McGRAW-HILL SERIES IN GEOGRAPHY

JOHN C. WEAVER, *Consulting Editor*

An Introduction to Climate

CLIMATES

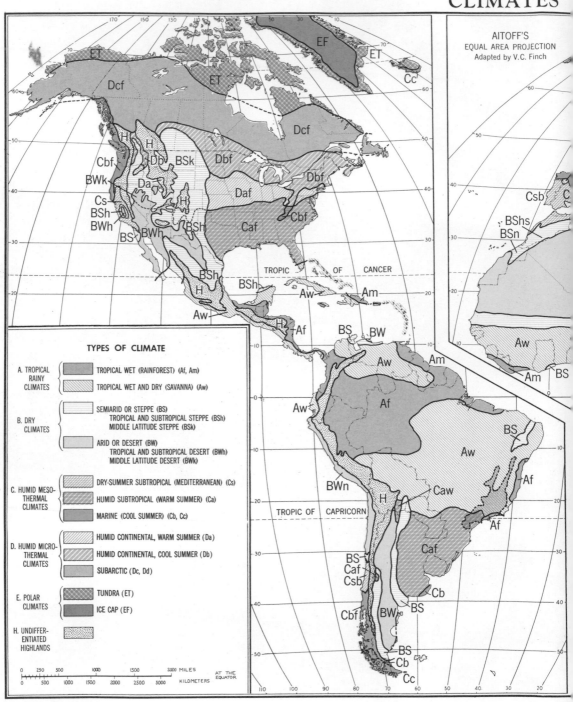

AITOFF'S
EQUAL AREA PROJECTION
Adapted by V.C. Finch

TYPES OF CLIMATE

A. TROPICAL RAINY CLIMATES
- TROPICAL WET (RAINFOREST) (Af, Am)
- TROPICAL WET AND DRY (SAVANNA) (Aw)

B. DRY CLIMATES
- SEMIARID OR STEPPE (BS)
  TROPICAL AND SUBTROPICAL STEPPE (BSh)
  MIDDLE LATITUDE STEPPE (BSk)
- ARID OR DESERT (BW)
  TROPICAL AND SUBTROPICAL DESERT (BWh)
  MIDDLE LATITUDE DESERT (BWk)

C. HUMID MESO-THERMAL CLIMATES
- DRY-SUMMER SUBTROPICAL (MEDITERRANEAN) (Cs)
- HUMID SUBTROPICAL (WARM SUMMER) (Ca)
- MARINE (COOL SUMMER) (Cb, Cc)

D. HUMID MICRO-THERMAL CLIMATES
- HUMID CONTINENTAL, WARM SUMMER (Da)
- HUMID CONTINENTAL, COOL SUMMER (Db)
- SUBARCTIC (Dc, Dd)

E. POLAR CLIMATES
- TUNDRA (ET)
- ICE CAP (EF)

H. UNDIFFER-ENTIATED HIGHLANDS

0   250   500   1000   1500   2000 MILES
0   500   1000   1500   2000   2500   3000
KILOMETERS
AT THE EQUATOR

PLATE I

THE SCHEME OF CLASSIFICATION IS MODIFIED
AND SIMPLIFIED FROM KÖPPEN

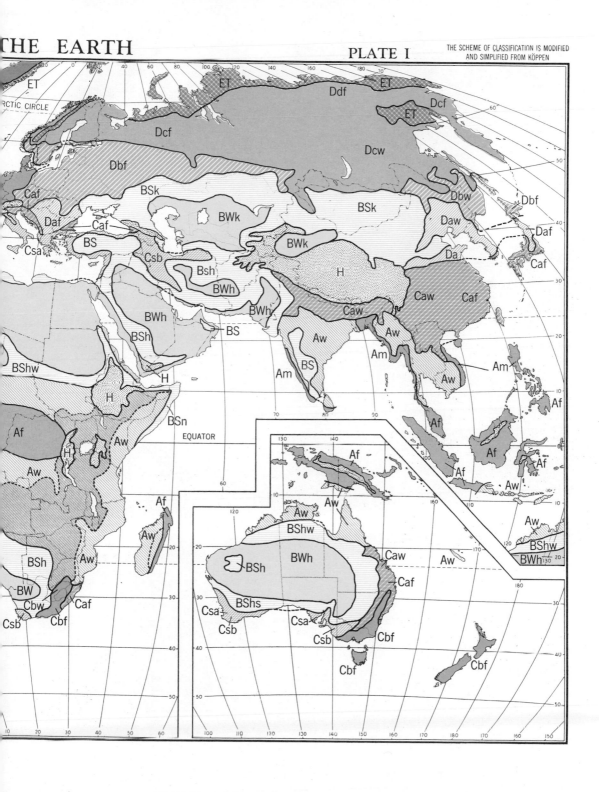

AN INTRODUCTION
TO CLIMATE

GLENN T. TREWARTHA

Professor of Geography, University of Wisconsin

THIRD EDITION

McGRAW-HILL BOOK COMPANY, INC.

NEW YORK   TORONTO   LONDON

1954

AN INTRODUCTION TO CLIMATE

Library of Congress Catalog Card Number 53-12438

IX
65149

Preface

In the more than a decade that has elapsed since the publication of the second edition of this book, added years of experience in teaching climatology to college students and a greatly expanded body of materials on the atmosphere have provided the author with new ideas relative to the selection and organization of the materials to be incorporated in this third edition. The shortened title, "An Introduction to Climate," it is believed, more accurately describes the content of the book.

Like the earlier editions this one also consists of two parts, Part I emphasizing the systematic aspects of climatology and Part II the regional features as revealed in the world pattern of distribution. A discussion organized on the basis of the individual continents is omitted, for the reason that such a treatment must of necessity be highly repetitious in character since the several climatic regions comprising a climatic type show much similarity. In Part I where the several elements of climate are treated individually, description and distribution are emphasized. This feature bespeaks the needs of geographers for whom the book has been designed. But description alone is deemed inadequate even for those disciplines whose focus is anthropocentric in character. For this reason sufficient background on the physical processes of the atmosphere is provided to make the patterns of distribution intelligible. For example, such items as upper-air waves and the jet stream are introduced because of their significance in understanding the distribution of atmospheric fronts and storms, which are significant ingredients of climate. It is the author's conviction that a climatology which omits, or seriously slights, gene-

sis and explanation is not only dull but is also inadequate for the geographers' needs.

The criterion employed in the selection of materials to be included in Part I has been their relative significance in contributing to an understanding of regional climates. The necessity for keeping the book brief and in the nature of an introduction or handbook will cause many instructors to feel the need for expanding the treatment of numerous topics here introduced. To this end brief bibliographic outlines with page references have been provided at the end of each chapter in Part I. In this way the book offers the instructor and student a framework upon which a more advanced or a more comprehensive treatment can be constructed.

In Part II the individual elements of climate are synthesized into climatic types and regions. Here it is the world pattern of climates which is emphasized as well as the reasons underlying this patternful distribution. Less attention is given to the departures from the world pattern and to the uniquenesses of individual climatic regions within a type. A modified Köppen system of climatic classification is employed as a vehicle for describing the distribution of climates. Throughout Part II less emphasis is placed upon an exact definition and location of climatic boundaries and more upon items of description, distribution, and explanation of core climates.

Following are some of the more significant modifications of the earlier editions which appear in this revision:

1. Large sections of Part I have been rewritten in order to bring the discussion of numerous topics into harmony with more recent

materials and points of view. Greater emphasis has been given to dynamic processes as genetic factors in climatic origins. The sections on surface winds have been expanded and modernized. More attention is given to upper-air phenomena as a basis for understanding surface climates.

2. A new chapter has been added on climatic classification.

3. The total number of illustrations has been increased by about 75; 114 new illustrations have been added and numerous old ones have been revised or redrawn.

4. Revised Part II places greater emphasis upon weather types as climatic features, stresses type locations of climates, and amplifies the discussion of regional peculiarities of climate.

Glenn T. Trewartha

Contents

PART ONE

The Elements of Climate

Introduction

1. The earth's atmosphere is a gaseous envelope several hundred miles thick which surrounds the solid and liquid earth. Most of the earth's life exists at the bottom of the atmosphere or at the zone of contact between the atmosphere and solid earth. Consequently, the earth's living things are greatly influenced by the characteristics of, and the changes that take place in, the air which lies above and around them. In fact, among the several elements (climate, terrain, economic minerals, soils, native vegetation, etc.) which in combination comprise the total natural equipment of any region for human use, climate probably is the single most important one causing variations in use potentialities between extensive regions of subcontinental size. This arises from the fact that not only is climate a highly important individual element of the total natural equipment of earth regions but also because it, more than any other element, influences the character of native vegetation, soil, drainage, and to a less degree the nature of the terrain or surface features as well. It is for this reason that extensive areas with similar climates are also likely to have strong resemblances in natural vegetation and soils.

2. Composition of the Atmosphere. Ordinary surface air is a mechanical mixture of a number of gases, chief among them being nitrogen and oxygen, which together comprise about 98 per cent of the volume. There are, in addition, smaller amounts of water vapor, argon, ozone, and carbon dioxide, and numerous organic and inorganic particles classed as dust. Of these ingredients, water vapor is by all odds the most important from a climatological standpoint, for this is the source of all forms of condensation and precipitation (clouds, white frost, rain, snow, sleet, and hail), is the principal absorber of solar energy and of energy radiated from the earth as well, is one of the large energy sources for the development and growth of storms, and greatly affects the stability of the atmosphere. Since water vapor is much more transparent to the sun's rays than to the energy radiated from the earth, it acts as a blanket to keep the earth relatively warmer than it otherwise would be, and freer from great extremes of temperature. The water-vapor content of the air is variable, reaching 4 or 5 per cent on very hot humid days. In the wet tropics the water vapor averages about 2.6 per cent of the total volume of the surface air; at latitude 50°, roughly 0.9 per cent; and in the vicinity of the 70° parallel, 0.2 per cent. Both water vapor and dust are concentrated in the lower atmosphere and show a rapid decrease with elevation. If all the water vapor in the air were condensed, it would be equivalent to a layer 1 in. deep over the whole earth. Even though nitrogen and oxygen comprise such a large part of the total volume of the atmosphere, they are of little consequence climatically.

Microscopic dust particles, the vast majority of which are too small to be seen even under a powerful microscope, tend to scatter the incoming sunlight and as a consequence are partly responsible for the sunset and sunrise colors, the blue of the sky, and the occurrence of twilight and dawn. Some of the dust particles which have hygroscopic (water-absorbing) properties provide the nuclei around which atmospheric condensation takes place. Among the more important kinds of hygroscopic dust are minute salt particles, derived from sea spray and the sands of seashores, and coal smoke. The more frequent and dense fogs over cities result in part from the abundance of condensation nuclei provided by the city's smoke. Over large cities smoke and dust also act as an effective screen against incoming sunlight. As an example, the university weather station at Chicago, Ill., receives during the three winter months (December through February) only 55 per cent of the solar energy recorded by the weather station in Madison, Wis., a smaller and less industrial city.

3. The Elements of Weather and Climate. The condition of the atmosphere at any time or place, *i.e.*, the weather, is expressed by a combination of several elements, primarily (*a*) *temperature* and (*b*) *precipitation* and *humidity* but to a lesser degree by (*c*) *winds* and (*d*) *air pressure* as well. These are called the *elements of weather and climate* because they are the ingredients out of which various weather and climatic types are compounded. The *weather* of any place is the sum total of its atmospheric conditions (temperature, pressure, winds, moisture, and precipitation) for a *short* period of time. It is the momentary state of the atmosphere. Thus we speak of the weather, not the climate, for today or of last week.

Climate, on the other hand, is a composite or generalization of the variety of day-to-day weather conditions. It is not just "average weather," for the variations from the mean, or average, are as important as the mean itself. "Certainly no picture of climate is at all true unless it is painted in all the colors of the constant variation of weather and the changes of season which are the really prominent features" (Kendrew). But as compared with meteorology, which is concerned primarily with the physics of individual weather events, physical climatology deals largely with the composite states of the atmosphere for the world or for certain parts of it. It emphasizes (*a*) characteristics and (*b*) distributions.

There are two methods by which the climatic picture may be created: (*a*) by averages of the several climatic elements, particularly temperature and precipitation, or (*b*) by a portrayal of the various types of weather which together comprise climate. By the first method climatic data in the form of daily, monthly, and annual averages are studied. Thus, Madison, Wis., has a January temperature of about 17° and a July, or hot month, average of about 72°. Its total annual precipitation approximates 32 in., with the cooler months having about 1 in. on the average and the midsummer months some 3 to 4 in.

But still another way to portray climate is to analyze the various weather types which go to make up these averages. Thus Madison's January temperature of 17° is composed of a great variety of weather types such as are exhibited on the daily weather map, including cold waves, moderately cold snowy days, January thaws, and many others. Probably both methods are needed to make a satisfactory picture of climate, although the one most often omitted or slighted is a comprehensive treatment of the weather types. Certain it is, however, that no adequate understanding of climate is possible without acquaintance with the daily weather, including the variety of atmospheric perturbations which are so obvious on the daily weather map.

4. The Controls of Weather and Climate. Weather varies from day to day, and climate differs from place to place, because of variations in the amount, intensity, and areal distribution of these several weather and climatic elements, more particularly temperature and precipitation. One may naturally inquire as to what it is that causes these several climatic elements to vary from place to place and season to season on the earth, resulting in some places and some seasons being hot and others cold, some wet and others dry. The answer is to be found in the *climatic controls*. These are (*a*) latitude or sun, (*b*) distribution of land and water, (*c*) the great semipermanent high- and low-pressure cells, (*d*) winds, (*e*) altitude, (*f*) mountain barriers, (*g*) ocean currents, (*h*) storms of various kinds, and a number of other more minor ones. It is these controls, acting with various intensities and in different combinations, that produce the changes in temperature and precipitation, which in turn give rise to varieties of weather and climate.

The following diagram may help to clarify the relationship among (a) *elements*, (b) *controls*, and (c) the resulting weather and climate.

characteristics, origins, and distributions of the individual elements which comprise the climatic complex. The first few chapters, dealing with air

Climatic Controls
1. Sun or latitude
2. Land and water
3. Semipermanent low- and high-pressure
   cells
4. Winds and air masses
5. Altitude
6. Mountain barriers
7. Ocean currents
8. Storms

Acting upon→

Climatic Elements
1. Temperature
2. Precipitation and
   humidity
3. Air pressure
4. Winds

Produce→

Types and varieties of
weather
and
climate

Although it is the composite of atmospheric conditions, called climates, and their world distribution, that is of principal interest to geographers, a description of climatic types will be more intelligible if preceded by an analysis of the

temperature, pressure and winds, moisture and precipitation, and storms, provide this background which is desirable for understanding the origin of various types of climate and their distribution over the earth.

GENERAL REFERENCES FOR PART I

Blair, Thomas A. "Weather Elements." 3d ed., Prentice-Hall, Inc., New York, 1948. An elementary, nontechnical meteorology.

Brooks, Charles Franklin. "Why the Weather?" 2d ed., Harcourt, Brace and Company, Inc., New York, 1935. A popularly written but scientific analysis of weather.

Brunt, David. "Physical and Dynamical Meteorology." 2d ed., Cambridge University Press, London, 1939.

Byers, Horace Robert. "General Meteorology." McGraw-Hill Book Company, Inc., New York, 1944. An excellent book on the atmosphere, for relatively mature students.

"Climate and Man." Yearbook of Agriculture, 1941. U.S. Department of Agriculture, Washington, D.C. See especially Parts 1 and 4.

"Compendium of Meteorology." American Meteorological Society, 1951. A relatively complete treatment of the recent developments in meteorological science written by specialists in their fields.

Conrad, V. "Fundamentals of Physical Climatology." Harvard University Blue Hill Meteorological Observatory, Milton, Mass., 1942.

Donn, William L. "Meteorology—with Marine Applications." McGraw-Hill Book Company, Inc., New York, 1951.

Garbell, Maurice A. "Tropical and Equatorial Meteorology." Pitman Publishing Corp., New York, 1947.

Hann, Julius. "Handbuch der Klimatologie." 4th ed. revised by Karl Knoch, J. Engelhorn's Nachfolger, Stuttgart, 1932.

Haurwitz, Bernhard. "Dynamic Meteorology." McGraw Hill Book Company, Inc., New York, 1941. A mathematical treatment of atmospheric physics.

Haurwitz, Bernhard, and Austin, James M. "Climatology." McGraw-Hill Book Company, Inc., New York, 1944.

Haynes, B. C. Meteorology for Pilots. *Civil Aeronautics Bull.* 25, Washington, D.C., January, 1943.

Hettner, Alfred. "Die Klimate der Erde." B. G. Teubner, Leipzig, 1930.

Kendrew, W. G. "Climatology." 3d ed. of "Climate," Oxford University Press, New York, 1949. A good treatment of the weather and climatic elements and their distribution.

Köppen, W., and Geiger, R. "Handbuch der Klimatologie." Gebrüder Borntraeger, Berlin, 1930. 5 volumes. The following sections of Vol. I, "Allegemeine Klimalehre," are valuable in the field of general climate: Milankovitch, M., Mathematische Klimalehre, Part A, 1930. Conrad, V., Die klimatologischen Elemente und ihre Abhängigkeit von terrestrischen Einflüssen, Part B, 1936.

Landsberg, Helmut. "Physical Climatology." The Pennsylvania State College, State College, Pa., 1941.

Namias, Jerome, and others. "An Introduction to the

Study of Air Mass and Isentropic Analysis."
5th ed., the American Meteorological Society,
Milton, Mass., 1940.

Petterssen, Sverre. "Weather Analysis and Forecasting." McGraw-Hill Book Company, Inc.,
New York, 1940.

Petterssen, Sverre. "Introduction to Meteorology."
McGraw-Hill Book Company, Inc., New York,
1941. An abbreviation and simplification of the
author's "Weather Analysis and Forecasting."

Suring, R. "Hann-Suring Lehrbuch der Meteor-ologie." 5th ed., Willabald Keller, Leipzig,
1937.

Taylor, George F. "Aeronautical Meteorology." Pitman Publishing Corp., New York, 1938. An
excellent book for relatively mature students.
Particularly good treatment of air masses of
several of the continents.

Ward, Robert De C. "Climate." 2d ed., G. P.
Putnam's Sons, New York, 1918.

Willett, H. C. "Descriptive Meteorology." Academic
Press, Inc., New York, 1944.

CHAPTER 1: *Air Temperature (Including Insolation)*

Solar Energy or Insolation

5. Source of Atmospheric Heat. The sun is the single noteworthy source of heat for the earth's atmosphere. Out into interplanetary space from this gigantic body, whose diameter is more than one hundred times the earth's and whose surface is estimated to have a temperature of more than 10,000°F., streams a tremendous mass of radiant energy. From each square yard of the sun's surface is being radiated energy equivalent to about 100,000 horsepower. Although the earth, nearly 93,000,000 miles distant, intercepts less than 1/2,000,000,000 part of the solar output, this fraction amounts continuously to 23,000,000,000,000 horsepower. The earth as a whole receives every minute as much energy as mankind utilizes in a year. Yet to this small percentage of the sun's total energy many of the physical, and all the biotic, phenomena of the earth owe their existence. Solar energy is the great engine that drives the winds and the ocean currents, generates the weather, and makes the earth a livable place for human beings. The wood, coal, water power, and oil that heat our homes and power our engines are only transformed sunlight. Every locomotive, ship, automobile, or airplane moves, and every factory wheel turns, only by the delayed drive of solar energy.

All bodies, no matter what their temperature, give off radiation in the form of electromagnetic waves that travel at a speed of about 186,000 miles a second. The hotter the body, the more intense its radiation and the shorter its wavelengths. Thus high-temperature radiation like the sun's is in the form of short waves, while low-temperature radiation, such as that from the earth, is in the form of longer waves. Only a comparatively narrow band of the total radiation spectrum is visible to the human eye in the form of light. All low-temperature radiation is invisible. The radiant energy received from the sun, transmitted in a form analogous to short waves (1/250 to 1/6,700 mm. in length), and traveling at the rate of 186,000 miles a second, is called *solar radiation*, or *insolation*. Less than one-sixth of the solar radiation spectrum can be perceived as light. But there are other waves, some shorter (ultraviolet), and others longer (infra-red), which cannot be seen. Since solar radiation is the single important source of atmospheric heat, its distribution over the earth is of outstanding significance in understanding weather and climatic phenomena, more especially those associated with temperature. In solar energy is to be found the *ultimate* cause of all changes and motions of the atmosphere. Certainly the sun, or

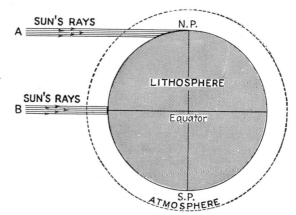

Fig. 1.1. The oblique ray (*A*) delivers less energy at the earth's surface than the vertical ray (*B*) because its energy is spread over a larger surface and because it passes through a thicker layer of absorbing, scattering, and reflecting atmosphere.

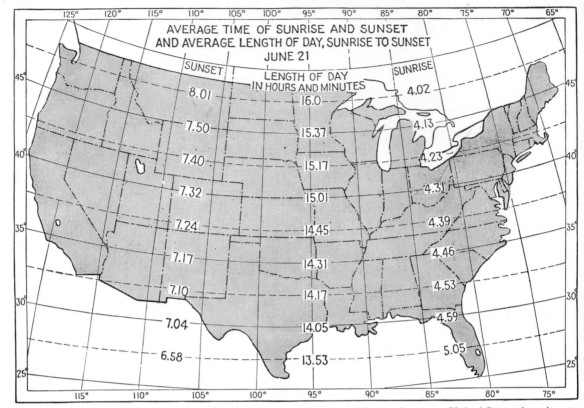

Fig. 1.2. At the time of the summer solstice, days are about 2 hr. longer in northernmost United States than they are in the extreme south.

insolation, is the single most important control of climate.

6. Major Factors Determining the Amount of Solar Radiation Received at Any Portion of the Earth's Surface. In order to simplify the problem of insolation distribution, imagine for the moment that the absorbing, scattering, and reflecting effects of the earth's atmospheric layers do not exist. Under that condition the amount of solar energy that any portion of the earth's surface received would depend primarily upon two factors: (a) *intensity of solar radiation*, or *the angle at which the rays of sunlight reach the earth* and (b) *the duration of solar radiation*, or *length of day*. Because an oblique solar ray is spread out over a larger surface than a vertical one, it delivers less energy per unit area (Fig. 1.1). Moreover, although for the moment the effects of an atmosphere are being omitted, it may be added that an oblique ray also passes through a thicker layer of scatter-

ing, absorbing, and reflecting air (table, p. 9). Winter sunlight, therefore, is much weaker than that of summer, since in late December the noon sun at Madison, Wis., located at 43°N., is only $23\frac{1}{2}°$ above the horizon, while in late June it has an elevation of $70\frac{1}{2}°$. As regards the second item, it would seem to require no further explanation of the fact that the longer the sun shines (length of day), the greater the amount of solar energy received, all other conditions being equal. Thus the longest summer days (15+ hr.) in the latitude of southern Wisconsin, which have 6+ hr. more of daylight than the shortest winter days (9− hr.), allow for much greater receipts of solar energy (Figs. 1.2, 1.3, 1.15). It is quite understandable, then, why in these latitudes summer temperatures are so much higher than winter temperatures, since (a) sun's rays are less oblique, and (b) days are much longer in summer.

Length of the Longest Day (Hence Also of the Longest Night) at Certain Latitudes

Latitude	0°	17°	41°	49°	63°	66½°	67°21′	69°51′	78°11′	90
Duration	12 hr.	13 hr.	15 hr.	16 hr.	20 hr.	24 hr.	1 mo.	2 mo.	4 mo.	6 mo.

Since length of day and angle of the sun's rays are equal on all parts of the same parallel, it follows that all places on a parallel (save for differences in the transparency of the atmosphere) receive the same amount of solar energy. By the same reasoning, different parallels or latitudes receive varying amounts of insolation, there being a decrease from equator to poles for the year as a whole. If insolation were the only control of atmospheric phenomena, then all places in the same latitude should have identical climates. While certainly not identical throughout, the strong climatic resemblances within latitude belts testify to the dominant, although not exclusive, rank of sun control.

7. Minor Factors Determining the Amount of Solar Radiation Received at the Earth's Surface. Other than length of day and angle of sun's rays, the less important factors determining the amount and distribution of solar energy at the earth's surface are (*a*) the fluctuations in solar output of radiation, there being a 1 to 2 per cent variation from the average of about 1.9 gram-calories per minute per square centimeter, and (*b*) the varying distances of the earth from the sun at the several positions in its orbit. Thus in January the earth is only 91.3 million miles from the sun, while in July they are 94.5 million miles apart. That there is a cold season in the Northern Hemisphere at the time when the earth is nearest the sun, and a warm season when it is farthest from the sun, tends to emphasize the fact that this item of distance is minor compared with length of day and angle of sun's rays.

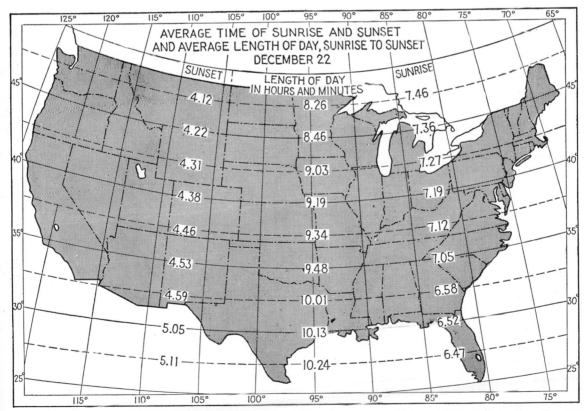

Fig. 1.3. At the time of the winter solstice days are about 2 hr. shorter in northernmost United States than they are in the extreme south.

8. Irregular Variations in Solar Radiation.
There is no doubt that the amount and quality of the solar radiation emitted by the sun does change from time to time. This is indicated by the changes that are to be observed in the sun's surface. On the other hand, the percentage change is so small, amounting to only 1 to 2 per cent, that it is still a much debated question whether the solar-constant measurements made at the surface of the earth are accurate enough to reveal the real magnitude or time of such variations. From the standpoint of the earth's weather and climate, the small percentage variation in the solar constant is probably not very important, certainly not nearly as significant as the variations in the amount of solar energy absorbed by the earth and its atmosphere. The solar energy reflected by the planet Earth varies so much that the energy absorbed may vary by $15 \pm$ per cent from the mean. This is to be compared with a 1 to 2 per cent variation in the solar constant.

While there is no question that the normal daily and seasonal variations in receipts of solar energy are the cause of the corresponding regular diurnal and seasonal sequences of weather over the earth, it is impossible at the present time conclusively to prove or disprove whether small irregular solar-radiation variations appreciably influence anomalous fluctuations in world weather. Studies of the sun reveal some characteristic features which do vary semicyclically. One of the solar phenomena, sunspot numbers, alternately increase and decrease with a period which averages about eleven years, although the period has varied from seven to seventeen years. Other features of solar variation have not been studied sufficiently to ascertain the number of cycles of variation. It is also recognized that there are world weather variations ranging from very short to very long periods. These changes in world weather patterns stem from changes in the general circulation of the atmosphere, but up to the present time it has not been demonstrated that there is any regular periodicity in these fluctuations. There is a possibility that irregular world weather patterns may be linked with solar variations, but so far the connection has not been established.[1]

9. Earth and Sun Relations; Rotation and Revolution. The earth is held in space by the combined gravitational attraction of other heavenly bodies and has motions that are controlled by them. The two principal earth motions are *rotation* and *revolution*. The earth rotates upon an imaginary axis which, owing to the polar flattening, is its shortest diameter. The ends of the axis of rotation are at the earth poles. The time required for the earth to rotate once upon its axis is 24 hr. During that time most places on the sphere are turned alternately toward and away from the sun, have experienced a period of light and a period of darkness, and have been swept over twice by the circle of illumination, once at dawn and again at twilight. The direction of earth rotation is toward the east. This fact has broad significance. Not only does it determine the direction in which the sun, moon, and stars appear to rise and set, but it is related to other earth phenomena of far-reaching consequence, such as the prevailing directions of winds and ocean currents, which will be studied later.

10. *Earth Revolution.* The rotating earth revolves in a slightly elliptical orbit about the sun, from which it keeps an average distance of about 93 million miles. The time required for the earth to pass once completely around its orbit fixes the length of the year. During the time of one revolution the turning earth rotates on its axis approximately $365\frac{1}{4}$ times, thus determining the number of days in the year.

An imaginary plane passed through the sun and extended outward through all points in the earth's orbit is called the plane of the ecliptic. The axis of the earth's rotation has a position that is neither parallel with nor vertical to that plane. It has instead a fixed inclination of about $66\frac{1}{2}°$ from the plane of the ecliptic (or $23\frac{1}{2}°$ from vertical to it). This position is constant, and therefore the axis at any time during the yearly revolution is parallel to the position that it occupied at any previous time (Fig. 1.4). This is called the *parallelism* of the axis.

The degree of *inclination* of the earth's axis and its *parallelism*, together with the earth's shape, its *rotation* on its axis, and its *revolution* about the sun, combine to produce several earth phenomena which are of vital importance among the conditions that surround earth inhabitants. One of the most fundamental of these is

[1] For an amplification of this topic, see "Compendium of Meteorology," pp. 18–19, 379–390.

the primary distribution of solar energy over the earth with its attendant change of seasons.

11. The March of the Seasons. The rotation and revolution of the earth and the inclination and parallelism of its axis have been discussed in the two previous articles. It remains to be analyzed, then, how these earth motions and positions act to produce the changing lengths of day and varying angles of the sun's rays, which in turn are the causes of the seasons (Figs. 1.4, 1.5).

12. *The Equinoxes: Spring and Fall.* Twice during the yearly period of revolution, on Mar. 21 and Sept. 23, the sun's noon rays are directly overhead or vertical at the equator (Fig. 1.5). At these times, therefore, the circle of illumination, marking the position of the tangent rays, passes through both poles and consequently cuts all of the earth's parallels exactly in half. One-half of each parallel (180°) consequently is in light, and the other half in darkness. For this reason, since the path described by any point on the earth's

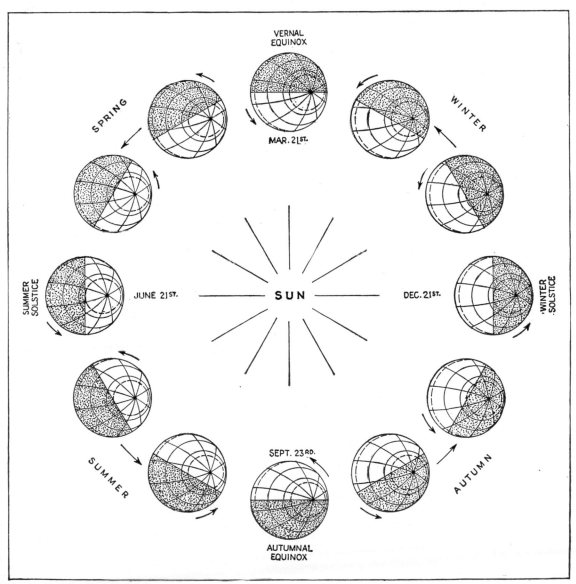

Fɪɢ. 1.4. The relation of the inclination and parallelism of the earth's axis to the change of seasons in the Northern Hemisphere.

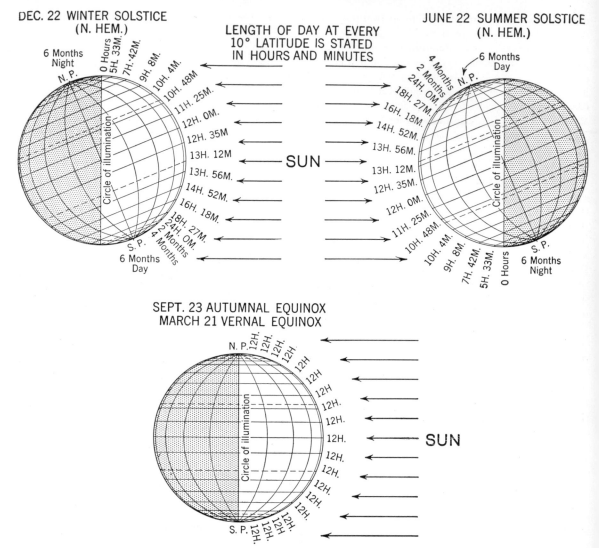

FIG. 1.5. On the equinoxes, when the sun's vertical rays are at the equator, the circle of illumination cuts all the parallels in half, and days and nights are equal in length over the entire earth. At this time insolation decreases regularly from equator to poles. See Fig. 1.6 for distribution of insolation from pole to pole at the time of the equinoxes. At the times of the solstices the sun's vertical rays have reached their greatest poleward migration. The circle of illumination cuts all the parallels (except the equator) unequally so that days and nights are unequal in length except at latitude 0°. See Fig. 1.7 for distribution of insolation from pole to pole at the time of the solstices.

surface during the period of rotation is coincident with its parallel of latitude, days and nights are equal (12 hr. each) over the entire earth. From this fact the two dates Mar. 21 and Sept. 23 get their names, the *equinoxes* (spring equinox Mar. 21, autumn equinox Sept. 23—Northern Hemisphere). At these seasons the maximum solar energy is being received at the equator, a latitude from which it diminishes regularly toward either pole where it becomes zero.

13. *The Solstices: Summer and Winter.* On June 22 the earth is approximately midway in its orbit between the equinoctial positions, and the North Pole is inclined $23\frac{1}{2}°$ *toward* the sun (Fig. 1.5). As a result of the axial inclination, the sun's rays are shifted northward by that same amount ($23\frac{1}{2}°$), so that the noon rays are vertical at the Tropic of Cancer ($23\frac{1}{2}°$N.), and the tangent rays in the Northern Hemisphere pass over the pole and reach the Arctic Circle ($66\frac{1}{2}°$N.), $23\frac{1}{2}°$

on the opposite side of it. In the Southern Hemisphere the tangent rays do not reach the pole but terminate at the Antarctic Circle, $23\frac{1}{2}°$ short of it. Thus while all parts of the earth north of the Arctic Circle are experiencing constant daylight, similar latitudes in the Southern Hemisphere (poleward from the Antarctic Circle) are entirely without sunlight. At this time, June 22, or the *summer solstice*, all parallels, except the equator, are cut unequally by the circle of illumination, those in the Northern Hemisphere having the larger parts of their circumferences toward the sun so that days are longer than nights. Longer days, plus a greater angle of the sun's rays, result in a maximum receipt of solar energy in the Northern Hemisphere at this time. Summer, with its associated high temperatures, is the result, and north of the equator June 22 is known as the summer solstice. In the Southern Hemisphere at this same time, all these conditions are reversed, nights being longer than days, and the sun's rays relatively oblique, so that solar radiation is at a minimum, and winter conditions prevail.

On Dec. 22, when the earth is in the opposite position in its orbit from what it was on June 22, it is the South Pole that is inclined $23\frac{1}{2}°$ *toward* the sun (Fig. 1.5). The latter's noon rays are then vertical over the Tropic of Capricorn ($23\frac{1}{2}°$S.), and the tangent rays pass $23\frac{1}{2}°$ over the South Pole to the Antarctic Circle ($66\frac{1}{2}°$S.). Consequently south of $66\frac{1}{2}°$S. there is constant light, while north of $66\frac{1}{2}°$N. there is a continuous absence of sunlight. All parallels of the earth, except the equator, are cut unequally by the circle of illumination, with days longer and sun's rays more nearly vertical in the Southern Hemisphere. This, therefore, is summer south of the equator but winter in the Northern Hemisphere (*winter solstice*) where opposite conditions prevail.

14. Distribution of Solar Radiation over the Earth. It is clear from the previous discussion that the belt of maximum insolation swings back and forth across the equator during the course of a year, following the shifting rays of the sun, with the two variables, (*a*) angle of sun's rays and (*b*) length of day, largely determining the amount of solar energy received at any time or place.

15. *Distribution of Solar Radiation from Pole to Pole along a Meridian at the Outer Limits of the Atmosphere.* The *total average annual insolation* reaches a maximum at the equator and diminishes gradually and regularly toward either pole (see table below and Fig. 1.6). At the poles the total

amount of solar radiation received for the entire year is about 40 per cent of that received at the equator.

Total Annual Insolation for Various Latitudes Expressed in Thermal Days (Effects of an Atmosphere Omitted)

(The Unit, or Thermal Day, Is the Average Total Daily Insolation at the Equator)

Latitude	Thermal Days	Latitude	Thermal Days
0°	365.2	50°	249.7
10°	360.2	60°	207.8
20°	345.2	70°	173.0
30°	321.0	80°	156.6
40°	288.5	90°	151.6

The latitudinal distribution of insolation at the time of the *equinoxes*, when the sun's noon ray is vertical at the equator and the tangent rays reach the poles, resembles that for the year as a whole since the maximum is at the equator and the minimum at the poles. Although the symmetrical curves representing annual and equinoxial latitudinal distributions of insolation are

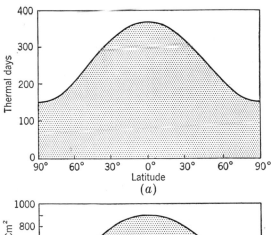

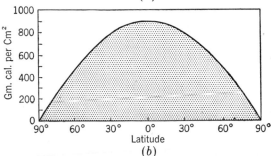

FIG. 1.6. The curves showing latitudinal distribution of insolation for the year (*a*) and at the time of an equinox (*b*) resemble each other both in general shape and in the location of maximum and minimum.

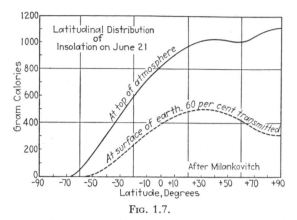

FIG. 1.7.

relatively similar in form, there is the difference that insolation declines to zero at the poles at the time of the equinoxes, while this is far from the case in the annual distribution. The symmetrical character of the distribution of insolation from pole to pole at the time of the equinoxes is of highest climatic importance. It is in spring and fall (equinoxes), the two intermediate seasons, that the latitudinal distribution not only of insolation but also of temperature, pressure, winds, and precipitation over the earth most closely resembles that for the year as a whole. This is to be expected since it is in these same transition seasons that the Northern and Southern Hemispheres are receiving approximately equal amounts of insolation. The result is that temperature conditions in the two hemispheres are most nearly similar at these same seasons, and pressure, wind, and precipitation conditions are likewise more in balance to the north and south of the equator.

At the time of the two solstices (June 22 and Dec. 22) when the noon rays of the sun are vertical on the $23\frac{1}{2}°$ parallels north or south and the length of day increases from $66\frac{1}{2}°$ in the winter hemisphere to the pole of the summer hemisphere,[1] insolation is very unequally distributed in the two hemispheres. At the solstices the summer hemisphere actually receives two to three

times the amount of solar radiation received by the winter hemisphere. Neglecting for the moment the effects of the atmosphere, on June 22 the insolation curve beginning at zero at the Antarctic Circle continues to rise steadily up to about the latitude 44°N. in spite of the fact that the sun's rays are increasingly more oblique north of $23\frac{1}{2}°$N. (Fig. 1.7). North of about latitude 44°, however, there is a slight decline in insolation up to about latitude 62°N. as a result of the more oblique sun offsetting the increased length of day. But the insolation curve again rises north of 62°N. and reaches an absolute maximum at the North Pole. The counterpart of this above-described insolation curve, but reversed as to hemisphere, prevails at the time of the winter solstice. This curve of insolation distribution from pole to pole at the time of the solstices is complicated because it is a compromise between the two important controls of insolation, angle of sun's rays and length of day, which do not coincide in their latitudes of maximum effect. Thus on June 22, although the sun's noon rays are vertical at parallel $23\frac{1}{2}°$N., days are longest beyond the Arctic Circle.

As shown in Fig. 1.7, the distribution of insolation from pole to pole at the *surface* of the earth is considerably affected by the reflective, absorptive, and scattering effects of the earth's atmosphere. The general effect of the atmosphere is to reduce the intensity of insolation while at the same time there are shifts in the latitudinal locations of the maximum amounts of solar energy. For example, a pole is no longer the region of maximum insolation at the time of a solstice, but instead there is a broad zone of maximum in the vicinity of latitude 40° and the pole receives less than the equator. In the summer hemisphere insolation is distributed rather uniformly with latitude so that there is no sharp maximum near any one latitude and most of the parallels receive more than do the regions near the equator. It is not unusual therefore that the maximum surface temperatures should occur on the land masses of the lower middle latitudes and not at the equator.

What has been just stated concerning insolation distribution from pole to pole at the time of

[1] By "summer" hemisphere is meant the hemisphere that has summer. Thus in July the Northern Hemisphere is the summer hemisphere and the Southern Hemisphere is the winter hemisphere. In January this situation is just reversed.

the solstices, times that represent the seasonal extremes of summer and winter, is of the greatest importance in furnishing the basic explanations for a number of the larger features of global weather and climate. Some of these are (a) the striking latitudinal shifting of temperature, pressure, wind, and precipitation belts from summer to winter following a similar migration of insolation; (b) the high temperatures of the lower middle-latitude continents in summer where insolation receipts are at a maximum in the summer hemisphere; (c) the much steeper latitudinal temperature gradients in the winter hemisphere as compared with the summer hemisphere, a situation which approximates the distribution of insolation; and (d) the greater storminess and increased variability of weather in the winter hemisphere as compared with the summer hemisphere, this condition being related to the steeper temperature gradients in the former.

16. *Annual Distribution of Solar Radiation for Selected Latitudes.* The annual curves of insolation for the several latitudes fall naturally into three groups, viz., the low, the middle, and

the high latitudes (Fig. 1.8). (a) The low-latitude, or tropical, type, which is characteristic of the areas lying between the Tropic of Cancer and the Tropic of Capricorn, remains constantly high and there is little seasonal variation. The prevailingly high temperatures of the tropics are the result of this abundant and constant insolation. During the course of a year all places situated between the two tropics are passed over twice by the vertical rays of the sun and as a result the insolation curve for the low latitudes shows two maxima and two minima. (b) The middle-latitude insolation curve, which prevails in those regions lying between $23\frac{1}{2}°$ and $66\frac{1}{2}°$ in each hemisphere, shows a single maximum and a single minimum, these extremes coinciding with the solstices. Like the tropics, the middle latitudes have no period when insolation is absent so that the curve does not reach zero at any time. Nevertheless, there are far greater seasonal extremes in the insolation curve for the middle latitudes, a condition which makes itself felt in greater seasonal extremes of temperature. (c) The polar type of insolation curve, which pre-

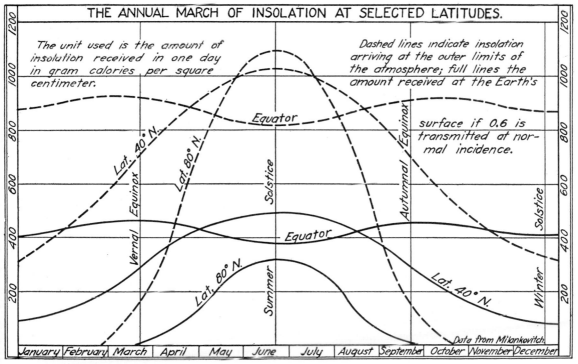

FIG. 1.8.

vails poleward of the Arctic and Antarctic Circles, resembles that of the middle latitudes in that it has one maximum and one minimum, coinciding with the summer and winter solstices. It stands in contrast to the other two curves by reason of the fact that it does reach zero, for during a portion of the year there is an absence of direct sunlight (Fig. 1.8).

17. Effects of an Atmosphere upon Insolation. In parts of the preceding description the problem of insolation distribution has been greatly simplified by assuming that solar radiation is received at the earth's surface without passing through an atmosphere. When that gaseous envelope is taken into consideration, numerous modifications and complications result. Chief among these is a weakening of insolation at the earth's surface due to (*a*) selective scattering, principally of the short wavelengths of blue light by very small obscuring particles (molecules of air, fine dust, etc.); (*b*) *diffuse reflection* of all wavelengths by larger particles (dust, cloud droplets, etc.); and (*c*) *absorption* of selected wavelengths, chiefly the longer ones, by water vapor and in a very minor degree by oxygen and ozone (see broken line in Fig. 1.7 and solid lines in Fig. 1.8).

When a beam of light or radiant energy passes through a transparent medium containing small obscuring particles or molecules, some of the light is deflected from the direct beam and sent in all directions from the particles. This phenomenon is known as *scattering*. True scattering occurs only when the diameters of the obscuring particles are smaller than the wavelengths of the radiation. The process is selective, the shorter wavelengths being affected most, so that various colors may result from the process. Thus the blue of the sky is the consequence of a more complete scattering, chiefly by molecules of air, of the shorter wavelengths in the insolation beam. On the other hand, the sun appears red when seen through a smoke screen, because the blue light has been subtracted. The ruddy cloud colors of sunset and sunrise result from cloud illumination by beams of light from which the blue portion of the spectrum has been removed by scattering. The importance of scattering is evidenced by the

small amount of ultraviolet light in cities as compared with the open country.

When the diameters of the obscuring particles are larger than the wavelengths of incident light, the effect is that of diffuse reflection, which is nonselective and therefore equally effective for all wavelengths. Thus the light reflected from a cloud when the sun is back of the observer is pure white, and the sun appears white when seen through a fog of water drops. It is worthy of emphasis that the scattered and reflected sunlight is still shortwave radiation and consequently is not readily absorbed by the atmosphere.

Absorption of solar energy by the earth's atmosphere is not very effective. To most of the wavelengths in the solar beam the atmospheric gases are transparent. Those gases that do absorb are selective in their action, absorbing more in some wavelengths than in others. Water vapor is the controlling agent in atmospheric absorption, although oxygen, ozone, and suspended particles, such as dust and cloud droplets, play a minor part.

Intensity of Insolation at Different Solar Elevations
(Coefficient of Transmission, 78 Per Cent)

Altitude of Sun	Relative Lengths of the Paths of Rays through the Atmosphere (Expressed in Atmospheres)	Intensity of Insolation on a Surface Perpendicular to the Rays	Intensity of Insolation on a Horizontal Surface
90°	1.00	78	78
80°	1.02	77	76
70°	1.06	76	72
60°	1.15	75	65
50°	1.31	72	55
40°	1.56	68	44
30°	2.00	62	31
20°	2.92	51	17
10°	5.70	31	5
5°	10.80	15	1
0°	45.00	0	0

A part of the solar energy which is scattered and reflected by the atmosphere and the earth's surface is sent back into space and is lost to the earth. This reflection from the earth is sufficient to cause the planet to shine with considerable brilliancy. It is this "earth shine" that illuminates the dark portion of the new moon so that one sees the earth-lit part as "the old moon in the new moon's arms." Some of the solar energy scattered and reflected in the atmosphere, however, reaches the earth's surface in the form of diffuse blue light of the sky, called diffuse daylight, and is transformed into heat and other forms of energy. It is this diffuse daylight which prevents absolute darkness on cloudy days, indoors, or in the shade where direct sunlight is absent. The energy transmitted to the earth in this form probably amounts to one-quarter of the energy of direct sunlight. The more oblique the ray of sunlight is, the thicker the layer of reflecting and scattering atmosphere through which it must pass. When the sun is only 4° above the horizon, the solar rays have to penetrate an atmosphere more than twelve times thicker than those coming from the sun at altitude 90°. This explains why one can look at the sun at sunrise and sunset without being blinded. It is in the higher latitudes, where the sun is never very high above the horizon, and direct sunlight is consequently weak, that diffuse daylight becomes of greatest significance, for in such regions it is the source of a large part of the solar energy received at the earth's surface. At Stockholm, Sweden, 25 per cent of the total solar energy in May, and 80 to 90 per cent of that in winter, is diffuse daylight. Probably not more than 18 per cent of the total solar radiation reaches ground level at the poles (Figs. 1.7, 1.8).

The amount of depletion of insolation by scattering, reflection, and absorption in passing through the atmosphere depends upon (a) the length of the passage, or, in other words, the angle of the sun's rays, and (b) the transparency of the atmosphere. The former factor can be arrived at mathematically, but the second is variable according to time and place. It is estimated that 35 per cent of the total insolation received at the outer limits of the atmosphere is returned to space in its original shortwave form by *scattering* and *reflection* from clouds, small dust particles, molecules of air, and from the earth's surface, and so has no part in heating either the earth or its atmosphere (Fig. 1.9). This is known as the earth's *albedo*. The 35 per cent is comprised of 2 per cent reflected from the earth's surface, 6 per cent reflected from the atmosphere, and 27 per cent reflected from the clouds. Fourteen per cent of the incoming insolation is absorbed by the atmosphere, most of it by water vapor, but small amounts by clouds, dust, and the permanent gases. The remaining 51 per cent reaches the earth's surface, is absorbed by it, and is available for heating the atmosphere from below. Of this 51 per cent, 34 per cent is in the form of direct

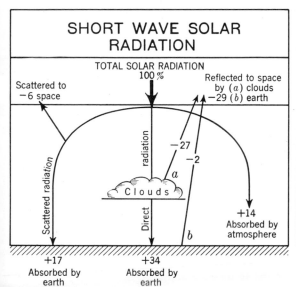

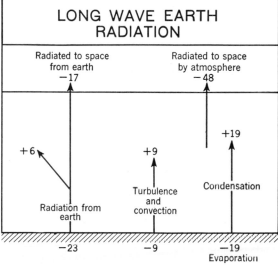

FIG. 1.9. Terrestrial heat balance. The effects of the earth's atmosphere and surface and of clouds upon incoming solar, and outgoing terrestrial, radiation. (*After Möller.*)

sunlight, while 17 per cent is diffuse daylight or sky radiation. From the preceding analysis it is obvious that only some 65 per cent of the total incoming solar radiation (14 per cent absorbed by the atmosphere directly and 51 per cent absorbed by the earth's surface) can be available for heating the atmosphere. Moreover, a much larger percentage (51 per cent) is absorbed by the earth's surface than by the atmosphere directly (14 per cent).

The solar energy absorbed by a unit area of the earth's surface, therefore, represents by far the largest part of the total solar energy absorbed by surface and atmosphere. Consequently most of the atmosphere's heat must be gained indirectly from the earth's surface. It must be realized, however, that the amount of insolation absorbed at the earth's surface varies greatly over short periods of time and from one region to another, chiefly because of variations in the amount of cloudiness which to a large extent determines the amount of solar energy reflected to space. These temporal and regional variations in the amount of solar energy absorbed at the earth's surface, resulting chiefly from variations in the amount of cloudiness, must have great climatic effects. For example, since the average surface air temperature lags behind the maximum solar radiation by about 4 to 8 weeks, it is obvious that a regional excess or deficiency of solar radiation at the earth's surface should have much to do with determining the future air temperature over a period of time such as week or month. The ground acts as a heat reservoir so that under the influence of solar radiation which it absorbs it is warmed to a considerable depth and it gives up its heat gradually to the atmosphere.

Absorption of Insolation at the Earth's Surface; Processes of Heating and Cooling the Earth's Surface and the Atmosphere

HEATING AND COOLING OF LAND AND WATER SURFACES

18. Land and Water Contrasts. Thus far the discussion has been concerned largely with distribution of solar energy, the single important source of atmospheric heat. But high-temperature sun energy is of such short wavelengths that only relatively small amounts (14 per cent) of it can be absorbed *directly* by the earth's atmosphere. In order to be readily absorbed by the air, insolation first must be converted into low-temperature terrestrial energy, which is composed of longer wavelengths. (Ratio of wavelengths of solar and terrestrial energy is roughly 1:25.) This conversion from short-wave solar to long-wave terrestrial energy takes place principally at the earth's surface, by which insolation is much more readily absorbed than it is by the relatively transparent atmosphere itself. Absorbed at the earth's surface, the solar energy is there converted into heat, after which the earth itself becomes a radiating body, but at a much lower temperature (average about 57°F.) than the sun, so that the wavelengths of radiation are longer. Thus the atmosphere receives most of its heat only *indirectly* from the sun but *directly* from the earth's surface, which in turn had previously absorbed and consequently been warmed by solar energy. It is obvious, therefore, that preliminary to a discussion of heating and cooling the atmosphere, it is necessary to understand the comparative reactions to solar energy (in terms of reflection, absorption, transmission) of the various kinds of terrestrial surfaces, and consequently their heating properties. It is clear that those surfaces which absorb relatively greater proportions of the incident solar energy and retain it in a relatively thin surface layer are the ones which will heat and cool most quickly.

There are, to be sure, considerable differences in the heating properties of even different kinds of land surfaces, depending on the relative amounts of solar energy reflected or absorbed and also on the conductivity of the materials. Thus snow reflects 70 to 90 per cent of the solar energy with the result that such a surface warms very slowly. By contrast grass reflects only 14 to 37 per cent, dry black soil 8 to 14 per cent, and a coniferous forest less than 10 per cent. Moreover, in the case of a vegetation surface a considerable proportion of the insolation is consumed in evaporating water transpired by the plants, which process prevents an excessive heating of the vegetation surface. But while the heating properties of different kinds of land surfaces are by no means identical, the contrasts of greatest magnitude are those between land and water, resulting in oceanic and continental climatic differences.

Of fundamental importance in understanding the differential heating and cooling of land and water is the fact that solid ground depends upon molecular heat conduction, while the heat exchange in fluids such as water and air is largely the result of dynamic convection or turbulence. Differences between land and water in terms of specific heat, transmission of solar radiation, reflection, and evaporation all appear to be relatively of much less importance compared with the mixing resulting from turbulence which takes place in water and of course is absent in land.

For the earth as a whole the loss of solar energy by *reflection* from the great variety of existing land surfaces is not greatly different from that of the oceans. The *specific heat* of water referred to the unit of volume is only 2.5 times greater than that of soil. The *transparency* of water to insolation suggests that a much greater volume of water should participate in heat transactions than is true of opaque soil, with the result that the land should heat more rapidly and intensely. Actually, however, the longer waves of solar energy do not penetrate the water to great depths so that the item of transparency or transmission is less important than might be assumed from the depth to which the visible rays penetrate the water body. Differential *evaporation* is also a factor moderating temperature variations in a water surface as compared with a land area, since over parts of the continental areas effective evaporation is less than potential evaporation. Over water, on the other hand, evaporation is always at a maximum. It is especially over the interiors of middle-latitude continents that actual evaporation is below potential evaporation. In the wet tropics, however, evaporation from the continents is greater than from the oceans. Large-scale evaporation and its retarding effects on excessive heating and cooling is therefore not restricted to the ocean surfaces.

While not neglecting the above-mentioned factors as affecting the differential heating of land and water surfaces, it needs to be emphasized that by far the most important factor causing the surfaces of relatively deep bodies of water to heat and cool slowly as compared with land is the fact of redistribution of heat by turbulence. In water bodies movements in the form of waves, drifts, currents, tides, and convectional systems tend to distribute the absorbed solar energy throughout a large mass with the consequence that surface heating and cooling are relatively slow. Obviously no such distribution and vertical mixing can occur in land areas. Therefore land and water surfaces with identical amounts of solar energy falling upon them do not acquire similar temperatures. Moreover, when a water surface begins to cool, vertical convectional movements are set up, the cooler, heavier surface layers sinking and being replaced by warmer water from underneath. Consequently the whole mass of water must be cooled before the surface layers can be brought to a low temperature. As a result, a larger mass of water (as compared with land) imparts its heat to the surrounding air, and the supply of heat is maintained for a longer period of time.

Observations show that the *daily* temperature variations do not penetrate more than about 3 ft. into the soil, while the *annual* changes go to a depth of only 47 ft. In quiet water *daily* temperature changes are felt at least 20 ft. below the surface. It is believed that, in oceans and deep lakes, owing to the movements that characterize water, a layer 600 to 2,000 ft. in depth is subject to annual temperature variations.

19. *Summary of Land and Water Contrasts.* From the above comparisons of land and water as regards their reactions to insolation, it becomes evident that, with the same amount of solar energy falling upon each, a land surface will reach a higher temperature, and reach it more quickly, than a water surface. Conversely, a land surface also cools more rapidly. Land-controlled, or continental, climates, therefore, should be characterized by large daily and seasonal extremes of temperature, while, on the other hand, ocean-controlled, or marine, climates should be more moderate (see Figs. 1.21, 1.22). The striking differences in the temperatures of marine and continental climates of middle and higher latitudes is principally due to the fact that the solid earth does not store any large amount of heat. The ocean, on the the other hand, has this potentiality of heat storage to an unusual degree, largely due to vertical mixing. The ocean surface probably changes temperatures not more than 1° between day and night, while seasonal changes also are very small. The relatively slower heating and cooling of water bodies quite naturally lead to a lag in the seasonal temperatures of marine climates.

HEATING AND COOLING THE ATMOSPHERE

20. The previous discussion having explained (a) the distribution of solar energy over the earth, (b) the contrasting reactions of land and water surfaces to this solar energy, and (c) the fact that the air receives most of its energy directly from the surface upon which it rests and only indirectly from the sun, the background is sufficient to proceed with an analysis of the processes involved in heating and cooling the atmosphere.

21. Absorption of Direct and Reflected Insolation. The earth's atmosphere is relatively transparent to direct and reflected solar radiation, which is short-wave energy, only about 14 per cent being absorbed and that chiefly by small amounts of water vapor. About one-half of this absorption takes place in the lower 2 km. of air where there is the strongest concentration of water vapor. But a layer of air 2 km. thick is a large mass through which to spread 7 per cent of the original solar radiation, so that the process is not very effective in producing the normal daytime rise in surface-air temperatures. Evidence of this is suggested by the fact that often on a clear, cold winter day, when the land surface is blanketed by a reflecting snow cover, air temperatures may remain extremely low in spite of a bright sun. At the same time, on the south side of an absorbing brick wall or building, where short-wave sun energy is being converted into long-wave terrestrial energy, it may be comfortably warm. Dust, an impurity in the air,

readily absorbs insolation, each particle thereby becoming a tiny focus for radiated terrestrial energy.

22. Conduction. When two bodies of unequal temperature are in contact with one another, energy in the form of heat passes from the warmer to the colder object until they both attain the same temperature. Thus, during the daylight hours, the solid earth (without a snow cover), being a much better absorber of insolation than air, attains a higher temperature. By conduction, therefore, the layer of air resting upon the warmer earth becomes heated. But air is a poor conductor, so that heat from the warmed lower layer is transferred very slowly to those above. Unless there is, through movement, a constant replacement of the warmed layer in contact with the earth, only the lower few feet will be heated by this process during the course of a day. Through air currents and winds, however, large masses of air are brought into contact with the heated earth's surface and consequently are warmed. Heating by conduction is primarily a daytime and a summer process.

Just as a warm earth on a summer day heats the air layer next to it by conduction, so a cold earth, chilled by terrestrial radiation on a winter night, has exactly the opposite effect. It not infrequently happens that, during clear calm winter nights, as a result of radiation and conduction, the atmospheric strata adjacent to the earth become colder than those at some distances above its surface. Conduction is not a major process of atmospheric heat transfer.

23. Radiation. A body at a given temperature emits radiation of different wavelengths. A body that at any given temperature emits the maximum amount of radiation at every wavelength is called a *black body*. This quality has nothing to do with the color of the radiating body. The earth's surface, for example, radiates as a black body. On the other hand, most gases, including those that comprise the atmosphere, do not radiate as black bodies, for at the same temperature they emit certain wavelengths but not others. This is called *selective radiation*. Gases not only radiate selectively, but they absorb selectively also, the wavelengths being the same in both processes. This selective absorption and radiation by the earth's atmosphere is a feature to be kept in mind in the discussion to follow.

The 51 per cent of the short-wave solar energy absorbed at the earth's surface is there transformed into heat. Through this absorption and conversion of insolation the heated earth becomes a radiating body whose average temperature is about 57°. As indicated previously, the spectrum of earth radiation is composed of long-wave energy ($\frac{1}{250}$ mm. to over $\frac{1}{20}$ mm.), so that it is not visible to the human eye. Although the atmosphere is capable of absorbing only relatively small amounts (14$\pm$ per cent) of short-wave incoming solar energy, it is, on the other hand, able to absorb perhaps as much as 85$+$ per cent of the outgoing long-wave earth radiation. Water vapor is much the most important of the atmosphere's absorbing gases, although carbon dioxide and ozone are of minor importance. Each of these gases absorbs selectively in the terrestrial radiation spectrum, being much more transparent to certain wavelengths than to others. The larger the amount of water vapor in the air, the greater the amount of absorption. This absorptive effect of water vapor upon outgoing earth radiation is illustrated by the rapid night cooling in deserts, the dry air and clear sky permitting a more rapid escape of energy. Obviously the effect of the atmosphere is analogous to that of a pane of glass, which lets through most of the incoming short-wave solar energy but greatly retards the outgoing long-wave earth radiation, thus maintaining surface temperatures considerably higher than they otherwise would be. This is the so-called *greenhouse effect* of the earth's atmosphere (Fig. 1.10). The greenhouse depends for a large part of its heating upon the principle that the glass roof and sides permit free entrance of solar energy but, on the other hand, prevent the escape of long-wave heat energy. A more universal experience illustrating the greenhouse effect is the superheating of the inside of a parked automobile that occurs on a sunny day if the car's windows are closed.

24. *Radiation under Clear Skies.* Under conditions of a clear sky, although much of the long-

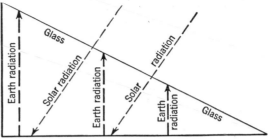

FIG. 1.10. Illustrating the "greenhouse effect" of the earth's atmosphere. The glass in the greenhouse, like the atmosphere, is relatively transparent to the short-wave solar radiation but is relatively opaque to the long-wave earth radiation.

wave earth radiation is absorbed by the water vapor in the atmosphere, a considerable portion passes directly through the atmosphere and out into space, none of the gases in the air being able to absorb in these particular wave lengths (Fig. 1.9). This portion of terrestrial radiation to which the earth's atmosphere is transparent may amount to as much as one-fifth of the total earth radiation. The remainder is absorbed largely by water vapor, but to a small degree by carbon dioxide and ozone. These gases in turn send out long-wave radiation both upward to the atmosphere layers above and downward to the earth's surface. Each successive absorbing layer of water vapor goes through this same process of absorption and radiation, resulting in a complexity of streams of radiation, the total effect being to retard the loss of heat from the earth. Since water vapor, which is the principal absorber of both solar and terrestrial radiation, diminishes rapidly with altitude (half of all the atmosphere's water vapor lies below 6,600 ft.), both the incoming and the outgoing radiation increase with altitude. For this reason high mountains may be called the "radiation windows" of the earth.

Radiation of terrestrial energy from the earth's surface upward toward space is a continuous process. During the daylight hours up to about midafternoon, however, receipts of energy from the sun are in excess of the amount radiated from the earth, with the result that surface-air temperatures usually continue to rise until two to four o'clock in the afternoon.

But during the night, when receipts of solar energy cease, a continued loss of energy through earth radiation results in a cooling of the earth's surface and a consequent drop in air temperature. *Being a better radiator than air*, the ground during the night becomes cooler than the air above it. When this condition prevails, the lower layers of atmosphere lose heat by radiation to the colder ground as well as upward toward space. This process is particularly effective during the long nights of winter when, if the skies are clear and the air is dry and relatively calm, excessively rapid and long-continued radiation takes place.

25. *The Effects of Different Surfaces.* If a snow cover mantles the ground, cooling is even more pronounced, for not only is most of the incoming solar radiation during the short day reflected, but at night, the snow, which is a good radiator but a very poor conductor of heat, allows little

Heat Conductivities of Various Substances

Substance	Conductivity, cal./cm./min./deg.
Air	0.003
Water	0.06
Snow	0.01
Sand	0.18
Rock	0.40

heat to come up from the ground below to replenish that lost by radiation. As a result, the snow surface becomes excessively cold, and then in turn the air layer resting upon it cools. Water, like land, is a good radiator, but the cooled surface waters keep constantly sinking to be replaced by warmer currents from below. Extremely low temperatures over water bodies are impossible, therefore, until they are frozen over, after which they act like a snow-covered land surface. Humid air tends to slow up the loss of heat from the earth by radiation so that air temperatures remain higher, and frosts are less likely on humid nights and especially when a cloud cover prevails. There are authentic cases in the dry air and under the cloudless skies of Sahara when day temperatures of 90° are followed by night temperatures slightly below freezing.

26. *Effects of a Cloud Cover.* When the sky is overcast by clouds, the radiation conditions are greatly altered from those prevailing under a clear sky even when the humidity is high. The cloud sheet, which is composed of water particles, contrasts with water vapor in that it is capable of absorbing and radiating in *all* the wavelengths that comprise the spectrum of earth radiation. Thus at the base of the cloud sheet all upward-moving radiation in all wavelengths is completely absorbed. Consequently in the returning stream of radiation from cloud to earth there are included all the wavelengths absorbed, including those to which water vapor is transparent. The principal effect of the cloud cover, therefore, is to put into the return beam from cloud to earth those wavelengths which pass out through the noncloudy atmosphere unabsorbed and consequently are not contained in the water-vapor radiation under a clear sky. Since more of the radiation is returned to the earth under a cloudy sky, the effect is greatly to retard the night cooling of the earth. Under the conditions of a night sky covered with low cloud the net loss of heat from the ground is only about one-seventh the loss with clear skies (Brunt). The higher the cloud cover, the less effective it is in retarding the loss of heat. Thus the net loss of heat from the ground under cirrostratus clouds at a height of about 4 miles was found to be nearly 80 per cent of that for clear skies, while, with nimbus and stratus clouds somewhat less than 1 mile high, the loss was only 14 per cent. A daytime cloud cover, with its high reflecting power of solar radiation has the effect of retarding surface heating, and hence reduces the stored-up energy in the earth.

27. Heating by Compression and Cooling by Expansion. When a mass of air descends from higher to lower altitudes, as, for instance, when it moves down a mountain slope or when subsidence occurs in a high-pressure system, it is being transferred from regions of lower atmospheric pressure to those where it is higher. Because there is an increasingly thicker layer of air pressing down upon it as lower altitudes are attained, the descending mass of air gradually is being compressed in volume. Work is being done upon it, and as a result of compression its temperature is increased.

Just as descending air heats as a result of compression, so rising air cools as a result of expansion. In the latter case the upward current is traveling from a lower altitude where atmospheric pressure is greater to a higher altitude where pressure is less. As a consequence, the rising air continues to expand as the weight of atmosphere upon it becomes less. It does work in pushing aside other air in order to make room for itself. This work done by the rising and expanding air consumes energy, which is subtracted from the ascending currents in the form of heat, resulting in a lowering of their temperature.

28. Heating by Additions of Latent Heat of Condensation. Large amounts of the solar energy which reaches the earth's surface is consumed in evaporating moisture from land surfaces and from vegetation. This transformed solar energy is thus contained in the water vapor of the atmosphere in a latent or potential form. When condensation takes place, this latent energy is again released into the atmosphere and heats it. Large-scale condensation, therefore, provides one of the principal sources of atmospheric heat. Of the total solar energy absorbed at the sea surface during the course of a year, it is estimated that 50 per cent is consumed in evaporating sea water and is therefore made available to the atmosphere in the form of water vapor. In view of this fact, and taking into consideration that the surface of earth is three-fourths water, it would appear that the latent energy represented by water vapor derived from ocean evaporation constitutes the most important single component of the atmosphere's heat budget.

29. Transfer of Heat by Vertical and Horizontal Currents in the Atmosphere. By means of the processes previously described heat is actually added to the atmosphere. There are additional processes, however, by which the acquired energy is transferred either vertically or horizontally and in the accompanying mixing processes changes in amtospheric temperature result.

30. *Vertical Mixing by Convectional Currents and Eddy Motions in the Atmosphere.* The surface air, after being heated by conduction and radi-

ation, expands in volume and consequently decreases in density. Because of expansion, a portion of the warmer, lighter column of air overflows aloft, thereby decreasing its own pressure at the surface and at the same time increasing that of the adjacent cooler air. This causes a lifting of the warmer, lighter air column by the heavier, cooler, settling air, which flows in at the surface to displace it. Such a circulation, as just described, and illustrated in Fig. 1.11 is called a convectional system. Warm surface air, expanded and therefore less dense, is like a cork that is held under water, *i.e.*, it is unstable and inclined to rise. This convectional principle (which applies to liquids and gases only) is employed in the ordinary hot-air and hot-water heating systems. The rising masses of warmed air on a hot summer day make air transport relatively bumpy, since the plane crosses alternately rising and sinking air columns. Though conduction and radiation are especially effective in heating the lower layers of atmosphere, convection, on the other hand, is capable of carrying terrestrial heat to the upper-air strata as well. It, too, is primarily a daytime and a summer process.

Eddy currents of random size and sequence are characteristic of the atmosphere for several miles above the earth's surface, and these also are effective agents for transferring upward the heat derived by the lower atmosphere from the earth. Turbulence set up by the roughness of the ground extends upward through an atmospheric layer 2,000 to 9,000 ft. deep. This is called the *friction layer*. Vertical mixing by convection, turbulence, and eddy currents is the most important method of distributing the warmed air

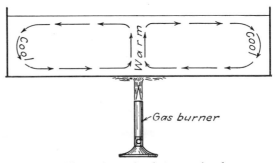

Fig. 1.11. Illustrating a simple convectional system.

close to the ground throughout the higher atmosphere.

31. *Horizontal Mixing by Advection Currents or Winds.* In the Northern Hemisphere middle latitudes a south wind is usually associated with unseasonably high temperatures. For example, as an air mass of tropical origin advances northward over central and eastern United States it conveys with it the temperature conditions acquired in its source region where high temperatures are normal. Such an importation of southerly warmth in winter results in mild weather, with melting snow and sloppy streets. In summer, several days of south wind may result in a hot wave with maximum temperatures of over 90°.

If tropical air masses with associated south winds from regions that are usually warmer import higher temperatures to the regions toward which they move, then polar air masses and accompanying north winds from colder, higher latitudes, or from the cold interiors of continents, should in turn bring lower temperatures. These importations are particularly effective where there are no mountain barriers to block the air movement. In eastern North America where lowlands prevail, great masses of cold polar air periodically pour down over the Mississippi Valley, occasionally carrying severe frosts even to the Gulf States. Both the advection of heat and of cold are accompanied by mixing processes which result in important temperature modifications.

HEAT BALANCE OF THE EARTH

32. Terrestrial Heat Balance. Referring to the left-hand portion of Fig. 1.9 which shows the effects of the atmosphere upon incoming solar radiation, it becomes clear that 65 per cent of the solar radiation received at the outer limits of the earth's atmosphere is absorbed by the atmosphere (14 per cent) or by the earth's surface (51 per cent). It is this part of the solar radiation, therefore, which is converted into terrestrial energy and made available for heating the atmosphere. The remaining 35 per cent is returned to space in the form of short-wave solar

radiation and has no part in heating the atmosphere. Since the yearly mean temperature of the earth as a whole is neither increasing nor decreasing, it is required that the 65 per cent of solar radiation shall be balanced by an equal amount of energy radiated back to space in the form of long-wave earth radiation. This is spoken of as *terrestrial heat balance.*

It must be kept in mind that 14 per cent of the solar radiation was absorbed directly by the atmosphere. Of the radiation from the earth's surface 17 units are indicated as escaping directly to space (Fig. 1.9) and these obviously play no part in heating the atmosphere. The six units of earth radiation shown as absorbed by the atmosphere is called the *effective radiation.*[1] It represents the difference between the ground radiation absorbed by the atmosphere and the back radiation from the atmosphere to the ground. The remaining 48 per cent is radiated to space by the earth's atmosphere. The atmosphere in turn receives 9 per cent by heat transport from the earth's surface through turbulence and convection currents. Another 19 per cent is transferred to the atmosphere from the earth's surface as evaporated moisture where it is released as latent heat of condensation; 14 (insolation absorbed directly by the earth's atmosphere) $+ 6 + 9 + 19 = 48$ per cent, which is the amount radiated to space by the atmosphere. This plus the 17 per cent radiated directly to space by the earth's surface amounts to 65 per cent, which just balances the 65 per cent of the solar radiation absorbed by the earth's atmosphere and surface. It should be emphasized that all the percentage figures used above are probably nothing more than good estimates and are subject to revision as more accurate measurements or computations are made.

[1] Actually only about 10 to 15 per cent of the radiation from the earth's surface escapes directly to space (17 units, Fig. 1.9), while 85 to 90 per cent is absorbed by the atmosphere. But of the 85 to 90 per cent absorbed by the atmosphere a large part is radiated back to the earth's surface. The six units of earth radiation shown in Fig. 1.9 as being absorbed by the atmosphere is the difference between the radiation from the earth's surface absorbed by the atmosphere and the back radiation from the atmosphere to the earth's surface.

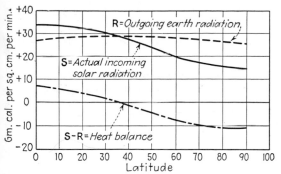

FIG. 1.12. Latitudinal heat balance. The annual balance between incoming solar radiation and outgoing earth radiation for various latitudes under conditions of average cloudiness. (*After Simpson.*)

33. Latitudinal Heat Balance. The mean annual temperature of the earth as a whole remains the same because, as shown previously, the amount of incoming solar radiation absorbed is just equaled by the amount of terrestrial energy radiated to space. On the other hand, with the data now available, it becomes clear that a balance between incoming and outgoing radiation is not true for most latitudes of the earth. Yet in spite of this latitudinal imbalance, no latitudes appear to be getting progressively warmer or colder. This situation requires some horizontal transfer of heat between the different latitudes.

It can be noted from Fig. 1.12 that, in the low latitudes, equatorward from about 37°, the incoming solar radiation exceeds the outgoing earth radiation, while poleward from 37° exactly the opposite is true. In other words, the continued excess of gain over loss in the low latitudes, and the reversal of this condition in the middle and higher latitudes, should, unless a transfer takes place, result in the former regions getting hotter and the latter regions getting colder. Since this does not occur, there must be a latitudinal transfer of energy from the region of excess to that of deficiency. In the following table the amount of heat given to the atmosphere by latitude belts, 10° in width, is shown. These values are not for unit areas but for girdles of equal width with very different areas. Where minus signs precede the value, they indicate that more heat is lost by terrestrial radiation than is gained from insolation. The smaller net losses poleward from 70° are due to the smaller areas covered by a 10° belt.

Latitude Belt	10⁹ Kilojoules per Second*
0 to 10	+1,109
10 to 20	+ 941
20 to 30	+ 544
30 to 40	+ 167
40 to 50	− 402
50 to 60	− 690
60 to 70	− 833
70 to 80	− 615
80 to 90	− 22

* One kilojoule is equal to 4,187 calories.

In order to maintain the heat balance in the various parts of the earth the following quantities of heat must be carried across the several latitude circles by an atmospheric circulation

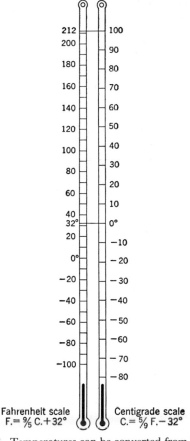

FIG. 1.13. Temperatures can be converted from Fahrenheit to centigrade, and vice versa, by using the conversion formula or by a direct comparison of the scales.

that will transfer heat horizontally from the low to the high latitudes:

Latitude	109 *Kilojoules per Second*
0	0
10	1,109
20	2,050
30	2,594
40	2,761
50	2,360
60	1,669
70	837
80	222
90	0

In this unequal latitudinal distribution of solar and terrestrial radiation is to be found the ultimate cause of the earth's atmospheric and oceanic circulation,[1] for it is only through the transfer of heat by winds and ocean currents that the latitudinal energy differences can be equalized. In the readjustments necessary to maintain the heat balance, not only is the great system of planetary winds involved, but also most of the other phenomena of weather and climate, including storms, which are the topics of study in the science of physical climatology. It is significant that the greatest transfer of heat is required in the middle latitudes (see previous table), for this helps to explain the greater turbulence and storminess of those regions where there is a maximum of air-mass movements.

Distribution of Temperature

TEMPORAL DISTRIBUTION

34. All average temperatures for a month, season, year, or even a long period of years are built upon the *mean daily temperature* as the basic

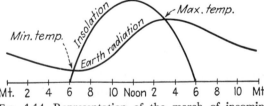

Fig. 1.14. Representation of the march of incoming solar radiation and of outgoing earth radiation for the daily 24-hr. period at about the time of an equinox, and their combined effects upon the time of daily maximum and minimum temperatures.

[1] Some European meteorologists feel that vertical temperature contrasts may be more important.

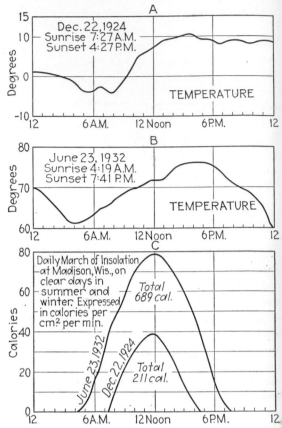

Fig. 1.15. Daily march of temperature (*A* and *B*) and of insolation (*C*) on clear days in winter and summer at Madison, Wis. The total solar energy recorded was $3\frac{1}{4}$ times as great on June 23 as on Dec. 22. Note that temperature lags behind insolation. South winds prevented normal night cooling on Dec. 22.

unit. The daily mean is thus the individual brick out of which the general temperature structure is composed. In some countries this basic unit of daily temperature is derived by computing the average of temperatures observed at certain definite hours during the day, as, for instance,

$$\frac{7:00 \text{ A.M.} + 2:00 \text{ P.M.} + 9:00 \text{ P.M.} + 9:00 \text{ P.M.}}{4}$$

The United States Weather Bureau at present uses the formula

$$\frac{\text{Maximum} + \text{minimum}}{2}$$

or, in other words, the average of the highest

and the lowest temperature recorded during the 24-hr. period.

35. The Mean Daily March, or Cycle, of Air Temperature. The mean daily march of temperature chiefly reflects the balance between incoming solar radiation and outgoing earth radiation (Fig. 1.14). From about sunrise until 2:00 to 4:00 P.M., when energy is being supplied by incoming solar radiation faster than it is being lost by earth radiation, the temperature curve usually continues to rise (Figs. 1.14, 1.15). Conversely, from about 3:00 ± P.M. to sunrise, when loss by terrestrial radiation exceeds receipts of solar energy, the daily temperature curve usually falls. It is noticeable, however, that the time of highest temperatures (2:00 to 4:00 P.M.) does not exactly coincide with that of maximum insolation (12:00 M. sun time). This lag results from the fact that temperature continues to rise as long as the amount of incoming solar radiation exceeds the outgoing earth radiation. Thus, although receipts begin to decline after the noon period, they continue to exceed the disbursements until 3:00 ± P.M. Moreover, it requires some time for the passage of heat from the ground to those elevations where the thermometers are located.

A perfect rise and fall of the daily temperature curve, corresponding to that for insolation, is many times not in evidence. Storms with their cloud covers, which obstruct both incoming and outgoing radiation, and their wind systems, which import air of contrasting temperatures from higher and lower latitudes, greatly modify the daily march of temperatures. In Fig. 1.15A south winds and a cloud cover prevented a normal decline of temperature on the afternoon and night of Dec. 22. In the stormy middle latitudes it is even possible for midnight to be warmer than noon. Along coasts, land and sea breezes may likewise impose modifications (Fig. 1.16).

36. The Annual March, or Cycle, of Temperature. The annual march, or cycle, of temperature reflects the daily increase in insolation (hence heat accumulated in the air and ground) from midwinter to midsummer and the decrease in the same from midsummer to midwinter (Fig. 1.17). Usually there is a temperature lag of 30 to 40 days after the periods of maximum or minimum insolation. This reflects the balance between incoming and outgoing energy. The lag is greater over the oceans in middle latitudes where August is often the warmest month and February the coldest (Northern Hemisphere). Even the most marine locations on land masses, such, for instance, as the west coasts

DAILY MARCH OF TEMPERATURE, SELECTED STATIONS

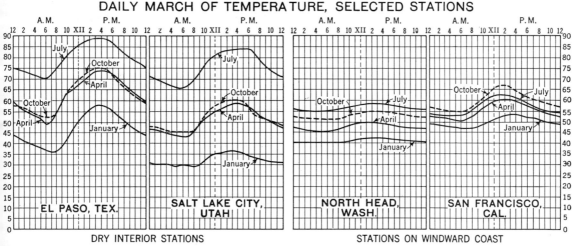

FIG. 1.16. Daily march of temperature at continental and marine stations as represented by the temperature for each hour of day. This is not the same as daily range, which is based on the daily extremes of temperature regardless of the hour of occurrence. Small daily variations in temperature are characteristic of marine climates (Northhead and San Francisco), while they are larger at continental stations. (*After Kincer, in Atlas of American Agriculture, U.S. Dept. of Agriculture.*)

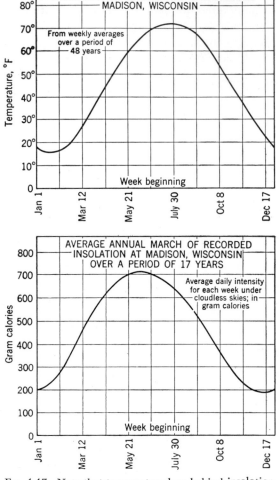

FIG. 1.17. Note that temperature lags behind insolation. Insolation curve has been smoothed slightly.

ing radiosonde, balloon, airplane, and kite ascents show that under normal conditions there is a general *decrease* in temperature with *increasing* elevation. While the rate of decrease is not uniform, varying with time of day, season, and location, the average is approximately 3.6°F. for each 1,000-ft. rise (Fig. 1.19). This is known as the *normal lapse rate*. The lapse rate, or vertical temperature gradient, is approximately 1,000 times greater than the average horizontal rate of temperature change with latitude. Paradoxically the steeper the lapse rate or the more rapid the vertical temperature decrease, the closer to a horizontal position is the temperature-altitude line on the graph chart (Fig. 1.19). A vertical temperature-altitude line indicates an isothermal condition in which there is no change in temperature with altitude. The fact that air temperature is normally highest at low elevations next to the earth and decreases with altitude clearly indicates that atmospheric heat is primarily received directly from the earth's surface and only indirectly from the sun. But the lower air is warmer, not only because it is closest to the direct source of heat, but also because it is denser and contains more water vapor, water particles, and dust, which cause it to be a more efficient absorber of terrestrial radiation than is the thinner, drier, cleaner air aloft. This lower few miles of the atmosphere where most of the mass of air is concentrated is called the *troposphere*. It is the turbulent convective stratum, contains a very large percentage of the dust, water vapor, and clouds, and is the locus of most of the weather phenomena. In it convection causes such a thorough mixing that there is a fairly rapid decrease in temperature upward from the earth's surface. The top of the troposphere varies in height, depending on latitude, from about 7 km. (4 miles) at the high latitudes to 18 km. (10 miles) at the equator (Fig. 1.20).

in middle latitudes, occasionally show this typical oceanic lag in seasonal temperatures. For the interiors of middle-latitude continents, however, July is almost universally the warmest month (Northern Hemisphere) and January the coldest. Annual temperatures are the average of the 12 monthly means, and each of these in turn is the average of the 28 to 31 daily means (Fig. 1.18).

GEOGRAPHICAL DISTRIBUTION OF TEMPERATURE: VERTICAL AND HORIZONTAL

Vertical Distribution

37. Temperature Decreases with Altitude.
Numerous temperature observations made dur-

There is still a good deal of uncertainty concerning temperature variations with altitude in the upper atmosphere, *i.e.*, above the troposphere. Until recently it was thought that everywhere over the earth temperature ceased to change with increasing altitude, above the

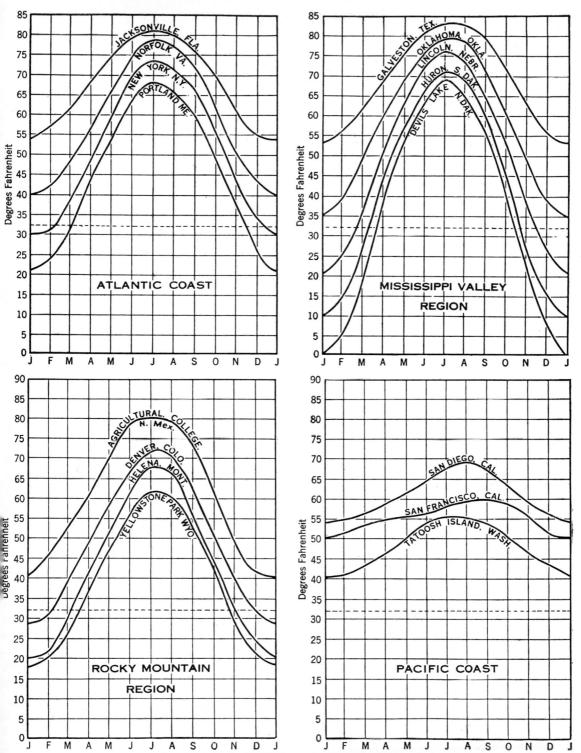

Fig. 1.18. Annual march of temperature at continental and marine stations. It represents the monthly changes in temperature for different parts of the United States and also the latitudinal gradient of the different seasons. The decrease in winter temperature from north to south is large at the interior and leeward-coast stations especially in the Mississippi Valley, whereas in summer the decrease is more moderate. Small seasonal changes in temperature are characteristic of marine climates (see Pacific Coast stations) but they are larger along leeward coasts and interior. (*After Kincer.*)

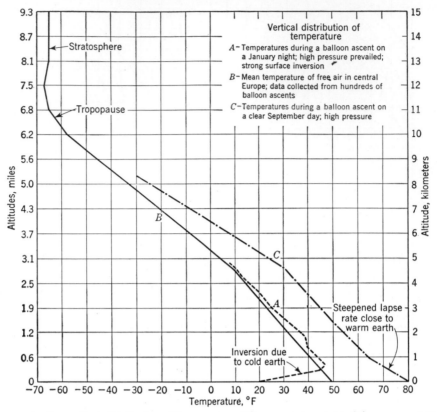

FIG. 1.19. Contrasts in the vertical distribution of temperature (A) on a winter night, (C) on a summer day, and (B) under average conditions. On the B curve the plotting of the temperature is continued up to 9+ miles so that the tropopause and the stratosphere are represented.

troposphere. This high-level isothermal layer was designated the *stratosphere*. Newer evidence seems to indicate that while in the middle and higher latitudes such an isothermal layer probably does prevail, in the tropical latitudes it is not so clearly defined.[1]

38. Inversions of Temperature. Although the normal condition in the lower several miles of atmosphere shows a decrease in temperature with increasing altitude, it not infrequently happens that this condition is reversed for certain strata of the atmosphere so that temperatures temporarily or locally increase with altitude. This condition in which the colder air is nearer the earth and the warmer air aloft is called a *temperature inversion* (Fig. 1.19A).

39. *Surface Inversion.* One of the commonest forms of temperature inversion is that which occurs close to the earth's surface and forms as a

[1] See "Compendium of Meteorology," pp. 303–310.

result of the radiation cooling of the lower air by the underlying surface. Since a land surface is a more effective radiating body than is the atmosphere, nighttime cooling is more rapid at the ground than in the atmosphere. As a consequence the coldest air may be found next to the earth's surface (Fig. 1.19A).

Ideal conditions for surface inversions are (a) long nights, as in winter, so that there will be a relatively long period when outgoing earth radiation exceeds incoming solar radiation; (b) a clear sky or only high cloud so that loss of heat by terrestrial radiation is rapid and unretarded; (c) relatively dry air that absorbs little earth radiation; (d) slight air movement so that little mixing shall take place, and the surface stratum will, as a consequence, have time, by conduction and radiation, to become excessively cold; and (e) a snow-covered surface which, due to reflection of solar energy, heats

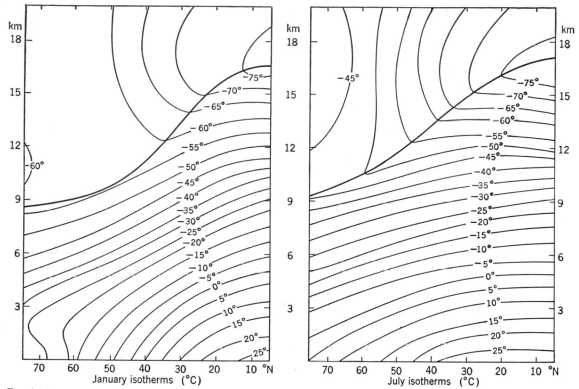

FIG. 1.20. Mean vertical distribution of temperature in degrees centigrade for the extreme months, January and July, Northern Hemisphere. (*After Wexler.*)

little by day, and, being a poor conductor, retards the upward flow of heat from the ground below.[1] At the Eiffel Tower in Paris there is, throughout the year, an increase in temperature upward from base to top between midnight and 4:00 A.M. Over the polar areas a temperature inversion is the normal thing, that condition prevailing in summer as well as winter. It is likewise normal for the night hours of the colder months over the snow-covered land masses of the higher middle latitudes (Fig. 1.21). Over oceans where the diurnal change in surface temperatures is very slight, inversions are most unlikely at night, and the nearest approach to an inversion condition occurs during midday (Fig. 1.22). The mean depth of the polar inversion layer is about 0.6 miles, while in the middle

latitudes it is normally only a few hundred feet. A very close relationship exists between surface temperature inversions and frost phenomena, for conditions favorable for the one are also ideal for the other.

The essential feature of an inversion is the marked stability of the air in which there is an increase in temperature with altitude, so that a pronounced inversion acts as a lid through which convection cannot penetrate and only minor turbulent mixing can take place. All upward and downward movement is suppressed by the stable inversion layer. During surface inversions over cities the smoke from numerous chimneys collects underneath the inversion to form dense smoke fogs. This phenomenon is very common on cold winter mornings. Frequently the smoke is carried upward by turbulence to the ceiling of the inversion where it spreads out laterally to form a definite smoke line. Since turbulence below the inversion ceiling tends to transport

[1] At Milton, Mass., on Feb. 9, 1934, C. F. Brooks recorded a temperature of $-27°$ on the surface of the snow and $+24°$ seven inches below the surface, a difference of $51°$.

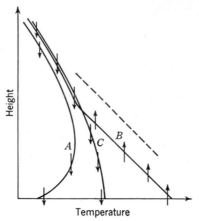

Fig. 1.21. Diurnal variations in vertical distribution of temperature and of stability over land. *A*, early morning; *B*, midday; *C*, evening; broken line, dry adiabat. Arrows indicate direction of the eddy transfer of heat. (*From Petterssen.*)

moisture upward, the relative humidity throughout the inversion layer is likely to be high, which condition favors fog formation. In strong inversions a layer of stratus cloud may form just below the inversion ceiling. While surface inversions are common on flattish land surfaces, they are, nevertheless, most perfectly developed in topographic depressions.

Temperature inversions at or near the earth's surface may also be produced by the horizontal invasion, or advection, of air masses. Such a *dynamic* type of surface inversion may be produced by the advection of cold air below or of warm air above. Inversions resulting from advection can be much more extensive than the local ones of radiation origin and consequently are often of greater climatic importance. The large and intense surface inversions which develop over the northern lowlands of Eurasia and North America in the cooler seasons can only be explained in terms of advected air masses.

40. *Diurnal Variations in the Vertical Distribution of Temperature over Continents and Oceans.* Since a land surface changes temperature sharply between day and night, it is to be expected that the lowest layers of the atmosphere lying closest to the earth will also show large diurnal variations in vertical temperature structure (Fig. 1.21). During daylight hours the lower air over land characteristically will show a greatly

steepened lapse rate with warmest air closest to the earth. At night, on the other hand, a surface temperature inversion will ordinarily prevail, so that the greatest diurnal variation in temperature is in the surface layers.

Since the ocean surface changes only very slightly in temperature between day and night, the air next to it does likewise. Somewhat higher up where temperature changes are controlled by radiation the diurnal variations in temperatures are somewhat greater. The result is that the steepest lapse rate and greatest atmospheric instability are characteristic of night (Fig. 1.22). This is just the reverse of the situation over the land surface.

41. *Surface Inversions and Air Drainage.* In regions of uneven surface configuration, the cold inversion stratum of air next to the earth's surface, because of its greater density, slips off the uplands and flows down into surrounding lowlands (Fig. 1.23). This phenomenon of the collecting of cold air, drained from the adjacent slopes, in valleys and lowlands is designated as *air drainage.* It is a well-known fact that the first frosts of autumn and the last in spring occur in bottom lands, while the lowest minima on calm, clear winter nights are found in similar locations. On one occasion, during a cold spell, a temperature of −8.9° was registered on top of Mount Washington, N.H., while records of −23 to −31° were recorded in the surrounding lowlands. Citrus orchards in California, which are

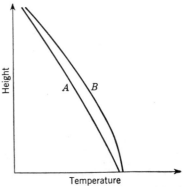

Fig. 1.22. Diurnal variations in vertical distribution of temperature over oceans. *A*, night; *B*, midday. Note that the lapse rate in the lower atmosphere is steeper at night than at midday, which is the reverse of conditions over land. (*From Petterssen.*)

quite intolerant of frost, are located on the upper slopes of alluvial fans where air drainage causes a slipping off of the dense frosty air, while the colder lower slopes and bottoms are given over to hardier deciduous fruits and nuts or to field crops. Coffee in Brazil is prevailingly planted on the rolling uplands, while the frosty valleys are avoided. Resort hotels in the Swiss Alps shun the cold, foggy valleys and choose instead sites on the brighter and warmer slopes above. So definite and sharp is the autumn frost line along certain of the valley slopes in the Blue Ridge Mountains that one can trace it by means of the color line between the darkened, frozen vegetation below and the brighter, living green of that above. At times the lower part of a bush may be frozen while the top is untouched.

42. Upper-air Inversions. Inversions may also develop in the free atmosphere as a result of large-scale subsidence of thick and extensive air masses and the spreading laterally of this descending air. In this subsidence aloft the descending air is heated by compression while the more turbulent lower air not involved in the subsidence is not affected. The result is the development of a warm, dry stratum of air aloft overlying a cooler stratum underneath so that an inversion has been developed. Such an upper-air inversion has the effect of stabilizing the air and preventing the development of deep convectional overturning. Upper-air inversions, therefore, are associated with drought conditions.

This type of upper-air inversion is very common in relatively stationary high-pressure anticyclonic systems such as the subtropical highs and the stationary seasonal highs which develop over the middle-latitude continents in winter. The poleward parts of the trade winds are also characterized by strong upper-air inversions resulting from subsidence, but the inversion becomes weaker and is located at higher levels as the trades approach the equatorial convergence zone. The above facts regarding the trade-wind inversion are significant in explaining the dry nature of the trades near their source regions in the subtropical highs and their increasing showeriness as they approach the equatorial convergence. Within the subtropical anticyclonic

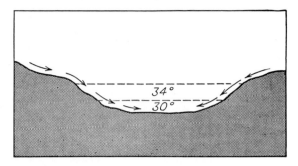

FIG. 1.23. Cold air, because it is denser, tends to settle into the valley bottoms. This drainage of cold air into depressions is the reason why frost is more prevalent and more severe in low places than it is on adjacent slopes.

cells the inversion is much stronger and exists at lower elevations in the eastern portions of the cells than along their western margins. Greater stability and intensified drought therefore characterize the eastern parts of the subtropical highs.

Horizontal Distribution

43. Isothermal Maps. Temperature distribution over the earth is shown on Figs. 1.24, 1.25, by means of isotherms, *i.e.*, lines connecting places of the same temperature. Thus all points on the earth's surface through which any one isotherm passes have identical average temperatures. It would be entirely feasible to cover the world map with figures representing the temperatures of hundreds of stations, but such a map would be very cumbersome to use. Without scrutinizing each figure it would be difficult to determine, for instance, the regions of highest or lowest temperatures. But if lines are drawn on such a map connecting places of the same average temperature, then one can see at a glance many of the significant facts of thermal distribution. On Figs. 1.24 and 1.25 all temperatures have been reduced to sea level so that the effects of altitude are eliminated. If this were not done, the complications and details induced by mountains and other lesser relief forms would render the maps so confusing that the general world-wide effects of latitude and of land-and-water distribution would be difficult to perceive. These maps of sea-level isotherms are not so useful to agriculturists, engineers, and others

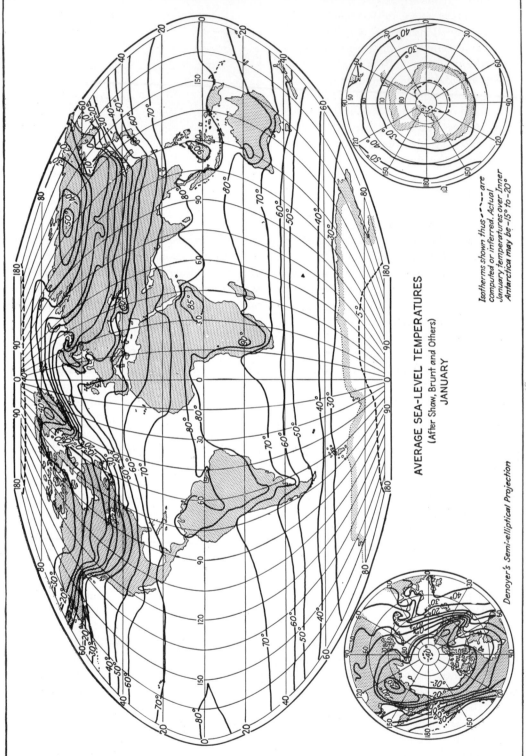

AVERAGE SEA-LEVEL TEMPERATURES
(After Shaw, Brunt and Others)
JANUARY

Denoyer's Semi-elliptical Projection

Isotherms shown thus —·—·— are
computed or inferred. Actual
January temperatures over Inner
Antarctica may be –15° to –20°

FIG. 1.24.

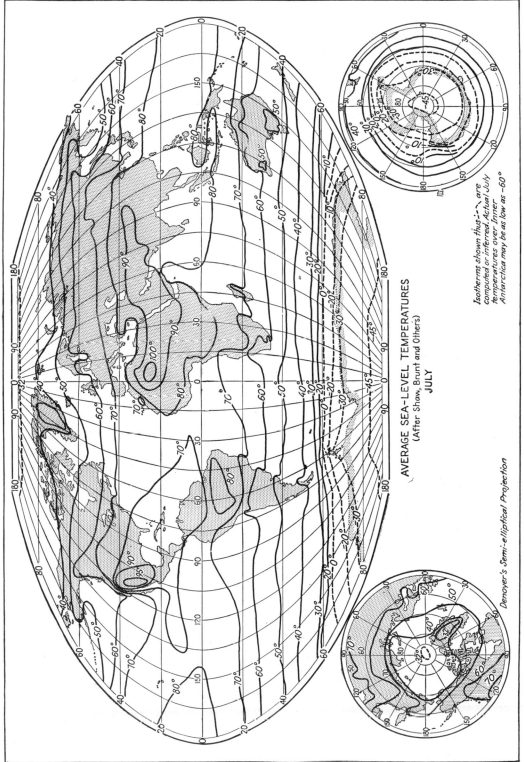

AVERAGE SEA-LEVEL TEMPERATURES
(After Shaw, Brunt and Others)
JULY

Denoyer's Semi-elliptical Projection

Isotherms shown thus ≈ are
computed or inferred. Actual July
temperatures over inner
Antarctica may be as low as −60°

FIG. 1.25.

who desire to put their data to practical use as those showing *actual* surface temperatures.

Isotherms in general trend east-west, roughly following the parallels (Figs. 1.24, 1.25). This is not unexpected, since, except for differences in the transparency of the atmosphere, all places in the same latitude, or along the same parallel, receive identical amounts of solar energy. This east-west trend of isotherms indicates that latitude is the single greatest cause of temperature contrasts. On no parallel of latitude at any season are temperature differences so great as between poles and equator.

It will be noted that there are some parts of the earth where the isotherms are closely spaced, indicating that temperature changes rapidly in a horizontal direction, and other parts where the isotherms are widely spaced, signifying slight horizontal temperature differences. The rate of change of temperature is called the *temperature gradient*. Closely spaced isotherms, therefore, signify a steep horizontal temperature gradient, and widely spaced isotherms represent a weak temperature gradient.

44. *Features of Annual Temperature Distribution.* The highest average annual temperatures are in the low latitudes, where, for the year, the largest amounts of insolation are received, while the average lowest temperatures are in the vicinity of the poles, the regions of least annual insolation (Figs. 1.24, 1.25). Some recently obtained vertical sections through the atmosphere seem to show that, in certain longitudes at least, there are only very slight temperature differences within a low-latitude zone of about 45° in width. This would indicate that there is a near absence of north-south temperature gradients within parts of the tropics. It is suggested that the heavier cloud cover near the equator reduces the amount of insolation so greatly as to diminish the heating in these rainier parts of the inner tropics compared with clearer areas farther away from the equator.

Isotherms tend to be straighter and are also more widely spaced in the Southern Hemisphere, the surface of which is more homogeneous, in this case largely water. The greatest deviations from east-west courses are where the isotherms

pass from continents to oceans, or vice versa. That is caused by the contrasting heating and cooling properties of land and water surfaces and the effects of ocean currents. After latitude or sun, land and water are the next greatest control of temperature distribution. Cool ocean currents off the coasts of Peru and northern Chile, southern California, and southwestern Africa make themselves conspicuous through the *equatorward* bending of the isotherms. Similarly, warm currents in higher latitudes cause isotherms to bend *poleward*, this condition being most marked off the coast of northwestern Europe.

45. January and July Temperatures. For the earth in general, January and July represent the seasonal extremes of temperature. Following are some of the more significant features of temperature distribution as shown on the seasonal maps (Figs. 1.24, 1.25). (*a*) From a comparison of the two maps it is obvious that there is a marked latitudinal shifting of the isotherms between July and January, following the latitudinal migration of sun's rays and insolation belts. (*b*) The migrations of isotherms are much greater over continents than over oceans because of the former's greater extremes of temperature. (*c*) The highest temperatures on both January and July maps are over land areas, while the lowest temperatures in January emphatically are over Asia and North America, the largest land masses in the middle and higher latitudes. (*d*) In the Northern Hemisphere the January isotherms bend abruptly equatorward over the colder continents and poleward over the warmer oceans, while in July exactly the opposite conditions prevail. (*e*) No such seasonal contrasts between land and water as exist north of the equator are to be found in the Southern Hemisphere, for there large land masses are absent in the higher middle latitudes. (*f*) The lowest temperature on the January map is over northeastern Asia, the leeward side of the largest land mass in higher middle latitudes. The next lowest temperatures are over Greenland and North America. (*g*) Temperature gradients (rates of change of temperature), like insolation gradients, are steeper in winter than in summer.

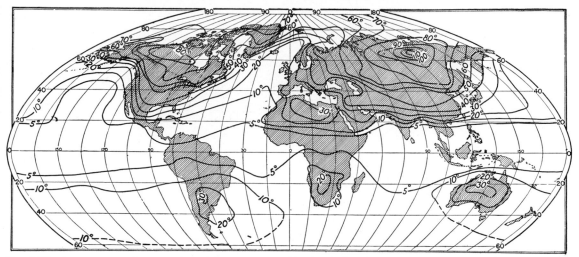

FIG. 1.26. Average annual ranges of temperature are smallest in the low latitudes and over oceans. They are largest over continents in the middle and higher latitudes.

Close spacing of isotherms is particularly conspicuous over the continents of the Northern Hemisphere in January.

46. Annual Ranges of Temperature. By the annual range of temperature is meant the difference between the average temperatures of the warmest and coldest months. The largest annual ranges of temperature are over the Northern Hemisphere continents which become alternately hot in summer and cold in winter (Fig. 1.26). Ranges are never large (*a*) near the equator, where insolation varies little; or (*b*) over large water bodies. For the latter reason ranges are everywhere small in the middle latitudes of the Southern Hemisphere. In general, they increase toward the higher latitudes but much more markedly over the continents than over the oceans.

47. Isanomalous Temperatures. An isothermal map for the world shows a temperature distribution, which is caused by (*a*) the balance between incoming solar radiation and outgoing earth radiation on a homogeneous earth's surface, upon which is superimposed (*b*) a field of disturbances produced by such terrestrial phenomena as unequal heating and cooling of land and water surfaces, ocean currents, prevailing streams of air flow, etc. If it is desired to separate the effects of these two temperature controls it may be done by (*a*) determining the

mean temperatures of the parallels, which presents a temperature distribution controlled by radiation on a homogeneous earth, and (*b*) subsequently determining the difference between the observed mean temperatures of places and the mean temperatures of their parallels. The difference between the mean temperature of any place and the mean temperature of its parallel is called its *thermal anomaly*, and it represents the amount of deviation from the normal caused by the terrestrial controls. If lines, called *isanomals*, are drawn on a world map, joining places of equal thermal anomaly, an isanomalous map is the result (Figs. 1.27 and 1.28).

The greatest thermal anomalies are in the Northern Hemisphere where extensive land masses and oceans occupy middle-latitude locations. In the relatively homogeneous Southern Hemisphere, temperature deviations from the mean for the parallel are much less. On the *January* map positive anomalies are found over the oceans and negative ones over the continents. The greatest positive anomalies are along the eastern sides of middle-latitude oceans and the adjacent western margins of the continents where warm ocean waters prevail. Northwestern Europe has the extreme positive anomaly on the earth, a little town on the Norwegian coast at 63°N., being 46° too warm for its latitude in January. The extreme negative anomaly is in

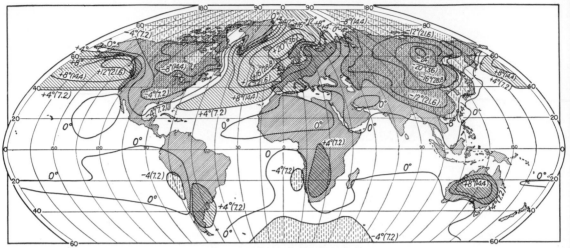

ISANOMALIES OF TEMPERATURE
IN DEGREES CENTIGRADE FAHRENHEIT EQUIVALENTS
IN PARENTHESES
(After Hann-Süring)

JANUARY

FIG. 1.27. Note that the principal negative anomalies are over the large Northern Hemisphere continents, while the important positive anomalies are over the Northern Hemisphere oceans, especially the eastern portions.

northeastern Siberia, which is 46° colder than the average for its parallel. Both the positive anomalies over the oceans and the negative anomalies over the continents are shifted away from the centers of the land or water areas toward the eastern or leeward sides.

In *summer* the situation is reversed and the continents have positive anomalies, while the oceans have negative ones. For the *year as a whole* the continents show negative anomalies poleward from about latitude 40°, and positive anomalies farther equatorward.

48. Air Temperature and Sensible Temperature. Correct *air temperature* can be obtained

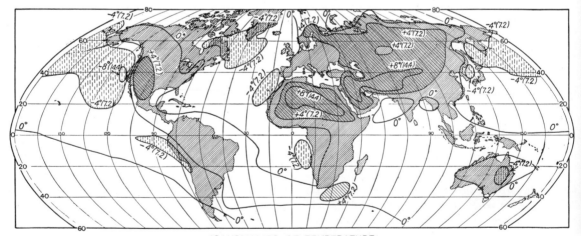

ISANOMALIES OF TEMPERATURE
IN DEGREES CENTIGRADE. FAHRENHEIT EQUIVALENTS
IN PARENTHESES
(After Hann-Süring)

JULY

FIG. 1.28.

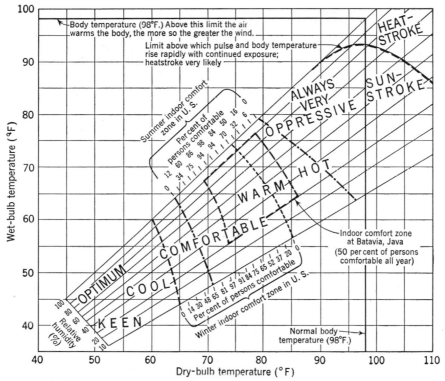

FIG. 1.29. Comfort and subjective sensations at various temperatures and humidities for normally clothed and resting persons according to indoor-chamber experiments and ordinary experience outdoors. The indoor comfort zones shown are based on controlled-chamber studies with almost still air and no sunshine; the effect of wind would be to shift the zone some degrees to the lower left of the chart, that is, toward lower wet- and dry-bulb temperature, while the effect of sunshine would be to shift the zone to the upper right (toward higher wet- and dry-bulb temperature). The terms in capital letters describing various subjective sensations, COOL, COMFORTABLE, WARM, etc., give the outdoor feelings of most people when the general outdoor temperatures are in the regions where the terms are located on the diagram, assuming average conditions of wind and sunshine, customary clothing, and moderate activity and that the individuals are used to those temperatures. There is considerable overlapping of the zones of neighboring sensations on the chart, owing to differences in sun and wind and in acclimatization and clothing of the individual. A comparison of the Java and United States winter indoor comfort zones indicates the magnitude of the shift in the comfort zone from the cooler climates to the Tropics or vice versa. Comparing the indoor with the outdoor sensations of warmth or coolness, one notes that with some sunshine, proper clothing, and physical exercise it is likely to be comfortable at lower temperatures outdoors than indoors at rest. On the too-warm side, however, exercise, sunshine, and clothing make one more uncomfortable at lower temperatures outdoors than indoors at rest. In the lower left of the diagram is an "optimum for civilization" zone, which extends to still lower temperatures (35°F.) than shown. This is roughly the climate which Ellsworth Huntington has suggested as most conducive to human physical and intellectual activity, for he found some evidence that people are healthier, produce more goods, and have more advanced culture in regions of the earth where mean temperatures in this approximate range prevail, along with sufficient yearly range and day-to-day variability to be stimulating. It is not a "comfort zone," however, as one can readily see. All the data for this figure are so crude and subject to so many limitations of interpretation that one should not attempt to read it in much detail; it rather serves to illustrate the general principles and very approximate order of magnitude of the contrasts. (*Courtesy of Robert G. Stone and the 1941 Yearbook of Agriculture.*)

only by an accurate thermometer *properly exposed*. One of the principal items of correct exposure is to see that the instrument is not in the sun; otherwise it receives energy not only from the surrounding air but from the absorption of insolation as well. It also should be protected from direct radiation from the ground and adjacent buildings.

49. *Sensible temperature* refers to the sensation of temperature that the human body feels, as distinguished from actual air temperature that is recorded by a properly exposed thermometer. Unlike a thermometer that has no temperature of its own, the human body, as well as that of every warm-blooded animal, is a heat engine, generating energy at a relatively fixed rate when at rest. Anything, therefore, that affects the *rate of loss* of heat from the body affects physical comfort.

A certain amount of heat produced by the body must be given off in order to maintain the proper heat balance. If the local climate is so hot as to prevent this heat loss the person feels uncomfortable, and a continuance of the condition may result in a heat stroke. On the other hand if the environment is so cold that heat losses from the body cannot be compensated for, then chilling and eventual death may result.

The factors controlling the heat comfort of the human body are numerous. Air temperature is the most important factor, but wind, relative humidity, and radiation are also influential. Thus a *humid* hot day is more uncomfortable than one of dry heat with the same temperature, since loss of heat by evaporation is retarded more when the air is humid. A *windy* cold day feels uncomfortable because the loss of heat is speeded up by greater evaporation and the more rapid conduction of heat from the body by a continuing removal of the warm air surrounding it and its replacement by cold air. A sunny day in winter feels less cold than it actually may be, owing to the body's absorption of direct insolation. Cold air containing moisture particles is particularly penetrating because the skin becomes moist, and evaporation results, while further loss of heat results from contact with the cold water. The rate of heat loss by radiation is greater in dry than in humid air. Because of its sensitiveness to factors other than air temperature, the human body is not a very accurate thermometer.

It is obvious that no instrument can measure accurately the human body's feeling with respect to a temperature condition (Fig. 1.29). Probably the best available instrument is what is known as a *wet-bulb thermometer*, which is simply an ordinary thermometer whose bulb is covered with saturated gauze or some other freely evaporating surface. The evaporation from the saturated gauze reduces the temperature of the wet-bulb thermometer below that of the dry bulb, and the amount of depression of the wet-bulb temperature varies inversely with the relative dryness of the atmosphere. The average depression of the wet-bulb thermometer in July, for southwestern Arizona, at the time of maximum temperature, is over 30°. This indicates a very dry atmosphere with ample opportunity for evaporation so that the extremely high temperatures of that region are not so oppressive as they might appear, since the sensible temperature has been reduced.

Other Temperature Data and Their Uses[1]

50. Means, Frequencies, and Deviations. The arithmetic mean, which is the sum of all observations divided by the number of observations, is the factor most often used to represent climatic conditions. Mean annual temperature, mean monthly temperature of January, July, or some other month, mean of the daily maximum temperatures for July or the minimum temperatures for January—these are illustrations of a few of the commonly used means. For example, the mean January temperature for Madison, Wis., may be computed by adding the average January temperatures for each of the 60+ years for which observations exist, and dividing this sum by the number of years represented.

[1] For a brief treatment of the use of climatological data, see Helmut Landsberg, "Physical Climatology," pp. 53–75. For a more detailed treatment, see V. Conrad and L. W. Pollok, "Methods in Climatology," 2d ed., Harvard University Press, Cambridge, Mass., 1950.

Means alone, however, give a very incomplete representation of actual climatic conditions. For example, the mean annual temperatures of Boston and Oxford (England) are both approximately 49°F.; yet the monthly means from which the annual means were computed are very different. In the case of Oxford the monthly means are grouped more closely about the annual mean, the coldest month being only 11° below and the warmest month 13° above the mean. For Boston,

Mean Monthly and Annual Temperatures

	J	F	M	A	M	J	J	A	S	O	N	D	Yr.
Boston	27	28	35	45	57	66	71	69	63	52	41	32	49
Oxford	38	40	42	47	53	59	62	61	57	49	44	40	49

on the other hand, the warm month is 22+° warmer, and the cold month 22° colder than the annual average. It is obvious that there are striking temperature differences between Boston and Oxford even though they have similar mean annual temperatures. The same criticism can be made of other temperature means and of means of rainfall, winds, and the rest of the climatic elements.

A much more satisfactory picture of climate is provided if, in addition to arithmetic means, the *frequency of occurrence* of certain climatic values is included. Frequency is defined as the number of times a certain value occurs within a specified interval; for example, the frequency of hours during which the temperature at a station was within a certain limit. A very important type of frequency is the number of occurrences of a certain deviation or departure from the mean. For example, the average temperature at Philadelphia for a period of 60 years was 54.4°. The departures of the individual yearly averages from 54.4° were computed and their mean determined with the results shown in the table below. The significance of such temperature deviations scarcely needs comment. When the same technique is applied to monthly means, the deviations are ordinarily more striking. For example, the mean departure of the monthly mean temperature for winter months in northern Russia is as much as 3.09° and in interior North America 2.54°.

Frequencies of Deviation of Annual Temperatures from 60-year Mean at Philadelphia
(From Landsberg)

Temp. deviation	−3°	−2°	−1°	0°	+1°	+2°	+3°
Number of cases	4	5	10	17	18	4	2

Mean Departures of Monthly Means
(From Hann)

	Winter	Summer	Mean
Interior of North America	2.54	1.20	1.95
Northern Russia	3.43	1.61	2.33
Northern Germany	2.02	0.93	1.28
Northern slope of Alps	2.28	1.06	1.56
England	1.41	0.95	1.24

51. The Annual Temperature Curve (March of Temperature). From the annual course or march of temperature, as represented by a line joining the 12 monthly means, one can discover a number of temperature characteristics.

One characteristic is the *range of variation, i.e.*, the difference between the temperature of the warmest and coldest month. Ordinarily this is

Fig. 1.30. Annual temperature curves of Barnaul, U.S.S.R., and San Diego, Calif.; to illustrate symmetry.

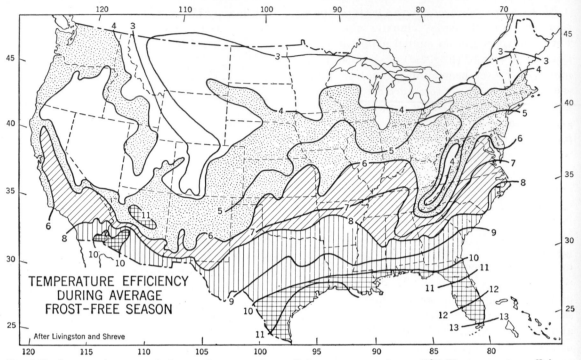

FIG. 1.31. In most plants growth does not become active until the temperature rises to 40°F. The temperature efficiency of an area is the effectiveness of temperature in promoting plant growth. It varies with the number of days having temperatures above 40° and with the amount of the temperature rise above that point. The numbers on the map represent efficiency units in hundreds.

called the *annual range*. A second characteristic is the *phase*, which refers to the month with the highest and the month with the lowest temperature. At most stations in the middle latitudes July is the warmest month and January the coldest, so that the lag of temperature behind insolation is about a month or a little less. But over the oceans and at various marine stations located on islands or on windward coasts, the phase is different, and August and February are not uncommonly the months of maximum and minimum. At San Francisco, for example, while January is the coldest month, September is the warmest. In regions of strong monsoons, such as India, the highest temperature is frequently in May, which precedes the time of maximum cloudiness and rainfall (June-July-August) when the amount of solar radiation reaching the earth's surface is greatly diminished.

A third characteristic of the annual temperature curve is its *symmetrical* or *asymmetrical* nature. There are two axes of symmetry, and

therefore symmetry can be analyzed in two directions. One axis of symmetry is the straight line *B*-7, which is the ordinate of the month of July. In a symmetrical curve the area 1-*A*-*B*-7 (Fig. 1.30) should equal the area 7-*B*-*C*-1. In the annual curve for Barnaul, a typical continental station, this is approximately true, but it is far from the case in the San Diego curve. At San Diego the latter half of the year is considerably warmer than the first half, so that fall is warmer than spring. The importance of this fact upon all biotic forms requires no discussion.

The second axis of symmetry (Fig. 1.30) is the straight line *ACD*, which is the mean of the monthly mean temperatures, and symmetry with respect to it is determined by measuring the stretch along the mean line covered by the upper part of the curve as compared with the lower part. For example, in the Barnaul curve *AC* is somewhat longer than *CD*, while in the San Diego curve *CD* is longer than *AC*. On the whole, curves that are above the mean a longer time than they are below indicate a longer period of vegetation growth.

52. Mean Duration of Certain Temperatures.

There are certain recognized temperatures such as 32°, the freezing point of water; 40 or 42°, the approximate temperature at which seeds germinate and plants begin to function; and perhaps 50°, often given as the lower limit of human comfort, which are relatively critical. The dates on which an annual temperature curve rises above such important thresholds and sinks below them, and the time between these dates, is of great significance climatically.

Although plants ordinarily are not killed by cool temperatures above 32°, it is true, nevertheless, that for many species growth does not become active until a temperature of about 40° is reached. The effectiveness of temperature in promoting plant growth, or the *temperature efficiency*, is therefore measured by the number of days with temperatures above 40°, and the amount of rise above that point (Fig. 1.31). A high-temperature efficiency is obviously an advantage, for with it the possibilities of crop diversification are greater.

Each crop has its own basic temperature at which growth begins and each crop also requires a certain number of heat units to bring it to maturity. Thus peas germinate at a temperature of 40°F. but for sweet corn 50°F. is required. As a rule the rate of maturing is approximately doubled for each 10°C., or 18°F., increase in temperature. For peas each Fahrenheit degree above a mean daily temperature of 40° is a *growing degree-day*, or heat unit. For sweet corn each unit above the mean daily temperature of 50° is a heat unit. For peas, therefore, on a day when the mean temperature is 52° there would accumulate 52 − 40 = 12 growing degree-days. Similarly on a day whose mean temperature is 70°, the growing degree-days would amount to 30. Data on growing degree-days serve as a guide in crop planting and in forecasting dates of crop maturity. If 1,500 heat units are required for maturity, the field of peas will theoretically be harvested when this number has actually accumulated. The application of the heat-unit theory is particularly suited to perishable crops

such as peas, sweet corn, lima beans, and spinach, leading to better scheduled plantings with a more orderly harvest (Fig. 1.32).

Heating engineers have discovered that the difference between 65°F. and the mean outside temperature for a day, a week, or any other period is an accurate index of the fuel required for heating a building. Thus the heating fuel consumed in a month having an average daily mean temperature of 15°F. as compared to a month with a corresponding temperature of

40°F. would be as $\frac{65 - 15}{65 - 40} = \frac{50}{25}$, or twice as

great. The unit used is the *heating degree-day*, which is defined as a departure of 1° per day from 65°. If the mean outside temperature for a day is 25°, the number of degree-days for that 24-hr. period would be 65 − 25, or 40. The degree-days for any longer period are computed by determining the number of degrees the mean temperature for each individual day falls below 65° and totaling them for the period. Degree-day records compiled over a period of many years

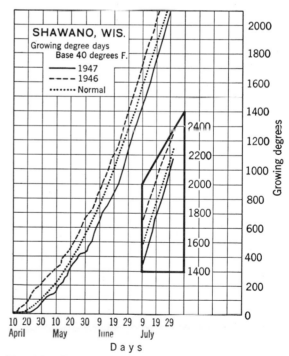

Fig. 1.32. Example of increase in growing degree-days at Shawano, Wis. (*Courtesy of U.S. Weather Bureau.*)

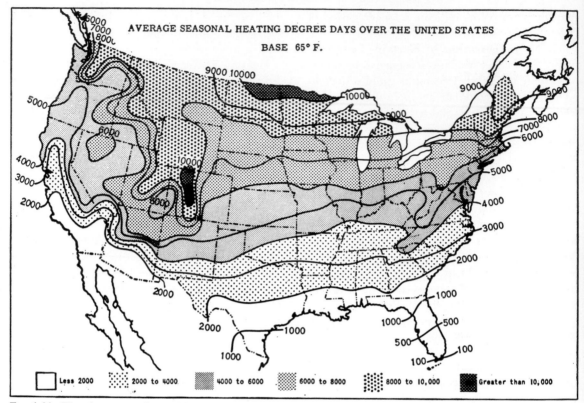

FIG. 1.33. The above map shows the average number of degree-days over the United States. The heavy lines connect points having approximately the same average number of degree-days per season. For example, every point through which the "5000" line passes has an average degree-day total of about 5000. The complex pattern in the western states is due to the influence of the mountains. (*Courtesy of U.S. Weather Bureau.*)

are used by the Weather Bureau in establishing monthly averages of degree-days for the entire country (Fig. 1.33). These form the basis for estimating fuel requirements and consumption. Shortly after the close of each month daily degree-day totals are computed and assembled by the Weather Bureau for more than 300 locations, and are published in the *Heating Degree-day Bulletin.*

53. *The Frost-free Season.* The duration of the period with temperatures above 32° is known as the frost-free period or growing season (Figs. 1.34, 1.35). A short frost-free period is a handicap to agricultural production, for it greatly limits the number and kind of crops that can be grown. The greater diversity of crops that is possible with a long frost-free season increases the stability of agriculture and tends to make it more profitable. Figure 1.35 purports to show in a

generalized way the duration of the frost-free period for the land areas of the earth. The extensive areas in the tropics where frost never occurs are, in general, not the regions of greatest present-day development. These regions do have great potentialities, however. Where the frost-free period is less than 90 days the opportunities for agricultural development are extremely meager. The *average* length of the frost-free, or growing, season may not be sufficiently refined data with which to plan agricultural production, for, if the departures from this average are relatively frequent and large, crop losses from spring and fall frosts may offset the profits accumulated in normal years. The length of period in which the chance of killing frost is small enough to permit profitable agriculture is the available growing season in four-fifths or nine-tenths of the years. This is sometimes called the *effective growing season* (Fig. 1.36). Usually it is, depending on the locality, between 15 and 50 days less than the average number of days without killing frost.

54. Frost and Frost Protection. The term "frost" may be applied either (*a*) to the white deposit of condensed water vapor in solid form (hoarfrost) or (*b*) to a temperature of 32° or below, even though there is no deposit of white frost. There are frosts of various degrees of severity; but it is the "killing frost," which may be defined as a temperature condition "of sufficient severity to be generally destructive to the staple products of the locality," that is of principal interest to geographers. When it is difficult by direct observation of destructive effects to determine the dates of the first killing frost in autumn and the last in spring, and thereby the length of the frost-free, or growing, season, the first and last dates on which a minimum temperature of 32° was recorded are accepted. Throughout most of the middle latitudes, frosts are of chief significance in autumn and spring, although in subtropical latitudes, such as California and Florida, midwinter frosts are critical because of the active growth of sensitive crops during that season. On the poleward margins of the intermediate zones, on the other hand, in such regions as northern Canada and northern Eurasia, summer frosts not infrequently do

serious damage to cereal crops. In tropical lowlands freezing temperatures are largely absent.

It is a general misconception that a Weather Bureau warning of frost conditions is equivalent to a forecast of general subfreezing air temperatures. On the contrary, local killing frosts may occur in favorable sites when the average temperature of the air, at several feet above the ground, over a wide area is still several degrees above freezing, or 32°F. It should be kept in mind that the Weather Bureau's forecasted temperature refers to conditions 5 or 6 ft. above the ground, so that it is quite possible to have below-freezing temperatures, and perhaps a deposit of white frost if the humidity is sufficient, at the ground and particularly in low places, while the general air temperature is above freezing.

55. Conditions Favorable for Frost. Ideal conditions for the occurrence of frost are those that are conducive to rapid and prolonged surface cooling, *viz.*, (*a*) a preliminary importation of a mass of chilly polar air, (*b*) followed by clear, dry, calm nights during which the surface air, by radiation and conduction, may be reduced below freezing. The original importation provides the necessary mass of cool air the temperature of which is already relatively low, although still somewhat above freezing, while further

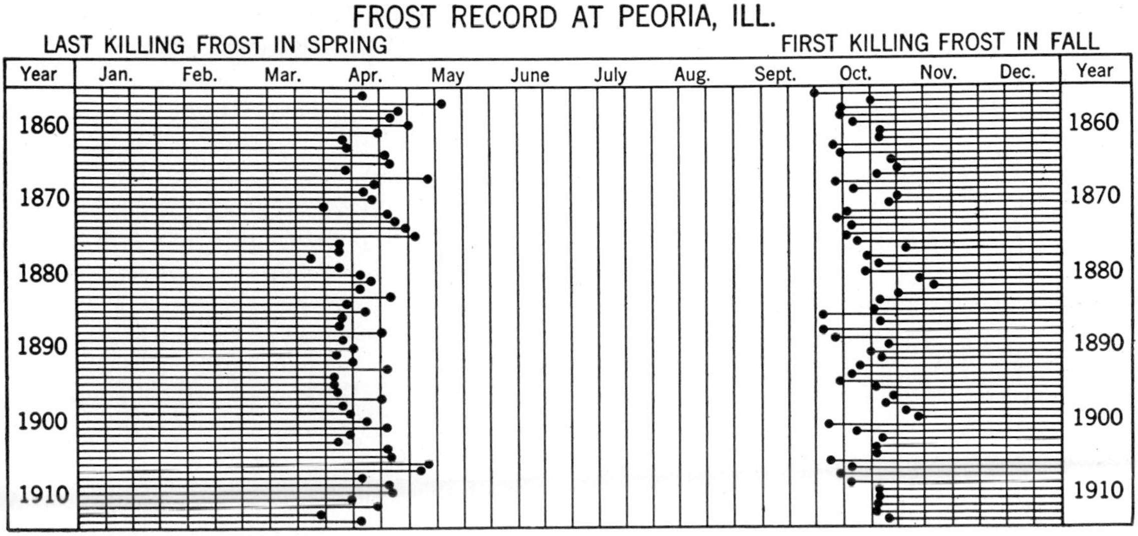

FROST RECORD AT PEORIA, ILL.

FIG. 1.34. (*From Atlas of American Agriculture, U.S. Dept. of Agriculture.*)

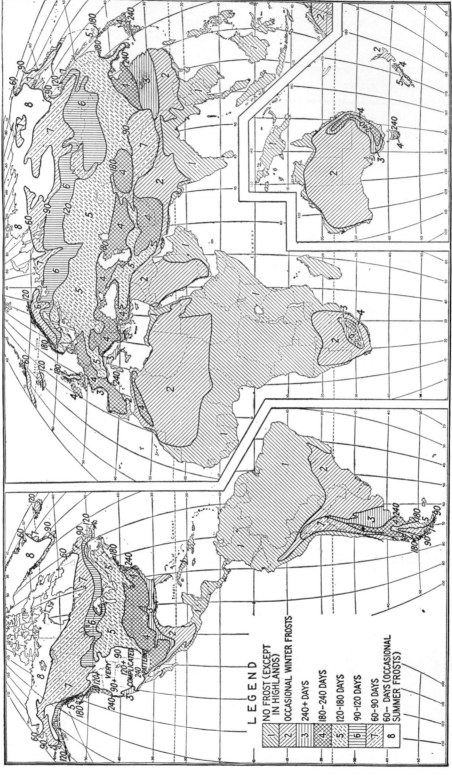

Fig. 1.35. Average length of the frost-free period, or growing season, in days. (*From Great Soviet World Atlas, Vol. I.*)

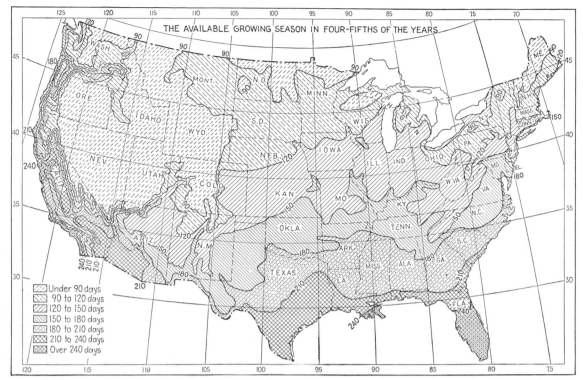

FIG. 1.36. The effective crop season in 4 years out of 5. (*From Atlas of American Agriculture, U.S. Dept. of Agriculture.*)

rapid loss of heat by earth radiation during the following clear night is all that is necessary to reduce the temperature of the surface air below freezing. But even though the generally favorable conditions for frost occurrence described above may prevail over extensive areas, the destructive effects very often are local and patchy. This is a matter chiefly of surface configuration and air drainage.

56. *Frost Prevention and Protection.*[1] The problem of artificial protection from frost is of genuine significance only in regions of highly sensitive and valuable crops which occupy restricted areas. It is obviously quite impossible to protect such extensively grown field crops as corn or small grains, even when Weather

[1] Rudolph Geiger, "The Climate Near the Ground," translation by Milroy N. Stewart and others, Harvard University Press, pp. 403–412, Cambridge, Mass., 1950; O. W. Kessler and W. D. Kaempfert, "Frostschaden-verhütung," *Wiss. Abhandl.*, Reichsamt für Wetterdienst, Berlin, 1940; Floyd D. Young, Frost and the Prevention of Frost Damage, *Farmers Bull.* 1588, U.S. Department of Agriculture.

Bureau warnings are issued 12 to 24 hr. in advance of the anticipated freeze. The highly valuable citrus groves of California and Florida, and important truck and market garden regions occupying only restricted areas, present a somewhat different problem, however. Most field crops in the middle latitudes are annuals planted late enough in spring to avoid frost. If fall-sown, they do not reach a stage of growth such as to be injured by frost until the danger from spring frosts is past. These crops of annuals ordinarily are harvested in summer or early fall before frosts are likely to occur, although in the latitude of southern Wisconsin, corn not infrequently is damaged by early frosts. Particularly sensitive annuals such as garden crops and orchards, and other fruit crops of the perennial type, are those requiring special precautions to minimize the danger of frost. This may be done either (a) by choosing a site for the sensitive crop where there is least danger of frost or (b) by adopting special measures for preventing frost occurrence. Two types of sites relatively freer

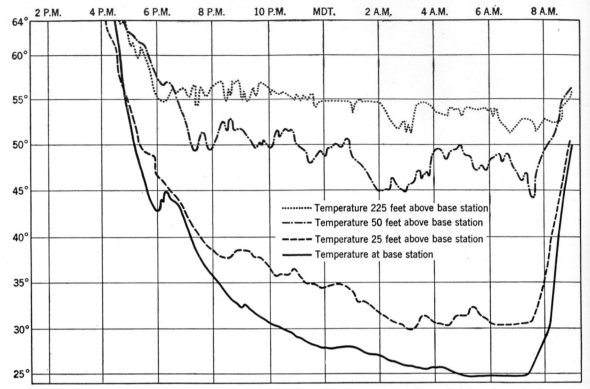

FIG. 1.37. Records of the temperature from 4 P.M. to 9 A.M. at the base and at different heights above the base of a steep hillside, showing the great differences that sometimes develop on a clear, still night. Although the temperature at the base was low enough to cause considerable damage to fruit, the lowest at 225 ft. above on the slope was only 51°F. (*Courtesy of U.S. Weather Bureau.*)

from frost than the immediate surroundings are (*a*) slopes and (*b*) coasts on the windward side of fairly large bodies of water (Fig. 1.37). The former are warmer because of the phenomenon of air drainage. The latter get their protection from the regulatory effects upon temperatures of adjacent bodies of water. These water influences are conspicuous only along the windward coasts. The important fruit belts along the southeastern shore of Lake Michigan, bordering Lake Erie, and along the south shore of Lake Ontario attest to this protective influence of water bodies against frost.

But dangerous frosts are occasionally inevitable even on the most favorable sites. Damage to sensitive crops over restricted areas may be prevented or lessened by (*a*) retarding the loss of heat from the earth by checking radiation or (*b*) maintaining a temperature above freezing immediately around the threatened crop by artificial heating. Radiation may be checked by spreading over the crop some nonmetallic covering such as paper, straw, or cloth, thereby intercepting the heat being radiated from the ground and plants. The purpose of the cover, quite obviously, is not to keep the cold out but to keep the heat in. This inexpensive type of frost protection is the one resorted to by the housewife in saving her garden plants from freezing. It is not so well suited to the protection of extensive orchard areas, however.

In California and Florida the huge losses in the citrus areas resulting from an occasional killing frost have inspired the most careful and sustained experimentation in frost-fighting methods. One single January frost in California resulted in a total citrus loss of $50,000,000. A considerable number of protective devices, most of them of little or no practical value, have been constructed and tried out in the citrus groves. The orchard heater, consisting of a sheet-metal cylinder containing about a gallon of diesel oil, is today, however, the only practical means known of obtaining complete protection from low temperatures in orchards. Smudging has proved ineffective. In the cranberry areas of Wisconsin and New England, the bogs are usually flooded if killing frost seems probable.

The water surface created by flooding cools more slowly than a land surface and thereby lessens the frost hazard. Moreover, a protective cover of light fog is likely to develop over the flooded fields.

57. Standard Seasons. The terms winter, spring, summer, and autumn are common to nearly all people of the middle latitudes. In

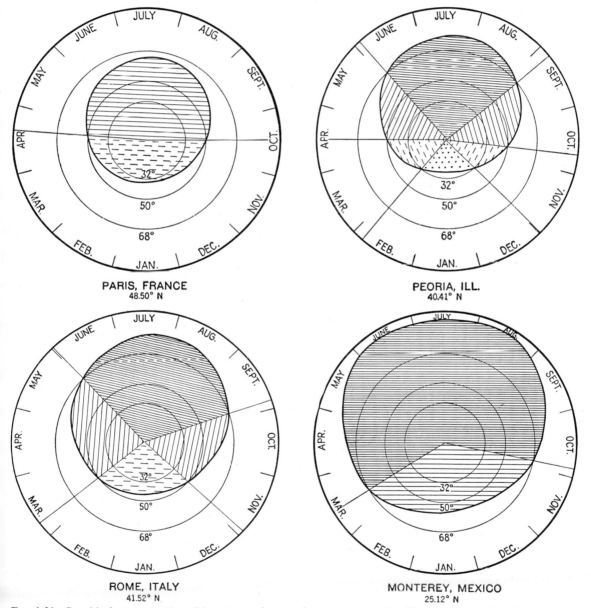

FIG. 1.38. Graphical representation of four types of seasonal temperature cycles. The four types of shading represent the four degrees of temperature seasons—hot, warm, cool, cold. (*After Hartshorne.*)

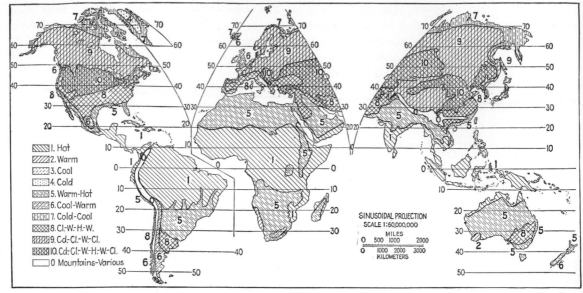

FIG. 1.39. Distribution of the 10 types of seasonal temperature cycles. (*After Hartshorne.*)

the Mediterranean lands as well as in Russia, winter and summer are the coldest and warmest seasons, while spring and autumn are intermediate in character. But only astronomers have defined these seasons, and for that reason it is the astronomer's definition that finds its way into the popular science of calendars and newspapers. But, even though the calendar may announce the arrival of spring on Mar. 21, the trapper on the Mackenzie River in Canada, still in the midst of ice and snow, may have his doubts; and equally unconvinced will be the citizen of Atlanta, Ga., where vegetation may have been in full bloom for several weeks (Fig. 1.38). It is clear that the season's names mean something very different to the layman and to the astronomer.

It has been suggested that there be recognized four kinds of seasons based on ranges of temperature as follows:[1]

Cold season	Mean daily temperatures below 32°. Snow and ice prominent
Cool season	Mean temperatures above 32°, but

[1] Mark Jefferson, Standard Seasons, *Ann. Assoc. Am. Geographers*, Vol. 28, pp. 1–12, 1938.
    Richard Hartshorne, Six Standard Seasons of the Year, *Ann. Assoc. Am. Geographers*, Vol. 28, pp. 165–178, 1938.

	below 50°. Frosts occur but do not dominate
Warm season	Mean temperatures above 50° but below 68°. Free from frost but without extreme heat
Hot season	Mean temperatures above 68 to 70°

Ten possible combinations can be found in different parts of the world throughout the year by employing these four kinds of temperature seasons. The distribution of these 10 types of seasonal cycles is shown on Fig. 1.39. The tropical lowlands are hot all year (Type 1), while the ice caps are constantly cold (Type 4). Very few lowland areas are either warm all year (Type 2) or cool all year (Type 3), but these types are common in tropical highlands. Types 5, 6, and 7 represent different combinations of two seasons, warm-hot in the outer tropics and the subtropics, cool-warm along windward coasts in middle latitudes, and cold-cool in the tundra. Types 8 and 9 are combinations of three temperature seasons, which, coming in sequence, form a four-season cycle. Cool-warm-hot-warm (Type 8) is characteristic of the lower middle latitudes, while cold-cool-warm-cool (Type 9) is dominant in higher middle latitudes. Four-season cycles prevail in most regions of European culture, but the cycles themselves are different. Only one type (10) has all four kinds of seasons, from hot through cold, and these four in sequence—hot, warm, cool, cold, cool, warm—form six seasons. Much of northern United States has this type.

SELECTED REFERENCES FOR FURTHER STUDY OF TOPICS CONTAINED IN CHAPTER 1

NOTE: References are inclusive. In order to avoid repeating long titles, reference is usually made to a particular book through the author's last name only. For the complete title of any book, its publisher, and date of publication, see reference list on pp. 5–6.

1. Solar energy; its nature, transmission, and distribution. Blair, 77–88; Byers, 1–22; "Compendium of Meteorology," 13–33 and 379–389; Conrad, 1–15; Haurwitz and Austin, 1–21; Landsberg, 84–98; Willett, 42–55.

2. Heating and cooling the atmosphere. Blair, 85–95; Byers, 22–38; Haurwitz and Austin, 14–22; Landsberg, 103–107; Petterssen, "Introduction to Meteorology," 68–81; Petterssen, "Weather Analysis," 138–140; Willett, 55–60.

3. Distribution of temperature over the earth. Byers, 39–53; Conrad, 16–38; Haurwitz and Austin, 23–43; Landsberg, 108–122; Willett, 60–70.

CHAPTER 2: *Atmospheric Pressure and Winds*

58. Importance of Pressure and Winds as Climatic Elements and Climatic Controls. Considering climate as one of the important elements of the resource equipment of the earth, it must be admitted that, compared with temperature and precipitation, atmospheric pressure and winds are of much less importance as climatic *elements*. All forms of life, including man, are little affected directly by the slight pressure changes which occur at the surface of the earth. To be sure, the changes in pressure with altitude are much greater and at high altitudes in mountains and plateaus the reduced pressure has important physiological consequences. Winds are of greater importance than pressure as a direct climatic element, for winds of high velocity may be destructive and winds directly affect the rate of evaporation and are an important element in controlling sensible temperatures. In general, however, these effects are of much less consequence than are the variable environments created by precipitation and temperature contrasts.

But although imperceptible to human beings, slight pressure differences are the cause of winds, and very small pressure changes may induce remarkable variations in general weather conditions. Therefore, while not directly of first importance as climatic elements, both pressure and winds are of the highest importance indirectly, acting as climatic controls, through the effects which they have upon temperature and precipitation, the two genuinely important elements of climate as far as life processes are concerned.

The sequence of events might be as follows: A minor change in pressure (of little consequence directly) acts to change the velocity and direction of wind (also not of major importance directly), and this in turn brings about changes in temperature and precipitation, which together largely determine the character of weather and climate. Whether it is a south wind or a north wind is chiefly consequential because of the contrasting temperature conditions induced. An onshore wind as compared with an offshore one is climatically significant because of differences in moisture and temperature. It is chiefly as *controls* of temperature and precipitation, then, rather than as *elements* of weather and climate, that pressure and winds are worthy of attention.

Winds serve two very fundamental climatic functions: (*a*) Through the transportation of heat from the lower to the higher latitudes they are the principal agent in maintaining the latitudinal heat balance of the earth in spite of an unbalanced condition of radiation between low and high latitudes. (*b*) They serve to provide the land masses with the necessary moisture supply for precipitation. It is the winds which transport the water vapor evaporated over the oceans to the lands where it is condensed and falls as rain. Because rainfall distribution over the earth is closely associated with the great pressure and wind systems, this chapter on pressure and winds precedes the one on moisture and precipitation. On the other hand, the discussion of atmospheric pressure logically follows the one on temperature, because some of the significant pressure differences and variations are induced by temperature.

59. Measurement of Air Pressure. A column of air 1 sq. in. in cross-sectional area extending from sea level to the top of the atmosphere weighs approximately 14.7 lb. This weight is balanced by a column of mercury 29.92 in., or 760 mm., tall having the same cross-sectional area. The value, 29.92 in., or 760 mm., is accepted as the normal value of atmospheric pressure at sea level at latitude 45°. Thus it is customary to measure air pressure in terms of its equivalent weight as expressed in inches of a column of mercury, in other words by a mercurial barometer. In the United States most barometers are calibrated in inches or millimeters of mercury, for scientists, other than meteorologists, continue to measure atmospheric density in terms of its equivalent in length of a column of mercury.

Another measure of atmospheric pressure, called a millibar, has within recent years been adopted by the Weather Bureau. The millibar is a force equal to 1,000 dynes per square centimeter, and a dyne is a unit of force approximately equal to the weight of a milligram. Sea-level pressure (29.92 in., or 760 mm.) under this newer system of measurement is 1,013.2 millibars (mb.). One-tenth of an inch of mercury is approximately equal to 3.4 millibars. On all United States weather maps published since January, 1940, pressure readings have been in millibars instead of inches. On these maps isobars are drawn for every 3 mb. of pressure

or winds, and winds in turn have important temperature and precipitation consequences, the question relative to what causes pressure changes and differences is climatically significant. If one knows the cause or origin, then the geographical distribution may appear more reasonable. These pressure differences may be observed on a variety of scales as applied to both time and area. For example, one may observe maps of over-all pressure distribution for the whole earth as it is developed in the extreme seasons of summer and winter. Here semipermanent high- and low-pressure systems are to be observed. Or, from observing a series of daily weather maps for the United States, it may be noted that there are numerous local high- and low-pressure systems, which, as they travel across the country, induce pressure changes which are associated with variations in the weather.

The principal types of pressure distribution are (a) high pressure and (b) low pressure. The areas of low pressure may be called *depressions*, *cyclones*, or merely *lows*. They are areas in which pressure is relatively low with respect to the surroundings. Elongated lows are called *troughs*. Areas of high pressure are called *anti-*

CONVERSION SCALE

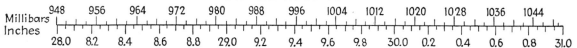

which closely corresponds to the interval of $\frac{1}{10}$ in. previously used. A conversion scale showing the relation of pressure in inches of mercury to pressure in millibars is printed on the weather map. A conversion table and scale are shown on this page.

Relation of Pressure in Inches to Pressure in Millibars

Inches	Millibars	Inches	Millibars	Inches	Millibars
27.00	914.3	29.00	982.1	29.92	1,013.2
28.00	948.2	29.50	999.0	30.00	1,015.9
28.50	965.1	29.75	1,007.5	30.25	1,024.4

60. Types and Causes of Pressure Changes and Differences. Since slight horizontal pressure differences are the cause of air movement,

cyclones or *highs*. An elongated high is called a *ridge* or *wedge*.

It must be admitted that at the present time there is no completely satisfactory explanation for the average condition of pressure distribution over the earth, or for the pressure changes which occur from day to day. Two types of origins will be mentioned.

61. *Thermal Origins.* The density and weight of a given volume of air vary with temperature. Thus when air is heated it expands and becomes less dense so that a column of warm, light air weighs less than a column of cold, heavy air, both having the same height and cross-sectional area. Changes in temperature produce changes in air density which set up vertical and hori-

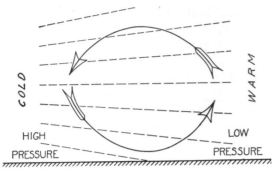

FIG. 2.1. The expected relationship of air temperature to atmospheric pressure and winds. Dashed lines indicate surfaces of equal pressure.

zontal movements resulting in differences in atmospheric pressure (Fig. 2.1). The above reasoning would lead to the logical conclusion that regions with high temperatures would be likely to have relatively low pressures and that regions with low temperatures would favor the development of high pressure. While there are numerous instances of this type of coincidence, there are also many examples of the opposite. Thermal highs and lows may result from surface chilling or heating of the air by conduction and radiation processes, from the horizontal advection of cold or warm air masses, and from temperature changes resulting from the addition of heat of condensation to an air mass. Examples of thermally induced pressure systems are the high pressures which develop over Asia and North America in winter, and the lows which are to be observed over the heated land masses of North America, Central Asia, and northern India in summer.

62. *Dynamic Origins.* In this case it is required that some outside agency such as friction or centrifugal force exert an effect upon the air. As an example, a pressure drop may be produced in a container of water if the container is rotated so that the frictional drag at the wall sets the water in motion. A dynamically induced pressure rise is likewise to be observed where the water in a river is piled up at the outside of a bend. Analogous mechanical processes probably produce pressure changes in the atmosphere. As far as pressure distribution and change are understood at the present time, it appears that

dynamic origins are more widespread and influential than are those arising directly out of thermal conditions.

Distribution of Atmospheric Pressure

63. **Vertical Distribution of Pressure.** Since air is very compressible, it almost goes without saying that there is a rapid decrease in air weight or pressure with increasing altitude. The lower layers of the atmosphere are the densest because the weight of all the layers above rests upon them. For the first few thousand feet above sea level the rate of pressure decrease is in the neighborhood of 1 in., or 34 mb., of pressure for each 900 to 1,000 ft. With higher altitudes the air rapidly becomes much thinner and lighter, so that at an elevation of about 18,000 ft. one-half the atmosphere by weight is below the observer, although the whole air mass extends to a height of several hundred miles (Fig. 2.2). The human body is not physiologically adjusted to the low pressures and associated small oxygen content of the air at high altitudes, and nausea, faintness, and nosebleed often result from a too rapid ascent. Oxygen tanks are a part of the normal equipment of aircraft operating at high altitudes.

64. **Horizontal Distribution of Pressure at Sea Level.** *Average Conditions.* Just as temperature distribution is represented by isotherms, so atmospheric pressure distribution is represented by *isobars*, *i.e.*, lines connecting places having the

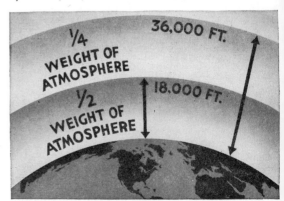

FIG. 2.2. Illustrating the decrease in atmospheric pressure with increasing altitude. (*Courtesy of U.S. Dept. of the Navy.*)

Standard Pressures, 1,000-ft. Levels

Feet	Inches	Millibars
18,000	14.94	506
17,000	15.56	
16,000	16.21	
15,000	16.88	
14,000	17.57	
13,000	18.29	
12,000	19.03	
11,000	19.79	
10,000	20.58	696.8
9,000	21.38	
8,000	22.22	
7,000	23.09	
6,000	23.98	
5,000	24.89	
4,000	25.84	875.1
3,000	26.81	
2,000	27.82	
1,000	28.86	
Sea level	29.92	1013.2

same atmospheric pressure at a given elevation. Pressure distribution charts are constructed for sea level and for a number of different pressure surfaces in the free atmosphere, usually the 700-mb. surface at about 10,000 ft. and the 500-mb. surface at about 18,000 ft. On the sea-level pressure charts the effects of different elevations on the continents have been eliminated by reducing all pressure readings to sea level. Where isobars are closely spaced a rapid change of pressure in a direction at right angles to the isobars is indicated. The rate and direction of change in pressure is called the *pressure gradient*, or barometric slope. Where isobars are widely spaced, the gradient is weak. The horizontal pressure gradient may therefore be defined as the decrease in pressure per unit distance in the direction in which the pressure decreases most rapidly (see Figs. 2.4 and 2.5).

Figure 2.3 is a very diagrammatic sketch of the arrangement of zonal sea-level pressure belts. This type of arrangement may be observed on an average annual chart of pressure for the earth, as well as on average seasonal maps of pressure for April (spring) or October (fall) when the disturbing effects of temperature contrasts between continents and oceans are least conspicuous.

Most of the so-called pressure belts are more accurately described as centers, or cells, of high and low pressure whose long axis is in general east-west. The centers of the cells of high pressure, elongated in an east-west direction, occupy relatively similar latitudes. The same is true of the centers, or cells, of low pressure. The total effect of this arrangement of the cells of similar pressure in similar latitudes is to produce a world pattern which is roughly zonal or belted in character (Fig. 2.3). In general, zonal belts of pressure are more in evidence in the Southern, or water, Hemisphere than in the Northern Hemisphere where the large continents with their seasonal temperature contrasts, their frictional effects, and their mountain barriers tend to emphasize the individual pressure cells more than zonal belts of pressure.

That zonal belts and cells of pressure chiefly exist in the form of statistical averages becomes evident from an inspection of daily weather charts. On these maps which show instantaneous pressure distributions, zonally arranged pressure cells are scarcely observable, since they are ob-

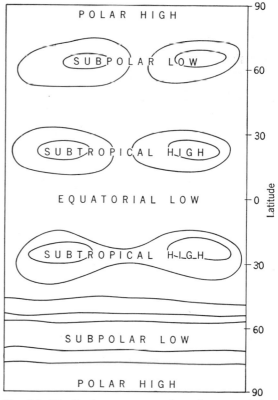

FIG. 2.3. Idealized arrangement of zonal pressure belts.

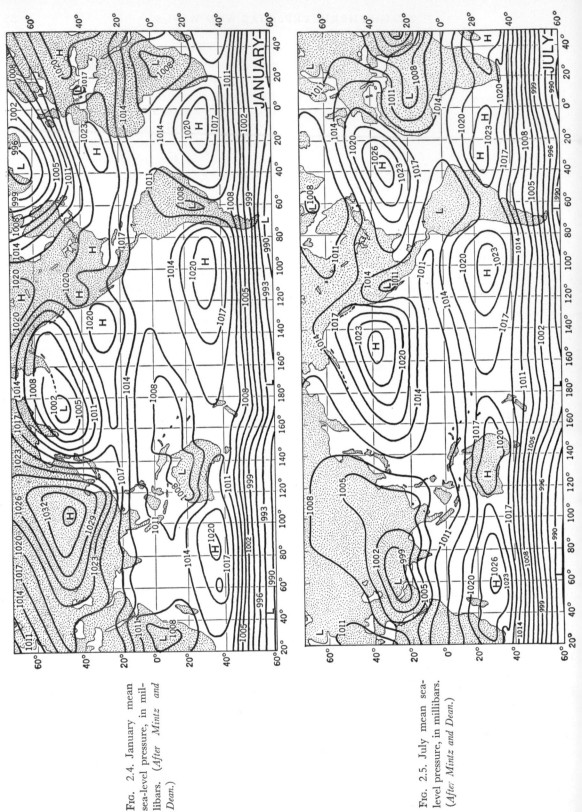

Fig. 2.4. January mean sea-level pressure, in millibars. (*After Mintz and Dean.*)

Fig. 2.5. July mean sea-level pressure, in millibars. (*After Mintz and Dean.*)

scured by the very complicated pattern of moving high- and low-pressure systems.

Following are the most noteworthy and characteristic features of average world-pressure conditions at sea level, diagrammatically represented by Fig. 2.3. (a) The dominant features of sea-level pressure are the series of high-pressure centers or cells which form irregular belts of high pressure, one in either hemisphere, located at about 30° N. and S. These are known as the *subtropical highs*. Although they represent what is probably the key element of the earth's surface pressure, these subtropical high-pressure systems are not wholly understood as to origin, except that dynamic rather than direct thermal causes are paramount. (b) Equatorward from the two subtropical high-pressure ridges surface pressure declines so that there is a general condition of low pressure in the vicinity of the geographic equator. This is known as the *equatorial trough of low pressure*. It appears to coincide rather closely with the region of highest annual temperature and is probably the result of these thermal conditions. (c) From the subtropical highs pressure likewise decreases poleward toward the centers, or cells, of low pressure located at about the latitudes of the Arctic and Antarctic circles. These are the *subpolar cells (troughs) of low pressure*. Individual oceanic cells of low pressure are characteristic of the Northern Hemisphere, but in the Southern Hemisphere a deep and continuous circumpolar trough of low pressure prevails. (d) Few reliable data on sea-level pressures exist for the high-latitude polar areas so that trustworthy generalizations are difficult to make. Most writers on the atmosphere represent the polar areas as being the sites of shallow, thermally induced highs, but it should be admitted that there is some recent contradictory evidence.[1] A profile of average sea-level pressure might be represented as in Figs. 2.6 and 2.7.

65. *Sea-level Pressure Distributions for January and July, Representing the Extreme Seasons* (Figs. 2.4 and 2.5). (a) On the January chart the mean

---

[1] Yale Mintz and Gordon Dean, The Observed Mean Field of Motion of the Atmosphere, *Geophysical Research Papers*, No. 17, pp. 37–42, 1952, Air Force Cambridge Research Center, Cambridge, Mass.

location of the equatorial low-pressure trough is somewhat to the south of the geographical equator, indicating a latitudinal shifting with the sun. The lowest pressures within this general trough are coincident with the continents of Australia, South America, and Africa which are especially warm at this period of the Southern Hemisphere summer. (b) The cells of subtropical high pressure are conspicuous over the oceans in the Southern Hemisphere, usually reaching their maximum development toward the eastern parts of the oceans. In the Northern Hemisphere individual cells of high pressure are less conspicuous in subtropical latitudes and there is more of a continuous ridge of high pressure. (c) The subpolar low-pressure trough is deep and continuous in the Southern Hemisphere. In the Northern Hemisphere, however, two well-devel-

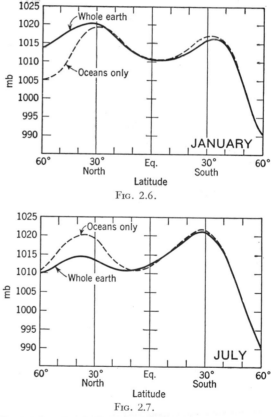

FIG. 2.6.

FIG. 2.7.

FIGS. 2.6 and 2.7. Seasonal profiles of mean sea-level pressure, averaged for all longitudes over the whole earth (continuous lines), and averaged for the oceans only (broken lines). (*After Mintz and Dean.*)

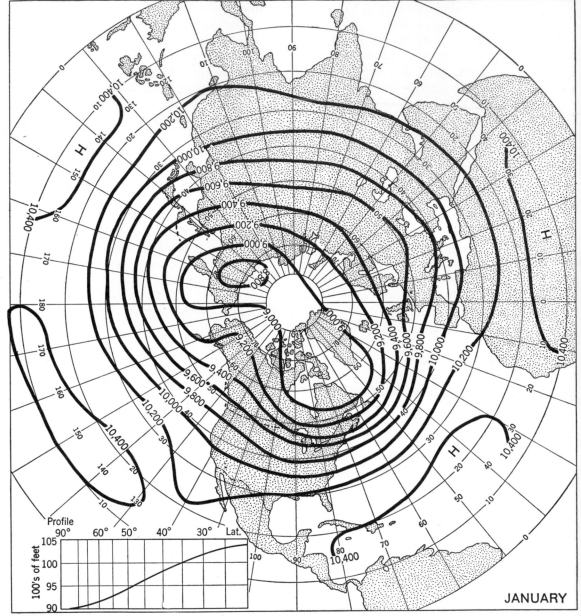

FIG. 2.8. January; 700-mb. pressure surface. (*After Namias and Clapp.*)

oped individual cells of low pressure occupy subpolar locations over the North Atlantic and North Pacific Oceans. These are known, respectively, as the Iceland Low and the Aleutian Low. (*d*) An extensive and well-developed high-pressure cell is centered over east-central Eurasia. This development is the result of the excessively cold continent. No such center of high pressure is indicated for the smaller continent of North America, although the trend of the 1,020-mb. isobar gives a hint of a weak high in that region also.

(*a*) On the July chart the equatorial low-pressure trough has followed the sun and is located somewhat north of the geographic equator in the summer hemisphere. (*b*) In fact, all the

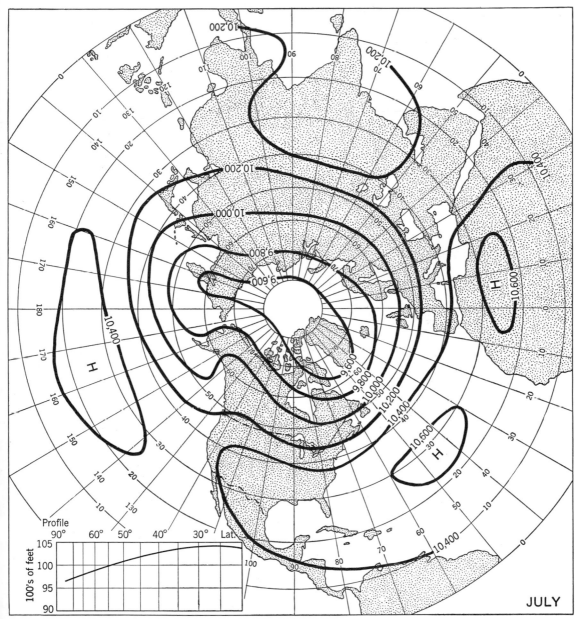

Fig. 2.9. July; 700-mb. pressure surface. (*After Namias and Clapp.*)

pressure systems experience a similar latitudinal shift as a consequence of solar-energy migration, northward in July and southward in January. (*c*) The subtropical belt of high pressure is somewhat more continuous in the Southern Hemisphere than it was in January, and an additional cell has developed over the continent of Australia. In the Northern Hemisphere unusually strong cells of high pressure exist over the subtropical North Atlantic and North Pacific Oceans and even extend their influence into the middle-latitude sections of the eastern parts of those oceans. (*d*) The subpolar low-pressure system continues as a deep and continuous trough in the Southern Hemisphere but in the Northern Hemisphere the oceanic lows are only faintly observable. (*e*) The heated continent of Asia, and to a lesser degree southwestern North America, show low-pressure centers of thermal origin. These continental lows have the effect of interrupting the subtropical high-pressure system in the Northern Hemisphere so that it is represented in the form of two distinct oceanic cells rather than as a zonal belt.

66. Seasonal Meridional Profiles of Sea-level Pressure. The seasonal pressure profiles, averaged for all longitudes of the earth, are shown in Figs. 2.6 and 2.7. From these figures the general latitudinal migration of the pressure belts from one extreme season to the other is clearly observable, as is the amount of north-south migration of the individual pressure belts. Note also that pressure gradients are generally steeper in the winter hemisphere so that the atmospheric circulation likewise is more vigorous. The unusual depth and permanence of the subpolar trough of the Southern Hemisphere compared with its counterpart in the Northern Hemisphere is also very striking. It becomes clear from the seasonal pressure variations as shown on these profiles that there is an enormous mass transfer of atmosphere from the warmer summer hemisphere to the colder winter hemisphere. It has been calculated that the July to January net flow of mass across the equator amounts to approximately 2 trillion tons, but this is only 1/2,500 of the mass of the earth's atmosphere.

67. Upper-air Pressure. With increasing elevation above the earth's surface the cellular pattern of pressure distribution, so conspicuous at sea level, becomes gradually less evident until in mid-troposphere, or the 700-mb. level, the cells are only faintly observable (Figs. 2.8, 2.9). On the January chart of the Northern Hemisphere showing the contours of the 700-mb. surface (about 10,000 ft.) there is a great circumpolar low with the highest pressures in the low latitudes near the equator. A profile of pressure from pole to equator at this level therefore reveals a general increase in pressure from high to low latitudes, with the most rapid change in pressure, or pressure gradient, occurring in the middle latitudes (see inset in Fig. 2.8).

The July map of pressure at about 10,000 ft.

differs from that of January in two respects: (*a*) The isobars are more widely spaced so that pressure gradients are weaker and (*b*) there has been a northward migration of the pressure systems following the sun (Fig. 2.9 and its profile inset). The July profile shows a broad plateau of high pressure in the low latitudes with slightly higher pressures at 20 to 30° than in the immediate vicinity of the equator. At this point it will be profitable to compare the upper-air latitudinal pressure profiles with those for surface pressure (Figs. 2.6 and 2.7).

Relation of Winds to Pressure

68. Pressure Gradient. In the discussion of heat balance in the atmosphere (see Chap. 1, pp. 25 to 26) it was pointed out that on the average there is a convective transport of heat from the lower air to the upper troposphere, and an advective or horizontal transport of heat from the lower to the higher latitudes. Such vertical and horizontal transfers indicate that large-scale atmospheric movement is a normal state of the atmosphere. While vertical motions are very important climatically because they are associated with the production of cloud and precipitation, their total magnitude is small in comparison with the horizontal movements of the atmosphere.

Wind is simply air in motion and in a direction which is essentially parallel with the earth's surface. Vertical air movements are more properly designated as currents. Wind is usually caused by differences in atmospheric density resulting in horizontal differences in air pressure. It represents nature's attempt to correct pressure inequalities. When horizontal pressure differences develop, a *pressure gradient* is said to exist. It is this pressure-gradient force which sets the air in motion and causes it to flow from high to low pressure. Pressure gradient has a direction as well as a magnitude. It is ordinarily measured in the direction of pressure decrease and is the most direct path from high to low pressure. It is, therefore, at right angles to the isobars. Steep gradients are revealed by a close spacing of the isobars which indicate a rapid change in horizontal pressure.

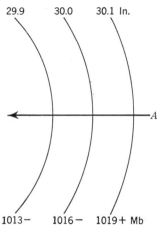

29.9   30.0   30.1 In.

→A

1013–   1016–   1019+ Mb

FIG. 2.10. Gradient is represented by a line drawn at right angles to the isobars.

Two very fundamental rules concerned with the relationships existing between pressure gradient and winds are as follows: (*a*) The *direction* of air flow is from regions of greater to those of less density, *i.e.*, from high to low pressure or down the barometric slope, which may be represented by a line drawn at right angles to the isobars (Fig. 2.10). In order to compare pressures at different stations and find the resulting gradient, it is necessary first to reduce all pressure readings to a common plane, usually sea level. Most weather maps employ sea-level isobars. If pressure-gradient force were the only force determining the direction of air movement, wind direction should always be at right angles to the isobars. On the rotating earth, however, there is another apparent force affecting direction of air movement, the Coriolis force, which causes the flow of air from high to low pressure to take a very oblique course and to cross the isobars at a narrow angle. In the free atmosphere, above the friction layer close to the earth's surface, the winds flow nearly parallel with the isobars. The deflective force of earth rotation and its effects upon wind direction will be described in greater detail in a later section. (*b*) The *rate* of air flow, or velocity of the wind, is indicated by the steepness of the pressure gradient or the rate of pressure change. When the gradient is steep, air flow is rapid, and when it is weak, the wind is likewise weak. Just as the ve-

locity of a river is determined largely by the slope of the land, or rate of change in elevation, so the velocity of wind is determined largely by the barometric slope, or the rate of change in air pressure, although air density, latitude, and friction are likewise involved. One can therefore determine the steepness of the pressure gradient, and consequently the relative velocity of air movement, by noting the spacing or closeness of the isobars. Closely spaced isobars, like those in the vicinity of the subpolar trough in the Southern Hemisphere (Figs. 2.4, 2.5), indicate relatively steep gradients, or marked pressure differences, and under these conditions winds of high velocity prevail. When isobars are far apart, gradients and winds are weak. Calms prevail when pressure differences over extensive areas are nil or almost nil. At such times there is nearly an absence of isobaric lines on the pressure map.

Since, except in the friction layer near the earth's surface, the winds blow nearly parallel with the isobars the air may be thought of as flowing between the isobars in the same way as water flows in a river. Where the river is narrow, the flow is faster, and where it is wider, the flow is slower. If we think of the space between the isobars as tubes of constant air transport, then the speed of the upper air is nearly inversely proportional to the space between the isobars (Fig. 2.11).

In higher latitudes, because of the greater **deflective force** of earth rotation, strong pressure gradients do not produce wind velocities equivalent to those in other latitudes. For example, a

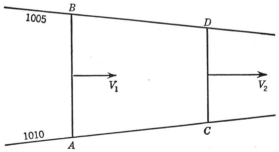

FIG. 2.11. The spaces between the isobars may be thought of as tubes of constant transport so that the amount of air that flows through section *CD* equals that which flows through section *AB*. Consequently the air must have a higher velocity at *CD* than at *AB*.

pressure difference of 0.1 in. in a distance of 100 miles results in a wind velocity of about 40 miles an hour on a nearly straight course at latitude 40°, 30 miles an hour at latitude 60°, and 25 at latitude 80° (Brooks). Cold air, because of its greater density, moves less readily and with greater friction than does warmer, lighter air.

Approximate Relation of Wind Velocity to Pressure Gradient near London, England*

Difference in Pressure per 15 Nautical Miles, Inches	Corresponding Wind Velocity, Miles per Hour
0.005	7.0
0.01	9.2
0.02	16.5
0.03	25.2

* W. J. Kendrew, "Climate," p. 73, Oxford University Press, New York, 1930. The nautical mile is 6,080 ft., or the length of 1′ of a great circle.

69. Wind Direction and Velocity. Winds are always named by the direction from which they come. Thus a wind from the south, blowing toward the north, is called a south wind. The wind vane points *toward* the source of the wind and so in a very general way toward the high-pressure area down the barometric slope of which the air is flowing. *Windward* refers to the direction from which a wind comes; *leeward*, that toward which it blows. Thus a windward coast is one along which the air is moving onshore, while a leeward coast has winds offshore. When

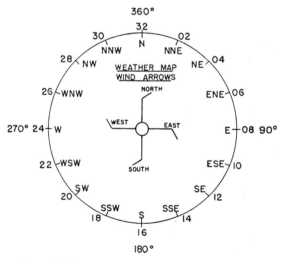

FIG. 2.12. Wind direction on a 32-point compass.

a wind blows more frequently from one direction than from any other, it is called a *prevailing* wind.

Wind direction is referred to directions on a 32-point compass and is expressed in terms of letter abbreviations of the directions, by the compass point, or by the number of degrees east of north (Fig. 2.12).

Wind velocity varies greatly with distance above the ground, and the change is particularly rapid at low elevations. Wind is not a steady current but is made up of a succession of gusts and

The Beaufort Scale of Wind Force with Velocity Equivalents

Beaufort number	Beaufort descriptive term	Land criteria	Velocity, miles per hour
0	Calm	Calm, smoke rises vertically	Less than 1
1	Light air	Direction of wind shown by smoke drift, but not by wind vanes	1 to 3
2	Light breeze	Wind felt on face; leaves rustle; ordinary vane moved by wind	4 to 7
3	Gentle breeze	Leaves and small twigs in constant motion; wind extends light flag	8 to 12
4	Moderate breeze	Raises dust and loose paper; small branches are moved	13 to 18
5	Fresh breeze	Small trees in leaf begin to sway; crested wavelets form on inland waters	19 to 24
6	Strong breeze	Large branches in motion; whistling heard in telegraph wires; umbrellas used with difficulty	25 to 31
7	Moderate gale	Whole trees in motion; inconvenience felt when walking against wind	32 to 38
8	Fresh gale	Breaks twigs off trees; progress generally impeded	39 to 46
9	Strong gale	Slight structural damage occurs (chimney pots and slate removed)	47 to 54
10	Whole gale	Seldom experienced inland; trees uprooted; considerable structural damage occurs	55 to 63
11	Storm	Very rarely experienced; accompanied by widespread damage	64 to 75
12	Hurricane		Above 75

lulls of variable direction. Close to the earth the gustiness is caused by irregularities of the surface which create eddies. Larger irregularities in the wind are caused by convectional currents. All forms of turbulence are important in the process of transporting heat, moisture, and dust into the upper air.

70. Isobaric Surfaces and Isobaric Lines. For the purposes of this discussion the atmosphere may be thought of as stratified, or composed of several successive layers of air, like onion peelings, each lower layer separately weighing about $\frac{1}{10}$ in. or 3.4 mb. But these successive layers can be weighed separately only by noting the decrease in pressure with ascent into the atmosphere, since at any elevation the air weight is only that of all the layers above. It is evident, in a mass of air conceived as being stratified into a series of layers, each of the same weight (say, $\frac{1}{10}$ in. or 3.4 mb.), that the hypothetical surface, or plane, that separates one stratum from another is an *isobaric surface; i.e.,* over it pressure is everywhere the same. Sometimes these isobaric surfaces are parallel with the earth's sea-level surface. Under these conditions the isobaric surface of 30.0 in. approximately coincides with the earth's sea-level surface. Above this are the successive parallel isobaric surfaces of 29.9, 29.8, 29.7, etc., each being $100 \pm$ ft. vertically distant from the one below. Under this arrangement of the isobaric surfaces, where they are horizontal and consequently parallel with the earth's sea-level surface, there is no horizontal isobaric gradient and consequently no air movement, calms prevailing. Everywhere at the same elevation pressure is the same (Fig. 2.13a).

But more frequently pressure differences do exist between regions, and under these conditions the isobaric surfaces, although still relatively parallel with one another, are inclined with respect to the earth's surface. At such times the inclined isobaric surfaces intersect the earth's sea-level surface, and the lines of intersection of the two planes are isobaric lines. Therefore, every isobaric line on a pressure chart should be thought of in terms of a tilted or inclined isobaric surface in the atmosphere intersecting the plane of the earth's sea-level surface. Under such conditions, since a horizontal pressure gradient exists, there is air movement. The steepness of this gradient, as expressed in the spacing of the isobaric lines on the pressure chart, is deter-

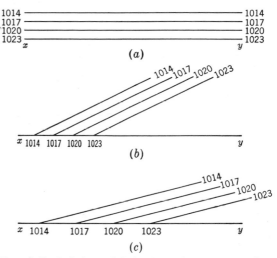

Fig. 2.13. Relation of isobaric surfaces in the free atmosphere to isobaric lines at the earth's surface (*xy*).

mined by the degree of inclination of the isobaric surfaces. When they are steeply inclined, they intersect the earth's plane at relatively frequent intervals, so that isobaric lines are close together, and the wind movement is rapid (Fig. 2.13b). Conversely, when the inclination of the pressure surfaces is slight, the isobaric lines are widely spaced, and winds are gentle (Fig. 2.13c). In a fluid mass of such low density and extensiveness as the earth's atmosphere, slight differences in pressure are sufficient to set it in motion. The slope of an isobaric surface sufficient to develop a strong wind is flatter than the gradients of any but the most sluggish rivers.

71. Deflection of Winds from a Gradient Course as a Result of Earth Rotation and Friction. Observation of a weather map, or of any map representing surface pressure distribution and winds, reveals that the surface winds do not follow a true gradient course and flow from high to low pressure along a route which is at right angles to the isobars. Instead the wind arrows make an oblique angle with the isobars (Fig. 2.14). In an earlier section it has been indicated that the reason why winds take the oblique course, or why they are deflected from a true gradient direction, is associated with the effects of earth rotation. This deflective force causes all winds to be turned to the *right* of the gradient in the Northern Hemisphere and to the *left* in the Southern Hemisphere. This will not be apparent from looking at the wind arrows unless it is kept in mind that one must

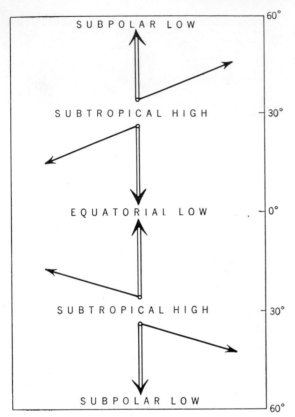

SUBPOLAR LOW — 60°

SUBTROPICAL HIGH — 30°

EQUATORIAL LOW — 0°

SUBTROPICAL HIGH — 30°

SUBPOLAR LOW — 60°

Fig. 2.14. Double-line arrows indicate wind direction as developed by the pressure gradient. Solid-line arrows indicate deflected winds resulting from earth rotation.

face *in the direction toward which the wind is traveling* in order to appreciate the proper deflection. Only at the equator is the deflective force of earth rotation absent, and it increases with increasing latitude reaching a maximum at the poles.

In considering the motions of the atmosphere and the forces that act on the air, it is necessary to keep in mind that the *observed winds always represent air movement relative to a rotating earth*. In other words it is relative, not absolute, motion that is observed. Actually the deflective force of earth rotation, or the Coriolis force, is not a force at all but is the resultant effect of two motions: (*a*) the rotational motion of the earth and (*b*) the movement of the body relative to the surface of the earth. This may be illustrated as follows: In Fig. 2.15 is shown a circular disk or plane rotating counterclockwise as indicated by the arrows. If an object at point *C* is moved toward point *P* beyond the rotating disk, an observer in space would see the object move from *C* to *P* along the straight dashed line. An observer *T* riding on the disk, however,

would be at point *T* when the object started from *C* but, because of rotation of the disk, would find himself at *T'* when the object arrived at *P*. It would appear to this observer on the disk that a force *F* had caused the moving object to be pushed to the right of its original path. This *apparent* force is the Coriolis force. Both observers would be right in their statements, for the one in space observed the absolute motion of the object while the one on the rotating disk observed its relative motion. The analogy to conditions on the earth may now be made.

Not only winds, but all objects moving over the earth's surface (except at the equator), no matter in what direction they travel, are affected by earth rotation. It is a fundamental law of motion that any frictionless body that is set in motion tends to keep the original straight-line direction given to it by its first impulse, while it continues to move, unless it is acted upon by some exterior force. Consequently when the pressure-gradient force causes a mass of air to be set in motion, it tends to travel in a straight line, keeping its original direction with respect to a point in space. As it happens, however, directions on the earth are not fixed with respect to a point in space but instead are determined by meridians and parallels which are constantly changing their positions and directions as the planet rotates. At any point on the globe, except on the equator, the plane of the horizon is rotating around that point from right to left in the Northern Hemisphere and from left to right south of the equator. This rotating horizon on the earth is comparable to the rotating disk in Fig. 2.15. The effects of this horizon rotation are most obvious when the chosen point is one of the poles, for here the speed of horizon rotation is that of the earth's rotation (Fig. 2.16). It decreases toward the equator where it becomes zero. Thus, as a wind moves across the earth's surface, the meridians and parallels (but not the earth) rotate

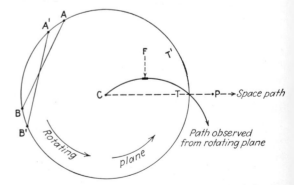

Fig. 2.15. Illustrating the Coriolis force, or the deflecting force of earth rotation.

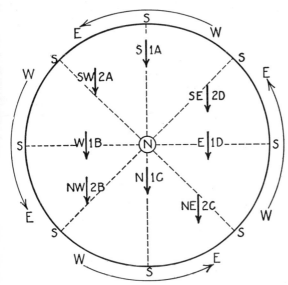

the globe tangent to it, say at latitude 60 to 70°, and parallel with a meridian or parallel. This may represent wind direction. If the ruler is kept constantly pointed at a fixed object so that its direction is unchanged and the globe is slowly rotated, it will be observed that the meridians and parallels rotate out from under the ruler. In other words, the ruler has *apparently* changed direction.

Not only north-south winds, but also those moving along east-west or even diagonal courses are deflected by earth rotation. This may also be illustrated by Fig. 2.15. If an object were moved from A to B, the observer at A would see it begin its course along the straight line AB. But while the object moves along the straight line AB, the observer arrives at A' and sees the destination in the direction $A'B'$. To him the course of the moving object would appear to be deflected to the right of the destination.

When air is set in motion by a pressure gradient, it is immediately acted upon by a number of forces that tend to deviate it from its initial path. One of these is the Coriolis force, or deflective force of earth rotation, and another is frictional force. If for the moment friction is omitted, then air flowing in a straight path over the earth is apparently deflected more and more to the right (Northern Hemisphere) of its original path until it blows exactly parallel with the isobars. Any further turning would make the wind blow from low to high pressure or up the gradient, and this is impossible. When air is blowing parallel to the isobars (called geostrophic wind), the Coriolis force is just balanced by the pressure gradient (Fig. 2.17). The Coriolis force is directly proportional to the mass, the

FIG. 2.16. Deflective effect of earth rotation at the North Pole. Illustrated is a flat disk tangent at the North Pole. The arrows paralleling the circumference indicate the west-to-east rotation of the earth. Any body that is set in motion in a given direction tends to keep that direction unless acted upon by some external force. Based upon the preceding principle, a south wind, illustrated by arrow 1A, continues to keep its direction constant as the earth rotates. When the earth has turned through 45°, the original south wind is still moving in the same direction with respect to space, for arrow 2A is parallel with 1A. But in terms of directions on the rotating earth whose meridians and parallels are constantly changing positions, the wind 2A is from the southwest. Similarly, the west wind 1B becomes northwest wind 2B; north wind 1C becomes northeast wind 2C; and east wind 1D becomes southeast wind 2D. (*After Koeppe.*)

out from under it, so that the wind apparently changes its direction, although actually it is the meridians and parallels that change theirs. Since the meridians and parallels rotate to the left in the Northern Hemisphere, this tends to give the winds an apparent right-hand deflection. In the Southern Hemisphere, on the other hand, where rotation about a point is clockwise, or to the right, winds appear to be deflected to the left.

This phenomenon of meridians and parallels changing their direction with earth rotation may be illustrated in the following manner: Attach to a terrestrial globe at some distance from its equator several paper disks an inch or two in diameter, each marked with strong east-west and north-south diametral lines. If the globe is slowly rotated, the diametral lines are seen to change direction, now pointing to one part of the room and now to another. Then place a ruler on

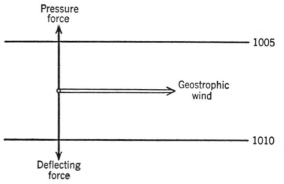

FIG. 2.17. A geostrophic wind results when pressure gradient is balanced by deflective force. The geostrophic wind blows parallel with the isobars with high pressure to the right (Northern Hemisphere). Its velocity is inversely proportional to the distance between the isobars. Winds are essentially geostrophic in character above 1,000 meters elevation.

straight-line velocity, and the angular velocity of the earth. It is always the same, no matter what the horizontal direction of movement, and, since it is at right angles to the direction of motion of the particles of air, it influences the direction but never the velocity of the movement.

The other important force, friction, modifies the effects of gravity and deflection. The velocity of a particle of air set in motion by pressure gradient continues to increase until friction balances the acceleration given to it by the gradient; its motion then becomes steady. The friction prevents winds on the earth's surface from attaining velocities that might be expected from pressure gradient. It also prevents winds from blowing parallel with the isobars as they would do on a frictionless earth. Friction through reducing the velocity of a wind diminishes the Coriolis force so that pressure-gradient force becomes greater than the deflecting force, and the winds consequently cross the isobars instead of paralleling them. The greater the friction, the greater the angle between winds and isobars. At elevations above 2,000 ft. the frictional effect of the earth's surface has practically disappeared, and winds blow nearly parallel with the isobars. Surface winds usually make an angle of 20 to 45° with the isobars over land areas, while over the oceans the angle is as low as 10°. This relation of pressure gradient and deflective force of earth rotation upon winds is stated in the following generalization, known as Buys Ballot's law: In the Northern Hemisphere, if an observer faces the wind, the region of lower pressure is to his right.

72. Cyclonic and Anticyclonic Circulations. A system of closed isobars with the lowest pressure at the center is designated as a cyclone. A similar system of closed isobars with the highest pressure at the center is an anticyclone. The pressure-gradient force plus the Coriolis force causes air flow in a cyclone to be a spiraling *convergent* system (Fig. 2.18); that in an anticyclone a spiraling *divergent* system. In cyclones air moves obliquely across the isobars and *in* toward a common center; hence a converging system of winds. In anticyclones air moves obliquely across the isobars and *out* from a common center; hence a diverging system of winds.

SURFACE WINDS

73. Diagrammatic Pattern of Surface Winds. On the generalized sketch of sea-level pressure as shown in Fig. 2.3 one can superimpose a very simple system of zonal winds. There are usually considered to be three great average wind systems. From the subtropical highs located at about 30°N. and S. surface winds flow toward the low pressure near the equator. The Coriolis force turns these into easterly winds and they are often designated as the *tropical easterlies.* They are also known as the *trade winds;* northeast trades north of the equator and southeast trades to the south (Fig. 2.19).

Poleward from the subtropical high-pressure ridges in each hemisphere winds flow down the barometric slope toward the subpolar troughs of low pressure. By Coriolis force these winds are turned so that they have a general direction from west to east. These are the middle-latitude *westerlies.* In the Northern Hemisphere their prevailing direction is from the southwest and in the Southern Hemisphere from the northwest.

Poleward from the westerlies the situation relative to the direction of surface winds is uncertain and confused. If it may be assumed that there are shallow highs of thermal origin in the general vicinity of the poles, outflowing easterly winds should characterize the very high latitudes poleward from the westerly winds. There is some

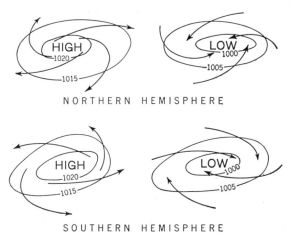

NORTHERN HEMISPHERE

SOUTHERN HEMISPHERE

Fɪɢ. 2.18. Cyclonic circulations are *converging* systems of air movement, counterclockwise in the Northern Hemisphere and clockwise in the Southern Hemisphere. Anticyclonic circulations are *diverging* systems of wind, clockwise in the Northern Hemisphere and anticlockwise in the Southern Hemisphere.

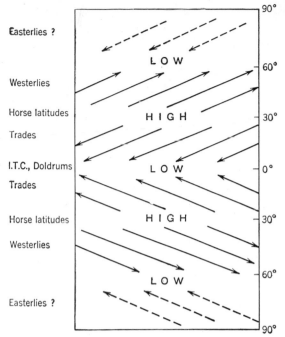

Easterlies ?

L O W — 60°

Westerlies

Horse latitudes

H I G H — 30°

Trades

I.T.C., Doldrums — L O W — 0°

Trades

Horse latitudes — H I G H — 30°

Westerlies

L O W — 60°

Easterlies ?

— 90°

FIG. 2.19. A very much idealized representation of the earth's surface winds.

74. Seasonal Surface Winds. The greatly idealized and simplified representation of surface winds as described above must now be modified in order to represent actual conditions more accurately. In Figs. 2.21 and 2.22 an attempt is made to portray the direction of the mean surface resultant wind[1] in January and July, the two extreme seasons, by means of atmospheric streamlines. It will be noted immediately that these charts portray a much more complicated pattern of surface wind direction than was indicated earlier when a simple zonal system of tropical easterlies and middle-latitude westerlies was described. On the streamline maps there is, to be sure, ample evidence of the dominance of easterly winds in the low latitudes and westerlies in the middle latitudes, but at the same time there also are indicated modification and departures from the elementary pattern heretofore outlined. It is noteworthy that no attempt is made in Figs. 2.21 and 2.22 to show the direction of the mean surface winds poleward of latitude 65°N. and 60°S., regions for which few reliable data exist.

From the seasonal maps of mean surface resultant winds one is impressed less with the zonal (east-west) pattern of surface winds than with their cellular arrangement. The circulation appears to occur not so much in belts as in the form of anticyclonic and cyclonic circulations around high-pressure and low-pressure centers, or cells. Some of these cellular circulations appear to persist throughout the year for they are in evidence on both the January and July charts.

evidence to support this concept of *polar easterlies*. On the other hand the number of reliable observations, both of pressure and winds, is relatively few so that the generalization does not rest upon a too secure foundation.

To summarize surface winds, there is a predominance of easterly winds in the tropics, or low latitudes, and a prevalence of westerly winds in the middle latitudes. In the high latitudes, or polar regions, the majority of authorities apparently believe that easterly winds prevail, although the evidence is meager and conflicting.

Between the converging trades in the vicinity of the equatorial pressure trough is an area of variable and weak winds. This transition area has been given various names such as *intertropical convergence*, *doldrums*, and *equatorial belt of variable winds and calms*. In the intermediate area between the trades and westerlies in the vicinity of the crests of the subtropical high-pressure ridges is another belt of weak and variable winds. These are the *horse latitudes* located at about 30° in each hemisphere. A third transition zone should exist in the vicinity of the subpolar troughs where westerlies and polar easterlies converge.

[1] Resultant winds are obtained by adding separately the north and south and the east and west components of the observed winds, averaging them, and then applying these average components to obtain a resultant (Fig. 2.20). This procedure is illustrated below. Here the vector pointing east (*E*) represents the average of the east and west components, while the vector pointing south (*S*) represents the average of the north and south components. *R* is the resultant of these two vectors.

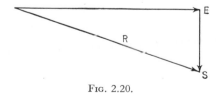

FIG. 2.20.

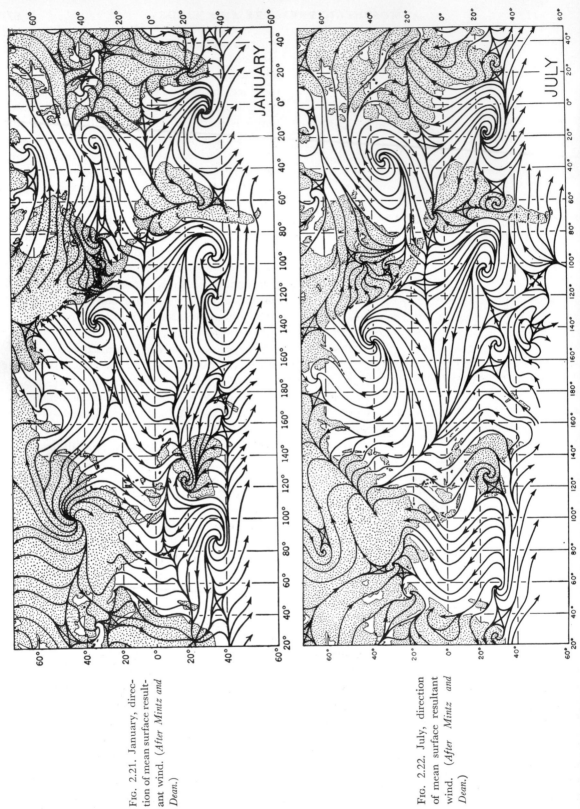

FIG. 2.21. January, direction of mean surface resultant wind. (*After Mintz and Dean.*)

FIG. 2.22. July, direction of mean surface resultant wind. (*After Mintz and Dean.*)

Others are definitely seasonal in character. As a general rule the cellular pattern of pressure and winds and the seasonal changes in the position and size of the centers of cyclonic and anticyclonic winds are not nearly so pronounced in the more homogeneous Southern Hemisphere, or water hemisphere, as they are in the Northern Hemisphere where extensive middle-latitude continents are present. In the latter the thermal contrasts between continents and oceans in winter and summer cause important modifications in the atmospheric circulation. Almost certainly the frictional effects of the continents, in conjunction with the blocking effects of their high cordilleran systems, impose important modifications upon wind-flow patterns which emphasize cellular (as contrasted with zonal) circulation north of the equator.

Without doubt the most prominent features of the mean surface wind flow are the large systems of divergent anticyclonic circulation concentrated in subtropical latitudes. The equatorward flow from these anticyclonic circulations is the well-known tropical easterlies or trades, while the poleward flow is the middle-latitude westerlies. The subtropical anticyclonic systems dominate both seasonal maps and no comparable systems of convergent cyclonic flow are to be observed. The nearest approach are the relatively small and weak centers of converging cyclonic circulation over the oceans in the higher latitudes of the Northern Hemisphere, especially in winter. This may seem strange in view of the well-developed low low-pressure centers which occupy these same areas, as shown on Figs. 2.4 and 2.5. In reality the winter lows over the North Atlantic and North Pacific are largely statistical in nature. They do not appear as permanent elements on the daily weather map in the same way that the subtropical highs do, but instead are largely the result of the passage of many small moving low-pressure centers so that the monthly average results in what appears to be a permanent low.

75. *On the January map* (Fig. 2.21) of surface winds divergent anticyclonic systems are relatively weak over the Northern Hemisphere subtropical oceans and they are largely confined to the eastern parts of the North Atlantic and North Pacific. In the Southern Hemisphere, by contrast, the subtropical anticyclonic circulations over the oceans are well developed and relatively continuous in an east-west direction. In addition to the anticyclonic wind systems over the subtropical oceans in both hemispheres, there is also one striking anticyclonic system elsewhere, *viz.*, that over mid-latitude eastern Asia (Fig. 2.21). This diverging circulation, the Asiatic winter monsoon, is associated with the establishment of a well-developed center of high pressure over the cold land and is a consequence of the increased density of the cold continental air.

January, which witnesses the weakening of the anticyclonic systems over the Northern Hemisphere oceans, also sees a spreading and deepening of the oceanic low-pressure centers and associated cyclonic circulations in somewhat higher latitudes. Convergent cyclonic circulations around the Aleutian Low over the North Pacific and the Iceland Low over the North Atlantic are best developed at this season. In the Southern Hemisphere, summer (January) witnesses the development of a relatively strong low-pressure cell and associated cyclonic wind system over heated Australia and somewhat weaker ones over South America and southern Africa.

76. *In July* well-developed highs and strong anticyclonic circulations cover much of the North Atlantic and North Pacific Oceans with their centers at about 35°N. and 40°N. (Fig. 2.22). The pattern of the subtropical anticyclonic circulations in the Southern Hemisphere has not greatly changed from what it was in January except that the cells are more continuous in an east-west direction as a result of the continental lows with their cyclonic circulations having been weakened over the cooled land areas.

In the Northern Hemisphere in July the oceanic lows in subpolar latitudes are weaker than in January and the associated cyclonic circulations over the northern parts of the Atlantic and Pacific Oceans are as well. On the other hand, over the heated lands of northwestern India, eastern Asia, and western interior North America thermally induced lows with cyclonic

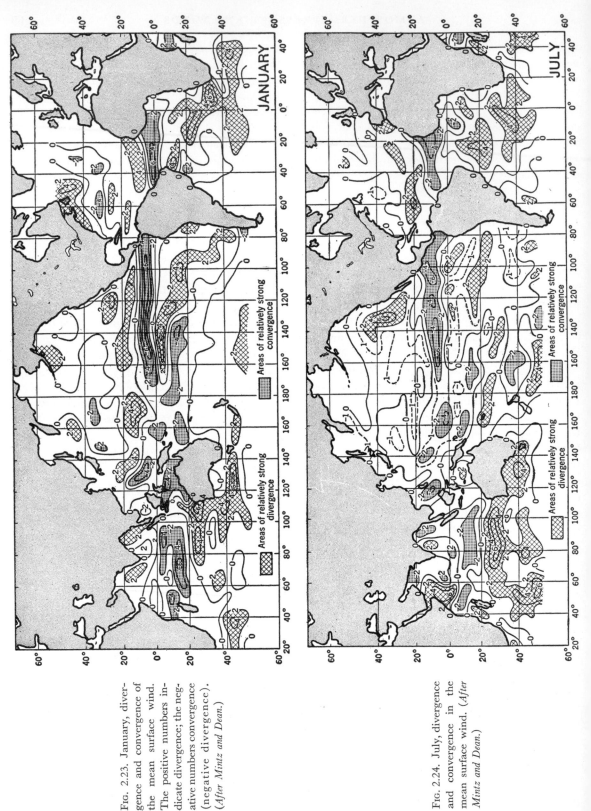

Fig. 2.23. January, divergence and convergence of the mean surface wind. The positive numbers indicate divergence; the negative numbers convergence (negative divergence). (*After Mintz and Dean.*)

Fig. 2.24. July, divergence and convergence in the mean surface wind. (*After Mintz and Dean.*)

circulations are in evidence. In India and eastern Asia this is the well-known summer monsoon.

77. *Lines and Areas of Horizontal Divergence and Convergence.* Very prominent in the pattern of surface wind flow as shown on Figs. 2.21 and 2.22 are the extended lines of divergence and convergence of wind direction. The most conspicuous of the great lines of divergence are those which pass through the centers of the anticyclonic systems and extend poleward and eastward, and equatorward and westward from these centers. Along such lines of divergence in surface wind flow there must of necessity be a compensating feeding in of dry air from aloft; in other words, vertical subsidence. Somewhat less well developed are the extended lines of convergence of wind direction associated with the centers of the smaller and less well-developed cyclonic circulations. Most prominent of all the extended lines of convergence of mean wind direction is that which lies between the subtropical anticyclones of the Northern Hemisphere and those of the Southern Hemisphere. It is situated between the trades, therefore, and in the vicinity of the geographic equator. In July this intertropical convergence of the streamlines of mean surface winds can be traced almost continuously around the world. The chief interruption is over the land area of southeastern Asia. In January the intertropical convergence is fairly continuous around the earth with some short interruptions over the oceans and with some sections of the *ITC* oriented north-south as over Africa and South America (Figs. 2.23, 2.24).

78. Geographical Distribution of the Zonal, or East-West, Component of the Mean Surface Wind. Examining Figs. 2.21 and 2.22, which show the direction of the mean surface wind, it is possible to determine the geographical distribution of its east-west component. This is shown in Fig. 2.25. Surface winds with an **easterly** component prevail in the tropics, or low latitudes, between about 30°N. and 30°S. Surface winds with a westerly component prevail poleward from about 30°N. and S. at least to about latitude 65°. In Fig. 2.25 the tropical easterlies are separated from the middle-latitude westerlies

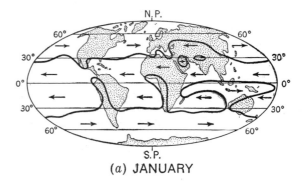

(a) JANUARY

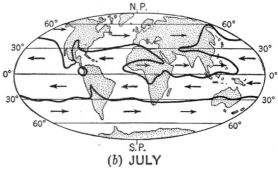

(b) JULY

FIG. 2.25. Geographical distribution of the west-east (zonal) component of the mean surface wind. The heavy lines separate the regions of tropical easterlies from those of the extratropical westerlies. (*After Mintz and Dean.*)

by heavy lines. These bounding lines extend in a nearly east-west direction in the winter hemispheres (January in the Northern Hemisphere; July in the Southern Hemisphere). In the summer hemispheres the bounding lines are less regular, for deep embayments of the westerlies are thrust into the tropical latitudes. Nevertheless, in both January and July almost equal areas of the earth's surface are covered by easterly and westerly winds. This fact confirms the earlier generalization regarding surface winds.

79. Velocity of Mean Surface Resultant Wind in January and July. By means of isovels (lines of equal velocity in meters per second) the speed of the resultant winds, over the oceans only, are represented in Figs. 2.26 and 2.27. The student needs to be cautioned that it is speed of the *resultant* wind which is here being analyzed and not average wind speed. The latter is a mean of the speeds of winds from any and all directions, while speed of the resultant wind expresses the rate of net transport of air in the direction of

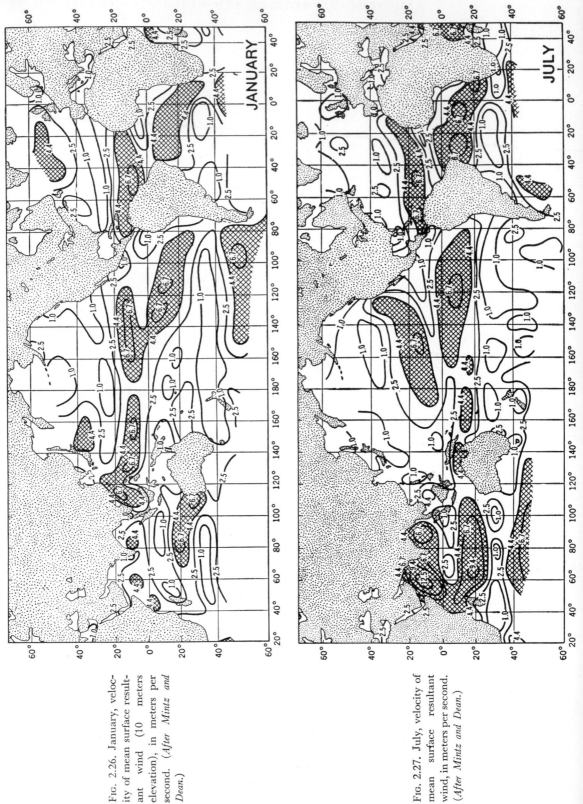

FIG. 2.26. January, velocity of mean surface resultant wind (10 meters elevation), in meters per second. (*After Mintz and Dean.*)

FIG. 2.27. July, velocity of mean surface resultant wind, in meters per second. (*After Mintz and Dean.*)

the resultant wind. Strong winds that come from a great variety of directions actually tend to cancel each other out so that the net transport in any direction may be small. Moderate winds with a strong directional prevalence will be represented by larger isovels than much stronger winds which are highly variable in direction.

The most extensive areas of high isovels are found in the tropical easterlies (trade winds) over the oceans. Other than in the tropical easterlies resultant winds of high velocity are found in the steady southwest monsoon winds of the Bay of Bengal and the Arabian Sea in July. Only small areas within the middle latitude westerlies show a large net transport of air, for these winds are variable in direction.

Small velocity values of the resultant wind are characteristic of (a) the major axes of the subtropical anticylcones, (b) the intertropical convergence zone between the trades, and (c) large areas in the westerlies where wind direction is inconstant.

80. Average Surface Wind Speed. If instead of considering the velocity of resultant winds which indicate net directional transport the average speed of winds *from any and all directions* is analyzed, the contrasts between the wind belts are not the same. (a) Highest average wind velocities are to be observed in the Southern Hemisphere westerlies in all seasons. Comparable velocities characterize the Northern Hemisphere westerlies in winter only, for in July average speeds are greatly reduced. (b) The tropical easterlies which showed the highest resultant velocities stand out as winds of only moderate average wind speed. (c) Between the tropical easterlies and the middle-latitude westerlies in the regions of the subtropical anticyclones are belts of average low wind speeds. (d) A similar condition of low average wind speed is characteristic of the intertropical convergence zone between the trades.

81. Zonal (East-West) Component of the Mean Surface Wind over the Oceans. Here the direction and speed of the mean resultant winds over the ocean surface have been averaged for all longitudes (Fig. 2.28). Negative wind speeds indicate easterlies and positive speeds in-

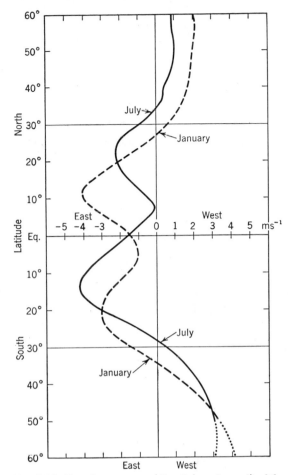

FIG. 2.28. Zonal component (direction and speed) of the mean surface wind, averaged for all longitudes over the oceans in meters per second. Negative speed represents easterly winds; positive speed, westerly. (*After Mintz and Dean.*)

dicate westerlies. (a) As is to be expected Fig. 2.28 shows that surface easterlies prevail in the low latitudes and surface westerlies farther poleward in the middle latitudes. (b) Easterlies, or trades, show a maximum in each hemisphere with a minimum between in the vicinity of the intertropical convergence. The maxima usually are located between 10 and 20°N. and S. (c) The position and intensity of the maxima in the easterlies shift with northward and southward migration of the insolation belts so that there is a latitudinal displacement of the ridges and troughs from July to January. This fact of the latitudinal migration of the zonal winds is of the

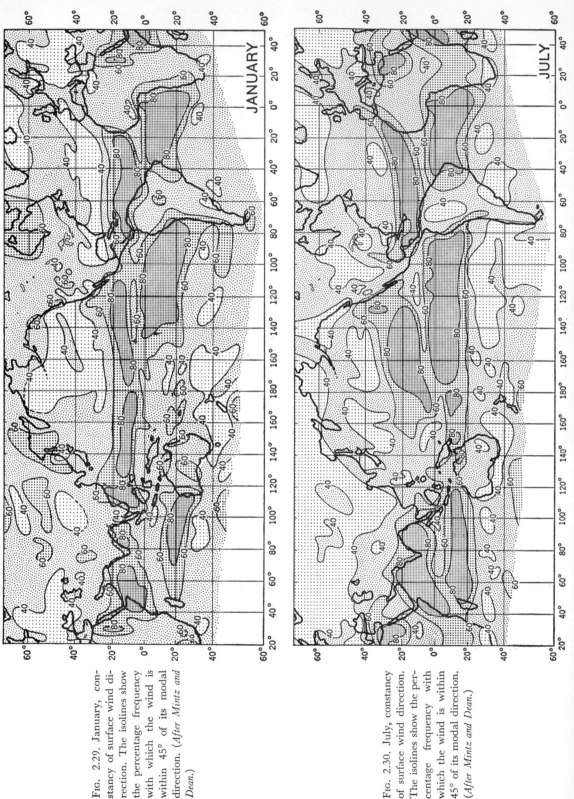

Fig. 2.29. January, constancy of surface wind direction. The isolines show the percentage frequency with which the wind is within 45° of its modal direction. (*After Mintz and Dean.*)

Fig. 2.30. July, constancy of surface wind direction. The isolines show the percentage frequency with which the wind is within 45° of its modal direction. (*After Mintz and Dean.*)

greatest importance climatically, for significant variations in seasonal weather and rainfall are associated with the displacement. (*d*) The maxima in the easterlies are strongest and closest to the equator in the respective late winter seasons. They are farthest from the equator and weakest in the respective late summer seasons. (*e*) The seasonal displacements and changes in velocity in the easterlies are smaller in the Southern Hemisphere than in the Northern Hemisphere. (*f*) The minimum between the two easterly currents moves north and south across the equator following the sun and hence in harmony with the trade-wind maxima. (*g*) In July and October the wind speed at the intertropical minimum is about zero, and between July and October there is a weak mean westerly current near the equator. Since the data employed apply to oceans only, and since the speed of the mean surface wind over the continents is not known, it is impossible at present to state whether the zonal wind averaged for all longitudes would show a mean westerly current near the equator at any season. (*h*) The boundaries between the tropical easterlies and middle-latitude westerlies (zero mean zonal wind) likewise are displaced north and south with the seasons, being farthest from the equator in late summer and closest to the equator in late winter of each hemisphere. The total width of the tropical easterlies remains about the same (60°) throughout the year. (*i*) Data are meager concerning the oceanic westerlies in the Southern Hemisphere. The data that are available suggest that these winds are more constantly westerly than their counterparts in the Northern Hemisphere. The speed of the southern westerlies is somewhat greater in January (summer), but the width of the belt is greater in July. (*j*) Owing to the size of the continents, the oceanic westerlies of the Northern Hemisphere cover much less longitude than those to the south of the equator. Their seasonal variations in velocity and width are great, with speeds in January twice those of July and with the width of the belt also greater in winter than in summer. (*k*) In the Northern Hemisphere the tropical easterlies and westerlies grow stronger and weaker together.

82. Constancy of Surface Winds.

Figures 2.29 and 2.30 show constancy in direction in terms of the percentage frequency with which the wind is within 45° (a 90° sector) of its modal or resultant direction. It is the variability in wind direction which is responsible for the differences between the speed of the mean resultant wind shown in Figs. 2.26 and 2.27 and the mean of wind speeds. (*a*) The tropical easterlies or trades are much the most constant of the zonal winds. Not all parts of the easterlies have a high constancy in wind direction, those of the western Pacific being especially deficient in this quality. (*b*) High constancy is also characteristic of the southwest winds (monsoons) of the North Indian Ocean in July and of the northeast winds in the same region in January. (*c*) Small constancy of direction is characteristic of some but not all of the subtropics. This regional variability seems to depend upon whether the anticyclone is a quasi-stationary feature or whether moving small anticyclones are characteristic. For example, the subtropical sections of the South Indian Ocean and the regions around Australia where moving small anticyclones predominate show low constancy. The same is true of winter (January) but not summer in the subtropical North Atlantic. The daily synoptic weather maps reveal the reason for this seasonal contrast, for in winter there is a constant migration of individual anticyclones across this region, while in summer the subtropical anticyclone is relatively stationary. (*d*) The intertropical convergence region is a region of moderate to low constancy. On the daily weather map this is not a continuous line of convergence on individual days. Instead, small individual areas of convergence and divergence move from east to west along this belt, with convergence dominating. The *ITC* therefore is in the nature of a statistical feature which appears in the mean wind field but is not conspicuous in the wind field for any day. (*e*) In general, the westerlies are regions of relatively low constancy of wind direction.

SUMMARY OF INDIVIDUAL SURFACE WINDS

In the previous treatment of the surface winds of the earth generalizations concerning direction, velocity, and variability of surface circulations have been developed through the use of world charts. It now remains to summarize the important characteristics of individual wind systems and those of particular latitudes or regions.

83. Winds in the Tropics. *New Concepts.* At the present time considerable confusion exists regarding the general pattern of tropical winds. During the Second World War, a sufficient number of new observations concerning both surface and upper-air winds in the low latitudes was collected to make many of the earlier notions concerning trades, doldrums, and anti-trades untenable. But at the same time these new observations are not sufficiently numerous, well distributed, or even reliable to permit of a reconstruction of a completely satisfactory new picture of wind patterns for tropical latitudes. Observations for continental areas in the tropics are particularly meager. The meagerness as well as the localism of the new observations has led some writers to make zonal generalizations based upon data applicable to a single meridian. The result of this practice has been contradictions and confusion.

There can be no doubt, however, that the earlier concept of steady easterly surface winds (trades) over the tropical oceans in both hemispheres, with an equatorial component which

The first of these is the discovery that the low latitudes are affected by many more nonperiodic types of weather disturbances than was previously thought to be the case. The severe hurricane type of disturbance has been recognized for a long time, but recently it has been discovered that some of these violent storms originate in the deep easterlies (trades) as well as in the doldrums. In addition it is now known that there are other types of disturbances or perturbations in the form of waves and weak cyclones which infest large parts of tropical latitudes. Hence, the earlier concept of tropical weather being almost exclusively periodic (diurnal and seasonal) in character must be changed, for there are numerous nonperiodic weather irregularities associated with wave and cyclone types of storms. Invasions of middle-latitude air masses in certain parts of the tropics add to the lack of uniformity in such regions.

A second circumstance which mars the classical picture of tropical wind and weather uniformity is the discovery that the really steady trades occupy only a fraction of the total oceanic area within the tropics, while the antitrades[1] aloft are found only in restricted areas.

That tropical easterlies with a high percentage of constancy do exist is clearly shown in Figs. 2.29 and 2.30 and in the table below. But it

Average Direction, Velocity, and Steadiness of the Southeast Trades within a 10° Rectangle
(10 *to* 20°S. *and* 80 *to* 90°E.) *in the Indian Ocean*
(N. = 0°, E. = 90°, S. = 180°, etc.)
(After Gallé and Conrad)

	J	F	M	A	M	J	J	A	S	O	N	D	Yr.
Direction, deg.	123	111	128	126	137	147	143	147	140	133	129	134	135
Steadiness, per cent	83	72	69	84	90	84	89	87	88	90	87	90	85
Beaufort velocity rating	3.65	3.01	2.86	3.86	4.11	3.97	4.82	4.70	4.75	4.60	4.25	4.12	4.07
Meters per second	5.66	4.32	4.06	6.11	6.64	6.34	8.24	7.98	8.09	7.75	6.96	6.67	6.55

causes them to converge near the equator, giving rise to a belt of variable winds and calms (doldrums) with cumulus clouds and heavy rainfall between the trades, must be revised. The previously held concept of zonal uniformity of winds and weather within the tropics is one that is no longer tenable. At least two circumstances shatter this previously held concept of zonal uniformity in winds and weather in the low latitudes.

is also observable from these same maps that the typical steady trades as described in textbook models of the general circulation are confined to more restricted areas in the tropics than is usually supposed. The uniform trades are limited to belts of latitude which are usually less than 10° in width (Figs. 2.29, 2.30) so that constancy in

[1] High-altitude winds above the surface trades flowing in an opposite direction to the trades.

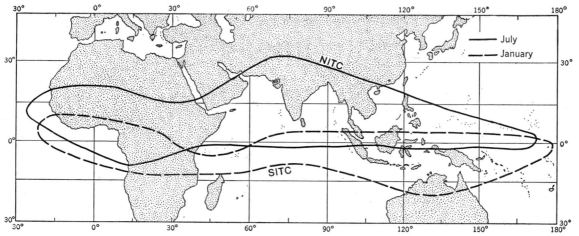

FIG. 2.31. Core area of the equatorial westerlies at the times of the extreme seasons. (*After Flohn.*)

both direction and velocity declines sharply on their poleward and equatorward margins. Equally important is the fact that the proverbially steady trades are chiefly characteristic of the *eastern* parts of the equatorial branches of the subtropical anticyclones. In the western parts of tropical oceans, or the western parts of the anticyclones, the tropical easterlies are much more variable in character, for in these parts they are interrupted more frequently by perturbations in the form of wave disturbances and cyclones. Even here they are certainly not so variable as are the surface westerlies of middle latitudes, but there are numerous disruptions of the wind field due to nonthermal causes.

In their westerly oceanic parts, not only are the trades less steady winds but in addition they have a smaller meridional (north-south) component and may not be directed toward the equator even in the mean. In some parts of the western tropical oceans the trades blow nearly parallel with the equator or are even directed away from it. Moreover, in these same westerly parts the west-to-east antitrades aloft are found at higher and higher levels and easterlies may prevail clear up to the top of the troposphere. There are no universal antitrades in the low latitudes and their best development appears to be toward the eastern margins of the subtropical highs. The typical trade-wind inversion is also found at increasingly higher elevations toward the western part of the trade circulation in each

anticyclone, so that there the air is more unstable and convection extends to higher elevations.

A somewhat controversial element of the tropical circulation has to do with the existence of an equatorial west-wind zone in the intertropical convergence area between the broader belts of easterlies (Fig. 2.31). By some, equatorial westerlies are considered to represent the normal situation in the inner tropics and are thought of as being located between a northern intertropical convergence (*NITC*) and a southern intertropical convergence (*SITC*) (Fig. 2.32).[1] With the data now available it does not seem possible to determine whether the zonal wind averaged for all longitudes would show a mean westerly current near the equator at any season. H. Flohn of the German Weather Bureau believes that such an equatorial west-wind zone is reasonably well established from the present observations for nearly 200° of longitude and extending from western Africa across the Indian Ocean and including the western Pacific (Fig. 2.31). Flohn considers the southwest monsoon of southern Asia to be only one element of the equatorial westerlies. Other students of the atmosphere are less certain that the equatorial westerlies are a part of a general circulation and suggest that, in

[1] R. D. Fletcher, The General Circulation of the Tropical and Equatorial Atmosphere, *Jour. Meteorology,* Vol. 2, 167–174, 1945; H. Flohn, Passat Zirkulation und äquatorial Westwindzone, *Arch. Meteorol. Geophys. u. Bioklimatol.,* Series B, Vol. 3, pp. 3–15, 1951.

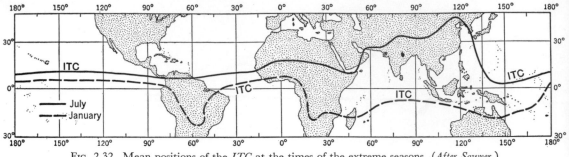

FIG. 2.32. Mean positions of the *ITC* at the times of the extreme seasons. (*After Sawyer.*)

the western equatorial Pacific at least, the mean drift of air from the west is the result of the passage of a large number of depressions.[1]

84. *Winds of the Equatorial Low-pressure Trough and Convergence Zone.* Previously this equatorial low-pressure trough, or convergence zone, was simply known as the doldrums, or equatorial belt of variable winds and calms. As the homogeneous northeast and southeast trades converge toward the equator it was assumed that they rose above the earth's surface, leaving between them at low elevations a condition of variable light and fickle breezes with much calm. The doldrum belt therefore was assumed to occupy the axis or valley of lowest pressure in the general equatorial low-pressure trough where pressure gradients are weak and variable. Much of the bad weather characteristic of this zone was assumed to be due to the instability of the stagnant, moist doldrum air which gave rise to abundant convection with cumulus clouds and thunderstorm rain.

It is now known, however, that the condition of calms and variable winds (doldrums) is not clearly marked all round the equator, nor does it exist at all times of the year. In places and upon occasions it may be reduced to the vanishing

point by encroaching trades or monsoons and then again it may expand to twice its normal width.

Three fairly persistent oceanic areas characterized by light and variable doldrum winds have been noted.[1] Much of the largest of these is located in the western Pacific and the Indian Oceans extending from about the 180° meridian to the east coast of equatorial Africa, a distance of some 10,000 miles, or over one-third the circumference of the earth (Fig. 2.33). These Indo-Pacific doldrums may prevail over an area approximating 10,000,000 square miles. Very extensive portions show a weak drift of air from west to east which has led some to designate this doldrum area as the largest and most representative region of equatorial westerlies. Two small doldrum areas are located off the west coast of equatorial Africa and off the west coast of equatorial Central America. These are in the form of wedges whose broad base is along the continental coast so that they taper to the west. In the western Atlantic and the central Pacific, beyond the "doldrum wedges," there are no zones of light and fickle winds between the converging trades.

[1] C. E. Palmer, Tropical Meteorology, "Compendium of Meteorology," pp. 876–877.

[1] P. R. Crowe, Wind and Weather in the Equatorial Zone, *Inst. British Geographers, Trans. and Papers, 1951, Publication* 17, pp. 21–76.

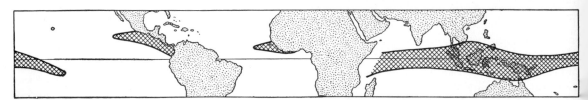

FIG. 2.33. Principal areas of doldrums. (*After Crowe.*)

Within the equatorial trough some longitudes appear to show a weak drift of air from the east and some from the west. Relatively small constancy of direction and velocity of air movement are characteristic, however. Essentially it is a convergence zone, and because of this fact there is a great deal of vertical movement of air, with the result that there is an abundance of cloud and precipitation in most parts of equatorial latitudes. It has been noted in an earlier section that the small constancy in wind direction agrees with the weather map condition, for on individual days a continuous east-west line of convergence does not exist. More accurately the picture is one of numerous small perturbations moving across the region, both convergences and divergences, with convergences dominating.

85. Fronts Near the Equator.[1] The question regarding the development of fronts between air masses of contrasting temperatures and densities within the equatorial zone is a very controversial question. Probably the majority of opinion favors the existence of fronts. Many insist, however, that while convergence is marked, the air masses involved in the convergence are too homogeneous to permit the development of real density discontinuity fronts such as exist in middle latitudes. The front most commonly recognized is the intertropical (equatorial) front (*ITF*) which is regarded as being formed in the equatorial convergence zone where the two trades meet (Figs. 2.34, 2.35, 2.36). Many prefer to designate it the intertropical convergence (*ITC*) rather than the intertropical front. By some the intertropical convergence is considered to be single and relatively continuous. Others describe it as discontinuous. Still others describe the *ITC* as double in character and insist that there is a northern intertropical front (*NITC*) and a southern intertropical front (*SITC*) with true equatorial air masses in the form of westerlies between the two fronts (Fig. 2.32). It has also been suggested

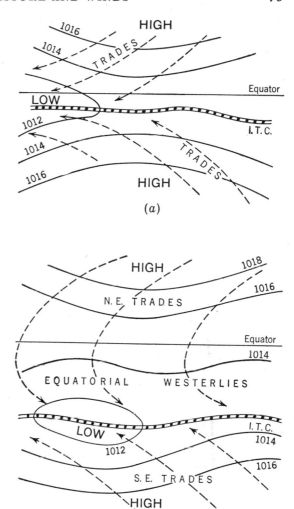

FIG. 2.34. Distribution of windflow and pressure: (*a*) when the *ITC* is near the equator; and (*b*) when the *ITC* is displaced some distance north or south of the equator. (*After Sawyer.*)

that the *NITC* and *SITC* are not single lines of convergence but instead are multiple in character (Fig. 2.36). Evaporation of the rain falling from the clouds developed at the convergence, and additional cooling of the air within the *ITC* by radiation from the cloud tops, may cause the *ITC* to become a cool source with descending air. The result is the formation of new *ITC*'s on either side of the original one which has subsequently become a cool source. The total result is the development of multiple *ITC*'s and the

[1] "Compendium of Meteorology," pp. 882–883; J. S. Sawyer, Memorandum on the Intertropical Front, *Meteorological Repts.*, No. 10, British Meteorological Office, 1952.

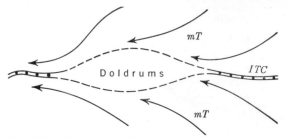

FIG. 2.35. Illustrating doldrums (equatorial air) and ITC. (*After Sawyer*.)

local northward and southward movements and the occasional jumps or displacements of the zone of convergence.[1] It must be admitted that the literature on the intertropical convergence and its possible fronts is very confusing and contradictory.

If and when density fronts do develop between the trades, they occur most frequently at those times when the trade from the winter hemisphere is beginning to advance across the equator into the summer hemisphere and also at the time when it is receding (just after the equinox). These are the periods, presumably, when the two trades, because of the nature of their sources and the lengths of their trajectories, have the greatest temperature and humidity contrasts.

86. *Tropical Easterlies, or Trades.*[2] The trade winds are not one homogeneous mass but have contrasting characteristics in different parts. In general, the poleward portion of the trades which are closest to the subtropical high-pressure cell, where there is a great deal of subsidence and divergence, are relatively dry, and fair weather is prevalent. As a result of subsidence, an inversion develops aloft which increases the stability. These poleward parts of trades are frequently designated as tropical air masses. As these stable tropical air masses of maritime subtropical origin move equatorward over the warm ocean surface, certain modifications occur. At least in the eastern parts of oceans, but less conspicuously in the western

parts, the equatorward-moving trades are passing over increasingly warmer surfaces, and hence both heat and humidity are being added at the base, tending to decrease the stability of the air. In the western part of tropical oceans, where latitudinal temperature gradients are very weak or absent, the heating from below may be less marked or even absent, but the moisture addition is still present. Thus as humidity and, in parts, heat as well are added at the base and are carried upward by convection currents to higher levels, an increasingly deeper air mass is being made unstable and therefore conducive to the formation of condensation and precipitation.

Of still greater importance in modifying the trade-wind air masses as they move equatorward is the fact that the air mass is gradually shifting from a high-pressure subsidence area toward a low-pressure convergent area. In the anticyclonic subsident area the total effect of the settling air is to stabilize it with the development of a strong temperature inversion at relatively low levels. As the trade wind approaches the convergent zone near the equator, elevation of the air mass takes the place of subsidence, with the result that the inversion gradually becomes weaker and is shifted to higher elevations so that the air mass becomes increasingly unstable. Thus while the trades are inclined to be dry, stable, and characterized by generally fair

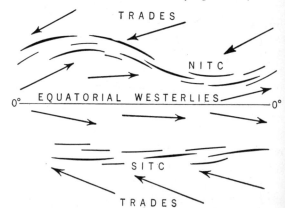

FIG. 2.36. Here the ITC is shown as consisting of two branches, a northern (NITC) and a southern (SITC) with equatorial westerlies between them. The ITC is represented not as a continuous convergence zone but as composed of multiple discontinuous convergences which shift their positions frequently. (*After Fletcher*.)

[1] Fletcher, *op. cit.*, pp. 172–174.

[2] P. R. Crowe, The Tradewind Circulation of the World, *Inst. British Geographers, Trans. and Papers, 1949,* Publication 15, pp. 37–56; The Seasonal Variation in the Strength of the Trades, *Inst. British Geographers, Trans. and Papers, 1950,* Publication 16, pp. 23–47.

weather and few storms on their poleward margins, they are likely to be more humid, unstable, and subject to disturbances accompanied by clouds and rain on their equatorial margins. Dry tropical air masses therefore are characteristic of the poleward margins of the tropical easterlies, but these are gradually transformed into unstable, humid tropical (equatorial) air masses farther equatorward. There is no specific line of demarcation (Fig. 2.37).

It is worthy of note that not only do the trades change in character latitudinally but also longitudinally. The typically dry trades are found toward the eastern ends of the subtropical anticyclones, where the easterlies have the greatest component toward the equator and where subsidence is at a maximum. Toward the western margins disturbances in form of waves and cyclones are more numerous, subsidence is less marked, and the upper-air trade inversion has disappeared or exists only at a relatively high elevation.

87. Winds of the Subtropics. As noted previously from Figs. 2.21 and 2.22, the subtropical latitudes (25 to 35°) witness the development of great anticyclonic circulations around a series of oceanic high-pressure cells which are elongated in a general east-west direction. These subtropical highs appear to be associated with longitudinal waves in the high-altitude jet stream and westerly wind vortex. The oceanic subtropical anticyclones are the most persistent and conspicuous features of the general circulation of the atmosphere. Their equatorward branches are the tropical easterlies, or the trade winds, while the circulation on their poleward sides is the westerlies of middle latitudes. The transition area between the easterlies and the westerlies is sometimes known as the *horse latitudes*.

As noted earlier, the centers of the subtropical anticyclones are associated with extended lines of mean surface wind divergence. Surface divergence in turn is accompanied by settling, or subsidence, of the air aloft in order to feed the surface flow so that the horse latitudes in general are regions of stable air which is opposed to

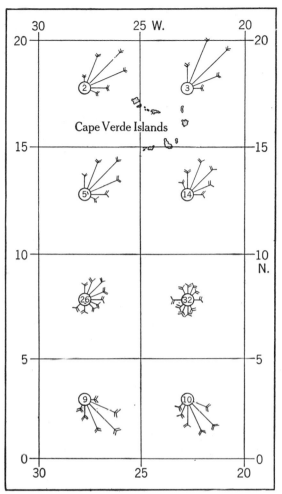

FIG. 2.37. Northeast and southeast trades and doldrums over the Atlantic Ocean, June, 1922. The wind rose is given for each 5-degree square. Arrows fly with the wind. The length of the arrow is proportional to the frequency of winds from that direction. The number of feathers on the arrow indicates the average force of the wind on the Beaufort scale. The figure in the center gives the percentage of calms, light airs, and variable winds. (*U.S. Hydrographic Office Pilot Chart.*)

condensation processes. In an earlier discussion of the earth's surface winds based upon a variety of world maps of wind characteristics, it has been noted that the centers of the subtropical anticyclones are regions of relatively low wind velocity (Figs. 2.26 and 2.27). The constancy of wind direction is also small (Figs. 2.29 and 2.30), for winds tend to come from a great variety of directions (Fig. 2.38). Consequently,

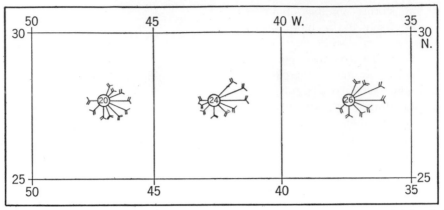

FIG. 2.38. The subtropical belt of variable winds and calms, or horse latitudes, over the North Atlantic Ocean, June, 1922. For explanation of symbols, see Fig. 2.37. (*U.S. Hydrographic Office Pilot Chart.*)

the resultant surface wind has a low velocity. Although constancy of direction is likely to be low for the horse latitudes in general, it does vary considerably from one subtropical center to another, depending upon the persistence of the high-pressure cell. When the particular anticyclone has a quasi-stationary character so that its size and shape remain much the same as seen on a large number of individual daily weather maps, the constancy of wind direction may be relatively high. On the other hand, where the subtropical anticyclonic cell is really a mean of a large number of anticyclones migrating across the area, the constancy of direction is much lower.

It is a general rule that the air-mass characteristic of the western portions of the subtropical anticyclonic systems are likely to be quite different from those along the eastern margins (Fig. 2.39). It is more especially in the

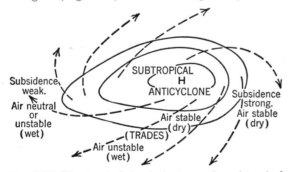

FIG. 2.39. The tropical circulation around a subtropical anticyclone showing prevailing areas of stability and instability.

eastern portions of the anticyclones that subsidence is most marked and the typical drought conditions of the horse latitudes are best developed. The strong subsidence in these eastern portions produces a marked inversion of temperature at about 500 to 1,500 meters above sea level. The air above the inversion is very dry and as a result of the dryness and the thermal inversion rainfall is very meager. Some of the driest regions of the earth are to be found along the west coastal margins of continents and the east sides of oceans at about 20 to 30°N. and S., which come under the influence of the strong subsidence in the eastern parts of the subtropical anticyclones. The intensified aridity of the coastal portions of the Sahara Desert in North Africa, the Kalahari in South Africa, the Chilean-Peruvian Desert in South America, and the Sonoran Desert in Mexico testify to the drying influence of the cell.

The western side of a subtropical anticyclone, by contrast, is usually characterized by moist unstable air and abundant rainfall. This condition is the exception as it applies to anticyclonic systems in general. Regions occupying positions coincident with the western ends of the oceanic highs are the lands bordering the Caribbean Sea and Gulf of Mexico in North America, eastern China and southern Japan in Asia, southeastern Brazil in South America, southeastern Africa and eastern Australia—all of them rainy areas and therefore standing in sharp climatic contrast to those arid regions along the western sides of the continents in similar latitudes which are influenced by the subsident eastern margins of the oceanic anticyclones.

It is not entirely clear why the eastern and western sides of the subtropical oceanic anticyclones are so greatly in contrast. Bjerkness and his Norwegian associates visualize the circulation in the subtropical cells at 1 to 8 km. as taking place in such a way that the planes of the ellipses that represent the trajectories of the air particles are tilted upward from east to west. The eastern end of the cell may be considered as tilted downward and the western end upward. A mass of air in the cellular circulation (Northern Hemisphere) consequently tends to subside as it moves eastward on the northern side of the cell and to be lifted as it moves westward on the southern side of the cell. The total vertical displacement that the air experiences in passing from one end of the cell to another may be in the neighborhood of three-fifths of a mile. It is to this tilted circulation in the subtropical oceanic cells, with subsidence prevailing at the eastern ends, and lifting at the western ends, that the Norwegian meteorologists would ascribe the contrasts in air-mass characteristics and also the climatic differences prevailing in the longitudinal extremes of the cell.

When the opposite moving currents of two adjacent cells overlap, as they frequently do in the cols between the cells, the one coming from the equatorial side of the eastern cell is warmer than the other coming from the northern side of the western cell, so that the former current is forced to ascend over the latter along an inclined surface of discontinuity whose slope is approximately 1:200. The cols therefore mark the boundaries between the cells and are characterized by converging air masses separated by discontinuity surfaces along which storms and rainfall may originate. These fronts formed in the cols between the cells are sometimes designated as *meridional fronts*, or *trade fronts*.

Although the horse latitudes resemble the intertropical convergence zone in many of their surface wind characteristics (small average wind speed, low constancy of direction, and small resultant wind velocity), these two regions

are relatively dissimilar in general weather conditions. Because the subtropical anticyclones, except in their western parts, are regions of upper-air subsidence and surface-wind divergence (compare with *ITC*), atmospheric disturbances are few, rainfall is meager, and, except where cool ocean currents prevail, skies are prevailingly clear and sunshine abundant. These conditions are considerably modified in the western parts of the subtropical anticyclones.

88. The Westerlies. Moving down gradient from the centers of subtropical high pressure to the subpolar lows (roughly 35 or 40° to 60 or 65°) are the stormy westerlies. Particularly is the poleward boundary of this wind belt a fluctuating one, shifting with the seasons and over shorter periods of time as well. The westerlies are distinctive among the wind belts in that they are uniformly neither strong nor weak but instead are composed of extremes. Spells of weather are one of their distinguishing characteristics. At times, and more especially in the winter, they blow with gale force, while upon other occasions mild breezes prevail. Moderate to strong winds (Beaufort 3 to 7) are most numerous but with stormy winds (Beaufort 8 to 12) more prevalent than weak winds (Beaufort 1 to 2). Calms are infrequent. Obviously the westerlies on the average are more boisterous than the trades.

Mean Wind Directions at Scilly Islands, 49.38°N., 6.16°W.

(Frequency in per cent)
(After Kendrew)

N.	5	E.	7	S.	6	W.	11
N.N.E.	5	E.S.E.	5	S.S.W.	5	W.N.W.	10
N.E.	5	S.E.	4	S.W.	6	N.W.	9
E.N.E.	4	S.S.E.	4	W.S.W.	7	N.N.W.	4
				Calm	3		

Although designated as *westerlies*, westerly being, to be sure, the direction of most frequent and strongest winds, air does blow from all points of the compass (Fig. 2.40). A comparison of the tables on pp. 76 and 87 shows trades of the Indian Ocean to have an annual constancy of 85 per cent while westerlies in the same ocean have only a 47 per cent constancy. The variability of winds, in both direction and strength, so

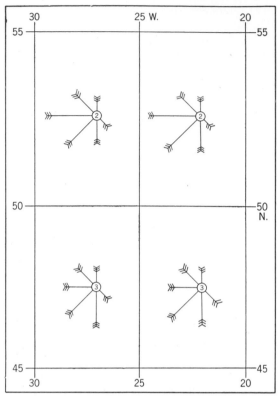

Fig. 2.40. The westerlies over the North Atlantic Ocean, January, 1922. For explanation of symbols, see Fig. 2.37. (*U.S. Hydrographic Office Pilot Chart.*)

westerly air currents. Moreover, on the eastern sides of Asia, and to a lesser degree North America, continental wind systems called monsoons tend to disturb the westerlies, especially in summer. It is in the Southern Hemisphere, where in latitudes 40 to 65° land masses are largely absent, that the stormy westerlies can be observed in their least interrupted longitudinal development. Over these great expanses of ocean, winds of gale strength are common in summer as well as winter. These are the "roaring forties" of the earlier mariners, while later penetration of higher latitudes discovered the "furious fifties" and the "shrieking sixties." In the vicinity of Cape Horn they are often so violent as to make east-west traffic around the Cape not only difficult but even dangerous. It is a wild region where gale follows gale with only brief intervening lulls; where raw chilly weather, cloudy skies, and mountainous seas prevail.

The westerlies of the Northern Hemisphere, where the great land masses with their seasonal pressure reversals cause the wind systems to be much more complex, are considerably less strong in summer than in winter. In the former season gentle to fresh breezes prevail, and winds come from a great variety of directions with almost equal frequency. But in winter they are like their counterparts in the Southern Hemisphere, being strong and boisterous with a greater prevalence of winds from westerly directions. The poleward margins of the westerlies near the subpolar troughs of low pressure are particularly subject to great surges of cold

characteristic of the westerlies, is largely the result of the procession of fronts and storms (cyclones and anticyclones) that travel from west to east in these latitudes. These storms, with their local systems of converging and diverging winds, tend to break up and modify the general

Average Wind Direction, Steadiness, and Velocity of the Westerlies of the Indian Ocean within a 10° Rectangle (35 to 45°S. and 70 to 80°E.)

(N. = 0°, E. = 90°, S. = 180°, W. = 270°, etc. Calms = Beaufort 0; weak winds = 1 and 2; moderate winds = 3, 4, 5; strong winds = 6, 7; stormy winds = 8, 9, 10, 11, 12; hurricane winds = 11 and 12. The numbers indicate frequency per 10,000 observations)

(After Gallé and Conrad)

	J	F	M	A	M	J	J	A	S	O	N	D
Direction, deg.	331	311	294	304	285	281	288	285	283	286	294	308
Steadiness, per cent	33	30	31	38	52	49	56	56	58	57	54	51
Weak winds	1,400	1,372	841	1,189	531	423	311	498	462	506	798	751
Moderate winds	5,972	5,363	5,263	4,982	4,309	3,697	3,073	3,741	3,207	4,026	4,723	5,609
Strong winds	2,081	2,420	2,779	2,457	3,293	3,308	3,640	3,621	3,632	3,668	3,106	2,766
Stormy winds	403	617	928	1,217	1,764	2,510	2,881	2,023	2,586	1,743	1,246	790
Hurricane winds	13	35	29	28	125	181	199	106	165	110	65	27
Calms	144	228	189	155	103	62	95	117	113	57	127	84

polar air in the winter season. The sinuous line of discontinuity, known as the polar front, which separates the cold, dry polar air from that warmer and more humid mass coming from the subtropics in the form of the westerlies is the zone of origin for a great many middle-latitude cyclones and anticyclones. It follows, therefore, that the poleward margins of the westerlies are much more subject to stormy, variable weather than are the subtropical margins. Since this polar front and the accompanying belt of storms migrate with the sun's rays, retreating poleward in summer and advancing equatorward in winter, it also follows that storm control of weather in the middle latitudes should be much more pronounced in the winter season.

89. Winds of the Polar Regions. The meagerness of direct observations makes it impossible, at the present time, to describe the mean surface circulation in the polar regions. It is still uncertain whether the zonal component of the mean wind in the high latitudes, averaged for all longitudes, is easterly or westerly. If one employed the U.S. Weather Bureau's pressure charts for the north polar region, one would conclude that mean easterly winds would prevail between latitude 60 or 65° and the North Pole. But if one used the Russian pressure charts, westerlies would appear to prevail.

Still less is known about the surface winds in the south polar regions. There is some evidence that surface easterlies prevail along the margins of the Antarctic continent, and westerlies over the major part of the high ice plateau where elevations of over 2,000 meters prevail.

90. Summary of the Major Wind Zones of Convergence and Divergence. In the preceding analysis of the surface circulation, it has been made clear that there are certain regions or latitudes of the earth where great wind systems converge horizontally and there are others where horizontal divergence is the rule. A cyclonic wind system is representative of horizontal convergence and an anticyclonic system of horizontal divergence; or wind systems may converge along an extended pressure trough so that the convergence area is in the form of a long, narrow zone. Thus it is common to speak of lines or zones of convergence and divergence. But convergence is not limited to narrow frontal zones or to restricted centers. It may operate over very large areas and give rise to widespread bad weather conditions. The facts of distribution of convergent and divergent wind systems is of utmost importance in world weather and climate. Convergence tends to make for temperature contrasts and steep temperature gradients so that the isotherms are closely spaced. This is true because the air coming from different latitudes tends to carry its temperature with it. In addition, convergence must of necessity result in an upward movement of the air involved. Such a lifting of large masses of air results in increased instability and cooling so that atmospheric disturbances in the form of storms, with accompanying cloud and precipitation, are likely.

Where horizontal divergence of surface winds is characteristic, there is of necessity a subsidence or settling of drier air from higher altitudes in order to feed the spreading surface currents (Fig. 2.41). Such a downward movement of dry air toward the earth's surface tends to warm and stabilize the air and is opposed to the development of storms, clouds, and precipitation. Regions of divergence consequently are more often than not characterized by fair weather and few storms.

A more realistic picture of the distribution of the horizontal convergence and divergence in the mean surface winds than heretofore given is provided by Figs. 2.23 and 2.24. Certain zonal elements in the distribution are very striking. Thus the strongest and most continuous convergent zone is the one located between the trades, the well-known *ITC*. Similarly the most conspicuous areas of divergence are asso-

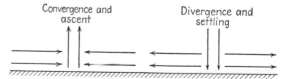

Fig. 2.41. Horizontal convergence produces ascending currents and horizontal divergence is associated with descending currents or subsidence.

ciated with the subtropical anticyclones. These features have been pointed out previously. Almost equally striking, however, is the fact that the distribution of surface wind convergence and divergence is not nearly as simple, and certainly not as zonal, as it may appear to be on an idealized atmospheric circulation which recognizes zonal trades, westerlies, horse latitudes, and doldrums. Conspicuous also are the very numerous nonzonal elements, or localisms, as shown in Figs. 2.23 and 2.24, and it is these which greatly complicate the general world pattern of climates, producing what appear to be zonal abnormalities. This is not the place to catalogue in detail the numerous nonzonal elements in the distribution pattern of convergences and divergences, but only to emphasize their importance to any understanding of world climates.

It must be emphasized, also, that not only convergence and divergence in *surface* winds are important climatologically but also those in the circulation aloft. The surface winds by no means supply all the answers to the student seeking to explain the distribution of world climates, although, to be sure, they do provide an important source of information.

General Circulation of the Atmosphere

91. Climatic Significance of Surface Winds and Winds Aloft. Any treatment of winds as a background for explanatory climatology must involve not only the surface winds of the earth but in addition the major circulation patterns of the free atmosphere. The surface winds, affected as they are by surface friction, may depart markedly in direction, speed, humidity characteristics, and vertical movement from those aloft. Surface winds have a velocity which ordinarily is much less than those of the winds aloft, where friction is greatly reduced. In addition the frictional effects tend to cause the surface air currents to cross the isobars at fairly large angles, especially over the continents, so that wind direction at the surface may depart markedly from that aloft. Also, surface ir-

regularities of the lands greatly modify the direction and speed of winds in the lower atmosphere. The air flow aloft, on the other hand, where the frictional effects are small, tends to approach the geostrophic wind, *i.e.*, it closely parallels the isobars, usually departing only 1 to 3° from them. This means that the circulation of the free atmosphere is predominantly zonal and only to a slight extent meridional.

Climatically speaking, surface air movement is chiefly important in terms of its effects upon surface air temperature as caused by advective processes. On the other hand, surface air movement may be of less assistance in understanding precipitation characteristics, for only thick air masses are capable of yielding large amounts of precipitation. Hence, it is principally in the winds in the free atmosphere that explanations of precipitation characteristics are to be sought.

92. New Concepts in the General Circulation. Anything like a complete and satisfactory outline of the mean circulation of the earth's atmosphere is not available at the present time. In part this arises from the fact that the observational network is halfway adequate only for North America and Europe. The tremendous gaps in our knowledge of the meteorology of the tropics (half the troposphere), of the high latitudes of the Southern Hemisphere, and of Asia make it impossible to construct satisfactory models of the general circulation.

The large amount of upper-air data collected during the Second World War, especially from the tropics, has had the effect of greatly stimulating research on the general circulation. But the first effect of these new data was to shatter many previously held concepts, which subsequently compelled the discarding of earlier models of the atmospheric circulation. Unfortunately, there has not been sufficient new data, nor even sufficient time, in which to create satisfactory new models to take the place of the discarded older ones.

The concept of a simple and direct thermally driven meridional circulation consisting of three principal units, a tropical, a middle-latitude, and a polar, has had its foundations badly undermined. The absence of antitrades in many longitudes within the tropics; the apparent lack of north-south temperature gradients within large parts of the tropics which would serve to drive the trade circulation; the fact that the winds in the free atmosphere, above about 500 to 1,000 meters, nearly parallel the isobars, and the existence of a cellular rather than a zonal circulation in the lower troposphere—all these facts seem to make the earlier model of a direct convectively driven meridional circulation untenable.

In place of the former tricellular vertical and meridional circulation some elements of a new horizontal exchange theory have been developed. According to this theory the exchange of air between the different latitudes takes place not so much through a series of vertical circulations directly thermally driven, but rather through irregular exchanges of polar and tropical air dynamically induced, the movements of which are primarily horizontal.

But although the concept of a direct thermally driven atmospheric circulation now appears untenable, it still remains true, however, that the basic reason for an atmospheric circulation is the fact that more solar energy is being received in the low latitudes near the equator and less in the high latitudes toward the poles. Winds are simply nature's attempt to correct this latitudinal imbalance of solar energy and thus prevent a cumulative excess of energy in the tropics and a deficit farther poleward.[1] Sir Napier Shaw aptly expresses this idea when he writes: "There is nothing but thermal convection to act as the motive power for every drop of rain that ever fell or for every wind that ever filled a sail or wrecked a ship since the world began." But although the *ultimate* cause of atmospheric circulation and winds may be latitudinal energy contrasts, it does not necessarily follow that the *direct* cause of the atmospheric circulation in all its parts is of thermal origin.

93. Normal State of General Circulation. The prevailing motion of the greatest volume of the earth's atmosphere is from west to east. There appears to be vast and deep circumpolar whirls of air, one occupying the Northern Hemisphere and another the Southern Hemisphere, and in each of them the predominant movement is from west to east. Because of turbulence, the presence of disturbances in the form of storms, and for other reasons as well, the westerly movement of the atmosphere may be somewhat obscured at the earth's surface. It becomes more pronounced and steadier with increasing elevation and reaches a sharp maximum of speed in the high troposphere or 10 to 12 km. above the earth's surface.

There is at least one, and perhaps two, major exceptions to the concept presented above which visualizes two great circumpolar whirls of westerly movement, and these exceptions exist chiefly in the surface winds. The first of these is the doubtful shallow easterly winds of the high-latitude, or polar, regions. These are known as the polar easterlies. They are generated in the shallow thermally induced polar high-pressure systems and flow toward the subpolar low-pressure cells. Normally they do not exceed 3 km. in thickness, and above them are the persistent westerlies. The other major exception to westerly movement of the atmosphere is found in the low latitudes, or tropics, where the surface winds likewise blow from east to west. These are the well-known tropical easterlies, or trade winds. They originate in the subtropical high-pressure cells and flow toward the equatorial low. The tropical easterlies, or trade winds, are much deeper and consequently extend to greater heights than do the questionable polar easterlies. Near the equator the surface easterlies may be as much as 10 km., or 6 miles, deep but they decline rapidly in depth away from the equator and cease to exist at about 35°N. and S.

A meridional cross section of the atmosphere from pole to pole is shown in Fig. 2.42. As indicated above, westerly movement of air is

[1] Some European meteorologists have suggested that the primary source of energy driving the atmospheric circulation is to be found in the vertical temperature contrast between the air near the earth's surface and that several miles up, while the temperature difference between equator and poles is of secondary importance.

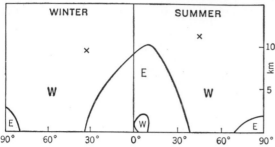

FIG. 2.42. Meridional cross section of the planetary wind belts. E = trades; W = westerlies; x = average location of jet stream; w = equatorial westerlies; e = polar easterlies. (*After Flohn.*)

characteristic of most of the earth's atmosphere, and this is especially true of the middle and higher atmospheric layers. These westerly currents actually reach down to the earth's surface only in the middle latitudes (35 to 70°).

94. The Jet Stream. The apparent point of departure for analyzing the later concepts regarding the general circulation of the atmosphere is the newly discovered jet stream and the narrow zone of steep pressure and temperature gradients associated with it. It was during the Second World War when American B-29's first began to bomb Japan that the pilots reported encountering such high-velocity head winds at 20,000 to 30,000 ft. that their ground speed was reduced to nearly zero. Similarly, when they turned downwind, their ground speed became nearly double their air speed. These reports were hard for meteorologists to believe, but subsequent high-altitude weather studies disclosed the presence of narrow bands of high-velocity winds of 200 to 300 miles an hour in other parts of the earth. The American bombers had experienced a new and previously unsuspected atmospheric phenomenon—the *jet stream* (Figs. 2.43, 2.44). This jet stream with its associated narrow belt of steep temperature and pressure gradients is the *planetary frontal zone*.

Although the origin of the jet stream is still obscure, recent observations have provided a fairly complete description of this spectacular phenomenon. The principal elements of the picture seem to be about as follows. The jet is essentially circumpolar in character and completely girdles the earth in a meandering course

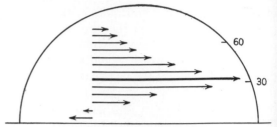

FIG. 2.43. High-altitude winds have a different pattern from those at low altitudes. At 40,000 ft., westerlies cover most of each hemisphere, their speeds increasing from the pole toward the equator until they reach a maximum at about 30°. This zone of maximum is the jet stream. (*After Namias.*)

in both the Northern and Southern Hemispheres. In places it appears to consist of several individual filaments of high-velocity air, and in other parts the filaments combine to form a single great stream of rushing air moving from west to east. These winds attain their highest velocities at elevations between 30,000 and 40,000 ft. Although the jet is sinuous in character, its average

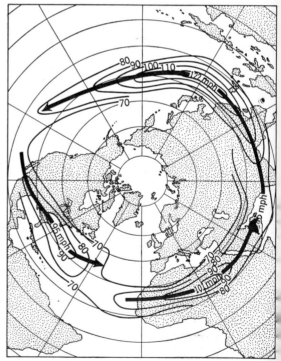

FIG. 2.44. Jet stream map for January in the Northern Hemisphere, showing average wind positions and speeds at elevations of 35,000 to 40,000 ft. (*After Namias.*)

location is about 30 to 35°. In the high troposphere the westerly winds increase in velocity
from the poles equatorward until they reach
a maximum speed at about latitude 30°, after
which they decline rapidly before reaching the
region of weak easterly winds. Thus, these high-
velocity winds aloft lie immediately above the
subtropical highs and horse latitudes at the surface, which are regions of variable and weak
winds.

The jet is not a freak but a component part of
the general atmospheric circulation. Its latitudinal position shifts with the seasons, for on
the average it is farther poleward (35 to 45°N.)
in summer than in winter (20 to 25°N.). Velocities also change seasonally, with the average
winter velocities being double those of summer.
The jet likewise has different velocities in different parts of its circumpolar course, with the
highest speeds in winter being found off the
Asiatic coast, over southeastern United States,
and in the region between North Africa and the
Indian Ocean. Across the jet horizontally, temperature changes very rapidly, so that very cold
air lies on its poleward side and very warm air
on its equatorward side.

95. Upper-air Waves. While the circumpolar vortex of westerly winds, including the jet
stream, is primarily zonal in character, *i.e.*,
paralleling the parallels, it does undergo north-
south undulations, however, so that the isobars
have a somewhat sinuous character (Fig. 2.45).
The very long ridges and troughs in the jet
stream and the west wind drift increase in amplitude with latitude and altitude in the troposphere. The smallest of the waves has a length
of about 4,000 miles and an amplitude of 550
miles; these waves are therefore the largest of all
atmospheric wave systems. The climatologist's
interest in these waves of the upper troposphere
is related to their believed connection with
surface weather phenomena, as will be shown
later.

Although the jet waves shift position and wax
and wane in strength, there is a tendency for
certain waves to be anchored in fixed geographical locations. It is believed that the origin
of the waves and the relatively fixed positions

of some of them is the result of distortions of the
westerly flow caused by the frictional effects of
land masses so that the waves are oriented with
respect to coastlines. More recently it has been
suggested that mountain barriers act in the same
capacity. Thus the continents set up a whole
series of somewhat continuous obstacles of varying importance to the westerly air flow all the
way round the earth. Each of the numerous
obstructions sets up a heterogeneous combination of waves (Fig. 2.46).

There is reason to believe that these dynamically induced waves in the upper westerlies
have a great deal to do with the cellular structure of pressure and atmospheric circulation at
the earth's surface. The troughs and ridges in
the high westerlies create convergences and
divergences which probably result in the
development of the great semipermanent centers
of high and low pressure at low levels. This
dynamic arrangement no doubt is modified
by the seasonal contrasts in surface heating over
continents and oceans, but fundamentally the
subtropical high-pressure cells and the subpolar
low-pressure cells appear to be the direct result
of nonthermal controls and are, as indicated
above, associated with convergences and divergences interrelated with the high-altitude
troughs and ridges. The shallow surface highs
of the polar regions, on the other hand, are the
result of surface cooling and the surface low-
pressure trough in the vicinity of the lowest
latitudes may likewise be thermally induced, at
least in part. This idea of a relationship between upper-air waves and surface pressure cells
is given credence by the fact that the waves in
the circumpolar vortex are much less pronounced (have a smaller amplitude) in the
Southern Hemisphere than in the Northern
Hemisphere and the cellular structure of sea-
level pressure is correspondingly less strongly
marked in the Southern Hemisphere.

**96. Nonseasonal (Irregular) Variations in
the Upper-air Circulation.** The normal, or
average, state of the general circulation as shown
on the hemisphere or world maps is one which is
never repeated in that precise form on any daily
weather map or in the mean for any week or

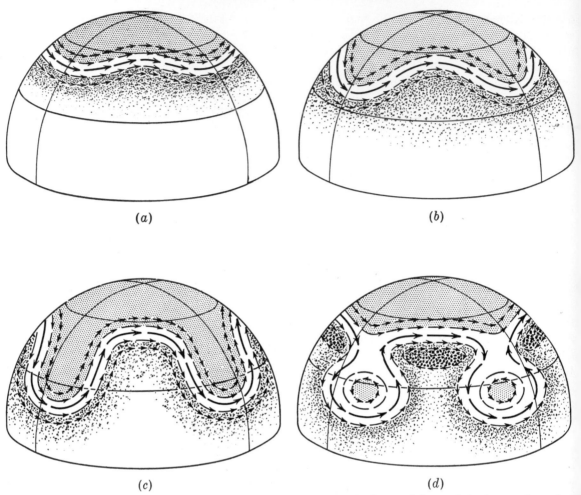

(a) (b)

(c) (d)

FIG. 2.45. Upper-air waves on the jet stream. Disturbances in the form of waves bring periods of unusual weather. The typical sequence, called an index cycle, is shown in the four diagrams. The undulating jet goes into increasingly large oscillations. North of the jet lies cold polar air and south of it warm tropical air. The oscillations carry polar air into the low latitudes and tropical air into the higher latitudes. Finally, the waves break loose, leaving cells of cold air in the south and of warm air in the north. (*After Namias.*)

month. The pattern on the normal map is only an average of very different circulations from week to week. These variations in the circulation pattern are not purely random, however, for there is some evidences of an observed sequence of types. The zonal jet wind speeds vary widely from week to week, the weekly variations being of the order of 50 to 150 per cent of the normal speed, while regional and shorter-period variations may be much greater, with occasional local jet speeds of three times the normal. Local or regional jets have been observed in latitudes ranging from beyond the Arctic Circle almost to the equator. It is these irregular variations in the position and intensity of the jet which, it is believed, are the cause of nonperiodic variations in surface weather conditions. They are, therefore, of unusual climatic importance.

The irregular or nonseasonal variations in the jet may be looked upon as contractions and expansions of the circumpolar westerly wind vortex toward and away from the pole. During these contractions and expansions the jet markedly changes its position and form. These periods of change are called *index cycles* and the cycle takes from 4 to 6 weeks to complete (Fig. 2.45).

In the first stage the jet stream lies well to the north and it takes a general west-east direction so that its waves or undulations are small. The cold polar air masses are confined to the higher latitudes, and much of the middle latitudes are covered by mild air. At this stage sea-level westerlies are strong and zonal in character and they lie poleward of their normal position. Pressure systems are oriented east-west, cyclonic activity is confined to the higher latitudes, and there is little latitudinal air-mass exchange between high and low latitudes. This stage is spoken of as representing a *high zonal index*.

In the second stage, the jet stream moves farther equatorward and its waves increase in amplitude. This results in thrusts of polar air equatorward and of tropical air poleward. A still later stage witnesses a further increase in the amplitude of the jet waves with associated strong north-south movements of tropical and polar air masses, causing great east-west con-

trasts in temperature. At this stage the mean position of the jet stream is much closer to the equator.

In the fourth stage of the index cycle the waves in the jet have so greatly increased in amplitude that immense pools of tropical air are cut off and isolated in higher latitudes, while equally large masses of polar air are left stranded in lower latitudes. This condition is described as one of *low zonal index* since the north-south contrasts in wind velocity and weather are small. There has been a complete fragmentation of the zonal westerlies into closed cellular centers; air mass and temperature contrasts are at a maximum in an east-west direction, and there is a north-south orientation of pressure centers and frontal systems. One author has described this period as the occasion of topsy-turvy weather when Alaska may be warmer than Florida. It bears reemphasizing that the great convolutions on the jet stream are a part of the mechanism of latitudinal heat balance on the earth. It represents nature's method, through mass exchanges of air between high and low latitudes, of

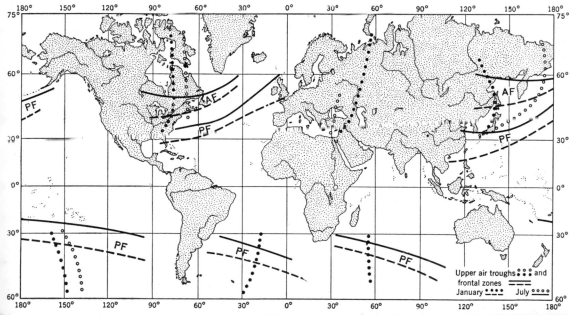

FIG. 2.46. Upper-air troughs are closely associated with the location of major frontal zones, which in turn are the regions of concentration of cyclonic storms. Eastern North America–western Atlantic and eastern Asia–western Pacific are two of the regions in the Northern Hemisphere showing a noteworthy concentration of upper air troughs, frontal zones, and cyclone development. (*After Flohn.*)

equalizing the radiation contrasts between the polar and equatorial regions. Thereby higher latitudes are prevented from becoming increasingly colder and the lower latitudes from becoming increasingly hotter.

97. The Jet Stream and Surface Weather. Without doubt the jet stream is closely associated with surface weather phenomena, although precisely what its connection is and how this connection operates are still highly controversial questions. The polar front, or planetary frontal zone, which separates tropical from polar air masses in the lower atmosphere characteristically intersects the earth's surface slightly equatorward of the high-altitude jet stream. The upper-air jet and the low-altitude frontal zone are believed to be closely related. Moreover, since the great planetary frontal zone is intimately associated with the development of storms, and hence of precipitation, it seems reasonable to believe that the jet stream must be an important element in the control of surface weather (Fig. 2.46). Well-developed middle-latitude cyclones appear to extend upward into upper air troughs. Rainfall seems to be concentrated in those areas lying below the jet, and cyclones tend to intensify when they follow a course which lies underneath the jet stream; but what part the jet plays in the production of the rainfall is not certain. The precise nature of the cause and effect relationship has not yet been made clear. It has been observed that the birth and subsequent development of cyclones is often associated with the jet, and likewise that an intensifying cyclone may apparently modify the location of the jet stream. The causal connection between these phenomena also remains obscure. It seems safe to say, however, that the jet has the effect of steering the storms, both cyclones and anticyclones, across the earth's surface.

To the jets also may be attributed the setting in motion of those deep and extensive air masses whose movements over the earth's surface bring in their train sustained periods of remarkable heat and cold, drought and flood. The ultimate cause of the varying patterns of the jet, with their important repercussions upon world weather, is also an unanswered question.

FURTHER TERRESTRIAL MODIFICATIONS OF THE SURFACE WINDS

98. It is interesting to speculate on what the characteristics of the earth's wind system would be if this planet's surface were completely water so that surface friction was reduced to a minimum and there were no mountain barriers to obstruct the free flow of air. Presumably the wind system on such a planet would be much more uniformly zonal in character than is the one which prevails on the present nonhomogeneous earth. Individual circulations, cyclonic and anticyclonic, around low- and high-pressure cells would be far less conspicuous, if they existed at all, for, as has been indicated in an earlier section, much of the nonzonal, or cellular, character of surface pressure and winds is thought to be associated with the effects of continents and their mountain systems upon upper-air flow.

There are additional terrestrial modifications of the surface winds, however, which perhaps can best be emphasized by setting them apart from the more general wind system. Some of these modifications, such as the seasonal monsoon winds and the seasonal north-south migration of winds, have been mentioned in the earlier discussion of surface winds. These require further elaboration, however. There are others which need to be introduced. Among the terrestrial modifications are some which are planetary in magnitude; others are of subcontinental size, while still others are relatively local. These terrestrial modifications result from (a) the inclination ($23\frac{1}{2}°$) and parallelism of the earth's axis, causing a uniform latitudinal shifting of the belts of solar energy following the seasons; (b) a nonhomogeneous surface composed of both land and water areas, having contrasting temperature, pressure, and wind characteristics; and (c) land areas, the surfaces of which are variable in configuration and altitude.

99. Latitudinal Shifting of the Wind Belts. Consequent upon the parallelism and inclination of the earth's axis, during the period of revolution the sun's vertical ray shifts from $23\frac{1}{2}°$N. (summer solstice) to $23\frac{1}{2}°$S. (winter solstice), a total of 47°. Of course it is not only the vertical ray that shifts but all the insolation belts as well, and along with them the temperature belts, which are largely sun-controlled. Pressure and wind belts, in part thermally induced, likewise may be expected to migrate latitudinally with the sun's rays. That there is such a north-south migration of surface wind belts is most clearly observed from an analysis of Fig. 2.28 which portrays the zonal component of the mean surface wind, averaged for all longitudes over the oceans.

This north-south shifting of the wind belts is by no means so simple a thing as it may appear to be from the above description, for it varies in amount and rapidity of shift from one part of the earth to another. In general, there is a lag of a month or possibly two behind the sun. Over the oceans and along coasts where the migration is more readily observable the total migration is not great, usually not much over 10 to 15°. Over continents, on the other hand, the total latitudinal shift is greater, and the lag is considerably less than over oceans. Then, again, surface wind systems are much confused over land masses, owing to surface irregularities and greater seasonal variations in temperature with associated monsoonal wind systems, so that the migration may be less readily observed. However, it is not safe to assume, because the greatly modified *surface* winds over land areas do not always give evidence of orderly latitudinal shifting, that a significant migration in above-surface winds has not occurred. Instead of a simple latitudinal migration, the seasonal changes in pressure and winds are often to be observed in terms of shifts in position and intensity of the great centers of action and in the seasonal prevalence of contrasting air masses.

100. *Latitudes Affected by More Than One Wind Belt.* This latitudinal shifting of the wind belts becomes climatically significant especially in those regions lying in an intermediate position between two wind systems of unlike weather conditions, as, for instance, between a convergent and a divergent system. Such an intermediate position assures the region of being encroached upon at the opposite seasons of the year by contrasting weather conditions. *Ideally,* three such transition regions should be present in each hemisphere, and there are evidences that they actually do exist, although in imperfect form and *certainly not as continuous zonal belts.*

a. Latitudes 5± to 15+° are intermediate in position between the equatorial convergence zone (*ITC*) with its numerous disturbances and abundant rainfall on the one hand and the divergent zone associated with the subtropical anticyclones, of which the trades are the tropical branch. With the seasonal north-south shift of insolation belts and winds, these latitudes are mainly under the influence of the *ITC* and its associated disturbances at the time of high sun (summer of the particular hemisphere) and of the divergent anticyclonic systems in the low-sun season (winter). One wet and one dry season should be the result.

b. Latitudes 30 to 40° over the eastern parts of oceans and the adjacent western sides of continents are intermediate between the stable eastern side of the subtropical anticyclones, where divergence and subsidence are pronounced, on the one hand, and the westerlies with their numerous moving fronts and cyclones, where the air flow is convergent, on the other. Divergence and drought are therefore characteristic of the high-sun period, or summer, and cyclones with rain of winter. This particular seasonal control is not usually observable over the same subtropical latitudes in the interiors and eastern sides of continents, and the western parts of oceans, for in such locations the subtropical anticyclones are not so well developed and divergence and subsidence are much less marked. Onshore monsoon winds with unstable air masses actually may develop along the subtropical eastern sides of large continents, giving rise to conditions favoring a summer maximum of rainfall.

c. Latitudes 60 to 70°, which mark the subpolar lows, are intermediate in position between the stormy westerlies and easterly winds of polar origin, so that latitudinal shifting of winds should allow this region during the course of a year to experience both. The numerous cyclones with their associated fronts which infest these latitudes tend to complicate and obscure any simple migration of wind belts. It is much more a region of alternating wedges of colder and warmer air as brought by the colder polar easterlies and the warmer westerlies, respectively. It is a fact, nevertheless, that in these higher latitudes there is a greater prevalence of cold polar air in winter and of warmer southwesterly currents in summer, suggesting a semblance of wind-belt and storm-belt migration.

Monsoons

101. Definition and Origin. Literally the term monsoon may be applied to any wind system in which there is a reversal of the prevailing wind direction between winter and summer. The name monsoon is said to be derived from the Arabic word *mausim*, meaning "season," and was first applied to the winds over the Arabian Sea which blow for approximately 6 months from the northeast and for 6 months from the southwest. If the above definition involving a seasonal reversal of wind direction of approximately 180° is employed, then there are numerous parts of the world not usually considered as having monsoon wind systems that must be included, *i.e.*, the German Baltic Sea Coast, northern Fenno-Scandia, and the north coast of Siberia. Flohn points out that, based upon the planetary system of winds and their annual latitudinal migration, there should be two principal world zones or latitudes where a seasonal wind reversal is a normal expectation. These are:

a. The transition region between polar easterlies and middle-latitude westerlies, *i.e.*, the region of the subpolar low pressure represented by Alaska, northwestern Canada, the Hudson Bay area, Norway, Kola, White Sea, and northern Siberia.

b. Subtropical latitudes transitional between the middle-latitude westerlies and the tropical easterlies or trades. California, Gulf of Mexico, Texas, South Africa, and South Australia are representative of such latitudes.

As the word monsoon is commonly used in climatological literature, however, it involves not only a seasonal wind reversal but also one of thermal origin arising from the differential heating of extensive land and water surfaces. According to this more restricted point of view monsoons are the result of the earth's surface being nonhomogeneous in character, for such monsoons could not develop if the earth's surface were composed of either all land or all water.

According to the standard explanation of thermally induced monsoons such a system of winds is simply a convectional system on a gigantic scale. The chain of events is from temperature through pressure and winds to rainfall. In the high-sun period, or summer, the land surface becomes warmer than the surface of the surrounding seas and this thermal contrast tends to set up surface pressure differences resulting in a low center over the land and higher pressure over adjacent seas. As a consequence the summer monsoon is a sea-to-land wind, the maritime air bringing to the land an abundance of moisture where it may be condensed to fall as rain as a result of being lifted in storms or over topographic obstacles. Summer therefore should be the rainy period (Fig. 2.47).

Conversely, the winter monsoon is a wind of land origin. As a result of the land being colder than the sea in the low-sun period, a shallow thermally induced high-pressure cell develops over the land with lower pressure over the adjacent ocean. A land-to-sea pressure gradient is thereby developed which causes cold, dry continental air masses to flow seaward. This cold, dry land air is poor stuff out of which to

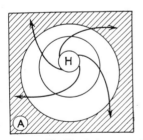
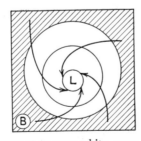

Fig. 2.47. Shaded areas represent oceans; white areas are continents. In winter (*A*) pressure is high over the cold continents, while in summer (*B*) it is low. The result is an outflow of continental air in winter and an inflow of maritime air in summer. This is a *monsoon* system. (*From Petterssen.*)

make abundant precipitation and as a result monsoon winters are, according to the classical explanation, likely to be not only cool or cold but also dry.

102. Modifications of the Monsoon Concept. There is some doubt, however, whether the above-described monsoon system of winds in its pure form actually is of common occurrence. Certainly the winter highs which develop over the cold continents are relatively shallow affairs, and the winter monsoon winds are likewise. Some contend that the same is true of the summer continental lows and their onshore monsoon winds. What seems probable is that the so-called monsoon winds of the earth are far more complex than was previously supposed. Supporting this conjecture is the discovery that the monsoon lows over the summer continents are not always evident as persistent features on the daily synoptic charts, even though they are conspicuous features on the mean summer charts of surface pressure. On the daily weather maps the monsoon lows show great variations in position and intensity from day to day which may be attributed to the number of cyclonic systems which move through the area. Many of these moving cyclonic storms seem to come in from the sea fully formed so that they cannot be described as heat lows. These local storms are characteristic of the summer season of such monsoon areas as India, China, Indo-China, and northern Australia.[1]

To a greater extent than was formerly thought to be the case the monsoons appear to be in the nature of various kinds and degrees of modification of the general planetary wind system. The thermally induced monsoon winds are always superimposed upon an original planetary system, which is usually the dominant one. If the monsoon represents a convectional system of gigantic proportions, the air flow aloft above the surface current should be opposite in direction to that at low levels, and in some instances this is not the case.

In the active discussion concerning monsoons which has developed in recent years, not only have many of the widely held facts regarding

[1] See "Compendium of Meteorology," p. 873.

their origins and wind systems been questioned, but also the efficacy of the summer monsoon itself as a rain bringer. The summer monsoon unquestionably does transport great quantities of evaporated moisture from the sea to the land, but this is not sufficient to produce precipitation. The weather in the summer monsoon is actually much more variable than most textbook accounts would lead one to assume. It does not rain continuously throughout the period of onshore winds by any means. There are frequent spells of fair weather, some of them lasting several days, during which the skies are relatively clear and no rain falls. Most of the monsoon rainfall over lowlands appears to be associated with atmospheric disturbance in the form of waves, cyclones, and convectional systems.

103. The Asiatic Monsoon. Owing to the greater size of the continent, and consequently the greater seasonal extremes of temperature, eastern and southern Asia is considered to be the classical monsoon region. Here the monsoon system of winds with its seasonal reversal of direction is most perfectly developed. Partly as a result of the well-developed monsoonal system of surface winds, tropical maritime in summer and polar continental in winter, coastal eastern Asia has greater seasonal extremes of temperature than other maritime regions in similar latitudes. Actually the Asiatic monsoon is not one but at least two monsoons, that of China and Japan being distinct from the tropical monsoon of South Asia. The system of high mountains and plateaus separating India and Pakistan from China makes any transport of air between the two regions unlikely.

104. *The East-Asia Monsoon.* There can be no doubt that the predominant winds of eastern Asia are from sea to land (east, southeast, and south) in summer and from land to sea (north, northwest, and west) in winter (Figs. 2.21 and 2.22). In both seasons there are numerous interruptions in the prevailing direction due to the passage of local cyclones or anticyclones with the constancy of direction being somewhat higher in winter than in summer (Figs. 2.29 and 2.30). The winter monsoon in China and

Percentage of Wind Frequency in North China
(After Kendrew)

	N.	NE.	E.	SE.	S.	SW.	W.	NW.
Winter	17	8	5	6	6	8	18	32
Summer	10	9	12	26	16	10	7	10

Japan is also much stronger than that of summer, the velocities of the mean resultant surface wind along the coasts being several times greater in January than in July (Figs. 2.26 and 2.27).

The weak summer monsoon of eastern Asia gives to that region its characteristically hot and humid summer weather. Average tropical maritime air of the summer monsoon at Nanking, China, has a temperature of 84°, a relative humidity of 78 per cent, and 19.6 grams of water per kg. (by way of contrast, see analysis of winter monsoon air, p. 97).

A considerable amount of controversy has developed in recent years concerning the depth of the East-Asia summer monsoon current and its effectiveness in producing precipitation. Flohn deduces from the upper-air data available to him that the summer monsoon in China and Japan has an average depth of only 400 to 700 meters, while above this shallow monsoonal inflow are westerly winds of continental origin. He argues that the rainfall of eastern Asia in summer cannot be of monsoon origin, for the monsoon current is too shallow to produce a large amount of rainfall. He therefore attributes

the abundant summer rainfall of China, Japan, and Korea not to the monsoon current but rather to convergence in the westerly currents aloft.[1] What are probably newer upper-air data suggest some modifications of the above picture. The summer monsoon of east Asia is not shallow in all parts but increases perceptibly in depth toward the south. Moreover, the westerly currents observed aloft are not necessarily of continental origin but instead may be deflected air currents from tropical southeastern Asia and consequently more humid than if they were of continental origin, and hence more conducive to precipitation. More numerous upper-air observations will be required to clarify the picture of the East-Asia monsoon and the nature of its air masses (Fig. 2.48).

The summer rainfall of eastern Asia is dubiously of *direct* monsoon origin. That is, it does not appear to be the result of humid surface air flowing over a warm continent with resultant surface heating and numerous convectional thunderstorms. Actually eastern Asia has many fewer thunderstorms than southeastern United States, even though the former area has much rougher terrain which should be conducive to triggering off convectional systems. Most of the rain of eastern Asia in summer appears to be associated with cyclonic disturbances which develop along fronts, although in regions of strong relief there is additional rainfall of orographic origin. It has been pointed out, however, that the stronger the summer monsoon, in South China at least, the less is the precipitation in the region. This again suggests that the rainfall is not directly monsoonal, but rather is of cyclonic or frontal origin. The nature of the convergences and the characteristics of the air masses involved cannot be stated with assurance at the present time. The migration northward of the polar front to a mean position in North China and Manchuria in midsummer brings to those regions a brief but heavy rainfall. In the south summer rains appear to be more the result of disturbances associated with

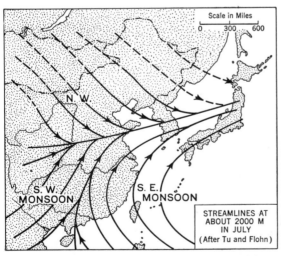

FIG. 2.48. Atmospheric stream lines over East Asia at about 2,000 meters in July. (*After Tu and Flohn.*)

[1] H. Flohn, Studien zur allgemeine Zirkulation der Atmosphäre, *Ber. deut. Wetterdienstes in der U.S. Zone,* No. 18, pp. 28–32.

the convergence of air masses of tropical and equatorial origin. Since the summer monsoon in northern China is approximately the northern limit of its penetration, and since its northern frontier is a pulsating migrating thing, it is obvious that these northern regions of Manchuria and North China should be areas of precarious and variable rainfall. It is noteworthy also that many stations in middle China and in Japan show annual rainfall curves with a secondary midsummer minimum. That is, late spring and early summer and also fall show more rainfall than midsummer. This would seem to indicate that the maximum rainfall occurs with the northward advance and the southward retreat of the polar front, while in midsummer this front is too far poleward on the average to produce as much precipitation in middle China.

The winter monsoon of eastern Asia is a land wind originating in the shallow thermally induced high of northeastern Asia. For most parts of eastern Asia it is classified as polar continenal air, but because of its passage over numerous topographic obstacles it has been modified considerably en route and is less cold and dry than it was at its source. At Peking, China, average fresh polar continental air in winter has a temperature of 10°F., a relative humidity of 22 per cent, and only 0.3 gram of water vapor per kg. This dry, stable air is not conducive to rainfall. In certain parts of coastal eastern Asia, more especially Japan, but in some other parts as well, the winter monsoon may have passed over various distances of water and as a result become considerably modified in its lower strata, with increased temperature and humidity. Where the winter monsoon is relatively strong and persistent, so that few fronts and cyclones develop, it results in unusually dry winters such as characterize the North China Plain and Manchuria. Farther south and toward the coast where the cold monsoon air may come into conflict with mild maritime air masses there are numerous cyclonic storms and more abundant rainfall. Japan and also China from the Yangtze southward have a relatively large amount of winter cyclonic rainfall. It

bears repeating that the monsoons of East Asia, both in summer and in winter, exist in the form of pulsations rather than as steady winds of uniform direction, for their constancy in direction and velocity is decreased by interruptions in the form of moving cyclones and anticyclones.

In summary, it may be stated that the two most important climatic effects of monsoon wind systems in middle latitudes are (1) to produce large seasonal temperature extremes and (2) to concentrate the annual rainfall in the summer season.

105. *The Tropical South Asia Monsoon.* The monsoon wind system of the two peninsulas— India and Pakistan and Farther India—of South Asia is different in some respects from that of East Asia. This is not to be wondered at since one is tropical and the other is middle latitude in location. Moreover, the India-Pakistan monsoon is very effectively separated from the monsoon of China by the highlands of the Himalaya system. To the east of India and Pakistan in the region known as Farther India, the separation of the tropical and middle-latitude monsoons is much less complete. It ed that less is known about the ver Farther India. Among the which the monsoons of India and is that of the strength and con- seasonal winds (Figs. 2.26, **2.27**, 0). Thus while the winter monsoon is stronger and more constant in direction than that of summer in eastern Asia, it is the summer monsoon which is much the stronger and more constant in India. In the latter region the winter monsoon is frequently only a gentle drift of air (2 or 3 miles an hour), while the average velocity of the summer monsoon at Bombay is 14 miles an hour and it is stronger over the sea (Fig. 2.49).

A further difference between the two Asiatic monsoons is to be observed in the locations of their controlling centers of action. The surface low of the Indian summer monsoon is located in superheated northwestern and northern India and Pakistan. This center of action formerly has been considered to be an example of a stationary thermal low, although recently

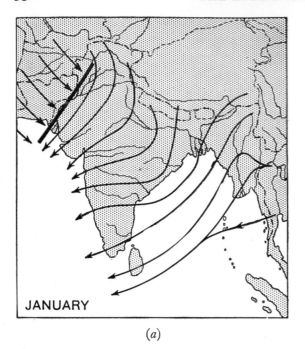

JANUARY

(a)

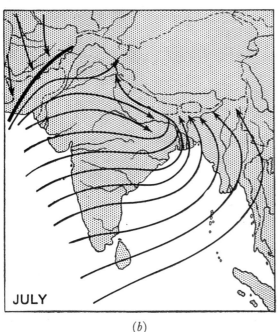

JULY

(b)

FIG. 2.49. Atmospheric streamlines over India and Pakistan in January (a) and July (b). These are the winter monsoon and the summer monsoon.

it has been suggested it may be, in part at least, a statistical phenomenon resulting from the passage of numerous cyclonic depressions through

the area. The tropical maritime air moving northward into India in summer is a deep current which has crossed several thousand miles of tropical sea and consequently is highly charged with water vapor. It advances rapidly northward over India as a definite front, its arrival being designated as the "burst of the monsoon." With the "burst" comes a complete change in the face of the weather, for heavy, squally rains accompanied by thunder and lightning ordinarily herald the arrival of the monsoon. In Farther India the northward advance of the monsoon is less abrupt and is accompanied by less severe weather disturbances. Weather is less turbulent during the height of the monsoon (although rainfall is greater) than during the advance and retreat of the monsoon at the beginning and end of summer. The retreat of the monsoon is often accompanied by hurricane types of storms. During the height of the monsoon much of the rainfall is associated with weak cyclonic storms which in turn appear to originate in zones of convergence.

Three main currents, or streamlines, of summer air flow may be recognized in India and Pakistan: (a) a main westerly current from over the Bay of Bengal meets the Western Ghats at nearly right angles and flows across peninsular India; (b) what appears to be a branch of this main current advances northward over the Bay of Bengal; (c) a third current from the southeast advances up the Ganges Valley to the south of the Himalayas (Fig. 2.49(b)). The main westerly current continues westward across Farther India. Excessively heavy rainfall results wherever these unstable monsoon currents are forced to ascend relief barriers such as the Western Ghats, the mountains of the northeastern regions of India and Pakistan, and the mountains along the west coast of Burma.

Flohn believes the tropical monsoon of tropical Asia is simply a modification of the planetary winds of the tropics.[1] He thinks of the

[1] H. Flohn, Passatzirkulation und äquatorial Westwindzone, Arch. Meteol., Geophys. u. Bioklimatol., Series B, Vol. 3, pp. 8–14, 1951; Studien zur allgemeine Zirkulation der Atmosphäre, Ber. deut. Wetterdienstes in der U.S. Zone, No. 18, pp. 34–40.

thermal low of northern India and the accompanying monsoon as simply an unusually great northward displacement of the northern intertropical convergence (*NITC*). The fact that the *NITC* is drawn so far northward to about latitude 30° may be associated with the unusually high temperatures over northern India and Pakistan. According to this interpretation the main westerly current of the monsoon is simply the expanded equatorial westerlies which lie embedded in the great mass of tropical easterlies or trades. The numerous rain-bringing storms are disturbances that develop along the oscillating *NITC* (Fig. 2.31).

The so-called winter monsoon of India and southeastern Asia is scarcely the result of any unusual development of a thermally induced high resulting from the cooler lands (Fig. 2.49(*a*)). Rather it seems to be a reestablishment of the normal trade-wind system of these latitudes as the heat equator and the *NITC* retreat southward.

106. Other Monsoon Areas. Partly owing to the great size of the continent, the monsoon system of winds is most perfectly developed over eastern and southern Asia, although monsoons in modified form, or *monsoon tendencies*, are characteristic of other regions as well. Within the tropics northern Australia, the Gulf of Guinea region of western Africa, and parts of tropical East Africa are extensive areas where monsoon tendencies are relatively striking. Flohn believes that all these tropical areas with winds from a westerly direction at the time of high sun are affected by the seasonal migration of the heat equator and intertropical convergence zone which puts them in the belt of equatorial westerlies during the period of highest continental temperatures. The "winter" monsoons are only the reestablishment of the normal tropical easterlies as the belt of maximum insolation retreats into the opposite hemisphere.

Southeastern United States, more especially the Gulf States, have a kind of monsoon circulation resulting in a wind reversal between winter and summer (Fig. 2.50). In summer the circulation over part of North America is weakly cyclonic, with the center of the thermal low at sea level located over heated southwestern United States and extending northward. The air flow is southerly over most of eastern North America in summer, but much of this inflow

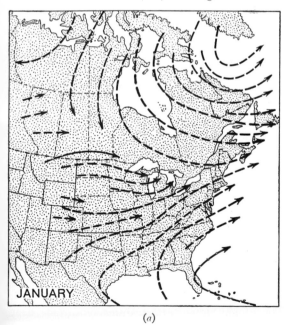 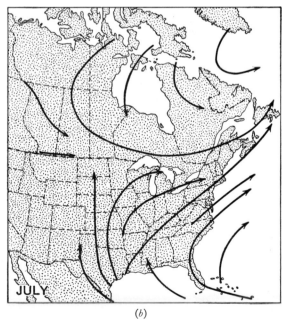

Fig. 2.50. (*a*) and (*b*), seasonal winds over central and eastern North America at the gradient level (about 500 meters). (*After Borchert.*)

into the eastern part of the continent is the result of an anticyclonic circulation around the western end of a strengthened and westward-displaced subtropical high-pressure cell (Azores High). Coming from the western end of the high-pressure cell, this southerly wind of summer over central and easterly United States is warm and moist and has the effect of providing a rich source of rainfall over this area. But while this southerly wind has the appearance and qualities of a summer monsoon, it is more anticyclonic than cyclonic in origin, which does not precisely fit the monsoon pattern.

The winter circulation over eastern North America is more definitely monsoon-like in character in that it is anticyclonic in origin. The thermal effect of the North American continent on pressure distribution is such that the prevailing wind over the central and eastern part of the continent has a strong component from the north. This, together with the open nature of the country from Arctic to Gulf results in recurrent

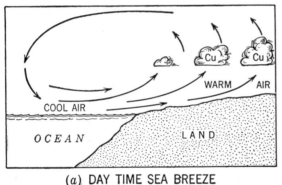

(a) DAY TIME SEA BREEZE

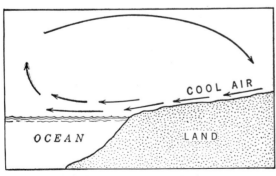

(b) NIGHT TIME LAND BREEZE

FIG. 2.51. Illustrating a type of diurnal wind.

outbreaks of cold, dry polar air associated with moving anticyclones. As these pass southward in the trough between the Rockies and Appalachians, they carry arctic air with freezing temperatures repeatedly to the American Gulf coast. These same surges of cold polar air extend their influence into the tropics and affect the weather and climate of the Caribbean and Gulf coasts of Mexico and Central America.

In the middle latitudes at least, regions with strong monsoon tendencies, showing onshore winds of maritime character in summer and offshore continental winds in winter, are much better developed on the eastern than on the western sides of continents. This is understandable, since the western, or windward, coasts are distinctly marine in character with only small seasonal temperature changes between summer and winter. It is, therefore, only on the more continental eastern, or leeward, sides of the great land masses that sufficiently large seasonal extremes of temperature can develop to produce marked wind reversals.

107. Minor Terrestrial Winds. *Land and Sea Breezes.* Just as there are *seasonal* wind reversals (monsoons) resulting at least in part from seasonal temperature contrasts between land and water, so there are *diurnal*, or daily, monsoons resulting from similarly induced temperature contrasts within the 24-hr. period. These are called *land and sea breezes*, or *diurnal monsoons.* Thus along coasts there is often a drift of cool air from land to water at night (corresponding to winter) and a reversed wind direction, sea to land, during the heat of the day (corresponding to summer). These diurnal monsoons represent a convectional circulation (Fig. 2.51).

The cause of the land and sea breezes is to be found in the different behavior of land and water under the conditions of an equal external heat supply. The slower heating and cooling of water surfaces compared with land surfaces is largely due to the fact of turbulent moving of the water by winds, currents, and waves which causes a continuous downward transfer of surface heat or cold, which results in relatively small temperature variations at the surface. In contrast with the rapid and strong daytime heating of the air over the coastal region, the air over the adjacent strip of water is much less warmed, so that a sharp temperature difference between them develops. Over the warmer land the isobaric surfaces are lifted with a resulting outflow of air aloft and consequently a decreased pressure at the surface. The daytime pressure gradient is therefore from cooler sea to warmer land, and the sea breeze is the result. Aloft the movement is reversed, and air flows from land to sea as it would in a normal convectional system.

Usually the sea breeze begins between 10:00 and 11:00 A.M., reaches its maximum velocity around 1:00 or 2:00, and subsides between 2:00 and 8:00, after which it is replaced by the weaker land breeze. The height to which the sea breeze extends varies with different climates and with local conditions. Sea breezes of large lakes may reach a depth of 200 to 500 meters, while along sea coasts in the subtropics and tropics it may reach depths of 1,000 to 2,000 meters. The land breeze is much shallower.

The depth of penetration of the sea breeze also varies greatly. Depths of 15 to 50 km. are typical of middle latitudes, while in the tropics, 50 to 65 km. are more characteristic, and maximum depths of over 100 km. have been recorded. The land breeze has a much smaller seaward range.

Velocities of the sea breeze also show great variations. In the middle latitudes speeds normally are not greater than 3 Beaufort, or 8 to 12 miles per hr., with maximum values up to 15 to 25 miles per hr. But along tropical coasts the sea breeze may reach storm intensity. It is particularly strong along those dry tropical coasts which are paralleled by cool ocean currents and where as a result the afternoon temperature contrasts between land and water are unusually strong.

Tropical coasts are the regions par excellence of strong and regular sea breezes and their importance climatically normally decreases with latitude. Particularly where skies are clear is the sea breeze a well-developed phenomenon, for such conditions favor large daily temperature contrasts between land and sea. The generally weaker prevailing winds in the low latitudes likewise interfere less with the development of the sea breeze than is the case in stormier regions farther poleward. In the middle and higher latitudes the sea breeze is pretty much confined to the warmer seasons. In the Baltic Sea region land and sea breezes are characteristic of only about 20 per cent of the days even in summer. In Jakarta (Batavia), Java, on the other hand, they are a year-round phenomenon and occur on 70 to 80 per cent of the days. At Karachi, Pakistan, along a dry coast, they occur on 100 per cent of the days from May to September inclusive.

The sea breeze is a remarkably important climatic phenomenon along tropical littorals, causing them to be more livable and healthy places than they otherwise would be. The beginning of the sea breeze may cause a drop in temperature of 15 to 20° within $\frac{1}{4}$ to $\frac{1}{2}$ hr. At Joal, Senegambia (West Africa), the temperature at 12:30 P.M. on one Apr. 14, was 100°F., with a land wind from the northeast and a relative humidity of 3 per cent. At 12:45 the wind direction was northwest, from the sea, temperature had dropped to 82°F., and the relative humidity had risen to 45 per cent (Hann). The most uncomfortable part of the day is frequently in the forenoon before the arrival of the sea or lake breeze. Coasts with well-developed sea breezes are inclined to have modified marine climates, with the daily temperature maxima much reduced. In cities like Milwaukee and Chicago the residents recognize two distinct belts of summer climate, a cooler marine type lying within a mile or so of Lake Michigan, and a markedly warmer one farther interior. Along certain coasts in the wet tropics and subtropics the sea breeze may cause a convergence, or front, resulting in increased cloud and precipitation.

108. *Mountain and Valley Winds.* Like land and sea breezes, these local winds have a distinct diurnal periodicity. In the vicinity of large mountain ranges the local temperature and wind conditions are so well developed that they strongly modify or even obscure the general wind and weather conditions. The local thermal differences in mountain areas tend to create a circulation which in the daytime consists of a lower current directed toward and up the mountains and an upper current in the opposite direction. This circulation pattern tends to reverse at night (Fig. 2.52).

The daytime surface current directed toward the mountains and upslope is composed of two elements: (*a*) the thermal *upslope wind* and (*b*) the *valley wind*. The former is the result of temperature differences between the air over the intensely heated exposed slopes and that over the center of the valley at the same altitude. The result is a strong rising of air along the mountain slopes. The upslope winds start shortly after sunrise, reach their maximum in midday, and reverse their direction shortly after sunset. As a result of the stronger insolation they are particularly well developed on southern slopes (Northern Hemisphere) and are weak or absent on northern slopes. The upslope wind is highly concentrated in the ravines and gullies. Evidence of the daytime upslope winds is the development of cumulus clouds over peaks and summits. These are the "visible tops of invisible ascending air currents." Daily afternoon cloudiness and showers are therefore common in mountains, and visibility, because of the cloud masses, is restricted during the warm hours of the day.

Closely associated with the slope winds are those which blow along the axes of the larger valleys and are designated as *valley winds*. They are especially well known in the wide and deep valleys of the Alps, where they have been studied in detail. They are best developed and most frequent during clear anticyclonic weather in summer. In daytime an up-valley or valley wind blows from about 9:00 or 10:00 A.M. until sunset, after which an opposite down-valley or *mountain wind* blows. Within large mountain valleys the diurnal temperature variations are more than twice as large as those in a similar air layer over the adjacent plains. This results in a pressure gradient from plains to mountain valleys during the day and from valleys to plains at night. Weather and climate in mountainous regions are greatly influenced by these local winds.

109. *Diurnal variation in wind velocity* is another terrestrial modification of surface winds with a daily periodicity. It is very noticeable that calm nights and early mornings in the warmer months are often followed by windy middays, the maximum wind velocity corresponding with the time of greatest heat. By sunset there is usually a marked calming of the atmosphere again. The boisterous midday winds are associated with convectional overturning, or interchange of air between upper and lower strata, which occurs at the time of greatest surface heating. Under

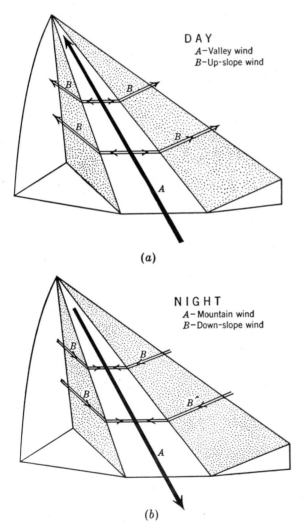

DAY
A—Valley wind
B—Up-slope wind

(*a*)

NIGHT
A—Mountain wind
B—Down-slope wind

(*b*)

FIG. 2.52. Illustrating a type of diurnal wind.

those conditions the lower air, entangled with the fast-moving upper air as a result of the ascending and descending currents, is dragged along at a rapid rate. It is noticeable that cumulus clouds are often numerous during the windiest hours when convection is at a maximum, a coincidence that has gained them the name of "wind clouds." During the night when the lower air is colder and heavier there is no tendency for it to rise. At that time interchanges between the upper and lower air are at a minimum, so that the surface air is relatively undisturbed by the fast-moving currents aloft. It is at the time of maximum vertical convectional interchange that surface winds reach their highest diurnal velocities.

110. *Gravity Winds.* Along the coasts of Greenland and Antarctica, which are backed by ice plateaus, there have been recorded unusually strong winds resulting from the descent of the cold dense air from the ice-cap plateau to the shore below. On the edge of the Antarctic Continent, Mawson reported an average wind velocity of 50 miles per hr., while velocities of over 100 miles an hour were frequent. Similar gravity winds on a smaller scale are characteristic of all regions where cold air accumulating at higher elevations is able to drain off to lower elevations of lower air density. Such a wind is the *bora* type, characteristic of the northeast coast of the Adriatic Sea. Here a narrow coastal plain is backed by a plateau where, under anticyclonic conditions of winter, the air becomes very cold. By reason of its density this plateau air slips through the passes and down the slopes of the plateau as a cold, gusty wind whose temperatures, even after warming by descent, are markedly colder than those along the coast below.

Oceanic Circulation and Its Effects upon World Climate

111. The discussion of the movement of ocean waters is included within the climatic section of this book chiefly because ocean drifts and currents are one of the controls of climate, and a knowledge of their characteristic systems is useful in an understanding of world climates. It should be added also, as a further reason for their inclusion at this point, that the surface drift of ocean waters is climatically induced, winds, temperature, precipitation, and humidity contrasts being the principal direct or indirect motivating agents. So, while to a large extent the atmosphere controls the oceanic circulation, the latter in turn exerts a significant influence upon world climates. The interaction between atmospheric and oceanic circulation is so complicated that it is often impossible to separate cause and effect.

112. *Drifts and Currents.* Much the larger part of the surface movement of ocean waters is in the nature of a slow, relatively inconspicuous transfer (average rate $2\frac{1}{4}$ miles per hr.) that affects only shallow depths. This is more correctly spoken of as a *drift*, in contrast to the deeper and more rapidly flowing *currents* that attain velocities two to three times the foregoing average. Currents, which are much less common than drifts, are usually confined to localities where discharge takes place through restricted channels, as, for instance, the Florida Strait, through which a portion of the "Gulf Stream," or Caribbean Current, emerges from the Gulf of Mexico.

113. Origin of Ocean-water Movements. There are two primary causes for the circulation of ocean waters. (*a*) Owing to the frictional effect of winds on the ocean surface, the relatively thin layer of top water is driven slowly in the general direction of the air movement. If winds are prevailingly from one direction, a steady drift of surface ocean water, moving in the same general direction, is usually the result. This relatively close parallelism between the great drifts of ocean water and the prevailing winds immediately suggests a causal connection and has led some oceanographers to conclude that winds are almost the sole cause of sea drift. (*b*) The second primary reason for ocean-water circulation is to be found in the different densities within the water itself, these contrasting densities being due to differences in temperature and in salinity. Atmospheric circulation is associated with differences in density or pressure, and it would seem logical to believe that much of the oceanic circulation is likewise. In all probability the system of water movement as we know it is largely the resultant of the combined forces of wind friction and contrasting densities, with the latter chiefly generating the great primary circulations, both vertical and horizontal, that take place throughout the entire hydrosphere, and the winds determining largely the details of surface movement. But although there is a general agreement between prevailing winds and ocean currents, the flow patterns of the two fluids are not identical. Modifying agencies affecting the general water circulation induced by the two principal causes are depth, degree of enclosure, and shape of the ocean basins; submarine barriers, trend of the coast lines, and the deflective force of earth rotation.

114. Mechanics of Ocean-water Circulation. *Temperature.* The observational material necessary for a complete understanding of oceanic circulation, more especially the differences of temperature and salinity at various depths in all the seas, is not yet available. In general it would appear as though temperature had more to do with the circulation than has salinity. The ocean waters in high latitudes are colder and therefore denser than those in the tropics, so that there is a constant exchange of waters between polar and equatorial regions. The Antarctic Ocean, having much wider connections with warmer seas than the more enclosed Arctic has, no doubt provides more cold water for the general circulation. The principal southern connection between the Arctic and warmer seas to the south is by way of the North Atlantic between Greenland and Eurasia, the warm surface waters flowing poleward on the eastern side of the basin, and cold return currents moving equatorward in the western North Atlantic, along both the eastern and the western margins of Greenland. In the North Pacific there is no such free connection with the Arctic Ocean, and as a result the oceanic circulation in the North Pacific is less vigorous, and both the warm and cool currents are much smaller in volume than they are in the North

Atlantic. In the latter ocean Cape Saint Roque in eastern South America so divides the equatorial current that much the larger part of its warm water is shunted northward to form the extraordinarily powerful Caribbean Current (Gulf Stream) and the North Atlantic drift.

115. *Salinity.* Differences in salinity tend further to complicate the thermally induced circulation. In the latitudes of the trades and the great permanent subtropical high-pressure centers, where rainfall is meager and evaporation great, salinity of the surface water is relatively high, and accordingly its density is greater. A constant sinking of the denser, saltier surface water of these latitudes is the result. On the other hand, both to the south and to the north of these dry belts with high evaporation are regions of relatively abundant rainfall, the wet tropics and the belts of westerlies. In these latitudes the surface waters are constantly being freshened, by direct precipitation as well as by runoff from the lands. As a result the surface waters are fresher and consequently less dense, with no tendency to sink.

116. Scheme of Surface Drifts and Currents in an Individual Ocean. Except in the polar seas, there is a tendency for all the other great oceans to exhibit general circulations of surface currents and drifts, which, in many of their broader aspects, greatly resemble each other (Fig. 2.53). As previously stated, the surface-water movement roughly parallels the circulation of surface winds. The scheme of ocean currents as developed in the North Atlantic, which is reasonably representative of the pattern of arrangement of those of other seas as well, will be taken as an example for analysis (Fig. 2.54).

The most conspicuous element of the North Atlantic circulation is probably the great, closed elliptical whirl about the subtropical Azores High. The trade winds on the equatorward sides of the subtropical highs in both hemispheres tend to drift the surface waters before them across the ocean. The deflective force of earth rotation, right in the Northern and left in the Southern Hemisphere, acts to make this a westward-flowing current, moving somewhat at an angle to the direction of the trades. This is the *Equatorial Current.* (There are really two equatorial currents, separated in the eastern part of the ocean by a minor countercurrent setting toward the east.) Checked in its westward progress by the South American continent, the Equatorial Current is divided, the larger part of it flowing northwestward, and the smaller part of it southwestward. Partly because of deflection (earth rotation) and trend of the coast line, and partly because of the wind direction around the western end of the subtropical Azores High (Figs. 2.53, 2.54), the warm northward-moving current gradually is bent more and more to the east. A part of it enters the Caribbean Sea and passes through the Straits of Yucatán into the Gulf of Mexico. This water returns to the Atlantic through the Florida Strait, where it joins the major part of the warm-water drift, which has kept eastward of the West Indies, to form the *Gulf Stream* (better designated as the *Caribbean* or *Florida Current*) which parallels the American Atlantic seaboard. At about latitude 40°N. westerly winds and deflection cause the warm surface waters to turn slowly eastward across the ocean in the form of a west-wind drift. In the eastern Atlantic the drift divides, a part of it being carried by the subtropical anticyclone's northwesterly and northerly winds southward along the coast of southwestern Europe and northwestern Africa, until it joins again the Equatorial Current and thus completes the low-latitude circuit. This is the relatively cool *Canaries Current* (Fig. 2.54). A considerable portion of the west-wind drift, however, is carried northeastward by the stormy southwesterlies along the northwest coast of Europe to form the *North Atlantic drift*, its relatively warm waters washing the coasts of the British Isles and Norway, and eventually entering the Arctic Ocean. The Arctic, compensating for this receipt of warm water from the eastern Atlantic, produces an outward surge of cold waters, in the western Atlantic on either side of Greenland, the western branch being called the *Labrador Current.*

It should be reemphasized that the picture given above is a greatly simplified one. Superimposed upon this generalized average flow are

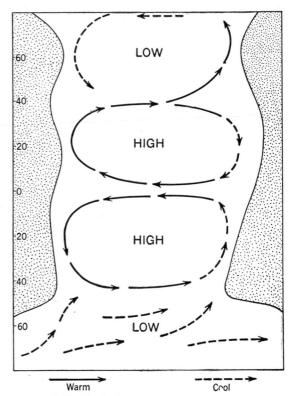

FIG. 2.53. Generalized scheme of ocean currents.

numerous eddies and surges, together with changes in direction and strength of currents following the seasonal shifting and reversals of winds.

117. *Convergences.* In oceanography the introduction of the concept of water masses has been as fruitful as the development of the concept of air masses in atmospheric science. Oceanographers recognize in both hemispheres three general contrasting water masses separated by relatively distinct lines of convergence or discontinuity. In the high latitudes are the polar waters which are characterized by low temperatures, low salt content, greenish color, and high plankton content. In the low latitudes are the contrasting tropical or subtropical waters high in temperature and salt, low in organic forms, and blue in color. Between the two extremes are the "mixed waters" of the middle latitudes. In both hemispheres, therefore, there must exist two principal lines of discontinuity or convergence where waters differing in temperature,

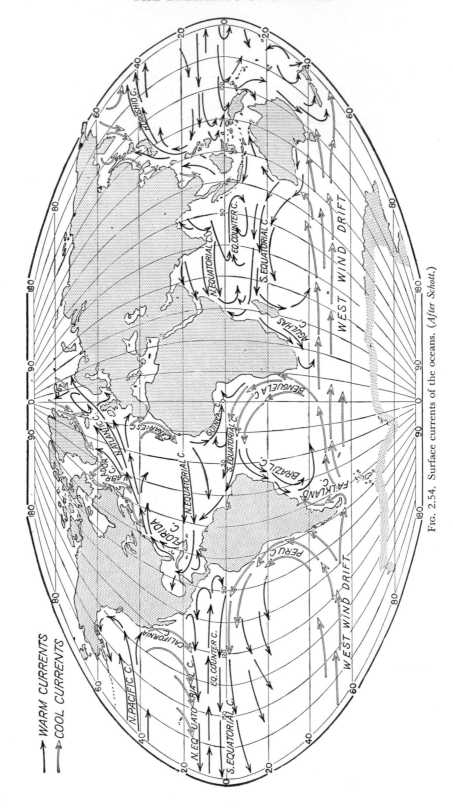

FIG. 2.54. Surface currents of the oceans. (*After Schott.*)

life forms, saltiness, and color are in contact. That line separating the westward-drifting tropical waters from the eastward-moving drifts of the middle latitudes is designated as the subtropical convergence, sometimes spoken of as the "polar front" of the oceans. Along these lines of convergence or discontinuity the heavier waters tend to sink and pass underneath the lighter ones.[1]

118. *Warm and Cool Currents.* If it is kept in mind that poleward-drifting surface waters, since they come from lower latitudes, are inclined to be *relatively* warm, while those from higher latitudes are likely to be cooler than the surrounding waters, the following generalizations may be made. In the lower latitudes (equatorward from about 40°) warm ocean currents tend to parallel the eastern sides of continents, while cool ocean currents parallel the western sides of continents (Figs. 2.53, 2.54). For example, along the west coast of the United States at about 40°N. the average surface water temperature near the coast is on occasions as low as 50°, while in the same latitude off the coast of Japan the sea temperature is 70° or higher. At 2°S. along the Peruvian Coast the water temperature is as low as 62°, whereas in a corresponding latitude on the coast of New Guinea the surface temperature is about 83°. In the middle and higher latitudes the reverse is more often the case, warm ocean currents affecting the western sides of land masses, and cool ones the eastern sides. Along east coasts (western sides of oceans), therefore, there is likely to be a convergence of contrasting currents, while along west coasts such currents tend to *diverge.*

119. *Upwelling.* It should be added that a part of the cool water along west coasts in lower latitudes (Peru and northern Chile, northwest and southwest Africa, southern California, and adjacent northwestern Mexico, and others) is the result of upwelling from some greater depths along the coast. These regions occupy positions along the eastern margins of well-developed subtropical high-pressure centers and their associated wind whirls, which are conspicuous features over oceans in these latitudes. Along their coasts, paralleling equatorward-moving winds from the subtropical whirls drive the surface waters toward lower latitudes. Owing to the deflective force of earth rotation, the ocean currents along these cool-water coasts have a component of movement away from the land. Colder water from below, therefore, rises to replace the surface water. Usually this overturn takes place within the upper 500 to 600 ft. so that upwelled water does not represent Arctic or Antarctic deep water.

120. Climatic Significance of Ocean Drifts and Currents.[1] *Temperature.* Since nearly three-quarters of the atmosphere is underlain by ocean, it is obvious that the climates of the world are greatly influenced by the nature of the sea surface, more especially its temperature. As pointed out previously, the great contrast between continental and oceanic climates of middle and high latitudes is mainly due to the much greater ability of oceans, as compared with lands, to store any appreciable amount of heat.

In order that an ocean current may have direct and marked effect upon the temperature of the adjacent land mass, it is obvious that the winds must be onshore. Such is the case in northwestern Europe where westerly winds throughout the year carry the oceanic influence far into the continent. Since much of this west wind has traveled over the warm North Atlantic drift, it is understandable why parts of coastal Europe are 30 to 40° too warm in January as compared with the normal for their latitudes. In contrast the warm waters paralleling the east coasts of the United States and subtropical Japan are much less effective as direct temper-

---

[1] Physics of the Earth, V, Oceanography. *Nat. Research Council Bull.* 85, pp. 358–360, Washington, D.C., 1932. Also H. V. Sverdrup, "Oceanography for Meteorologists," pp. 155–222, Prentice-Hall, Inc., New York, 1942.

[1] H. V. Sverdrup, The Currents of the Pacific Ocean and Their Bearing on the Climates of the Coasts, *Science,* Vol. 91, pp. 273–282, Mar. 22, 1940; Sverdrup, "Oceanography for Meteorologists," pp. 223–235; Physics of the Earth, V, Oceanography, *Nat. Research Council Bull.* 85, 457–519, Washington, D.C., 1932.

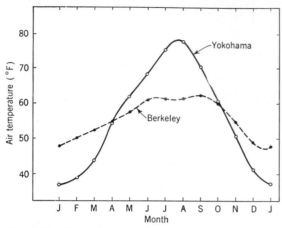

FIG. 2.55. Illustrating the effects of ocean currents on the temperature characteristics of opposite coasts; Berkeley with a west coast location and Yokohama on an east coast. (*From Sverdrup, Science, Mar. 22, 1940.*)

Temperature Contrasts of Stations on East and West Coasts in Similar Tropical and Subtropical Latitudes
East Coast Stations Bordered by Warm Currents, West Coasts by Cold
(After Süring)

East Coast		Diff. E.-W.	West Coast	
Station	Warm month		Station	Warm month
North Atlantic Basin				
Jacksonville, Fla. 31°2′N.	81.9°	+13.5	Mogador 31°5′N.	68.4°
South Atlantic Basin				
South Brazil 30°7′S.	75.7°	+15.3	Port Nolloth 29°2′S.	60.4°
Pacific Basin				
Shanghai 31°2′N.	80.6°	+11.7	San Diego 32°7′N.	68.9°
Port Darwin 12°5′S.	84.4°	+10.6	Lima 12°1 S.	73.8°

ature controls, because the winter winds are prevailingly offshore. Nevertheless, the not infrequent east winds on the fronts of cyclonic storms create sporadic importations along these east coasts from off the mild waters and thereby tend to raise somewhat the normal winter temperatures, although they are still much more continental than they are marine (Figs. 2.55, 2.56).

Where cool ocean currents parallel coasts, temperatures along the adjacent littorals are likely to be markedly lowered. Thus the coast of Peru, which is paralleled by the cool Peruvian Current, is 10° cooler than the coast of Brazil in a similar latitude, where a warm current prevails. Kushiro in eastern Hokkaido (Japan) which is bordered by the cool Okhotsk Current has an August temperature of only 63.7°, while Sapporo near the west coast of the same island shows an average temperature of 69.4° for the same month.

It has been stated previously that there is a tendency for cool and warm ocean currents to converge along the western sides of oceans and to diverge along the eastern sides. Where contrasting currents *converge*, the effect is to squeeze the isotherms closer together, making for marked latitudinal temperature contrasts, steep temperature gradients, and advection fogs. This condition is found, for instance, along the east coasts

of Asia and North America. Where contrasting currents *diverge*, they tend to spread the isotherms, making for milder temperature gradients. This is the case in the eastern Atlantic. It must not be inferred, however, that ocean currents are the principal cause of these temperature-gradient phenomena on the opposite sides

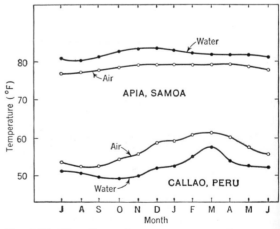

FIG. 2.56. The effects of ocean currents on air temperature. (*From Sverdrup, Science, Mar. 22, 1940.*)

of oceans; at best they are only auxiliary causes cooperating with more powerful marine and continental influences.

121. *Fog and Precipitation.* Cool-water coasts in low latitudes often present the unusual situation of being characterized by both fog and aridity— an apparently contradictory combination. The surface fog is the result of warm air from over the ocean proper being chilled by blowing over the cool current lying alongshore and mixing with the cool air above it. It may then be drifted in over the land, but usually it is confined to a narrow, coastal fringe. High-level fog, or stratus cloud, is likewise common in these areas of tropical and subtropical west coasts bordered by cool currents, so that even when low-lying fog is absent the skies may be gray and overcast. Such high-level fog is associated with a low-level subsidence layer in the eastern end of the subtropical anticyclone which characteristically occupies these coastal areas. The intense aridity of these cool-water tropical coasts with their stable air masses is well known. To what extent the stability of the air is the result of the cool water is somewhat controversial. Formerly it was attributed to the chilling effects of the cool waters upon the lower layer of the tropical maritime air as it moves landward from the ocean proper over the cool waters adjacent to the continent. More recently doubt has been

expressed relative to the effectiveness of the short trajectory of tropical air over a cool current in producing a thick stability layer and consequent aridity. At the present time the stabilizing effects of the cool water seems to be viewed as an auxiliary process rather than as the primary one. The effective aridifying agent is probably the strong upper-air subsidence in the high-pressure cell whose eastern margins are located over these tropical and subtropical west coasts.

122. *Summary of Climatic Effects.* In summary the following generalizations may be made concerning the climatic influences of ocean waters (Fig. 2.57):

a. West coasts in subtropical and tropical (except close to equator) *latitudes,* bordered by cool waters, have relatively low average temperatures and small annual and diurnal ranges of temperature. They are foggy but arid.

b. West coasts in middle and higher latitudes, bordered by warm waters, have strikingly marine climates. Cool summers, mild winters, and small annual ranges of temperature are the rule. Precipitation is adequate.

c. East coasts in the tropics and subtropics, paralleled by warm currents, have warm and rainy climates. Here the western margins of the subtropical anticyclone are relatively unstable.

d. East coasts in lower middle latitudes (leeward

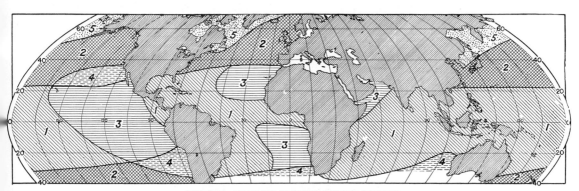

NATURAL CLIMATIC REGIONS OF THE OCEANS
(After Marcus)

1. RELATIVELY WARM TROPICAL OCEAN
2. RELATIVELY WARM TEMPERATE OCEAN
3. RELATIVELY COOL TROPICAL OCEAN
4. RELATIVELY COOL TEMPERATE OCEAN
5. RELATIVELY COLD POLAR OCEAN

FIG. 2.57. Classification of oceanic regions relative to temperature. (*After Markus.*)

side), even though bordered by warm waters, have modified continental climates with relatively cold winters and warm to hot summers.

e. East coasts in higher middle latitudes, paralleled by cool ocean currents, are noteworthy for their cool summers.

123. *Indirect Climatic Effects of Ocean Currents.* Indirectly ocean currents may affect the general climatic and weather conditions of a region by their influence upon the locations of the great frontal zones, and consequently the tracks of cylconic storms. Two of the main frontal zones in winter are those lying off the eastern coasts of North America and Asia roughly between latitudes 25 and 50°. Both these locations are where an abundance of tropical water is being transported into middle latitudes and where as a result energy is being supplied to the atmosphere in great amounts. It is in these same locations that temperature gradients are unusually steep,

the cold eastern sides of the great continent and the warm waters offshore providing marked thermal contrasts. The fact that frontal zones appear to be located where unusual amounts of energy are being supplied to the atmosphere suggests that the cyclones developed along these fronts are at least partly of thermodynamic origin. Fassig points out that the two principal hurricane paths in the Caribbean region coincide with warm waters, one following the inside Gulf Stream route, and the other the route of the warm waters off the northern and eastern coasts of the Greater Antilles and Florida. Extratropical cyclones in the United States are attracted by warm waters in fall and early winter and are repelled by water bodies in spring when the water is colder than the land. Similarly European storm tracks follow water bodies in fall and winter especially, when the land is colder and the water warmer than usual.

SELECTED BIBLIOGRAPHY FOR FURTHER STUDY OF TOPICS CONTAINED IN CHAPTER 2[1]

1. Atmospheric pressure. Blair, 129–131, 145–148; Byers, 227–231; Brunt, 6–12; Petterssen, "Weather Analysis and Forecasting," 148–153.

2. General Circulation of the Atmosphere. Namias, Jerome, The Jet Stream, *Scientific American*, Vol. 187, pp. 27–31, October, 1952; "Compendium of Meteorology," pp. 541–567; Flohn, H. Studien zur allgemeine Zirkulation der Atmosphäre. *Ber. deut. Wetterdienstes in der U.S. Zone*, No. 18, 1950; Flohn, H. Neue Anschauungen über allgemeine Zirkulation der Atmosphäre und ihre klimatische Bedeutung, *Erdkunde*, Vol. 4, pp. 141–162, 1950; Brooks, C. E. P., *et al.* Upper Winds over the World, *Geophys. Mem.*, No. 85, British Meteorological Office, 1950.

3. Surface winds and their characteristics. Conrad, 252–277; Haurwitz and Austin, 44–63; Mintz,

Yale, and Dean, Gordon. The Observed Mean Field of Motion of the Atmosphere. *Geophysical Research Papers*, No. 17, Air Force Cambridge Research Center, Cambridge, Mass., 1952; "Atlas of Climatic Charts of the Oceans," U.S. Weather Bureau, 1938; Sawyer, J. S., Memorandum on the Intertropical Front. *Meteorological Repts.*, No. 10, British Meteorological Office, 1952; "Compendium of Meteorology," 859–887.

4. Local winds. "Compendium of Meteorology," 655–672.

5. Ocean drifts and currents. "Oceanography," *Nat. Research Council Bull.* 85, 358–383, 457–514, 515–519 (bibliography); Conrad, 292–306; Schott, Gerhard. "Geographie des atlantischen Ozean." C. Boysen, Hamburg, 1912; and Schott, Gerhard. "Geographie des indischen und stillen Ozeans." Deutsche Seewarte, Hamburg, 1935; Sverdrup, H. U. "Oceanography for Meteorologists." Prentice-Hall, Inc., New York, 1942.

[1] For complete titles of reference books, see pp. 5–6.

CHAPTER 3: *Atmospheric Moisture and Precipitation*

Humidity

124. Importance of Water Vapor. Humidity refers to the water vapor in the atmosphere. Although water vapor comprises only a very small part of the total atmosphere, averaging less than 2 per cent of the total mass, it is the single most important component of the air from the standpoint of weather and climate. The proportions of most of the gaseous constituents that compose the atmosphere near sea level are relatively constant from place to place at the surface of the earth. One in particular, water vapor, is highly inconstant, varying from nearly zero up to a maximum of almost 5 per cent. This variability in the atmospheric content of water vapor, as to both place and time, is of outstanding importance for at least four reasons: (*a*) The amount of that gas in a given mass of air is an indication of the atmosphere's potential capacity for precipitation, one of the two most important climatic elements. (*b*) Water vapor, through its absorptive effects on terrestrial radiation, is a regulator of rate of heat loss from the earth, and thereby significantly affects temperature phenomena. (*c*) The greater the amount of water vapor, the larger the quantity of latent or potential energy stored up in the atmosphere for the origin and growth of storms; it frequently determines, therefore, whether an air mass will be stable or unstable. (*d*) The amount of water vapor is likewise an important factor affecting the human body's rate of cooling, *i.e.*, the sensible temperature.

125. Evaporation is the process through which water in its liquid or solid form is converted into the gas, water vapor. It is through evaporation that all the water vapor suspended

in the atmosphere is obtained. The amount and rapidity of evaporation from a water surface depends upon the aridity of the air, its temperature, and its movement. The higher the wind velocity and the higher the temperature, the more intense the evaporation. Air which is near the saturation point, or approaching its capacity for water vapor, is not an effective evaporator. If the evaporating air remains stagnant, it gradually becomes saturated with moisture, and no more evaporation can occur. But if movement occurs, horizontal or vertical, so that the humid surface layer is constantly being replaced by drier air, evaporation is able to continue. When the air is colder than the underlying water surface, evaporation will be most effective since the vapor pressure of the atmosphere will always be less than that over the warmer water. Moreover, under these circumstances the air is heated from below by contact with the warm water so that it becomes unstable, turbulence increases, and with it evaporation. It is for this reason that evaporation is greater over oceans in winter than in summer.

Data on evaporation are scanty and unreliable. For the earth as a whole it has been estimated that the annual evaporation is about 29 in. Since the annual average rainfall is estimated to be 39 in., it is probably true that the evaporation figure is too low and the precipitation figure too high.

From the table on p. 112 the following observations may be made concerning the distribution of actual evaporation. (*a*) Evaporation over oceans is greater than over the continents, reflecting the unlimited supply of water at the ocean surface. Over many land areas, on the other hand, the water supply is meager or absent. (*b*) In the very low latitudes, between about 10°N. and 10°S. there is more evaporation over the lands than over the water. This reflects the abundant supply of water available in these rainy regions where in addition the vegetation cover is relatively dense and transpiration from the plant life great. (*c*) The zone of maximum evaporation over the oceans is at 10 to 20° north and south rather than at the equator. This reflects the stronger and steadier winds in these latitudes than is true nearer the equator and also the greater aridity of the air. Over the continents, where the winds are weaker, the belt of maximum evaporation is closer to the equator.

Zonal Distribution of Actual Evaporation, Inches
(After Wüst)

Latitude	60°–50°	50°–40°	40°–30°	30°–20°	20°–10°	10°–0°
Northern Hemisphere						
Continent	14.2	13.0	15.0	19.7	31.1	45.3
Ocean	15.7	27.6	37.8	45.3	47.2	39.4
Mean	15.0	20.1	28.0	35.8	42.9	40.6
Southern Hemisphere						
Continent	(7.9)	(19.7)	20.1	16.1	35.4	48.0
Ocean	9.1	22.8	35.0	44.1	47.2	44.9
Mean	8.8	22.8	33.5	39.0	44.5	45.7

126. Sources of Water Vapor. Like all the other gases in the atmosphere, water vapor is invisible. The primary source of atmospheric humidity is the great oceans that cover approximately three-quarters of the earth's surface. By winds and diffusion methods, the water vapor evaporated from these bodies of water through the expenditure of solar energy is carried in over the continents. Less important, but nevertheless significant, secondary sources of atmospheric moisture are the moist land surfaces, the vegetation cover, and the minor bodies of water. Plants give off more moisture to the air than does bare ground but not so much as a freely exposed water surface. A constant turnover is forever in progress in the atmosphere's water vapor, additions being made through *evapotrans-*

piration of water in its solid and liquid states, while some is being lost to the atmosphere by *condensation* and *precipitation*. By the process of condensation, water vapor, a gas, is changed back into the liquid or solid state, while through evaporation the liquid (or solid) water is converted into invisible gaseous water vapor. As winds carry the moisture in gas form from the oceans to the land, so winds, rivers, and glaciers deliver it again in gaseous, liquid, or solid form to the seas. Half the water vapor in the air lies below an altitude of 6,500 ft.

127. *The Hydrologic Cycle.*[1] Through careful observation it has been discovered that the amount of water precipitated upon the continents is far in excess of the runoff from those same areas in the form of rivers and glaciers. Since roughly only 30 per cent of the land precipitation is removed by runoff, it follows that close to 70 per cent must be returned to the atmosphere by evaporation from the ground, inland bodies of water, and the vegetation cover. From these data it might be concluded that the oceans contribute to continental precipitation only that proportion included in the runoff, while local continental evaporation must provide the other 70 per cent. This reasoning neglects a fundamental consideration, *viz.*, that, if winds can transport water vapor from the oceans to the lands, then winds also can transport it from lands to the oceans (Fig. 3.1). Actually continental precipitation is derived very largely not from land-evaporated moisture, but chiefly from great humid maritime air masses whose moisture was evaporated from the sea.

Most of the moisture evaporated from the lands does not remain intact or stagnant to be eventually returned to the continent as precipitation. Local evapotranspiration is of very minor significance as a source of moisture for the precipitation of an area. In the general circulation of the atmosphere in middle latitudes and in the

[1] Benjamin Holzman, Sources of Moisture for Precipitation in the U.S., *U.S. Dept. Agr. Tech. Bull.* 589 October, 1937; C. W. Thornthwaite, The Hydrologic Cycle Reexamined, *Soil Conservation*, Vol. 3, No. 4 October, 1937; "Compendium of Meteorology," pp 1048–1054.

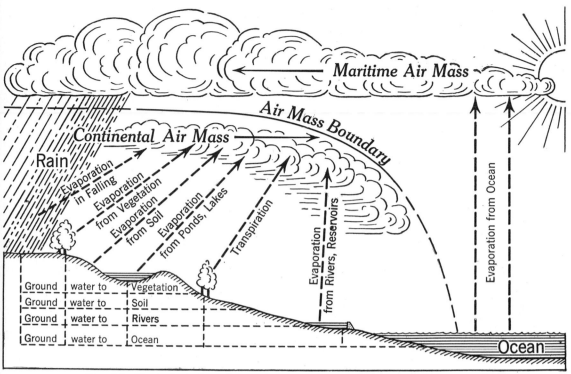

FIG. 3.1. The hydrologic cycle correlated with the air-mass cycle. (*After Holtzman.*)

cycle of atmospheric exchange between land and sea, humid tropical maritime air masses traveling poleward become cooled, precipitate most of their moisture, and are ultimately converted into polar continental air masses. Conversely, polar continental air masses in passing equatorward over land areas become warmed, absorb much land-evaporated moisture, and eventually are transformed into warm, moist, tropical maritime air masses over the oceans. Not only the rivers, then, carry land-precipitated moisture back to the oceans, but also these dry polar continental air masses that pass entirely across the continent from north to south without any reprecipitation. Holzman has calculated the amount of evaporation by these polar continental air masses by measuring the difference in their moisture content between where they cross the Canadian border and their arrival at the Gulf of Mexico. He found the water content of the southward-moving polar continental air at Ellendale, N.D., to be equivalent of 0.44 in. of rainfall, and at Pensacola, Fla., to be 0.97 in., a gain of 0.53 in.

in the 3-day journey southward across the country. If these figures are correct, the water removed by polar continental evaporation from the Mississippi drainage basin reaches the astounding figure of 5,909,000 cu. ft. per sec., which is nine times the average discharge of the Mississippi River. It appears, therefore, that polar continental air masses moving southward across the country to the Gulf are great invisible rivers transporting vast amounts of water vapor from the lands to the ocean, where it is precipitated, later to be evaporated from the sea and returned to the continents as part of the great tropical maritime air currents.

128. Latent Energy in Water Vapor. It is common knowledge that energy is required in the form of heat to change ice (solid) into water (liquid) and water into vapor or steam (gas). The unit of heat energy, the calorie, is the amount of heat required to raise the temperature of a gram of water one degree centigrade. But it takes 79 calories to convert a gram of ice into a gram of water at freezing temperature.

and 607 calories to evaporate the gram of water at 32° and convert it into water vapor at the same temperature. Since energy is required to change the solid into a liquid, and likewise the liquid into a gas, it follows that water vapor contains more potential energy than liquid water, and water in turn more than ice. This stored-up energy in water vapor is known as *latent heat*, or *latent energy*. For the most part it is transformed sun energy, which has been employed in evaporating water, ice, or snow and converting them into water vapor. The energy lost to the liquid during evaporation does not warm the resulting gas but is used only in producing the change from a liquid to a gas state. One reason why bodies of water heat slowly is that so much energy is consumed in evaporating at their surfaces. That evaporation requires heat is evident from the cool sensation experienced when the skin is moistened with water or, even better, with alcohol. In this case heat is subtracted from the skin to convert the liquid into a gas. If energy is consumed in the process of evaporation then, conversely, energy should again be released during condensation. This released heat, known as the *latent heat of condensation*, is an important source of energy in the growth of storms and in the production of precipitation. On a night when condensation takes place, cooling is retarded by the liberation of so much latent heat.

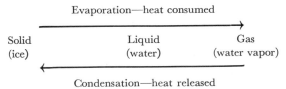

Evaporation—heat consumed

Solid (ice) — Liquid (water) — Gas (water vapor)

Condensation—heat released

129. Atmospheric Humidity. The capacity of the air for water vapor depends very largely upon its temperature.[1] That the capacity advances at an increasing rate with higher temperatures is indicated by the following table. Thus by increasing the temperature of a cubic foot of air 10°, from 30 to 40°, the moisture capacity is

[1] Although it is customary to speak of the *capacity of the air* for water vapor, actually the air itself has practically no effect in this respect. A cubic foot of space and a cubic foot of air at the same temperature can contain essentially the same amount of water vapor.

Maximum Water-vapor Capacity of 1 Cu. Ft. of Air at Varying Temperatures, Grains

Temperature °F.	Water Vapor, Grains	Difference between Successive 10° Intervals
30	1.9	
40	2.9	1.0
50	4.1	1.2
60	5.7	1.6
70	8.0	2.3
80	10.9	2.9
90	14.7	3.8
100	19.7	5.0

advanced only 1 grain, while a similar 10° increase, from 90 to 100°, results in an increase of 5 grains. It is evident that the air on a hot summer day is able to contain much more moisture than is cold winter air, and it has, therefore, greater potentialities for abundant precipitation. Air over Madison, Wis., in July has a water-vapor capacity seven to eight times what it is in January. When a given mass of air contains all the water vapor that it is capable of retaining, it is said to be *saturated*. The condition of the air as regards water vapor is spoken of as *humidity*. If air is completely dry, its humidity is zero.

130. Measurement and Distribution of Humidity. The moisture content of the atmosphere may be expressed in various ways. *Vapor pressure* is that part of the whole atmospheric pressure which is due to the water vapor. It is expressed in the same units as total air pressure, *i.e.* in millibars, or in inches or millimeters of mercury. *Specific humidity* is defined as the weight of water vapor per unit weight of air and is usually expressed as the number of grams of water vapor contained in one kilogram of natural air. *Specific humidity* is nearly proportional to the water vapor pressure so that in the discussion on distribution of humidity to follow, the two terms specific humidity and vapor pressure may be used interchangeably. *Absolute humidity* refers to the weight of water vapor per unit *volume* of air as for example, grains in a cubic foot or grams in a cubic centimeter. It is less frequently used by meteorologists since volume changes as an air mass is elevated or subsides, and as a result the absolute humidity varies with contraction or expansion of the air.

Because the source of all atmospheric humidity is the earth's surface, it is to be expected that much of the water vapor will be concentrated in the lower layers and there will be a rapid decrease upward into the free atmosphere. The *zonal distribution* of the water-vapor content of the air is shown in Fig. 3.2. Here the scale has been adjusted to indicate the relative size of the latitude belts. The atmosphere's water-vapor content, expressed as specific humidity or vapor pressure, is highest at the equator and lowest at the poles. This reflects a similar distribution of temperature which largely determines the capacity of the air for water vapor. It is the temperature control also which causes the specific humidity of any latitude to be higher in summer than in winter so that all values are displaced northward in July and southward in January (Fig. 3.2), the former being larger. Distribution of water vapor is by no means entirely zonal in character, for along the same parallel a dry continental area may have a lower specific humidity than the oceans and it is these contrasts which cause the minor irregularities in the relatively symmetrical zonal curves (Fig. 3.2). It bears mentioning in this connection that the water-vapor content of desert air is not necessarily low in an absolute sense, for the superheated air of the Sahara in summer may contain more moisture than the cool maritime air farther poleward.

For most regions of the earth the *annual variation* of specific humidity closely parallels that of temperature and therefore is highest in summer and lowest in winter. Over north central United States July air contains three to six times as much water vapor as does the January air (Figs. 3.3, 3.4). The *diurnal variation* of the specific humidity is more complicated, for while over the oceans it follows the temperature change, over the lands there are two maxima and two minima within the 24-hr. period. The secondary minimum in midday is the result of convective turbulence which transports so much water vapor upward away from the earth's surface as to offset the effect of the high afternoon temperatures.

131. *Relative Humidity.* Relative humidity is always expressed in the form of a ratio, frac-

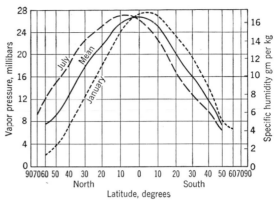

FIG. 3.2. Zonal distribution of the water-vapor content of the air. Specific humidity is highest in the vicinity of the equator and decreases toward the poles. There is a northward displacement in July and a southward displacement in January due to a similar distribution of temperature. Specific humidity at each latitude is higher in summer than in winter. (*After Haurwitz and Austin.*)

tion, or percentage. It represents the amount of water vapor actually present in the air (absolute humidity) compared with the maximum that could be contained under conditions of saturation at the given temperature and pressure. When relative humidity reaches 100 per cent, the air is said to be saturated. As an illustration: Air at 70° can contain approximately 8 grains of water vapor per cu. ft. If it actually contains only 6 grains (its absolute humidity), then it is only three-fourths saturated, and its relative humidity is 75 per cent. Relative humidity can be altered either by changing the amount of water vapor or by varying the capacity of the air, *i.e.,* changing its temperature. The following table

Temperature, °F.	Absolute Humidity, Grains	Relative Humidity, Per Cent Saturated
40	2.9	100
50	2.9	71
60	2.9	51
70	2.9	36
80	2.9	27
90	2.9	19

shows how air, which was saturated at 40°, acquires successively lower relative humidities simply by increasing its temperature, the water-vapor content remaining unchanged. Relative humidity is an important determinant of the amount and rate of evaporation, and hence is a critical climatic factor in the rate of moisture

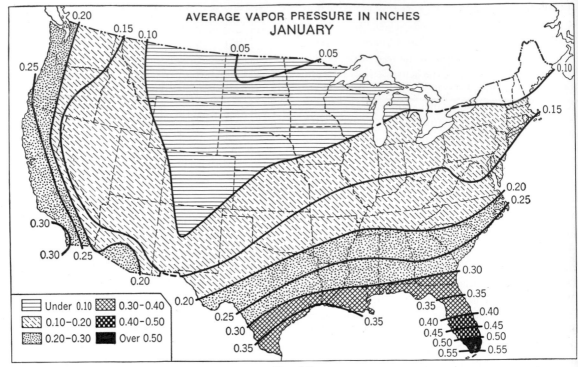

Fig. 3.3.

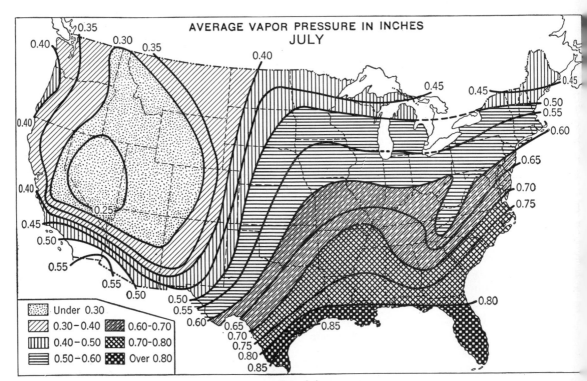

Fig. 3.4.

and temperature loss by plants and animals, including human beings. Various humidity relationships are illustrated by Fig. 3.5. Figure 3.5(a) shows a cubic foot of air subject to three different temperatures. At 0°F. only $\frac{1}{2}$ grain of invisible water vapor can exist in a cubic foot. If the temperature rises to 40°F., nearly 3 grains of water vapor can exist in that same cubic foot of air, and at 80°F. there can be nearly 11 grains of water vapor in the same space. In all these cases, saturation conditions, or 100 per cent relative humidities, are assumed. If any of the cubes in Fig. 3.5(a) is cooled appreciably, the invisible water vapor will be condensed out as visible water or ice particles.

In Fig. 3.5(b) the same cubic foot samples are shown except that they now represent unsaturated conditions; i.e., they do not contain all the water vapor possible at those temperatures. The cube on the extreme left has only $\frac{1}{4}$ grain of water vapor. Since this is only one-half of what can be present under saturated conditions (see cube at left in Fig. 3.5(b)), the relative humidity is therefore $\frac{1}{4}$ grain divided by $\frac{1}{2}$ grain, or 50 per cent. The middle cube in Fig. 3.5(b) contains only $\frac{1}{2}$ grain of water vapor as compared with nearly 3 grains at saturation, making a relative humidity in this case of about 17 per cent. The same reasoning gives a relative humidity of about 91 per cent for the cube on the extreme right. A comparison of the cube on the extreme left in Fig. 3.5(a) with the center cube in Fig. 3.5(b), *both of which contain an identical amount of water vapor*, reveals the former with 100 per cent

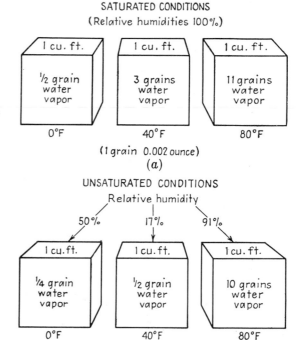

SATURATED CONDITIONS
(Relative humidities 100%)

(1 grain 0.002 ounce)

(a)

UNSATURATED CONDITIONS
Relative humidity

(b)

Fig. 3.5.

relative humidity and the latter with only 17 per cent. This explains why relative humidity ordinarily goes down as temperature rises on a hot summer day and rises as temperature falls on a cool night.

The *zonal distribution* of relative humidity is quite different from that of specific humidity (compare Figs. 3.2 and 3.6). The highest maximum of relative humidity is at the equator, and there is a decrease poleward toward the latitudes

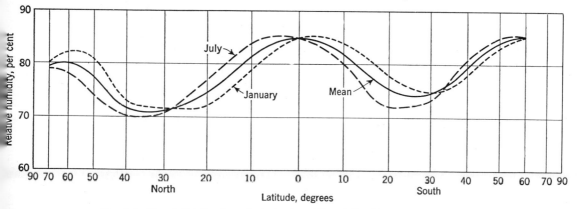

Fig. 3.6. Zonal distribution of relative humidity. (*After Haurwitz and Austin.*)

of the subtropical anticyclones, in whose subsiding and diverging air masses the lowest values occur. From about 30° poleward relative humidity increases, this being a result of the decreasing temperature. There is a shift of the belts of highest and lowest relative humidity northward in July and southward in January following the course of the sun. The *seasonal distribution* of relative humidity varies with latitude. In the low latitudes, from about 30°N. to 30°S., average relative humidity is higher in summer than in winter, while at higher latitudes the reverse is true. The latter situation is caused by the low winter temperatures, especially over the continents. The *diurnal variation* in relative humidity is generally the reverse of that of temperature, with a maximum occurring in the early morning and a minimum in about midafternoon.

132. *Dew Point and Condensation.* If air that is not saturated is sufficiently cooled, its capacity for moisture thereby being reduced, a temperature is eventually reached at which the mass of air has a relative humidity of 100 per cent, even though the amount of water vapor has not been altered. The air is then said to be saturated. This critical temperature at which saturation is reached is called the *dew point.* If air is cooled below the dew point, then the excess of water vapor, over and above what the air can contain at that temperature, is given off in the form of minute particles of water (if above 32°) or ice (if below 32°), and *condensation* has taken place. For example, when the temperature of the air is 80° and the absolute humidity 8 grains of water vapor per cu. ft., then the relative humidity is 73 per cent (table, p. 114). If this mass of air is gradually reduced in temperature so that its capacity for water vapor is lowered, it eventually reaches the dew point 70° and is therefore saturated at that temperature. Further cooling below the saturation point leads to condensation, the amount of water vapor condensed being the difference between the capacity of air at the different temperatures. Thus a cubic foot of saturated air at 70°, if reduced to 60°, will result in 2.3 grains of water vapor being condensed, this being the difference between the capacities of a cubic foot of air at those two temperatures.

An equivalent amount of cooling of saturated air at different temperatures does not, however, yield the same amount of condensed water vapor. If a cubic foot of saturated air at 90° has its temperature reduced 20° (to 70°), 6.7 grains of water vapor are condensed (table, p. 114), but a further cooling of 20° (to 50°) releases only 3.9 grains, and the next 20° drop only 2.2 grains. It is obvious that warm summer air has greater potentialities for abundant precipitation than does cold winter air.

Condensation

133. The only method known whereby significant amounts of water vapor in the atmosphere can be converted into the liquid (condensation) or solid (sublimation) state is to reduce the temperature of the air close to or *below the dew point.* If the atmosphere is cooled, its capacity for water vapor is lowered, and, if it is sufficiently reduced, condensation must result. The dew point of any mass of air is closely related to its relative humidity. When the relative humidity is high, and the air is close to saturation point, only a slight amount of cooling may be required before the dew point is reached and condensation begins. On the other hand, when relative humidity is low, as it usually is over the hot deserts, a large amount of cooling is required before dew point is reached. Condensation therefore depends upon two variables: (a) the amount of cooling and (b) the relative humidity of the air. If the dew point is not reached until the temperature falls below 32°, some of the condensed water vapor may be in the form of tiny ice crystals (white frost, snow, and some clouds) if condensation occurs above the freezing point it will be in the liquid state (dew, fog, and cloud). Observations seem to indicate that while condensation in solid form may occur at any temperature below 32°, actually most condensation down to about −40°F. is in the liquid form.

FORMS OF CONDENSATION AND ASSOCIATED METHODS OF COOLING THE ATMOSPHERE

134. Cooling of the atmosphere so as to cause condensation may be brought about by several methods. By such processes as radiation and conduction from the overlying air to the cold earth, and by mixing of two unlike air masses of contrasting temperatures and humidities, relatively shallow layers of air may have their temperatures lowered below condensation level. But the condensation forms (dew, white frost, and fog) resulting from these types of cooling are usually confined to air layers close to the earth's surface and represent relatively small scale condensation. Appreciable rainfall probably never results from such cooling. The one process capable of sufficiently reducing the temperature of great masses of air so as to bring about condensation on such a scale as to result in abundant precipitation is the expansion associated with rising air currents—adiabatic cooling.

135. Classical Condensation Theory vs. Condensation Conditions in the Free Atmosphere. According to the classical condensation theory it is assumed that (a) water in the atmosphere is entirely in vapor form until saturation or 100 per cent relative humidity is reached; further cooling results in some of it being changed to liquid or ice; (b) liquid condensation droplets do not exist in the atmosphere at subfreezing temperatures, and any such droplets present when the freezing point is reached are immediately frozen into ice pellets; (c) at temperatures below freezing all condensation is directly from the gas to the solid state (sublimation). All three of the above assumptions are only partially correct. Actually the formation of fog is likely to begin before 100 per cent relative humidity is reached, although the process goes on much more rapidly as saturation is approached. Smoke fogs over cities sometimes occur at relative humidities below 90 per cent. Liquid condensation droplets do exist in great numbers in the atmosphere at temperatures below freezing, while condensation of new liquid droplets takes place as a common occurrence at temperatures below 32°, although under those conditions direct sublimation may also occur. The formation of ice on aircraft clearly indicates the existence of clouds composed of supercooled liquid droplets. Fogs composed of water droplets have been observed at temperatures as low as −20°. More-

over it is now believed that most clouds (except those associated with rapidly ascending air) down to a temperature of −40°F. have a predominance of liquid droplets. The reason for the persistence of the liquid state at such low temperatures is not entirely clear, but it is thought that a condition of colloidal stability prevents the freezing.

136. Condensation on Hygroscopic Nuclei. For several decades it has been known that condensation would take place only when very microscopic nuclei were present around which the droplets could form. At first it was believed that any microscopic dust was sufficient, but it was soon shown that ordinary dust is totally inactive as condensation kerns. It is only particles, called hygroscopic substances, having a high affinity for water vapor that are effective condensation nuclei. Most important of these is salt sprayed up from the oceans and distributed inland by winds, and smoke, particularly that associated with the combustion of sulfurous compounds such as coal and oil.

The most universal nuclei of condensation are salt from ocean water. This is much more widespread than combustion compounds. It is self-explanatory then why hygroscopic nuclei are most numerous over the oceans, along coasts, and in the vicinity of cities. In such localities the presence of almost innumerable nuclei permit of condensation in the form of numerous very tiny droplets, which accounts for the density of resulting fogs. Such tiny droplets remain in suspension for very long periods and may not be entirely dissipated until a mass of new dry air displaces the older foggy one. It is probably true that hygroscopic nuclei are seldom so few as to retard the processes of condensation, although fogs are ordinarily less frequent and less dense away from cities and coasts.

Condensation apparently is a continuous process, for strongly hygroscopic particles begin to attract water around them even at low relative humidities. Light haze is the first evidence of such subsaturation condensation. As the relative humidity approaches 100 per cent, the growth in size of these droplets increases rapidly so that the haze thickens and gradually develops into fog. Haze, then, is often the forerunner of fog, although the ordinary dust haze of dry weather does not have this association. Fog and cloud are the two significant above-surface forms of condensation.

Condensation at or near the Earth's Surface

137. Dew and White Frost. Ideal conditions for the formation of dew or white frost, which are deposited on solid surfaces, are a clear sky, little or no wind, a fairly moist atmosphere, and relatively long nights. Under these conditions radiation of terrestrial energy proceeds rapidly so that the earth's surface, which radiates in all wavelengths rather than selectively and therefore is a better radiator than air, soon becomes colder than the atmospheric layer resting upon it. The adjacent air layer in turn becomes chilled by radiation and conduction to the earth's cold surface. Cloudless skies, or only high cloud, are essential to this process, since they permit a rapid loss of heat from the earth. Windy nights are not conducive to surface-air cooling, for under these conditions there is a constant "churning" of the lower air so that it does not remain long enough in contact with the earth's surface to be markedly cooled. Moreover, the cooling is distributed throughout a larger mass of air. It is a well-known fact that both dew and frost are much more likely to occur on nights that are clear and calm than on those when the sky is overcast and a wind is blowing. If the temperature of the lower few inches of surface air is reduced below the dew point, condensation takes place. This may be in the form of (a) *dew* (if the dew point is above 32°) or (b) *white frost* (if the dew point is below 32°), both of which collect on cold objects close to the earth.

138. Fog. Unlike nimbus clouds and precipitation, most fogs are formed by cooling processes that do not involve ascent and consequent expansion of the rising air. Radiation, conduction, and mixing of warm and cold air masses are the usual forms of cooling involved in fog formation. Since fog is merely a stratus cloud so close to the ground as to affect surface visibility, the problem of fog formation is one involving the cooling of air masses of high moisture content close to the surface. This usually takes place through lowering the temperature below the dew point. It may, however, result from the addition of water vapor to the atmosphere until the rising dew-point temperature coincides with the actual air temperature. In Willett's[1] classification the two principal types of fog are distinguished on the basis of which of the two processes is of greater importance in bringing air temperature and dew point together. These two classes are (a) intra air-mass fogs, which are usually formed by lowering the temperature, and (b) frontal fogs in which the more important factor usually is the addition of water vapor to the air by precipitation.

A modified and simplified form of Willett's classification of fogs is given below:

A. Intra air-mass fogs
   1. Radiation types
   2. Advection-radiation types
B. Frontal fogs

139. *Radiation Fogs.* The very common type of land fog, *radiation ground fog*, results from simple radiation and conduction cooling of relatively humid air overlying a chilled land surface. There are two main conditions favorable for radiation fog: (a) The air has been under a cloud cover, preferably with precipitation falling through it, the day before the fog occurs. (b) Pools of air, cooled to an excessive degree, have collected in depressions or valleys due to air drainage. The latter condition (b) becomes ideal if there is much nearby low land along a river or lake. The presence of the cloud cover in the daylight hours preceding the formation of the night fog is necessary in that it prevents an excessive heating and drying of the air under the cloud canopy, while precipitation falling through the air greatly aids formation of fog through the humidifying of the surface air.

Additional nighttime conditions which favor radiation fogs are (a) a surface inversion of temperature must be present, (b) air movement must be slight but not absolutely calm, and (c) skies

[1] H. C. Willett, Fog and Haze, Their Cause, Distribution, and Forecasting. *Monthly Weather Rev.*, Vol. 56, pp. 435–467, November, 1928. See also "Compendium of Meteorology," pp. 1179–1189.

should be cloudless. If low clouds cover the sky, they will absorb a large part of the earth radiation and reradiate it back to the earth's surface where it will be absorbed and as a consequence reduce the net loss of heat. The inversion is necessary to prevent the fog from rising. Whenever a warmer layer of air rests upon a colder one, a "lid," or "ceiling," is formed which rising smoke, dust, and fog particles find it difficult to penetrate. Fogs of the radiation type cannot form when the wind velocity is greater than 6 to 10 miles an hour. Some slight turbulence and mixing appear to be necessary, however, in order to develop a fog of moderate density. When air movement is considerable, the turbulence associated with the wind carries heat downward and thus prevents formation of an inversion.

Radiation fogs build up by gravitation. For this reason they are much more prevalent in valleys and depressions where, as a result of air drainage, the colder, heavier air tends to collect. Thus it often happens that while the slopes and uplands of a region are clear the adjacent lowlands may be damp and foggy. From an elevation one may view these numerous "lakes" of fog occupying the surrounding depressions. On a convex surface air drainage reduces the likelihood of temperature inversion and fog formation.

Radiation ground fog has a distinct diurnal periodicity and is usually short-lived. It grows and deepens from the bottom upward as the night progresses, only to burn off and disappear as the temperature inversion is dissipated and the moisture particles are evaporated by the ascending sun during the following morning. Ordinarily fog is not formed at temperatures well below freezing, since the heat of fusion retards the cooling process. Radiation fog is at its worst in the vicinity of large cities where the air is rich in hygroscopic smoke particles. The abundant condensation nuclei result in tinier fog particles which make for greater fog density. London fogs of this type are particularly famous, the chilled air collecting in the Thames Valley. Their darkness and persistence are partly the result of the pall of oily smoke that collects underneath the "lid" of a temperature inversion

and prevents the penetration of sunlight, which would evaporate the moisture particles. Obviously ground fog, and more especially its occurrence in the vicinity of landing fields, presents one of the greatest hazards to commercial aviation.

A variety of radiation fog is known as *high-inversion fog*. In this type not only is the inversion layer much deeper than in the radiation ground fog, but in addition the temperature inversion commonly is located at an elevation of 400 to 2,000 ft. above the earth's surface. During the day a deck of low stratus cloud, or "high fog," may mark the inversion level, but at night this cloud changes into a dense surface fog. Ideal conditions for such fogs are similar to those for a ground fog except that they are due to cooling, resulting not from one night's radiation, but from a cumulative net loss of heat by radiation. Polar maritime air that has become stagnant over a continent provides ideal temperature and moisture conditions for such fogs. Thus western Europe open to direct invasion of polar maritime air is characterized by much high-inversion fog in winter. The stratus deck formed at the inversion level is an excellent reflector by day and an equally good radiator at night. This further tends to intensify the inversion so that the high fog, reaching ground level at night, may persist for days or even weeks. Under such conditions air transport may be practically halted for days at a time.

140. *Advection-radiation fogs* always involve the transportation of air, and usually warm moist air, over cold surfaces. Loss of heat by radiation is likewise an essential part of the fog-forming process. Ideal locations for such fogs are to be found along sea coasts and along the shores of large inland bodies of water such as the Great Lakes. Advection fogs are most common over oceans and large inland bodies of water in summer, and over lands in winter. This is because the horizontal contrasts in temperature are more marked over land masses in winter. Over oceans, on the other hand, temperature contrasts are greater in summer, since the northern waters are kept cool by melting ice. The diurnal periodicity so conspicuous in radiation fogs is not characteristic of the advection type as a class.

A common form of advection fog is the *sea fog* which forms over the open water as a result of warm, moist air moving over colder waters. It is especially prevalent in those parts of the ocean having cool currents. Sea fogs may be carried inland a few miles and thereby affect the coastal margins of continents. The very foggy weather in the vicinity of the Newfoundland Banks is caused by air from the south, where warm water prevails, passing over the cool waters of the Labrador Current. Many of the earth's cool currents are found along coasts with the result that a great deal of sea fog is found near land. The fogs of the Peruvian Coast are of this origin.

Advection-radiation fogs of a somewhat different origin are also characteristic of a wider belt of land bordering oceans and large lakes. In this case the width of the fog belt may be defined as that distance which the moist lower air layers from the water body may reach in one night's travel from the water. The inland limits of such fogs has been found to be about 200 to 250 miles in winter and 150 miles in summer. Both factors, advection and radiation, are required in the formation of these fogs.

Still another type of advection-radiation fog results when a moist tropical air mass is transported poleward over a cooler surface. It is commonest in middle latitudes where latitudinal temperature contrasts are most marked. Such fogs are common over both sea and land. Since they are related to an extensive air mass, they usually cover large areas. Mist or even drizzle is a familiar accompaniment of this type. They are common in north central United States in winter when a cyclone traveling on a northern track draws tropical air northward over a snow-covered surface.

An additional type of advection fog is formed when very cold stable air passes over a warmer water surface. It is a common phenomenon over patches of open water in the arctic ice pack and over rivers and inland lakes in cold spells of early winter. Under these conditions water evaporates quickly and fills the surface air with vapor. Water vapor pours forth from the water surface to condense in the cold air as a dense steam fog. It is said that arctic explorers by means of steam fogs are often able to locate and avoid dangerous stretches of open water.

141. *Frontal Fogs.* These fogs are associated with the passage of the boundaries separating unlike air masses, these boundaries being known as fronts. The fog is formed both (*a*) as a result of forced ascent due to convergence and (*b*) by saturation of the cold surface layer of air by rainfall from the overrunning warm air aloft. There is little difference between warm-front and cold-front fogs since both are largely the result of evaporation and cooling from the falling rain. In general the belt of precipitation along a cold front is narrower than that associated with a warm front, and the fog belts vary in a similar fashion.

142. *Local Dissipation of Natural Fog.*[1] It is recognized that the hazards associated with the landing of aircraft in fog could be greatly reduced if relatively small clearings could be made artificially in the fog. The minimum dimensions of such a useful cleared space over a landing field are considered to be 1,600 to 3,250 ft. long, 100 to 160 ft. wide, and 30 to 65 ft. deep. To maintain such a clearing under typical wind conditions, fog must be removed at the rate of about 70,000 cu. ft. per sec. A study of the various methods of fog removal has led to the conclusion that there are three reasonably feasible methods of fog removal in very restricted areas such as the runway of an air field: (*a*) the direct application of heat, (*b*) the use of hygroscopic materials to dry the air, and (*c*) the dropping of electrically charged materials through the fog. There is no longer any doubt that fog can be dispelled very locally by artificial means. The fundamental problem lies in the economics of fog dispersal, for the costs are relatively high. It seems doubtful whether a method will be found which will clear fog from extensive areas with the consumption of only a small amount of energy.

[1] H. G. Houghton, and W. H. Radford, On the Local Dissipation of Natural Fog, *Mass. Inst. of Technology and Woods Hole Oceanographic Inst., Papers in Physical Oceanography and Meteorology,* Vol. 6, No. 3, October, 1938.

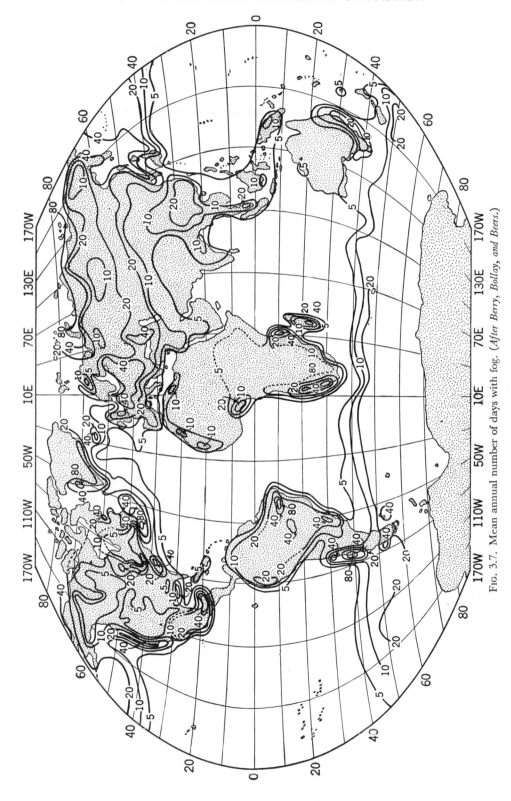

Fig. 3.7. Mean annual number of days with fog. (*After Berry, Bollay, and Beers.*)

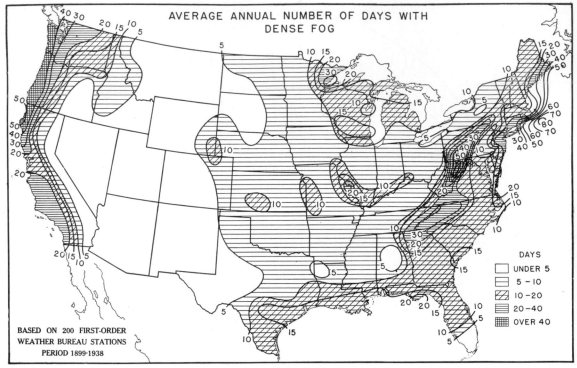

FIG. 3.8. (*Courtesy of U.S. Weather Bureau.*)

143. *Distribution of Fog.* For the earth as a whole fogs are much more common over the oceans than over the lands. These are advection fogs and result when air from warmer regions blows over cooler waters. A study of fog distribution over the ocean obviously involves a knowledge of ocean temperatures and the system of ocean currents. From the world pattern of ocean currents one can make important generalizations regarding the distribution of sea fogs. Since in the low latitudes, including the subtropics, cool ocean currents are concentrated along the eastern sides of oceans (west sides of continents), these regions are some of the foggiest regions of the earth. Much fog likewise develops over the middle-latitude oceans as a result of warm tropical air moving poleward in the warm sectors of cyclonic storms. Such fogs are common in the North Atlantic, especially its eastern parts, and in the North Pacific near the Aleutian Islands and the Gulf of Alaska. Summer fogs are particularly prevalent in the Newfoundland area of the North Atlantic and in the region

northeast of Japan in the North Pacific where warm and cool ocean currents converge (Fig. 3.7).

In the United States there is a definite regional pattern of fog frequency.[1] The regions of maximum fog are to be found along the North Atlantic Coast, the Pacific Coast, and the Appalachian Highlands (Fig. 3.8). Minimum fogginess is characteristic of the dry western country where the air masses ordinarily contain a small amount of moisture. Secondary regions of relatively high fog frequency are the upper Great Lakes states, the bottom lands of the Mississippi and Ohio Rivers in the vicinity of Illinois and Indiana, and the Gulf and Atlantic Coastal Plain. Western Europe which is freely open to the invasion of maritime air has a high percentage of winter fogs of the advection types. The British Isles, surrounded by warm seas, are

[1] For a relatively comprehensive analysis of fog in the United States, see R. G. Stone, Fog in the United States, *Geo. Rev.*, Vol. 26, pp. 111–134, 1936; Horace Robert Byers, "General Meteorology," pp. 519–533.

particularly subject to winter fogs. In certain industrial valleys such as the Ruhr, the Saar, and the Thames around London, the smoke pollution intensifies fog formation.

The seasonal variation in fog frequency differs for continental and marine locations. Continental stations usually experience a maximum of fog in winter and a minimum in summer, while the reverse is true of marine locations. Winter favors the development of radiation ground fogs over land areas because of the greater frequency of large anticyclones at that season. The clear calm air of the anticyclone and the long winter nights provide ideal conditions for strong radiational cooling and hence for fog formation. The fewer anticyclones and shorter nights of summer provide less favorable conditions for the development of radiation fog. Advection fogs also are more frequent over land areas in winter because at that season the moist maritime air masses entering a continent are chilled at the base as a result of moving over a relatively cold land surface. Over oceans radiation fog is infrequent and advection fog is at a maximum in summer since at that season the water surface is cooler than the land.

The Formation of Clouds and Associated Precipitation in Ascending Air Currents

144. Adiabatic Temperature Changes. It is necessary at this point to consider the very important changes in the temperature of air which occurs as it is moved upward away from the earth or downward toward the earth. As air moves upward away from the earth, it comes under lower pressures, for there is less weight of air upon it, and consequently it expands. Conversely as air moves downward toward the earth from higher elevations it encounters higher pressures and contracts in volume. Thus if a mass of dry air at sea level, under an atmospheric pressure of approximately 1,016 mb., or 30 in., rises to an altitude of 17,500 ft., the pressure on it is reduced about one-half and consequently its volume is doubled. A cubic foot of air at sea level would then, if carried to that altitude, occupy

2 cu. ft. Through these expansion and contraction processes associated with changes in elevation the temperature of the moving air changes even though there is no actual addition or withdrawal of heat. This type of temperature change resulting from internal processes is called *adiabatic* change.

According to the molecular theory a gas such as air is composed of molecules which are in a state of constant motion, so that there are persistent collisions between individual molecules. The impact of the colliding gas molecules produces the pressure of the gas. The pressure, therefore, depends upon the number and mass of the molecules and the speed at which they are moving, which in turn is determined by temperature. If the temperature is high, the molecular velocity is greater and the number of collisions more frequent. Therefore, the gas pressure is greater at high temperatures than at low temperatures.

Some of these principles indicating the relationship between pressure, temperature, and volume (hence also density) in gases may be expressed in the form of physical laws as follows:

a. In a gas kept at constant temperature the volume is inversely proportional to the pressure. If pressure on the gas is doubled, its volume is reduced one-half.

b. In a gas kept at constant pressure the volume varies directly with the absolute temperature. Therefore, as the temperature of a gas increases, its volume also increases, and as its temperature is lowered, its volume is decreased.

In making use of the above gas laws, it becomes clear that a mass of air which is lifted will experience a decreased pressure upon it, so that its volume is increased. In addition, work is done by the expanding air in making room for itself and this work done in pushing aside the surrounding air requires energy which results in a lowering of the temperature of the rising air. Since the volume of the expanding air has been increased, the collision of the molecules is less frequent and temperature consequently falls; conversely when air descends, its volume is decreased by the greater air pressure and its temperature and density are increased.

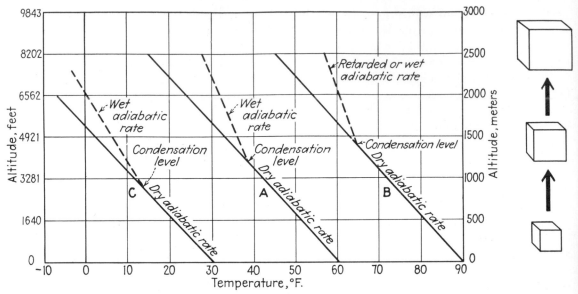

FIG. 3.9. Illustrating adiabatic cooling in rising air of different temperatures.

The rate of adiabatic heating and cooling of dry or nonsaturated air masses through vertical movement is constant, no matter what the temperature of the air. It is approximately 5.54°F. per 1,000 ft. change in altitude or 10°C. per 1,000 meters. This is known as the dry adiabatic rate, for it applies only to air which is not saturated. The rate of cooling of ascending air, therefore, is considerably more rapid than is the normal vertical decrease in temperature (lapse rate) which is about 3.3°F. per 1,000 ft. or 6°C. per 1,000 meters. These two rates should be clearly distinguished as being very different things, for one represents the cooling of a rising and therefore vertically moving air mass, while the other applies to the change in air temperature that would be recorded by a thermometer carried up through the atmosphere.

145. *The Moist or Retarded Adiabatic Rate.* As indicated previously, the adiabatic rate of cooling for unsaturated air is the same, no matter what the temperature. For this reason the three dry adiabats in Fig. 3.9 are all parallel. But as the unsaturated air continues to rise and cool, it is likely to reach a temperature at which condensation begins. This is called the condensation level. It will be noted in Fig. 3.9 that the condensation levels for the three rising air masses, each of a different temperature, are not the same. This results from likely differences in relative humidity. Thus the cooler air, *C*, which normally would have the highest relative humidity, reaches condensation level first or at the lowest elevation. The warmest air, *B*, which has the lowest relative humidity has to rise higher and reach a lower temperature before the saturation point is reached and condensation begins.

After the rising air reaches the condensation level, where clouds begin to form, the then saturated air as it continues to rise cools no longer at the previous dry adiabatic rate, but at one which is somewhat slower. This is called the *retarded*, or *wet adiabatic*, rate. Above condensation level where water vapor is being converted into clouds composed of liquid and ice particles, heat of condensation is released into the atmosphere. It is this added source of energy which slows up the rate of cooling in the rising air. Two counteracting processes, one resulting in cooling and the other in heating are proceeding simultaneously, for while the saturated air continues to cool by expansion, the heat liberated as a result of condensation acts as a brake on the cooling process. Of the two processes, the cooling due to expansion is the primary one, with the result that the rising saturated air continues to cool but at a slower rate.

It may be observed from Fig. 3.9 that the retarded, or wet adiabatic, rate is not constant, but varies with the temperature of the air. The same amount of cooling will result in the condensation of a greater amount of moisture when air temperature is high because the specific humidity of warm air is higher than that of cool air. As a result, the amount of liberated heat of condensation is much greater at high temperatures and as a consequence the wet adiabatic lapse rate is smaller in 90° air than in 30° air. When air temperatures are extremely low, the moisture content is so low that the wet adiabatic lapse rate is almost the same as the dry adiabatic rate. At high temperatures the wet adiabatic rate may be in the neighborhood of one-half the dry adiabatic rate, or about 3° per 1,000 ft.

146. Adiabatic Cooling and Precipitation.
Air which because of its instability and buoyancy rises voluntarily, will continue to rise until it reaches air layers having its own temperature and density. *This process of cooling, by the expansion associated with rising air, is the only one capable of reducing the temperature of extensive and thick masses of air below the dew point.* It is the only one, therefore, which is capable of producing condensation on such a large scale that abundant precipitation results. There is no doubt that nearly all the earth's precipitation is the result of expansion and cooling in rising air currents. The direct result of cooling due to ascent is *clouds,* a form of condensation characteristic of air at altitudes usually well above the earth's surface, just as dew, white frost, and fog are forms characteristic of the surface air. Fog and cloud are identical except for differences in height above the ground. Not all clouds, to be sure, give rise to precipitation, but all precipitation has its origin in clouds and is the result of processes that are additional to those causing condensation.

147. Stable and Unstable Atmospheric Conditions and Their Relation to Precipitation. Since practically all precipitation may be ascribed to vertical movements of the atmosphere, the conditions that tend to promote or hinder such movements are of prime importance. Although the concept of atmospheric stability and instability has been touched upon previously, it is elaborated again at this point because of its close association with the processes of condensation and precipitation. The concepts of stable and unstable air are slightly mathematical to be sure, and in a book of this kind some may wonder at their inclusion. But to omit a discussion of this topic would be to skip some of the veriest fundamentals of all atmospheric science.

Air is said to be stable, and consequently antagonistic to precipitation, if it resists vertical displacement, or if, following forced vertical displacement, it tends to return to its former position. A rocking chair at rest is in stable equilibrium, for, if it is rocked slightly, it immediately returns to its original position. Vertical motions are largely absent in stable air. On the other hand, if displacement results in a tendency to further movement away from the original position, a condition of instability prevails. Under such conditions vertical movement is prevalent. A cone balanced upon its apex is in unstable equilibrium, for the slightest impulse would cause it to move farther away from its original position. Whether an air mass is stable or unstable depends upon a comparison of its lapse rate with the adiabatic rate. When the lapse rate exceeds the dry adiabatic ($5\frac{1}{2}$°F. per 1,000 ft.), as it may possibly do on a bright, hot afternoon, the surface air is unstable and inclined to rise. But when, for example, over a cold middle-latitude continent in winter, the lapse rate is less than the adiabatic, the air is stable, and it resists displacement and tends to remain in its original position. Note that it is the lapse rate which is the variable. The dry adiabatic rate is the same at all times and under all conditions. In Fig. 3.10, the solid lines AB and XY represent conditions of stability and instability, respectively. The dashed lines $X'Y$ and $A'B$ indicate the dry adiabatic rate, which, of course, is the same for unsaturated air, no matter what the temperature. These latter lines are therefore parallel.

148. *Instability.* If a particle of air from point Y with a temperature of 85° is caused to rise, its

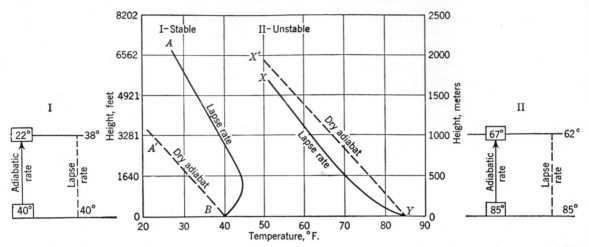

FIG. 3.10. Illustrating atmospheric stability and instability. When the lapse rate exceeds the adiabatic rate, instability prevails. When the reverse is true the air is stable.

rate of cooling will be represented by the line $X'Y$ (Fig. 3.10). At any point along this line it will be warmer and therefore less dense than the surrounding air represented by XY, and it will therefore continue to rise freely of its own accord after an initial upward impetus has been given it. The condition when the lapse rate throughout is greater than the dry adiabatic rate of $5\frac{1}{2}°$F. per 1,000 ft. illustrates what is known as *absolute instability*. Moderately unstable air will not begin to rise voluntarily, but, if an updraft is once started, or "triggered off," by intense surface heating by the sun or by upward deflection by a mountain slope or a cold air mass, the ascent will continue of its own accord because of the buoyancy forces involved (Fig. 3.11). When the lapse rate exceeds 19°F. per 1,000 ft., the upper air is actually denser than that underneath, and automatic overturning occurs without any initial forced displacement. This condition, known as *mechanical instability*, is of rare occurrence in nature. It may play a part in violent line squalls or tornado weather.

149. *Stability.* When an air layer has a lapse rate that is less than the dry adiabatic—say $3\frac{1}{2}°$F. per 1,000 ft.—a *stable* condition is present, and there is opposition to vertical movement. If, in Fig. 3.10, an air particle from point B, temperature 40°, is forced to ascend, at any point along dry adiabat $A'B$ it will be cooler than the surrounding air whose vertical temper-

ature structure is represented by line AB, and consequently it will tend to sink back to its former position. It would never have risen except under compulsion (Fig. 3.11). If the lapse rate is less than about $2\frac{1}{2}°$F. per 1,000 ft. the air is said to be *absolutely stable*. This air resists vertical displacement even when condensation takes place. A common instance of absolute stability is the temperature inversion. An inversion is so stable that it acts as an aerial "lid" to halt ordinary rising currents. Rising col-

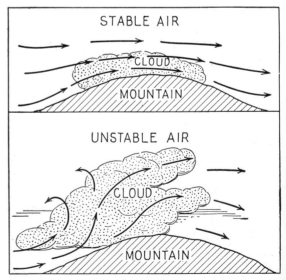

FIG. 3.11. Illustrating cloud formation in saturated air, stable in one case and unstable in the other.

umns of smoke or growing clouds are forced to spread out horizontally beneath the base of the inversion.

150. *Conditional Instability.* It has been pointed out in the previous discussion that a lapse rate greater than 5½°F. per 1,000 ft. represents *instability*, while a lapse rate of less than about 2½°F. indicates absolute *stability*. If an air layer has an actual lapse rate between the dry adiabatic (5½°F. per 1,000 ft.) and the wet adiabatic (2½°F. per 1,000 ft.) rates of cooling, its instability is conditional upon the relative humidity of the air at all levels. The lapse rate shown in Fig. 3.12 represents a state of *conditional instability*. The rising air particle while still unsaturated follows the dry adiabatic rate of cooling. The lapse rate is less than the dry adiabatic rate, so that during this phase the rising air is cooler than its surroundings. It is, therefore, stable and resists lifting, and any rising is the result of forced ascent. But, when the rising air reaches condensation level and latent heat is added, any further cooling takes place at the retarded, or wet adiabatic, rate, which is less than the lapse rate. As a result of the lapse rate

being greater than the wet adiabatic rate, from point *B* upward the rising air is warmer than the surrounding air and consequently is unstable so that it rises freely of its own accord. In other words, conditionally unstable air performs like stable air until after condensation begins. Somewhat above condensation level it behaves like unstable air.

151. The preceding discussion may be summarized as follows:

a. Absolute stability prevails when the temperature lapse rate is less than 2½°F. per 1,000 ft.

b. Stability prevails in a relatively *dry* air mass when its lapse rate is less than the dry adiabatic rate (lapse rate between 2½ and 5½° per 1,000 ft.).

c. Conditional instability prevails in a relatively *moist* air mass when its lapse rate lies between the dry and the wet adiabatic rates (lapse rate between 2½ and 5½° per 1,000 ft.).

d. Absolute instability prevails in an air mass when its lapse rate is greater than the dry adiabatic rate (lapse rate greater than 5½° per 1,000 ft.).

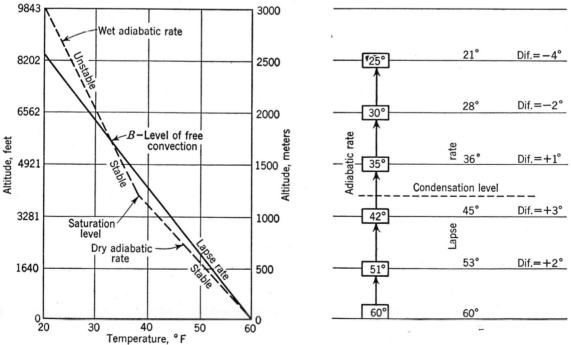

Fig. 3.12. Illustrating conditional instability.

e. Mechanical instability prevails in an air mass when its lapse is greater than about 19°F. per 1,000 ft.

It bears repeating that these concepts of atmospheric stability, instability, and conditional instability are basic and fundamental to an understanding of the origin of precipitation and of the nature of air masses as related to precipitation.

152. Vertical Displacements of Deep and Extensive Air Masses. Previously the discussion has been concerned with the rising or subsidence of isolated particles or currents of air. The bodily lifting or sinking of an entire air mass several thousand feet thick and covering thousands of square miles, however, involves expansion or contraction of the air mass as a whole, with consequent changes in its vertical thickness which are of great importance meteorologically. In addition to the general cooling of the air mass with ascent and heating with descent, there will be differential rates of cooling and heating at different heights within the layer. In the lifting process the upper layers of the air mass expand more than the lower ones and as a result are cooled more. This differential cooling tends to steepen the lapse rate within the air mass. Conversely, during subsidence the lower strata are less involved in the vertical movement than are

those aloft, so that adiabatic heating is not so marked at the lower levels. The result of this differential heating at the different levels is to decrease the lapse rate of the air mass and make it more stable. These effects upon the lapse rate of lifting and subsidence are illustrated by Fig. 3.13. When the layer of air lying between the 1,000- and 900-mb. surfaces is lifted sufficiently so that there has been a decrease in pressure amounting to 300 mb. and its bounding isobaric surfaces are 700 and 600 mb., the vertical thickness of the air mass has increased. This is because the density of air is less at higher altitudes, and consequently the isobaric surfaces are farther apart. In the lifting process (Fig. 3.13) the lower part of the layer at *A* will cool to *A'*; and the upper part with the temperature *B* will cool to *B'*. The result is that the lapse rate has been steepened from *AB* to *A'B'*, and the air mass is less stable. If the layer under the condition *A'B'* is caused to sink, the reverse process is followed, and the lapse rate is made more stable (*AB*). Actually the lapse rate *AB* shows an inversion condition, so that absolute stability prevails. *As a general rule, then, lifting steepens the lapse rate and therefore increases instability, while subsidence or sinking decreases the lapse rate and so makes stable air all the more stable.*

An additional factor tending to change the lapse rate in ascending or subsiding air is the divergence, or horizontal spreading. This process usually accompanies subsidence. By horizontal spreading the thickness of the air mass is decreased as its area increases, with the result that its stability will be greatly increased, and a strong temperature inversion will be formed. Subsidence and divergence are a very common way by which air masses are stabilized and temperature inversions formed.

153. *Convective Instability.* It frequently happens that the lower layers of an air mass have a much higher relative humidity than those aloft. When lifting takes place in an air mass in which relative humidity decreases rapidly with elevation, the lower part reaches condensation level first, and as a result of added heat of condensation it cools much more slowly than the upper layers, which are following the dry rather than

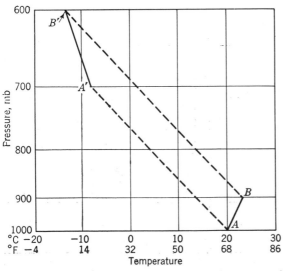

FIG. 3.13. Illustrating the effects upon the lapse rate of the lifting and subsidence of thick air masses.

the wet adiabatic rate. A greatly steepened lapse rate within the air mass follows; so much so that it becomes unstable. Such an air mass is said to be *convectively unstable*. In Fig. 3.14 the air mass lying between the 1,000- and 900-mb. levels has a lapse rate as indicated by line *AB*. Because the air at *A* has a higher relative humidity than that at *B*, after ascent begins it reaches condensation level sooner than *B* and therefore cools at a retarded rate. If the air mass with lapse rate *AB* is lifted so that its pressure is reduced 300 mb., *A* will have cooled to *A'* and *B* to *B'*. *A'B'*, which represents the new lapse rate of the ascending air layer, is considerably steeper than the old lapse rate *AB* and represents a condition of greater instability.

The importance of convective instability lies in the fact that even masses of air that were originally stable may be converted into convectively unstable air masses, provided there are marked vertical contrasts in water-vapor content, through a forced vertical motion of the air mass as a whole. Such forced vertical displacement of extensive air masses takes place along the windward sides of mountain ranges, and also along frontal surfaces in cyclonic storms where cold and stable air masses act as the obstacle to produce forced ascent. Widespread and abundant rainfall is commonly associated with the vertical displacement of convectively unstable air masses.

154. Vorticity and Its Relationship to Lifting and Subsidence of Air Masses. Winds that flow parallel with the isobars need have no convergence or divergence, but this is not true of the actual winds which even in the free atmosphere above the friction layer continue to cross the isobars at a small angle. The drift of air across the isobars causes an inflow of air toward cyclonic areas and outflow from anticyclonic areas. The air that converges must ascend and cool, while the air which diverges must descend or subside and heat. Hence cyclonic areas, or regions of convergence, are likely to be characterized by clouds and precipitation, while anticyclones, or regions of divergence, are, in general, areas of fair weather.

Convergence or divergence in the horizontal

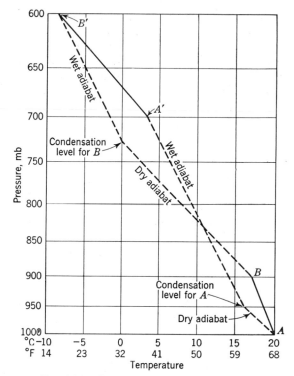

FIG. 3.14. Illustrating convective instability.

flow may result from other causes. Horizontal air currents in the free atmosphere develop vorticity or spin (angular velocity) which causes them to move in curved or sinuous courses instead of in a straight line. The spin or vorticity is developed in part because of earth rotation. This effect is at a maximum at the poles and becomes zero at the equator. In addition, horizontally moving air develops spin or angular velocity as a result of the curved streamlines and the wind shear. The vorticity resulting from curved streamlines is expressed by the formula c/r where c = the speed of the rotating air particles and r = the radius of curvature. Therefore either an increase in speed (c) or a decrease in the radius (r) will result in increased spin or vorticity.

By wind shear is meant the change in wind speed at right angles to the direction of flow. When wind speed decreases toward the left looking downstream, there is said to be cyclonic shear and as a result cyclonic, or anticlockwise (Northern Hemisphere), curvature of the air particles results. Conversely, when wind speed decreases toward the right looking downstream, the anticyclonic shear results in a clockwise, or anticyclonic, flow. To summarize, it may be said that at a given latitude increasing cyclonic vorticity (or decreasing anticyclonic) must be accompanied by lateral convergence and lffting. Conversely, decreasing cyclonic vorticity (or increasing anticyclonic) must be accompanied by lateral divergence and subsidence.

Changes in vorticity, with resulting modification in lateral convergence and divergence, also occur as a result of horizontal air flow in northerly or southerly directions. This is occasioned by the latitudinal change in the Coriolis force, or deflective force of earth rotation. As a result of decreasing Coriolis force toward the lower latitudes, an equatorward moving air current tends to develop increasing cyclonic curvature or vorticity, while one moving poleward tends to develop increasing anticyclonic vorticity.

From a climatic standpoint the significance of the above discussion of vorticity is associated with the fact that cyclonic vorticity or spin in a horizontally moving air mass is associated with convergence and vertical lifting and hence is related to areas of cloud and precipitation. In contrast, anticyclonic vorticity or spin, where divergence and subsidence are present, is likely to be associated with fair weather. Thus the nature of the air flow in the free atmosphere in terms of its cyclonic or anticyclonic vorticity or curvature is of the highest importance in understanding rainfall phenomena at the surface of the earth.

CLOUD TYPES

155. Classification of Clouds. Clouds very clearly reflect the physical processes taking place in the atmosphere. They are, therefore, indicators of weather conditions. A comprehensive treatment of cloud types and their usefulness in weather forecasting lies outside the province of this book, which is primarily climatological. Only brief mention is made here of the 10 principal cloud types recognized in the international classification of clouds that has been adopted by most countries, including the United States (Fig. 3.15). A modest acquaintance with cloud types

is of value in understanding weather types, which in turn are the units out of which the composite climatic picture is composed.

Family A: High Clouds (Mean Lower Level 20,000 ft.)

1. Cirrus (Ci)—thin featherlike clouds with a fibrous structure and a delicate silky appearance. When detached and arranged irregularly in the sky, they are harbingers of fair weather. On the other hand, when they are systematically arranged, as in bands, or connected with cirrostratus or altostratus, they usually foretell bad weather. They are always composed of ice crystals.

2. Cirrostratus (Cs)—a thin whitish sheet of cloud covering the whole sky and giving it a milky appearance. These clouds commonly produce a halo around the sun and moon and usually are the sign of approaching storm.

3. Cirrocumulus (Cc)—small white flakes or small globular masses, usually without shadows. They are usually arranged in groups, lines, or ripples resulting from undulation of the cloud sheet. Called mackerel sky.

Family B: Middle Clouds (Mean Upper Level, 20,000 ft.; Mean Lower Level, 6,500 ft.)

4. Altostratus (As)—a uniform sheet cloud of gray or bluish color, frequently showing a fibrous structure. It is like thick cirrostratus and often merges gradually with it. Through it the sun and moon shine only very wanly and with a faint gleam. Altostratus commonly is followed by widespread precipitation of a relatively continuous type.

5. Altocumulus (Ac)—flattened globular masses of cloud, arranged in lines or waves. Differs from cirrocumulus in consisting of larger globules, often with shadows.

Family C: Low Clouds (Mean Upper Level, 6,500 ft.; Mean Lower Level Close to Earth's Surface)

6. Stratocumulus (Sc)—large globular masses or rolls of soft gray clouds with brighter interstices. The masses are commonly arranged in a regular pattern.

7. Stratus (St)—a low uniform layer of cloud resembling fog, but not resting on the ground.

8. Nimbostratus (Ns)—a dense, shapeless, and often ragged layer of low clouds from which continuous precipitation commonly falls.

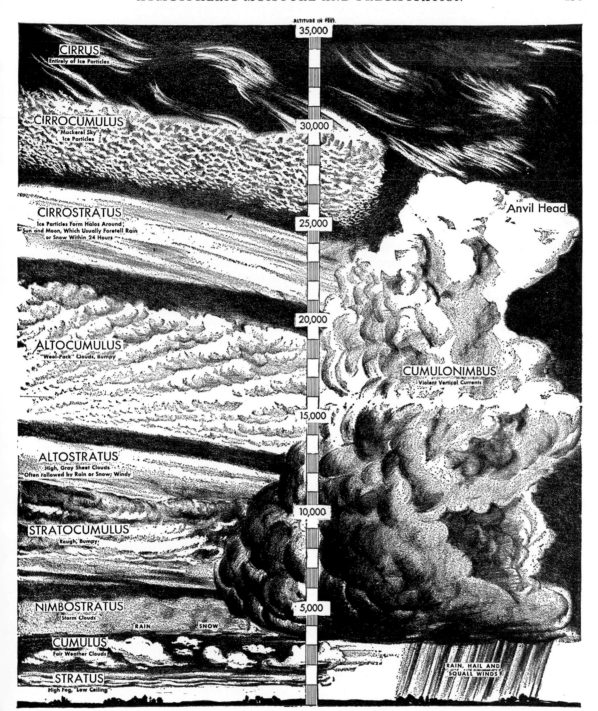

Fig. 3.15. Very generalized vertical arrangement of cloud types. (*From "Atmosphere and Weather Charts," published by A. J. Nystrom Co.*)

Family D: Clouds with Vertical Development (Mean Upper Level, That of Cirrus; Mean Lower Level, 1,600 ft.)

9. Cumulus (Cu)—a thick, dense cloud with vertical development. The upper surface is dome-shaped with a cauliflower structure, while the base is nearly horizontal. Much cumulus cloud is of the fair-weather type, although towering cumulus may develop into cumulonimbus or thunderheads.

10. Cumulonimbus (Cb)—heavy masses of cloud with great vertical development whose summits rise like mountains, towers, or anvils. They are accompanied by sharp showers, squalls, thunderstorms, and sometimes hail.

156. Distribution of Cloudiness. Cloudiness is expressed in terms of the amount of sky covered by clouds and is usually given in tenths of total area of the sky. A cloudiness of 0 indicates a cloudless sky, and a cloudiness of 10 represents a sky completely covered by clouds.

Zonal Distribution of the Annual Means of Cloudiness, Per Cent

(After C. E. P. Brooks)

Latitude	90–80°	80–70°	70–60°	60–50°	50–40°	40–30°	30–20°	20–10°	10–0°
Northern Hemisphere									
Ocean	63	70	72	67	66	52	49	53	53
Land	..	63	62	60	50	40	34	40	52
Mean	..	66	63	62	56	45	41	47	53
Southern Hemisphere									
Ocean	..	64	76	72	67	57	53	49	50
Land	..	..	..	70	58	48	38	46	56
Mean	..	..	..	72	66	54	48	48	52

One might expect that the zonal distribution of cloudiness would closely parallel that of rainfall, and it does to a considerable degree. Thus there is a modest maximum of cloudiness in the equatorial latitudes where horizontal convergence is strong (see table above). But the equatorial maximum in cloudiness is not as strong as is the rainfall maximum for this same region. The predominance in the low latitudes of convective clouds which are local in character and cover only a part of the sky is the reason for this disparity between rainfall and cloudiness. There is a strong minimum of cloudiness in the latitudes of the subtropical anticyclones, as there is of rainfall. Poleward from the subtropics both cloudiness and rainfall increase, but while rainfall reaches only secondary maxima in the middle latitudes of both hemispheres (Fig. 3.18), cloudiness, on the other hand, reaches its primary maxima in these middle and higher latitudes. This is explained by the fact that the cloudiness and rainfall of the middle latitudes are associated with cyclones and fronts in which the cloud cover is extensive and covers the whole sky.

The *annual variation* in cloudiness, in a large measure, follows the rainfall regime. Thus, in the tropics, the cloudiness maximum coincides with summer rainfall maximum and along subtropical west coasts, as California, cloudiness and rainfall are both at a maximum in winter. In the interiors of middle-latitude continents, however, the situation is frequently reversed so that summer is likely to experience the maximum rainfall, but the minimum of cloudiness. This situation reflects the greater amount of local convective cloud in the hot season and of stratiform frontal clouds in winter.

The *daily variation* in cloudiness is complicated because of the contrasts in origin of cumulus and stratiform cloud types. Since the former develop as a result of surface heating, they tend to reach a maximum in the early and midafternoon hours. Stratiform clouds, by contrast, are favored by stable atmospheric conditions so that their maximum occurs in the early morning hours and their minimum in midday.

ORIGIN AND FORMS OF PRECIPITATION

157. Origin. It is possible for ascending air to reach and pass somewhat beyond the condensation level, with a resulting formation of clouds, and still yield no precipitation. Cloudy condensation probably does not occur without at least a slight degree of supersaturation. As relative humidity exceeds 100 per cent, condensation occurs first on the largest hygroscopic nuclei, and if condensation remains slow, only the largest nuclei will be activated. But if condensation is increased, then additional and smaller nuclei will collect condensation. Thus condensation takes place around almost innumerable hygroscopic nuclei so that the individual cloud particles are too small to fall to earth as rain. Clouds may be regarded as colloidal suspensions of water in air. As long as the droplets do not coalesce but tend to remain floating in the air, the cloud is colloidally stable and precipitation does not occur. When the droplets have a tendency to coalesce and thereby become so heavy that they cannot be kept afloat, the cloud is unstable and precipitation occurs.

The air usually contains so many condensation nuclei, thousands to the cubic centimeter, that the first cloud droplets are only about $\frac{1}{100}$ mm. in diameter. Even a very slight ascent of air would be adequate to keep such minute particles in suspension. Moreover, if they did succeed in falling below condensation level, in all probability they would be evaporated before reaching the earth. It is obvious then why there can be so many gray, overcast days on which rain does not occur. Some explanation is required as to how sufficiently large drops are produced to cause precipitation. Precipitation cannot be formed by a simple continuation of the condensation processes which produce clouds. Other processes are required. Cloudy condensation results in the formation of a high concentration of very small condensation particles. The precipitation processes must result in the combining of these myriads of small particles into a smaller number of larger units capable of falling to earth. The mass of a small raindrop 1 mm. in diameter may be a million times that of a cloud droplet, so that any precipitation process must be capable of causing a rapid coalescing of a large number of cloud particles.

Two precipitation mechanisms are believed to account for most of the combining of cloud particles to form raindrops. The first of these is the result of cloud instability brought about by the coexistence of water droplets and ice particles in a cloud at temperatures below 32°F. If this is true, then for an appreciable amount of precipitation to occur, the ascending air must rise above the freezing level where some of the liquid droplets will be changed into ice and where likewise direct sublimation (gas to solid) may take place. The difference in vapor pressure over the liquid droplets and over the ice particles leads to evaporation of the former and resulting condensation around the ice particles as nuclei. As water accumulates around the ice nucleus, it eventually reaches such a size that it can no longer be held up by the ascending currents and so falls to earth. The drop then continues to grow until it leaves the cloud, unless it is broken up by the speed of its descent. The best evidence supporting this theory is the sudden release of precipitation when a cumulus cloud grows into a cumulonimbus as it reaches the glaciation, or ice-nuclei, level. This glaciation of the upper part of the cloud results in a change from the typical boiling, cauliflower top to one that is veil-shaped or anvil-shaped in appearance.

The second precipitation mechanism is the coalescence of drops as they fall in the cloud. If the drops are of nonuniform size, they will fall at different velocities, which fact accounts for their collisions. Thus the rate of growth by this process depends upon the size, size distribution, and concentration of the drops in the cloud.

A good-sized raindrop contains as much water as 8,000,000 cloud particles and falls 200 times as fast (Brooks). The maximum size to which a raindrop can grow is about $\frac{1}{5}$ in. (5 mm.) in diameter, for at that size its rate of fall is about 18 miles per hr., and above that size and speed drops begin to break up. In gently ascending air currents condensation is relatively slow, and even small drops can fall to earth through the slowly rising air, so that light rain or drizzle is the result. On the other hand, the strong upward surges in a violent thunderstorm produce very vigorous condensation and are able to support drops of great size. As a result the first few isolated drops that fall preceding the general downpour produce sizable splashes. Raindrops are usually larger than $\frac{1}{50}$ in. in diameter, and in still air they fall faster than 10 ft. per sec. Drizzle droplets are less than $\frac{1}{50}$ in. in diameter.

158. Solid Forms of Condensation and Precipitation. In rising air solid condensation forms may appear in the atmosphere either as a result of the freezing of liquid condensation or by the direct condensation (sublimation) from the vapor to the solid phase. It is believed that down to a temperature of about −40°F. liquid condensation is more common than ice. Thus clouds composed of supercooled water droplets are much more common than ice clouds at temperatures down to 15°F. and they have been observed down to −30°F. and even below.

Snow is precipitation in the solid form that occurs at temperatures below freezing. It may originate from a waterdrop cloud, or, on the other hand, it may be formed by the direct sublimation of ice crystals from water vapor. The fundamental form of snow is the intricately branched flat hexagonal crystal in an almost infinite variety of patterns. A snowflake is simply an agglomeration of snow crystals matted together as a result of a film of water on the individual crystals. Since very cold air contains little moisture, heavy snowfalls are usually associated with surface temperatures not much below freezing. Large wet flakes fall under conditions of comparatively high temperatures, while fine hard snow is characteristic of very cold regions and periods. As a rough approximation it requires about 1 ft. of snow to equal 1 in. of rain, although the ratio may vary from 5 to 1 to 50 to 1, depending on the density of the snow. If snow is formed at fairly high levels while the surface temperatures are considerably above freezing, it will melt before reaching the ground and therefore arrive at the surface as rain. A considerable proportion of the rainfall reaching the ground in middle latitudes originated as snow.

Data on the amount of snowfall and the duration of the snow cover are very scanty and fragmentary for much of the earth so that a satisfactory description of the distribution of snow is impossible. Köppen indicates that a snow cover of appreciable duration is characteristic of regions where the temperature of the cold month is 27°F. or below. A permanent snow cover exists at very high altitudes even in the tropics and the height of the snow line declines poleward. Thus at 68°N. in Norway permanent snow

is found at an elevation of about 3,500 ft., while on Mount Kilimanjaro in tropical East Africa at 3°S. the snow line is at about 18,400 ft. Obviously, the height of the snow line depends not alone on temperature, but also on the amount of snowfall, for if the snowfall is sufficiently heavy a permanent snow cover may prevail even where the average summer temperatures are above freezing.

Sleet is frozen or partly frozen rain and appears as particles of clear ice. *Glazed frost* is actually not a form of precipitation but is the accumulation of a coating of ice on surface objects. Fortunately it is not of common occurrence, for the so-called ice storm that produces glazed frost is one of the most destructive of the cool-season weather types. It occurs when supercooled rain or drizzle strikes surface objects and is immediately converted into ice. The weight of the ice accumulation may become so great that trees are often wrecked; telephone, telegraph, and electric wires are broken and their poles snapped off. *Rime* is composed of white layers of ice crystals deposited on windward edges or points of objects, generally in supercooled fog or mist. *Hail*, although the heaviest and largest unit form of precipitation existing in solid form, is almost exclusively the product of vigorous convection such as characterizes thunderstorms, which in turn are features of the warm season. Hailstones are composed of concentric layers, or shells, of clear ice alternating with opaque layers of partially melted and refrozen snow.

TYPES OF AIR ASCENT AND PRECIPITATION RESULTING

It already has been noted that rising air cools and that, if the temperature of sufficiently large masses of humid air is reduced well below the dew point, abundant condensation, and probably precipitation, will result. It remains now to analyze the conditions under which large masses of air may be caused to ascend. Three types of ascent and the precipitation characteristics associated with each will be noted. It needs to be emphasized, however, that the three ways of causing air to be lifted are not mutually exclusive, so that precipitation is not necessarily the result of one form of ascent. In reality, most of the earth's precipitation is the result of two or more causes of lifting rather than of one.

159. Convectional Precipitation. As a result of the heating of surface air it expands and is forced to rise by the cooler, heavier air above and around it. Ordinarily such rising air, since it cools at nearly double the rate of the normal vertical temperature decrease, will rise only a few thousand feet before its temperature has been reduced to the point where it is the same as that of the surrounding air. At that point where the rising air reaches air strata of its own temperature and density, further ascent ceases. But if abundant condensation begins before this stage is reached, then heat of condensation is released, so that, with this added source of energy, the rising air will be forced to ascend much higher before reaching atmospheric strata of its own temperature. Thus on a hot, humid summer afternoon, when surface heating is intense and condensation abundant, the towering cumulonimbus clouds resulting from convectional ascent may be several miles in vertical depth, and precipitation from them may be copious. Convectional ascent due to diurnal heating over land is usually associated with the warm season of the year and the warm hours of the day. Clearing toward evening is characteristic. If the convection is caused by the advection of air toward warmer regions, the daytime concentration of rainfall is less obvious. Since it is essentially a vertical movement of warm, humid air, cooling is rapid, and the rainfall resulting is likely to be in the form of heavy showers. Because a cumulonimbus cloud usually covers only a relatively small area, it quickly drifts by, so that the associated shower is not of long duration.

Convectional rain, because it comes frequently in the form of heavy showers, is less effective for crop growth, since much of it, instead of entering the soil, goes off in the form of surface drainage. This is a genuine menace to plowed fields, since soil removal through slope wash and gullying is likely to be serious. On the other hand, for the middle and higher latitudes, convectional rain, since it occurs in the warm season of the year when vegetation is active and crops are growing, comes at the most strategic time. Moreover, it provides the maximum rainfall with the minimum amount of cloudiness.

Of a somewhat different origin is rainfall resulting from the overrunning of warm and less dense air by colder, denser currents aloft. When warm, moist air is thus entrapped below an overrunning cold wedge, extremely steep lapse rates and accompanying instability are the result. Severe storms are sometimes associated with the vigorous overturning that takes place when the colder, heavier air sinks to earth, forcing the warm air to rise, often violently. Heavy downpours may result.

Without doubt a considerable part of the earth's precipitation is from conditionally unstable and convectively unstable air in which convection is associated with other forms of ascent. Since such air is originally stable and remains so until after condensation level has been reached, it requires an initial lifting through horizontal convergence or by some obstacle such as a mountain range or a cold wedge of air to bring it to the stage of instability. After this stage has been attained, convective ascent carries the conditionally and convectively unstable air to still higher levels, with further cooling resulting in continuing condensation and probably showery precipitation. Rainfall from conditionally and convectively unstable air clearly is of complex origin, involving, in addition to convection, orographic and frontal (cyclonic) genesis. Much convectional precipitation, therefore, is not the result of simple surface heating, but is associated with the lifting of air in convergences, along fronts separating unlike air masses, and in the vicinity of orographic barriers.

160. Orographic Precipitation. Air also may be forced to rise when landform barriers, such as mountain ranges, plateau escarpments, or even high hills, lie athwart the paths of deep and extensive air masses. Since water vapor is largely confined to the lower layers of atmosphere and rapidly decreases in amount upward, heavy orographic rainfall is the result of such forced ascent of air, associated with the blocking effect of landform obstacles. Witness, for

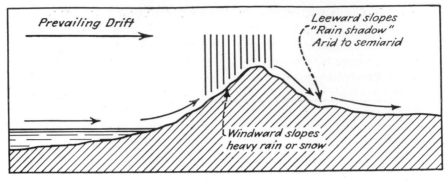

FIG. 3.16.

example, the very abundant precipitation along the western, or windward, flanks of the Cascade Mountains in Washington and Oregon, along parts of the precipitous east coast of Brazil which lies in the trades, or bordering the abrupt west coast of India which the westerly currents of the summer monsoon meet practically at right angles. The *leeward* sides of such mountain barriers, where the air is descending and warming, are characteristically drier. This is called the *rain shadow* (Fig. 3.16). The blocking effect of a mountain is normally felt at some distance out in front of the abrupt change in slope, the approaching wind riding up over a mass of stagnant air along its front. The belt of heaviest orographic rainfall along a mountain front usually is not far above the point where precipitation begins, although its elevation varies with the season, exposure, and latitude. The ideal condition for producing heavy orographic rainfall is when a high and relatively continuous mountain barrier lies close to a coast, and the winds from off a warm ocean meet the barrier at right angles. Orographic rains have less seasonal and daily periodicity than do those of convectional origin. In monsoon regions, very naturally, the maximum is at the time when air is moving from sea to land, usually high sun, or summer. In other regions the strength of the winds, the angle at which they meet the mountain barrier, or the contrast between land and water temperatures may determine the season of maximum orographic rainfall.

It seems likely, however, that a large part of the precipitation associated with highlands is not solely the result of the direct forced ascent of the prevailing winds. In other words, it is not purely orographic in type but instead is highly complex in origin. Certainly of great importance are such indirect effects as (*a*) the production of daytime convectional currents up mountain slopes and valleys as a result of strong convectional heating; (*b*) the "pinching" or "blocking" effect upon cyclonic storms; (*c*) orographically conditioned convergence in horizontal currents; and (*d*) the providing of a trigger effect that gives the initial upthrust to conditionally or convectively unstable air masses. Sometimes only a slight amount of lifting is necessary to bring such air masses to the condensation level, after which as a result of added heat of condensation they become unstable and buoyant and so continue to rise, yielding abundant rainfall. Thus highlands of less than 3,000 ft. elevation, although probably inducing no great amount of purely orographic precipitation, may by these indirect means become much rainier areas than the surrounding lowlands.

Recently it has been pointed out that even the frictional effects of coastal land areas that are relatively low in elevation may produce a convergence and lifting effect upon onshore air masses such as to cause increased precipitation along coasts that are not distinctly elevated.[1]

161. Convergent, Frontal, and Cyclonic Precipitation. Where convergence exists in the

[1] Tor Bergeron, The Problem of Artificial Control of Rainfall on the Globe, II, The Coastal Orographic Maximum of Precipitation in Autumn and Winter, *Tellus*, Vol. 1, No. 3, pp. 15–32, August, 1949.

horizontal flow of thick and extensive masses of the atmosphere, a slow upward movement of air must result. Such slow ascent of air in a convergence zone, such as that which occurs in the surface low-pressure trough near the equator, tends to increase the instability of the lifted air and as a consequence make it more conducive to the development of cumulus clouds and showery precipitation. Areas of horizontal convergence and lifting, therefore, are in general likely to provide conditions favorable to the development of clouds and precipitation.

In many convergent areas, especially those of the middle latitudes, the converging air masses are likely to be characterized by contrasting temperatures and densities, so that true density fronts may be formed in the zone of air-mass conflict. Where two horizontally converging air masses of contrasting temperatures and densities meet, the warmer and less dense air mass is forced to ascend over the colder, denser air along a mildly inclined surface of discontinuity (Fig. 3.17).

Some of the most common convergent and frontal areas are to be found associated with moving low-pressure vortex storms called depressions, or cyclones, and with atmospheric waves. Unlike convectional ascent, which involves direct vertical lifting, along fronts and in cyclones the warmer air more often rises obliquely, and therefore slowly, along mildly inclined surfaces of colder, denser air, and cooling as a consequence is less rapid. As a result of the slower ascent and cooling, precipitation in cyclones is characteristically less violent than in thunderstorms and is inclined to be more widespread, steadier, and longer continued. The dull, gray overcast skies and drizzly precipitation of the cooler months in middle latitudes, producing some of the most unpleasant weather of those seasons, are usually associated with fronts and cyclones. When overrunning of warm surface air by cooler currents aloft occurs heavier downpours may occur. Cyclonic storms and their associated fronts are most numerous and best developed during the cool season. Where they dominate weather conditions, therefore, they tend to produce fall or winter maxima in precipitation curves. Most of the winter precipitation of lowlands in the middle latitudes is primarily cyclonic, or frontal, in origin, although convection is also involved when the displaced air mass is conditionally or convectively unstable. In the tropics, as well as in the middle latitudes, cyclones are important generators of precipitation. It bears repeating that horizontal convergence of air masses and consequent ascent are characteristic of all low-pressure storms, whether in low or in middle latitudes.

NOTE: The last major topic in this chapter, dealing with the distribution of precipitation over the earth, may well be postponed for study until after completion of the following chapters on air masses and storms. Unless one is acquainted with the characteristics and distribution of the more important types of rain-bringing storms—thunderstorms, cyclones, and hurricanes—precipitation distribution is apt to be much less intelligible.

Distribution of Precipitation

160. Important Precipitation Data. At least three items concerning precipitation of a region are of outstanding importance: (*a*) its total average amount, or depth, for the year (Fig. 3.19); (*b*) its seasonal periodicity; and (*c*) its dependability, both annual and seasonal.

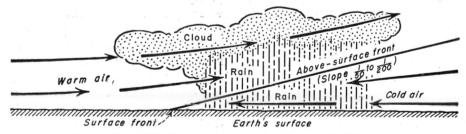

FIG. 3.17. Illustrating the origin of frontal rainfall.

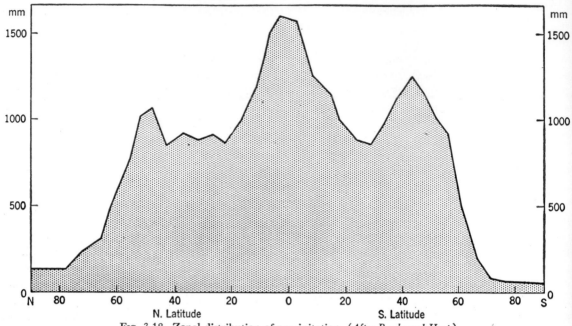

FIG. 3.18. Zonal distribution of precipitation. (*After Brooks and Hunt.*)

163. *The amount of annual rainfall* varies widely over the earth, numerous stations recording on the average less than 5 in., while there are a few where it exceeds 400 in. It is this total average yearly amount of rainfall which usually receives the principal attention, although this practice cannot be defended. Geographically speaking, the fact that Omaha, Neb., receives 30 in. of rainfall annually is no more significant than the fact that 17.4 in. (58 per cent) falls during the months from May to August and only 3.3 in. (11 per cent) falls during the period November to February.

164. *Seasonal distribution of precipitation* becomes of greatest importance in the middle latitudes where there is a dormant season for plant growth imposed by low temperatures, *i.e.*, the winter season. In the tropics where frost is practically unknown except at higher elevations, rainfall is effective for plant growth no matter at what time of year it falls. In the middle latitudes, however, only that proportion of the annual precipitation which falls during the frost-free season may be effective. In the more severe climates a strong concentration of rainfall in the warmer months when plants can use it is desirable. Time of occurrence, therefore, is coequal

in importance with the amount of rainfall.

165. *The dependability*, or reliability, of the annual or seasonal precipitation is an expression of its variability (Fig. 8.2). Data on rainfall reliability are scarcely less important than those concerned with amount and seasonal distribution. Variability may be defined as the deviation from the mean computed from 35 years or more of observations. In humid climates the annual variability is usually not greater than 50 per cent on either side of the mean, *i.e.*, the driest year may have about 50 per cent of the normal value, while the wettest year may have 150 per cent. In dry climates these values vary between about 30 and 250 per cent. It is the general rule that variability increases as the amount of rainfall decreases. It is an inverse ratio. Variability of precipitation must be taken into consideration when agricultural plans are made, for it is only normal that there will be years when the precipitation is less than average. In semiarid and subhumid climates where crop raising normally depends on a small margin of safety, variability is of utmost concern. Moreover, the agriculturist in such regions must bear in mind that negative deviations from the mean are more frequent than positive ones, which indicates that a greater

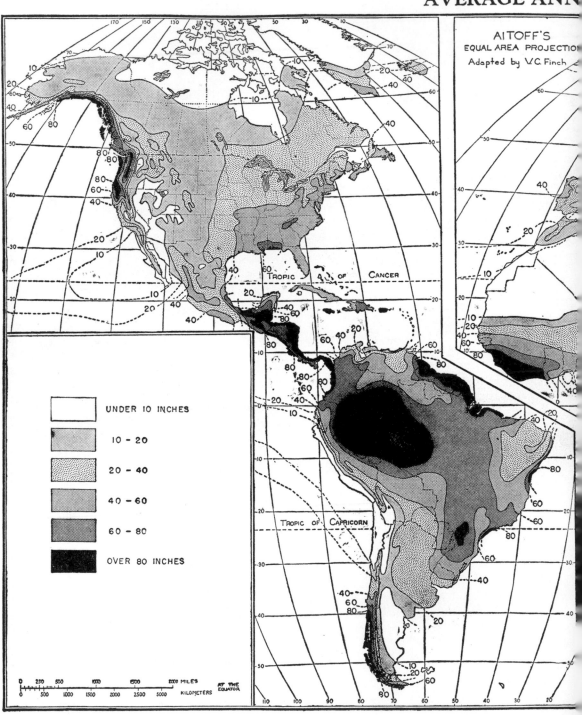

AITOFF'S
EQUAL AREA PROJECTION
Adapted by V.C. Finch

UNDER 10 INCHES

10 - 20

20 - 40

40 - 60

60 - 80

OVER 80 INCHES

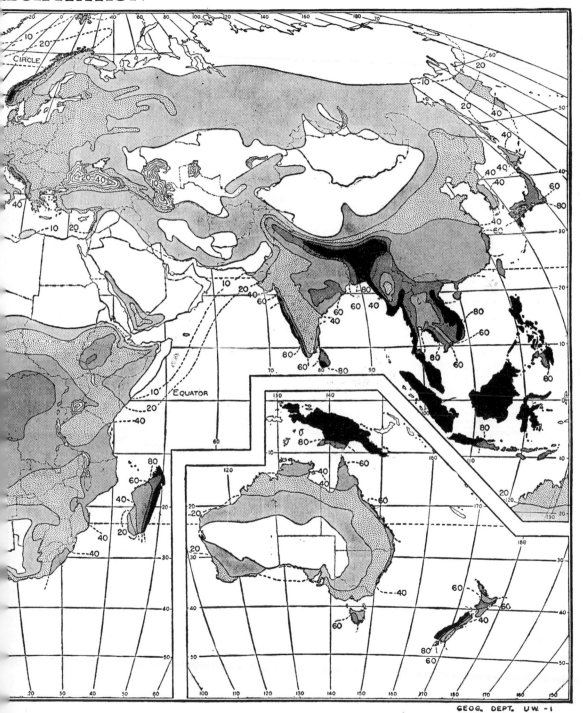

GEOG. DEPT. U.W. -1

number of dry years are compensated for by a few excessively wet ones. Variability of seasonal and monthly amounts is even greater than that for annual values.

166. *Intensity and Probability.* There are many other types of useful precipitation data, although most of them are probably of less value than the three mentioned previously. For example, the number of rainy days (defined as one having at least 0.01 in. of rainfall) compared with the total amount of annual rainfall is an indication of the way the rain falls, or its *intensity*. At London, England, the annual rainfall of about 25 in. is spread over 164 rainy days which indicates a lower intensity than the conditions at Cherrapunji, India, where 440 in. falls in 159 days. The probability of rainy days is a kind of data which has considerable value to such people as farmers and resort owners. This may be readily computed by dividing the number of rainy days in a month or a year by the total number of days.

167. Zonal Rainfall Pattern. Practically all the precipitation of the earth is the result of cooling of ascending air masses. Since the great zones of horizontal convergence of winds are also regions of large-scale lifting of thick and extensive air masses, one might expect these zones of convergent air to show up as belts of maximum precipitation on a meridional profile of world rainfall (Fig. 3.18), and so they do, as will be described later. However, there are reasons for ascent of air other than horizontal convergence, such as (a) the windward sides of highlands and (b) local convectional systems which result from diurnal surface heating. These latter influences are not distributed over the earth in a zonal pattern as are the belts of horizontal convergence, and hence they tend to modify and complicate any zonal arrangement of rainfall belts.

World rainfall distribution in reality is very complicated and no single explanation will suffice, for while most precipitation results from the lifting and cooling of thick air masses, the amount of rainfall resulting from the lifting also depends upon the nature of the air being lifted, especially whether it is dry or moist, and the nature of its vertical stratification as it relates to temperature and moisture. Precipitation distribution consequently is associated not only with regions favoring ascent, but also is influenced by such items as (a) the maritime or continental origin of prevailing air masses and (b) the seasonal shift of the zonal pressure and wind belts.

To summarize, it may be stated that there are three primary controls affecting precipitation distribution: (a) the great latitudinal zones of horizontal atmospheric convergence and divergence, (b) the distribution of land and water, and (c) highlands. The first control named is chiefly important in affecting the zonal pattern of rainfall distribution, while the other two operate in such a way as to produce modifications in the zonal pattern (Fig. 3.19).

The average yearly precipitation for the whole earth is estimated to be 975 mm., or about 39 in., which represents a total volume of water of $4,971 \times 10^{11}$ cubic meters. Over the lands where the humidity of the continental air is less, the yearly precipitation is estimated to be only about 26 in., while over the much more extensive oceans the comparable figure is 44 in.

A meridional profile of average annual rainfall amounts, showing the means for different parallels around the entire earth and consequently including precipitation over both continents and oceans, suggests some of the most fundamental facts of rainfall distribution. Figure 3.18 is such a profile. To be sure much is omitted in such a meridional profile which emphasizes only zonal features of distribution, for it shows none of the variations in amount of rainfall in an east-west direction, *i.e.*, along a parallel. Figure 3.18 indicates the existence of a strong primary maximum (70 to 80 in.) of precipitation in a belt about 10° wide in the vicinity of the equator, the region of the great intertropical convergence and of warm, humid air masses. From the equator amounts decline poleward in each hemisphere and belts of lower rainfall are noted at latitudes 20 to 30°N. and S. Here the average rainfall is only 32 to 36 in. These are the latitudes of the great subtropical anticyclones with their diverging system of winds and associated vertical subsidence. Since these are the latitudes in which some of the earth's great deserts are located, it may seem odd that the average zonal rainfall is not lower than it is. It must be kept in mind, however, that the western sides of the subtropical highs are far from being dry, and these heavier rainfalls tend to raise the average for the subtropical latitudes as a whole. Poleward from the subtropics rainfall again increases and secondary maxima with an average precipitation of 40 to 50 in. are indicated for latitudes 45 to 55°. This is the region of the middle-latitude convergence with which is associated the polar front and its belt of maximum cyclonic activity. The average zonal rainfall in the Northern Hemisphere in these latitudes is less than it is in the Southern Hemisphere because of the extensive interior deserts in Eurasia and North America. This effect is particularly emphasized if the land rainfall alone is considered for which there is no middle-latitude maximum in the Northern Hemisphere (Fig. 3.18). Poleward from about latitude 50 to 55° precipitation declines sharply so that an absolute zonal minimum of less than 10 in. is reached in the cold regions of the very high latitudes beyond about the 75° parallel.

Although the total amount of the annual precipitation is about the same in the Northern and Southern Hemispheres, some contrasts in zonal distribution may be observed. The most conspicuous difference is the higher precipitation amount from 0 to 10°N. as compared with 0 to 10°S. This reflects the fact that the intertropical convergence is mostly located north of the equator throughout the year. The secondary maximum of precipitation at about latitudes 40 to 60° is considerably higher in the Southern Hemisphere than in the Northern Hemisphere, which is explainable by the much larger proportion of ocean in these latitudes in the Southern Hemisphere.

The second principal factor affecting zonal rainfall amounts is the distribution of oceans and continents. For the earth as a whole the average amount of precipitation is much higher over the oceans than over the continents, the respective figures being about 44 in. as compared with 26 in. Taking into consideration the fact that

71 per cent of the earth's surface is water and only 29 per cent land, it has been computed that only 19 per cent of the earth's total annual precipitation by weight falls on land surfaces and 81 per cent on water. It is in the Northern Hemisphere, where there is a more equal distribution of land and water areas, that the zonal patterns of rainfall distribution for oceans and continents are most in contrast. Continental rainfall, for example, shows no secondary middle-latitude maximum north of the equator, while this same zonal maximum is very sharp over the oceans.

168. Zonal Variations in Seasonal Rainfall. Figure 3.20 is a diagrammatic representation of the principal zones of convergence and divergence associated with the general atmospheric circulation. Parts A and B indicate the maximum latitudinal displacement of the several elements of the circulation such as would occur at the extreme seasons. Figure 3.20C purports to show the zonal belts of rainfall such as would result from a regular north-south migration of the zonal elements of the circulation. It is worthy of study, even though it is inadequate, for it is incapable of showing those important seasonal variations in precipitation which are the result of longitudinal differences in the atmospheric circulation pattern and of such terrestrial influences as land and water contrasts and highlands.

The zonal pattern of seasonal rainfall variations is most conspicuous in the tropics (Figs 3.20, 3.21). In the subtropics and middle latitudes, the contrasts in a longitudinal direction, especially over the continents, tend to cancel out each other in the zonal averages. In the very low latitudes near the equator, rainfall is abundant and falls throughout the year so that there is no dry season (Fig. 3.20C, Zone 1). From about latitude 10° out to 15 or 20°, there is a decreasing amount of rainfall and characteristically the high-sun period, or summer, is wet and winter is dry (Zones 2 and 3). Zone 4, shown in Fig. 3.20C as dry in all seasons, is not the prevailing situation around the earth in subtropical latitudes, for the anticyclones and their associated subsidence and drought are not continuous. Zones 5 and 6 for which a winter maximum i

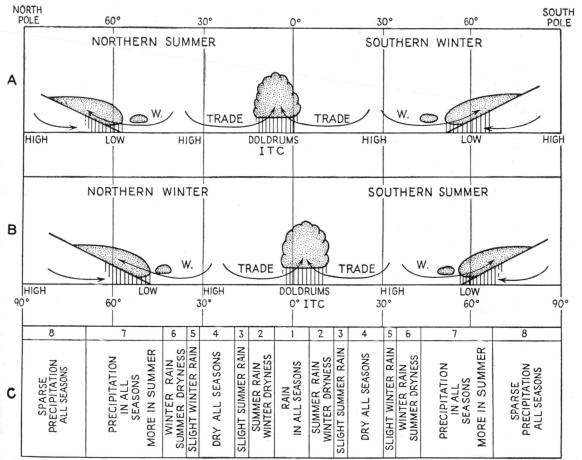

FIG. 3.20. Schematic cross section through the atmosphere showing the main zones of ascending and descending motion; *A*, during the northern summer; *B*, during the northern winter; *C*, zones of precipitation. Many nonzonal features of the earth's rainfall distribution cannot be represented on this type of diagram. (*From Petterssen, "Introduction to Meteorology," McGraw-Hill Book Company, Inc., New York.*)

indicated are explained by assuming that these latitudes are influenced by the drought-producing subtropical anticyclones in summer and the polar-front convergence in winter. This condition is likely to prevail toward the western margins of most of the continents in these subtropical latitudes, and in the Mediterranean Sea region it extends far interior, but as a zonal mean the winter maximum probably does not exist. Poleward of the subtropics, zonal variations in seasonal rainfall are not distinct, and it is for this reason that Zones 7 and 8 are described only as having rainfall throughout the year. In the middle latitudes of the Southern Hemisphere, where the earth's surface is predominantly water, and

in similar latitudes over the Northern Hemisphere oceans, the cooler months ordinarily show a maximum of precipitation. However, the reverse is the case for the Northern Hemisphere continents.[1]

169. Nonzonal Aspects of Seasonal Rainfall Distribution. *Latitudes 20 to 30°.* In the preceding section objection was offered to designating latitudes 20 to 30° as zonal belts which are dry throughout the year (Zone 4, Fig. 3.20*C*). These

[1] C. E. P. Brooks and Theresa M. Hunt, The Zonal Distribution of Rainfall over the Earth, *Mem. Roy. Meteorological Soc.*, Vol. 3, No. 28, 1930.

Fritz Möller, Vierteljahrskarten des Niederschlags für die ganze Erde, *Petermann's geograph. Mitt.*, Vol. 95, pp. 1–7, 1951.

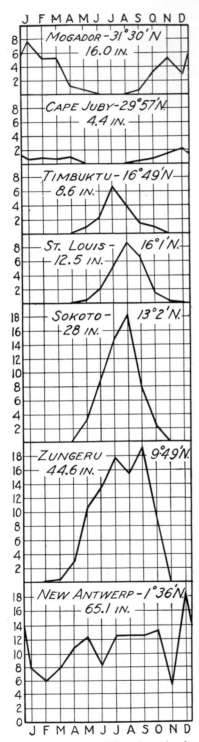

FIG. 3.21. Illustrating rainfall regimes in the low latitudes (Africa) north of the equator. The stations are arranged according to latitude with Nouvelle Anvers (New Antwerp) closest to the equator.

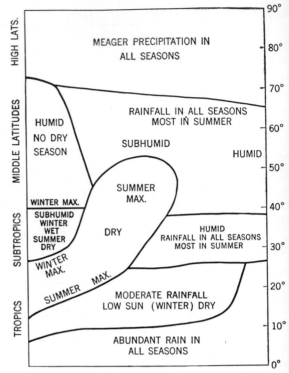

FIG. 3.22. Distribution of precipitation types on a hypothetical continent.

latitudes 20 to 30° in each hemisphere are the regions of the subtropical anticyclones which are the cause of lower average zonal rainfall than in regions farther north and farther south. Moreover, these are the latitudes of the great tropical and subtropical deserts such as the Sahara and Kalahari in Africa, the Australian Desert, Arabia, dry southwestern United States and northwestern Mexico, and the Peruvian–north Chilean Desert. However, the fact that the belts contained between parallels 20 and 30°N. and S. have an average zonal rainfall of 30 to 35 in. indicates that some longitudes within these belts must be genuinely humid. The dry or desert conditions within these belts are especially well developed in those *eastern* and *central* parts of the subtropical anticyclones where upper-level subsidence is particularly strong. This includes the *western* parts of the continents in these latitudes (15 to 30°) and the oceans adjacent (Fig. 3.22).

But toward the *eastern* sides of the continents and the western parts of oceans in these same latitudes where subsidence aloft is less marked, the air actually has an ascending component, and the air masses are warmer and more humid and rainfall is relatively abundant. Moreover, the eastern sides of continents are the windward sides, being constantly under the influence of maritime air masses associated with the tropical easterlies or trades. Although found in the same latitudes as the tropical dry type, these rainy eastern sides of the continents represent a totally different rainfall type. In the zonal arrangement shown on Fig. 3.20C this humid tropical type of latitudes 15 to 30° is not shown (see Fig. 3.22). Perhaps it may be considered as simply a poleward extension of the tropical rainy types.

In the middle latitudes, where the polar-front convergence with its numerous cyclones is a principal cause of precipitation, seasonal rainfall distribution is less zonal than longitudinal.

170. *The Subtropics* (30 to 40°N. and S.). A Mediterranean type is the one which is most clearly distinguishable. It is located along the western margins of the land masses in an intermediate position (latitudes 30 to 40°) between the middle-latitude convergence zone with its fronts and cyclonic storms on the poleward side and the dry subtropical anticyclones farther equatorward (Figs. 3.22, 3.23(a)). It is a subhumid rainfall type in which the winters are rainy and the summers are dry (Fig. 3.20C,

Zone 6). The wet winters coincide with the equatorward migration following the sun of the middle-latitude storm belt in the westerlies, while the aridity of summer is associated with the poleward retreat of the storm belt and the reestablishment of anticyclonic control with its strong upper-air subsidence (Fig. 3.21, Mogador).

The eastern sides of the continents in these same subtropical latitudes (30 to 40°), however, are very different in their precipitation characteristics (Fig. 3.23(b)). Normally, they have more rainfall than the western sides and in addition the winter maximum and summer drought have entirely disappeared. Here it is the western margins of the subtropical anticyclones with their unstable air masses which are in control, so that rain falls throughout the year and summers with their tendency to onshore monsoon winds are likely to have more precipitation than winters.

171. *Latitudes Poleward of* 40°. The *western*, or windward, side of continents in the westerlies (poleward from about 40°) are distinctly marine in character. Normally, they have adequate or even abundant precipitation, the amount depending in part upon the elevation of the land along the coast. The absence of a genuinely dry season is characteristic, there being adequate rain throughout the year (Figs. 3.22, 3.24(a)). Along the immediate coasts there is commonly

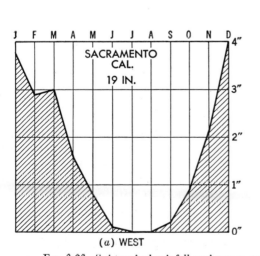

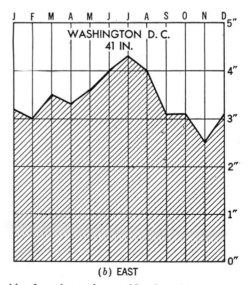

FIG. 3.23. Subtropical rainfall regimes; *a*, west side of continent; *b*, east side of continent.

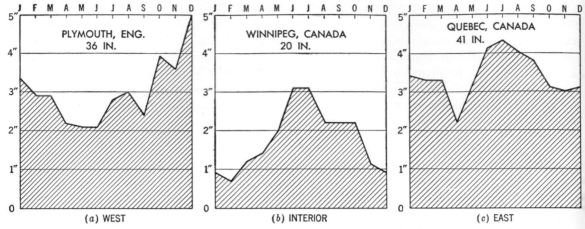

Fig. 3.24. Middle-latitude rainfall regimes.

a winter maximum of precipitation. This is a characteristic feature of oceanic climates in middle latitudes and is associated with the intensified cyclonic activity in the cooler seasons.[1] Since these regions are within the middle-latitude convergence zone, much of the rainfall of west-coast lowlands is frontal in origin. Where coasts are bordered by highlands, heavy orographic rains are added to those of cyclonic, or frontal, origin.

Interiors of continents in the middle latitudes are drier than either the western or the eastern margins. This is to be expected, since the centers of land masses are farther away from oceans, the major sources of atmospheric moisture. The normal succession of rainfall amounts from coasts to interior is humid, subhumid, semiarid, and arid. The emphasis is upon too little rainfall rather than too much. Although there is precipitation at all seasons (Fig. 3.20C, Zone 7), summer is likely to have more than winter in these continental climates (Figs. 3.22, 3.24(*b*)). The summer maximum is a distinctive feature of land-controlled climates. This fact is associated with (*a*) the low winter air temperatures which reduce the possible water-vapor capacity, (*b*) the greater prevalence of anticyclones in winter at

the time of greatest cold, and (*c*) the tendency toward monsoonal outflows of continental air in the winter season. In summer, on the other hand, surface heating causes greater convective activity, the warm air has a higher moisture capacity, strong anticyclones are less pronounced, and there is a tendency toward a monsoonal indraft of warm, humid air from the oceans.

Even though they are on the leeward side of continents in the westerlies, the *eastern* margins of large continents in middle latitudes are characteristically humid. This fact is associated with (*a*) the location of major frontal zones and regions of cyclogenesis in close proximity to the eastern sides of both North America and Asia and (*b*) the tendency toward monsoonal indrafts of warm, humid maritime air in summer. When the monsoon control is extraordinarily well developed and continental cyclones are fewer, as is the case in eastern Asia, precipitation shows a marked summer maximum. On the other hand, where monsoons are less dominant and cyclonic control is better developed, as in eastern North America, there is rainfall throughout the year and a less emphatic seasonal periodicity (Fig. 3.24(*c*)). Summer rains are both cyclonic and convectional. In winter, precipitation is largely cyclonic or frontal. Dry Patagonia, in the rain shadow of the Andes and lacking in monsoons, is the noteworthy exception to humid eastern margins of middle-latitude continents.

[1] Bergeron suggests that the frictional effects of a land surface upon on-shore winds in winter may cause convergence and lifting of the air, with a resulting coastal maximum of precipitation. In this connection, see Tor Bergeron, The Coastal Orographic Maximum of Precipitation in Autumn and Winter, *Tellus*, Vol. 1, No. 3, pp. 15–31, 1949.

Precipitation in the very high latitudes is characteristically meager, owing to the low temperatures and to the anticyclonic circulation. The maximum precipitation probably occurs during the season of least cold, since at that time there is more moisture in the air and cyclonic influence can penetrate deeper (Fig. 3.20, Zone 8).

172. Effects of Highlands on Precipitation. Next to the distribution of land and water, highlands are the greatest control of nonzonal rainfall distribution over the earth. Along windward sides of highlands extensive and thick air masses may be forced to ascend, resulting in greatly increased precipitation. Highlands, therefore, are usually coincident with areas of increased precipitation. This relationship is readily observable on the annual rainfall map (Fig. 3.19). Leeward from highlands, however, where there is a descending movement of the air, precipitation is likely to be below normal. As indicated in an earlier section, the heavier precipitation associated with highlands is far more complex in origin than had formerly been suspected. At least a part of it appears to be associated with orographically induced convergence, frictional effects, and convective turbulence.

The amount of precipitation increases with altitude, at least up to a certain elevation. In the tropics it appears to be fairly well established that there is a zone of maximum precipitation in highlands, beyond which, as a result of the decreased temperature and moisture content of the air, the increase ceases and a decrease sets in. Such a zone of maximum precipitation is less in evidence in middle-latitude highlands, although this is still something of a controversial topic.

173. The diurnal variation in precipitation is a relatively complicated phenomenon although two general types may be recognized, viz., (a) the continental type and (b) the maritime type. Over land masses more of the rainfall is likely to occur in the warmer hours of the day when thermal convection is at a maximum. By contrast, oceans tend to experience a maximum of precipitation during the night or early morning when there is the greatest instability in the maritime air (Fig. 1.22). The most striking midday maximum over land masses occurs during the summer season in middle latitudes and throughout the tropics where the intensity of insolation is greatest. The surface temperature of oceans, unlike those of continents in summer, changes very little from day to night and as a result the surface air also changes little in temperature. At some distance above the ocean surface where the air temperature is largely controlled by radiation the atmosphere is warmer by day and cooler by night so that the lapse rate is steepest at night and convective activity consequently greater. The above generalizations are illustrated in the table showing the diurnal variation in the amount of precipitation for Valencia, Ireland, a marine station in middle latitudes, Pavlovsk, U.S.S.R., a continental station, and San José, Costa Rica, located in the tropics.

Diurnal Variation in Precipitation, in Thousandths of Total Amount
(After Köppen)

Place	Hours					
	0–4	4–8	8–12	12–16	16–20	20–24
Valentia, Ireland, 52°N.	181	183	160	149	162	163
Pavlovsk, U.S.S.R., 60°N.	148	156	144	201	185	157
San José, Costa Rica, 10°N.	13	6	44	342	485	84

SELECTED REFERENCES FOR FURTHER STUDY OF TOPICS CONTAINED IN CHAPTER 3[1]

1. Atmospheric humidity and condensation. Willett, 1941, 71–99; Byers, 106–160; Blair, 38–60; Petterssen, "Introduction to Meteorology," 43–46, 49–67; Haurwitz and Austin, 83–96; "Compendium of Meteorology," 165–175, 192–197, 199–205, 1179–1189.

2. Precipitation: origin and kinds. "Compendium of Meteorology," 175–179; Petterssen, "Introduction

[1] For complete titles of reference books, see pp. 5–6.

to Meteorology," 46–48; Petterssen, "Weather Analysis and Forecasting," 43–47.

a. Distribution. Blair, 111–127; Petterssen, "Introduction to Meteorology," 207–211; Haurwitz and Austin, 64–83; Brooks, C. E. P., and Hunt, Theresa M. The Zonal Distribution of Rainfall over the Earth, *Mem. Roy. Meteorological Soc. (Great Britain)*, Vol. 3, No. 28, pp. 139–154, 1930; Möller, Fritz. Vierteljahrskarten des Niederschlags für die ganze Erde, *Petermann's Geograph. Mitt.*, Vol. 95, pp. 1–7, 1951.

b. Artificial production of precipitation. "Compendium of Meteorology," 235–241; Bergeron, T. The Problem of Artificial Control of Rainfall on the Globe, *Tellus*, Vol. 1, No. 1, pp. 32–43, 1949; Elliott, Robert D. Increasing Precipitation through Cloud Seeding, *Weatherwise*, Vol. 4, No. 4, pp. 88–90, August, 1951; Houghton, Henry G. An Appraisal of Cloud Seeding as a Means of Increasing Precipitation. *Bull. Am. Meteorological Soc.*, Vol. 32, No. 2, pp. 39–46, February, 1951.

CHAPTER 4: *Air Masses and Fronts*

Origin and Classification

174. Origin and Nature of Air Masses. An understanding of the origin and characteristics of air masses is essential to a comprehension of many of those atmospheric disturbances, or storms, which are the topic for discussion in the following chapter. These migratory disturbances, which are responsible for a large proportion of the earth's precipitation, characteristically develop along the contact zones between contrasting air masses, and the weather characteristics of such storms depend largely upon the nature of the interacting air masses. It is not only along the frontal or contact zones where migratory storms develop that air masses determine the weather, but also in those extensive areas dominated by a single air mass between the bounding frontal zones. Thus the prevailing air mass in any region largely determines that region's general weather. It becomes clear, therefore, that a knowledge of air mass types, their distributions, and the general locations of their contact zones is essential to an understanding of the regional climates of the continents which is the theme of Part II of this book.

It is worth emphasizing that the air-mass concept is in the nature of a refinement of the earth's wind system. Thus specific air masses are likely to be associated with a particular wind belt or belts. Maritime tropical air, for example, is characteristic chiefly of the trades but also of the intertropical convergence zone and the subtropical anticyclones. But likewise within the trades are found both tropical maritime and tropical continental air masses with quite different properties. And within the westerlies there can in certain places and at certain periods be discovered air of both tropical and polar as well as of continental and maritime origin. The discussion of the air masses of the earth which follows is, therefore, an amplification of the earlier discussion on winds (Chap. 2) and may be thought of as supplementary to it.

An air mass is a thick and extensive portion of the atmosphere whose temperature and humidity characteristics are approximately homogeneous in a horizontal direction at different levels. When in motion air masses are evident as large-scale currents of polar or tropical origin. These deep and extensive currents are the units of exchange by which the general circulation effects the transfer of heat from tropical to polar regions.

The weather characteristics of an air mass depend upon two basic properties: (*a*) its vertical temperature distribution and (*b*) its moisture content. Vertical temperature distribution indicates not only the general warmth or coldness of an air mass, as reflected in its surface temperatures, but also its stability characteristics. And since stability is closely associated with vertical movement within the air mass, it is evident that the distribution of moisture upward, the nature of the condensation forms, and the amount of precipitation are all related to this same item of vertical temperature distribution.

175. Source Regions. Extensive air masses such as appear on the daily weather map originate when the atmosphere remains sufficiently at rest over an extensive area of uniform surface for such a time that the air is able to acquire the temperature and moisture characteristics peculiar to the underlying surface. These extensive areas of the earth's surface where air masses develop are designated as *source regions*.

Since relative horizontal uniformity in temperature and moisture is the essential characteristic of an air mass, the ideal source region (a) should have a reasonably uniform surface and (b) the large-scale surface air movement should be light and divergent (anticyclonic) in character. An area of uneven terrain or one composed of both land and water surfaces is not satisfactory. Nor is one in which there is strong convergent air flow, for in most parts of the earth outside the inner tropics converging winds are likely to transport unlike temperatures toward the zone of convergence, resulting in steep temperature gradients. Anticyclonic circulations, on the other hand, with their subsidence and horizontal divergence tend to develop horizontal temperature uniformity. Examples of good source regions are the snow-covered arctic plains of North America and Eurasia in winter, the extensive subtropical and tropical oceans, and the Sahara in summer.

It is of greatest importance to note that air masses, once having formed over their source regions, do not long remain there. The necessity for a general atmospheric circulation requires that sooner or later a movement outward from the source region shall occur, so that the weather of invaded areas is bound to be affected. Such an extensive and horizontally homogeneous body of air is able to travel for long distances over the earth's surface from its region of origin and still retain many of the physical properties attained at its source. It is conservative in character. Because of its great size, and the slowness with which it is modified, it is possible to trace the movement of an air mass from day to day

and at the same time to note any gradual changes in it which are being induced by the new environment into which it is moving. Usually such changes are small and gradual compared with those which occur along the boundary zones that separate different air masses. When an air mass moves away from its source region, not only is it modified by the new environment, but it, in turn, modifies the weather of the region into which it is moving.

In addition to being influenced by the surfaces over which they move, and the different amounts of radiation which they receive, air masses are also greatly modified by vertical movements which occur within them. These profound modifications arising from subsidence and lifting within a thick air mass greatly complicate the use of air masses in climatological work.

176. Surfaces of Discontinuity and Fronts. When air masses having different properties in temperature and moisture are brought together, they do not mix freely with each other, but tend rather to remain separate with more or less distinct sloping boundary surfaces, called surfaces of discontinuity or fronts, between them (Fig. 4.1). The location of these boundary surfaces in the atmosphere and the nature of the contrasting air masses on either side of them are of great significance in weather analysis, for along such fronts most weather changes originate.

There are two conditions necessary for the formation of fronts, and unless both are operating simultaneously, frontogenesis cannot occur. These conditions are (a) the air masses separated by the front must have contrasting temperatures so that one is colder and denser than the other; (b) the atmospheric circulation is of such a nature that a convergent flow is present and the air masses are transported toward each other at the front line. The decay and disappearance of fronts is caused (a) whenever the temperature contrast between the air masses weakens and eventually disappears or (b) the wind system no longer brings about convergence of the air masses.

Surfaces of discontinuity, or fronts, are not mathematically abrupt transitions, but rather zones of appreciable width, within which

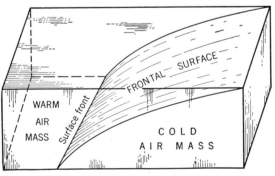

FIG. 4.1. Three-dimensional representation of an atmospheric front.

changes in the weather elements are much more rapid than within the air masses themselves. Marked changes in temperature and humidity usually can be observed as one crosses such an air-mass boundary zone. Most of all the front represents a temperature discontinuity, for it is chiefly through temperature contrasts that differences in air-mass densities are maintained. The width of fronts varies between about 3 and 50 miles. Because of turbulence that causes mixing of the air on either side of the front, these discontinuity zones cannot be narrower than about 3 miles, and if they are wider than 50 miles they are better called zones of transition than fronts. In a very narrow front between a warm tropical and a fresh, cold polar air mass, the temperature gradient is very steep, occasionally amounting to 20 to 30° within a distance of 5 miles.

It might be expected that the surface of discontinuity separating two contrasting air masses would be horizontal, just as would be the case with oil and water in a tank, where the former less dense fluid would overlie the latter. Because forces other than gravity (chief of which is the deflective force of earth rotation) are acting upon atmospheric currents, two unlike air masses may be separated by a sloping boundary in such a way that the cold air underlies the warm air in the form of a wedge, and still the air masses may be in equilibrium, i.e., with no vertical displacement. When for some reason the front is thrown out of equilibrium, vertical movement takes place. Where these sloping surfaces of discontinuity in the free atmosphere intersect the earth's surface, *surface fronts* are formed. The drawing of fronts on a weather map is simply a charting of these intersections.

It rarely happens that the discontinuity surfaces between unlike air masses will remain very long in a stationary condition. Usually one air mass begins to advance into the domain of the other so that the front itself begins to shift. Two principal types of fronts are recognized: (*a*) where there is an active upward ascent of lighter warm air over cold dense air; and (*b*) where there is a passive ascent of warm air over cold, owing to active underrunning and lifting

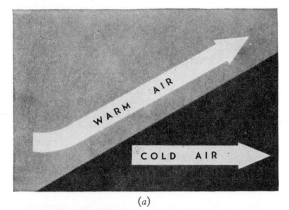

(a)

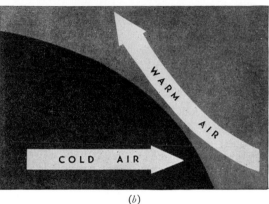

(b)

Fig. 4.2. Illustrating (*a*) warm and (*b*) cold fronts. (*Courtesy of the U.S. Weather Bureau.*)

by the cold air. These are the well-known *warm fronts* and *cold fronts* (Fig. 4.2). Their detailed analysis, and the types of weather characteristic of them will be postponed to the later chapter on storms.

The whole concept of fronts within the tropics is at present a topic about which there is much confusion and dispute.[1] In general, this has been the result of trying to apply to the low latitudes concepts of air masses and fronts developed for the middle and higher latitudes. Outside the tropics fronts are boundary areas separating air masses of contrasting densities resulting from temperature differences. Along such fronts pressure gradients have oppositely directed components so that there is a wind shift associated with the passage of the front, with accompanying changes in temperature and humidity. A

[1] See C. E. Palmer, "Tropical Meteorology," in "Compendium of Meteorology," pp. 859–880.

striking feature of these fronts is the occurrence of an organized system of clouds extending over immense horizontal distances.

But in the tropics there appear to be many wind shifts accompanied by extensive cloud development in which there are no appreciable temperature differences across the "fronts." Such zones of convergence in the tropics must differ in many respects from the density fronts of the middle latitudes, and their associated weather phenomena must be in contrast as well. The literature on tropical fronts and air masses published in the last 10 years, unfortunately, does little to clarify the picture.

CLASSIFICATION OF AIR MASSES

177. Basis of Classification. The attributes of an air mass which determine its characteristic weather features are largely acquired from its source region and to a less degree from those other influences which continue to modify the air mass as it moves away from its source region. Any useful classification of air masses must serve to express their weather characteristics and consequently must be based upon the nature of their source regions and the subsequent modifications to which they are subjected.

The primary air-mass source regions are either those of the high latitudes, or polar (P), or those of the low latitudes, or tropical (T). It is only in the high latitudes and low latitudes that extensive homogeneous surfaces characterized by light air movement can be found, and hence it is the polar and tropical (including subtropical) regions that provide the only true air-mass source regions. The middle latitudes are the scene of intense interaction between the air masses from polar and tropical latitudes and, hence, lack the uniformity of conditions essential to a source region. Nearly all air masses in middle latitudes if traced back to their source regions are found to be either polar or tropical. As polar air moves equatorward and tropical air moves poleward, each is gradually modified by the new environment encountered.

It may be noted in the primary classification of air masses into P and T, as suggested above, that arctic and equatorial air masses are not recognized as separate types as is done in some classifications. In order to keep the classification simple, arctic air is here considered to be only a modified form of polar continental air and equatorial air as unstable tropical air.

The polar and tropical air masses may be further subdivided into maritime (m) and continental (c) groups, depending upon whether they originated over oceans or over continents. The m or c symbol indicates whether the air mass left the source region with moist maritime characteristics so that condensation forms are likely, or whether it originated as a dry continental air mass in which condensation will be meager. When a continental air mass moves out over an ocean surface, it is transformed rapidly into a maritime air mass as a result of evaporation into the dry air mass. The transformation from m to c is ordinarily much slower since there is necessarily no immediate cause for the large-scale removal of moisture from a maritime air mass which moves inland over a continent. From what has been suggested above, it will be evident that there are four principal types of source regions and four corresponding principal air masses, viz., mP, cP, mT, and cT.

178. Modifications of Air Masses. At any particular locality the properties of an air mass depend not only on the nature of the source region but also on the modifications of the source properties which the air mass has experienced en route from the source region to the place of observation. These modifications may be of great importance in determining the nature of the weather which will occur within the air mass. Two principal types of air-mass modification are recognized: (a) those which are thermodynamic in origin and (b) those which are mechanical in origin. Actually these modifications do not occur separately but usually in combinations.

179. *Thermodynamic modifications* characteristically result from the transfer of heat between the bottom of an air mass and the surface over which it moves. The degree of modification depends upon the nature of the underlying surface, the trajectory or path of the air mass as it leaves its source, and the number of days it has traveled in arriving at the observation point. If an air mass moves over a surface that is warmer than its own ground temperature, there will be a consequent warming of the lower air layers which will result in an increased lapse rate with associated instability. This condition favors ascent of the heated lower air with the possibility of condensation and precipitation. There is a differential rate of heating with the maximum change occurring in the lower layers. Conversely, when an air mass moves over a surface that is colder than its own ground temperature, there is a chilling of the surface air, and the development of a surface inversion with a consequent increase in the stability of the air mass. Such a condition is opposed to the ascent of air and consequently also to the formation of clouds and precipitation. It is clear that polar air masses will most frequently experience the first type of modification, while tropical air masses will normally undergo the second type.

The above modifications of the source properties of an air mass are indicated by the letters W (warm) or K (cold, or *kalt*). The letter W indicates that the air mass is warmer than the underlying surface, while K shows that the air mass is colder than the underlying surface. It needs to be reemphasized that these designations offer no evidence as to whether the air mass has a high or low temperature but indicate only its relative temperature with respect to the surface beneath.

The depth to which the surface thermal influence extends up into the air mass depends on its W or K character. Since surface cooling tends to produce stability, vertical turbulence and convective transport are restricted, so that the W character or the chilling of the air is confined to a fairly shallow layer, usually the first few thousand feet. The K characteristic, in which an air mass is being warmed at the surface, by its convective nature usually extends to a much greater height. In an air mass which is moderately unstable aloft, there is almost no limit to which the surface convection and its attendant transport of water vapor can extend into the troposphere.

Further thermodynamic modification results from the addition of moisture to an air mass by evaporation from a moist underlying surface (particularly a water surface) or from raindrops which fall through the air mass from an overrunning air current. Turbulence and vertical convection will distribute the moisture through a moderately thick layer of the atmosphere. This is another way, in addition to a direct temperature increase, of adding heat to the lower atmosphere and increasing its instability, for the evaporated moisture represents potential energy in the form of heat of condensation.

180. *Mechanical air-mass modifications* of several kinds are also instrumental in causing stability changes. Turbulence resulting either from the frictional effects of the earth's surface or from thermal differences tends to mix the atmosphere vertically. By this means heat and moisture may be carried upward from the surface so that a thick layer of atmosphere is thereby modified.

Of greater importance, however, are the modifications of an air mass resulting from large-scale horizontal convergences and divergences which occur well above the earth's surface. Such circulations produce ascending and descending movements of air and thereby affect air-mass stratification. Horizontal divergence, or spreading, is associated with subsidence in the free atmosphere, and subsidence results in increased stability, which is opposed to condensation forms of a type leading to precipitation. By contrast, horizontal convergence is accompanied by ascent of air, a steepening of the lapse rate, a trend toward instability, and possibly cloud and precipitation. Consequently an air mass which is a part of an anticyclonic circulation with associated upper-air subsidence is thereby rendered more stable. Likewise, air which descends on the leeward side of a mountain barrier is made more stable by the subsidence. On the other hand, an air mass which enters a cyclonic circulation where convergence and lifting are dominant is made more unstable. Lifting over highlands has a similar effect. The changes described above mainly affect those parts of an air mass above the surface, or friction, layer and are likely to be independent of those other modifications resulting from surface heating or cooling. In order to represent air mass qualities associated with stability and instability conditions aloft, a fourth letter has been added to the air-mass classification symbol, viz.: *s* = stable air aloft; *u* = unstable air aloft. Under most conditions one can associate the *s* symbol with anticyclonic circulation and the *u* symbol with cyclonic circulation.

Based upon the elements of air-mass classification described above, the following diagrammatic representation of air-mass types is possible. *P* indicates polar, *T* tropical, *m* maritime, *c* continental, *K* heated from below, *W* cooled from below, *s* stable aloft, *u* unstable aloft.

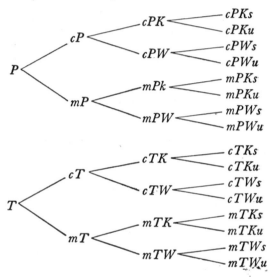

Sixteen possible air-mass types are represented on the above classification scheme, for each of which a brief written summary of the following types might be made:

cPWs—a cold, dry continental air mass whose lower layers are stable through cooling from below and whose upper strata are stable as a result of subsidence associated with anticyclonic circulation.

cPKu—a cold and unstable continental air mass whose instability is partly the result of surface heating and partly the result of ascent aloft associated with strong cyclonic circulation.

The *mP* air masses differ from *cP* mainly in their higher surface temperatures and larger moisture content. Tropical air masses are characterized by higher temperatures at all elevations and *mT* air by more moisture. *K*, *W*, *s*, and *u* have the same meaning when associated with tropical air as they do with polar air.

The World Pattern of Frontal Zones and Air Masses

Figures 4.3 and 4.4 attempt to give a very generalized picture of the distribution of the principal air masses and the average locations of the major fronts and zones of convergence at the two extreme seasons. (Compare with Figs. 2.21 and 2.22 showing resultant surface winds. See also the discussion of lines of convergence under the general topic of surface winds in Chap. 2.) It needs to be emphasized that these seasonal charts of air masses are a bird's-eye view at best, so that only the most conspicuous elements are represented. In addition they are able to show only *mean* positions of the frontal zones which are constantly shifting. At any particular time both frontal zones and air masses may occupy positions far removed from those shown on the charts.

181. Major Fronts. Three types of fronts are indicated on the Figs. 4.3 and 4.4. The *intertropical*, or *equatorial*, *front* (*ITF*, or *ITC*) is regarded as formed in the equatorial convergence zone where the trade winds from the Northern and Southern Hemispheres meet. There is a great deal of controversy regarding its nature and the literature on the subject is contradictory and bewildering. At most times the converging air masses along this front have very small temperature and density contrasts so that strong cyclonic development is not characteristic. Numerous weak cyclones are present, however. The *ITF* is more correctly designated a zone of convergence (*ITC*) than as a genuine density front. The *polar front* appears as a number of disconnected zones of convergence separating polar and tropical air masses. The mean position coincide with pressure troughs. Air-mass temperature contrasts are strongest along the polar front and cyclonic storms are numerous and well developed. Along the high-latitude *arctic* an *antarctic fronts* the converging air masses are polar in origin; in some places polar continental and polar maritime air are in conflict and in other places contrasting polar maritime air masses. Normally, the temperature contrasts are smaller than along the polar front and cyclogenesis is weaker. There is a tendency for the fronts to migrate with the seasonal shifts in solar energy, being farther poleward in summer than in winter.

A detailed analysis of seasonal air masses and fronts of the earth as a whole is purposely omitted at this point, for the climatic usefulness of these charts (Figs. 4.3 and 4.4) is more obvious as the topic of types of climate and the distribution of climates on the continents is discussed in a later section of the book. Only certain of the more obvious facts pertaining to world distribution are discussed at this point.

182. Tropical Air Masses and Fronts. Some students of the atmosphere recognize the existence of three types of fronts within the tropics. Two of these, the intertropical front (*ITF*, or *ITC*) and the meridional fronts between the subtropical high-pressure cells, have been discussed in a preceding section in Chap. 2 dealing with winds. A third type, called *subsidiary front*, is more local in character and is thought of as occurring within a homogeneous air mass due to diversions of air streams by orographic obstacles. Such local fronts or lines of convergence fluctuate rapidly in position and are difficult to detect and to follow. They may be of great importance, however, in producing local weather phenomena. On Figs. 4.3 and 4.4 only the intertropical, or equatorial, front is shown.

There is diversity of opinion concerning air masses in the tropics as there is concerning fronts. By some, four principal types are recognized:

1. Tropical maritime air of the subsident type *mTs*).

2. Tropical maritime air of the neutral type *mT*).

3. Tropical maritime air of the convergent type (*mTu*); sometimes designated as *equatorial maritime air*.

4. Tropical continental air (*cTs*).

mTs air is characteristic of the *central* and *eastern* parts of the subtropical anticyclones over oceans and the adjacent poleward parts of the trades over the eastern oceans. Here upper-air subsidence is particularly intense and the inversion level low so that stability is pronounced. Ordinarily *mTs* air is dry aloft and warm, but where cool coastal waters prevail the surface layer may be cool and moist (Figs. 4.3, 4.4).

Neutral *mT* results when *mTs* air has experienced a long journey over warm waters as it travels westward in the tradewind circulation. Hence, neutral *mT* air is characteristic of the western parts of the subtropical anticyclones and the trades and therefore the symbol *mT* is common over the *western* parts of tropical and subtropical oceans. This air has been thoroughly moistened in its lower layers although its upper strata may still be relatively dry. Upper-air subsidence is weak or has disappeared, and as a consequence the high inversion is absent or only weakly developed. *mT* air is conditionally and convectively unstable so that when there is a relatively strong trigger action in the form of intense surface heating or orographic lifting vigorous convection and heavy rainfall will result.

Tropical maritime air of the convergent type (*mTu*) is characteristic of equatorial latitudes over continents as well as oceans. Here the moisture has been carried to greater heights so that a deep air mass is highly charged with humidity. Equally significant is the fact that the convergent wind system close to the equator has increased the instability aloft. Such air is capable of producing abundant cumulonimbus clouds and heavy showers, even in the absence of strong trigger action. Thus while neutral *mT* air usually requires strong trigger action to produce heavy showers, convergent *mTu* air provides an environment in which strong convection is easily induced.

Tropical continental (*cTs*) air is characteristic of the subtropical anticyclonic circulations over the low-latitude continents. Subsidence aloft produces a dry, stable air mass in which condensation forms are unlikely. The extensive low-latitude deserts are characterized by air of this

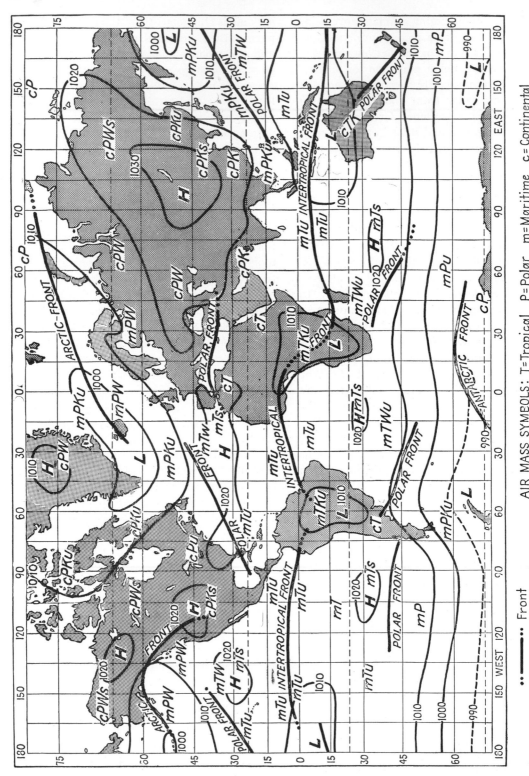

AIR MASS SYMBOLS: T=Tropical P=Polar m=Maritime c=Continental
W=Warmer than, K=Colder than underlying surface s=Stable aloft u=Unstable aloft

FIG. 4.3. Air masses and fronts in January. (*After Haurwitz and Austin.*)

•••— Front

mb— Isobar

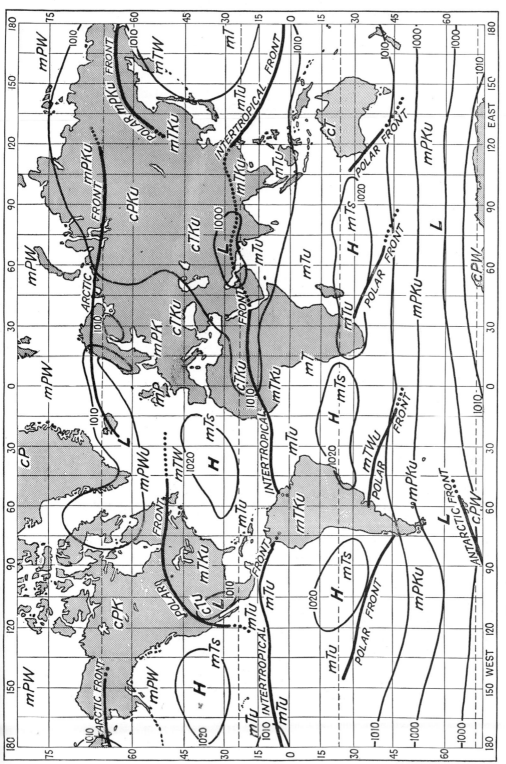

AIR MASS SYMBOLS: T=Tropical   P=Polar   m=Maritime   c=Continental
W=Warmer than, K=Colder than underlying surface.   s=Stable aloft   u=Unstable aloft

FIG. 4.4. Air masses and fronts in July. *(After Haurwitz and Austin.)*

type. In some of these desert areas summer heat results in surface thermal lows with shallow cyclonic circulations. However, the dry subsident stable air still prevails aloft above the surface layer.

183. Air Masses and Fronts in the Middle and High Latitudes. Outside the tropics, air masses show much greater contrasts in temperature and density, fronts are consequently better developed, and seasonal contrasts in source regions and their air masses are more pronounced.

On the January map over the Atlantic and Pacific Oceans (Fig. 4.3) polar maritime air (*mPKu*) is being warmed over the water surface and the cyclonic circulation makes for instability aloft. Over the great continents of Eurasia and North America the dry polar continental air masses are somewhat different in the northern and southern parts. Over the southern parts the continental air is being warmed by the land surface so that the symbol *cPKs* is prominent. The *s* indicates stability associated with upper-air subsidence. Farther north, however, the air is being chilled by the cold snow-covered surface so that the air mass is represented as *cPWs*.

On the July map (Fig. 4.4) the northern parts of the Atlantic and Pacific Oceans have a predominance of *mPW* or *mPWu*, for the air is warmer than the underlying water surface and

is being stabilized as a result of cooling at the base. Over the continents of North America and Eurasia *cPK* or *cPKu* air masses prevail in the northern parts, signifying that the air is being heated from the surface. *mTKu* air prevails to the south of the polar front in the eastern parts of both continents.

184. *Vertical Extent of Frontal Zones.* Ordinarily frontal surfaces have an inclination with the horizontal of the magnitude of about 1:100. In height they may extend from the earth's surface up to the top of the troposphere, although most of them do not. Their vertical extent depends upon the depth of the winds that form them and upon the processes that create the air masses. A front formed between genuine tropical air masses, which extend to great heights, and any other air mass is likely to be deep. On the contrary, boundary surfaces of less vertical extent are formed between shallower polar continental and transitional air masses. As a general rule, air masses that originate through cooling from below are shallow, while those that form as a result of heating from below are deep. Figure 4.5 represents the principal features of the main frontal zones in the troposphere in a meridional cross section.

North American Air Masses

WINTER AIR-MASS PROPERTIES

185. *cP* (**polar continental**) **air masses** originate over the snow- and ice-covered areas of interior Canada north of latitude 50 or 55° Alaska, and the frozen arctic seas (Figs. 4.6 4.7). Uniformity of surface and relatively light anticyclonic air movement make this an ideal source region. The high latitude and the snow surface cause insolational heating to be negligible so that the surface is always much colder than the overlying air. To the west the Rocky Mountains and other highlands act as natural barriers obstructing invasions of milder maritime air from the Pacific. As a result of (*a*) radiational cooling from the cold snow surface below which is typically colder than the air and (*b*) subsidence aloft in the strongly anticyclonic circulation, *cP* air at its source is always very

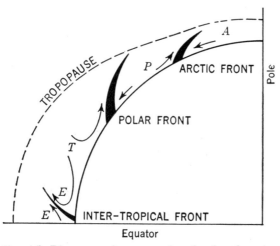

FIG. 4.5. Diagrammatic cross section showing the principal frontal zones and air masses in the Northern Hemisphere. (*From Petterssen, "Introduction to Meteorology," McGraw-Hill Book Company, Inc., New York.*)

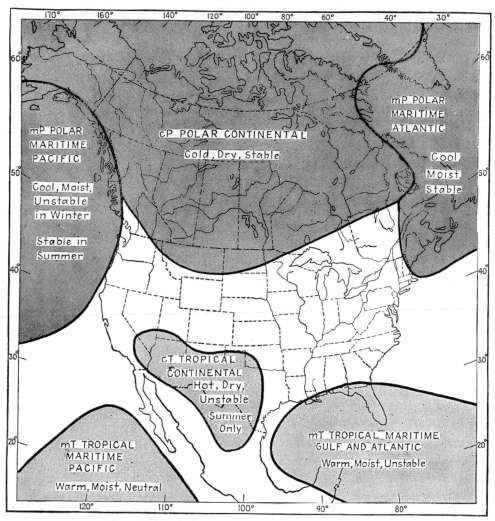

FIG. 4.6. North American air masses and source regions.

old, dry, and stable (*cPWs*). Clouds are largely absent. The strong radiational cooling from below results in a marked surface inversion of temperature which extends up to a mile or more above the ground.

cP air enters the United States from Canada, usually between the Rocky Mountains and the Great Lakes. On the weather map it takes the form of a rapidly moving cold polar anticyclone. The open nature of the continent between the arctic plains and the Gulf of Mexico makes it relatively easy for these outbreaks of polar air to move rapidly southeastward carrying abnormally cold weather to the subtropical latitudes of east-central United States. The first frosts in fall, the last frosts in spring, and the cold waves over most of the country are associated with *cP* air. This same open nature of the continent makes central and eastern North America an ideal region for the clash of polar and tropical air masses. For this reason the middle latitudes of North America are the world's most noteworthy continental region of cyclogenesis in winter. The storminess of this region is proverbial.

186. *Modified cP Air in Southern and Eastern United States.* The three important modifying agents of *cP* air as it travels southward and eastward from its source region are:

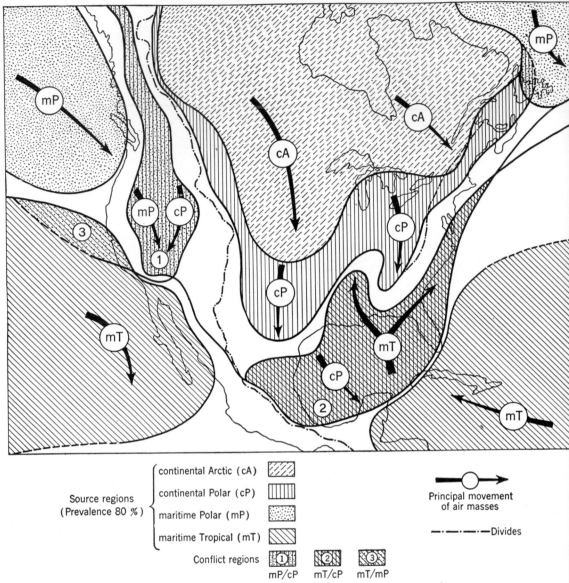

Fig. 4.7. Air mass distribution in winter. (*After Brunnschweiler.*)

a. Addition of heat and moisture at the surface so that the lower air becomes somewhat less stable and *K* begins to replace *W* in the air-mass symbol.

b. Continuing subsidence aloft serves to maintain upper-level stability in the air mass so that *s* persists in the air-mass symbol.

c. Mechanical turbulence, especially in regions of rough terrain, or where the movement of the air mass is rapid, tends to disrupt the sur-

face inversion and raise the surface temperature. As the wind dies down, however, the surface inversion is reestablished and exceptionally low minimum temperatures, associated with clear skies, are the rule.

As long as the *cP* air, in its southward movement, is continuing over a snow-covered surface, the extent of its modification is slight. But when, at about the latitude of central Illinois, the air mass passes from a snow-covered surface to one

Classification of North American Air Masses

Classification by local source regions				General classification after Bergeron (international)	Local air-mass names
Source by		Local source regions	Season of frequent occurrence		
Latitude	Nature				
Polar	Continental	Alaska, Canada, and the Arctic	Entire year	cP or cPW, winter cPK, summer	Pc, polar continental
		Modified in southern and central United States	Entire year	cPK	
	Maritime	North Pacific Ocean	Entire year	mPK, winter mP or mPK, summer	Pp, polar Pacific
		Modified in western and central United States	Entire year	cPW, winter cPK, summer	
		Colder portions of the North Atlantic Ocean	Entire year	mPK, winter mPW, spring and summer	Pa, Polar Atlantic
		Modified over warmer portions or the North Atlantic Ocean	Spring and summer	mPK	
Tropical	Continental	Southwestern United States and northern Mexico	Warmer half of year	cTK	Tc, tropical continental
	Maritime	Gulf of Mexico and Caribbean Sea	Entire year	mTW, winter mTW or mTK, summer	Tg tropical Gulf
		Modified in the United States or over the North Atlantic Ocean	Entire year	mTW	
		Sargasso Sea (Middle Atlantic)	Entire year	mTW, winter mTW or mTK, summer	Ta, tropical Atlantic
		Modified in the United States or over the North Atlantic Ocean	Entire year	mTW	
		Middle North Pacific Ocean	Entire year	mTW, winter mTW or mTK, summer	Tp, tropical Pacific
		Modified in the United States or over North Pacific Ocean	Entire year	mTW	

Winter Characteristics of Some American Air Masses

Air mass	Station	Weather element	Elevation above sea level				
			Surface	1 km.	2 km.	3 km.	4 km.
cP	Ellendale, N.D.	Temp., °F.	−15	−13	−4	−7	−13
		Sp. humid., g./kg.	0.32	0.35	0.60	0.50	0.45
		Rel. humid., %	82	80	75	63	71
	Boston	Temp., °F.	21	6	0	−9	−20
		Sp. humid., g./kg.	0.9	0.6	0.5	0.3	0.2
		Rel. humid., %	43	50	50	44	48
mP	Seattle	Temp., °F.	46	32	18	7	−2
		Sp. humid., g./kg.	4.4	2.7	1.5	0.8	0.4
		Rel. humid., %	66	64	64	52	35
	Ellendale, N.D.	Temp., °F.	30	45	34	19	7
		Sp. humid., g./kg.	3.0	3.0	2.2	1.5	1.1
		Rel. humid., %	83	43	44	48	60
mT	Miami, Fla.	Temp., °F.	77	68	55	46	37
		Sp. humid., g./kg.	16.3	13.3	9.8	6.2	5.2
		Rel. humid., %	82	82	83	66	67
	Boston	Temp., °F.	57	57	48	36	25
		Sp. humid., g./kg.	8.8	6.5	6.2	4.6	2.9
		Rel. humid., %	88	59	70	75	65
mT	San Diego	Temp., °F.	68	59	50	43	34
		Sp. humid., g./kg.	11.9	9.8	6.8	4.0	2.1
		Rel. humid., %	86	81	70	51	33

that is free of snow, rapid insolational heating and humidification of the surface air occurs by day. These seaward moving streams of cP air are essential elements of the hydrologic cycle. But this surface heating and humidification are by no means sufficient to overcome the stability (s) aloft so that the air mass remains stable and cloudless (cPKs).

Even as the cP air advances over the warm waters of the Gulf of Mexico, with large additions of heat and moisture at the surface, its s characteristic persists as long as the circulation remains anticyclonic and subsidence prevails. Over the Gulf of Mexico the cPKs air is transformed into mPKs and mTKs air with which there may be associated a low cloud cover and showers of a heavy drizzle type. Only when this air becomes involved in a cyclonic type of circu-

lation involving ascent and consequent insta bility, as along frontal zones, do heavy loca rains develop. These polar outbreaks may arriv in Central America and Mexico as a stron norther from the Gulf either as cool mTKu ai accompanied by heavy convective precipitatio or as anticyclonic mTKs air with drizzle or eve no rainfall.

Eastward from the Great Lakes to the Atlanti Seaboard cP air has significantly different prop erties from those usually observed in centr United States. Surface temperatures are usuall higher, as is the specific humidity, and cloud and snow showers are more prevalent. Thre principal modifying agents are involved. Th first of these is the weakening of the stabilit aloft as a result of the increasingly strong c clonic circulation of the polar current eastwar from the Great Lakes, so that upper-level subsidence is weak or absent and the *s* element gradually disappears from the air-mass symbol.

The other two modifying influences on eastward moving *cP* air are the Great Lakes and the Appalachian Highlands. Both of these cause a warming of the surface layers. Over the open water of the Great Lakes in winter the surface air is humidified as well as heated, resulting in some surface instability so that heavy snow showers are characteristic of this *cPK* air on the windward coasts of any of the Great Lakes. The rough terrain of the Appalachian country results in a thorough mixing of the lower few thousand feet of air so that the surface temperature inversion is eliminated and surface temperatures are comparatively high. On the western slopes of the eastern highlands the forced ascent of modified *cP* air from over the Great Lakes causes general cloudiness and heavy local snowfall as long as there is a strong flow of cold air. Heat of condensation acts to warm the air mass. As it descends the eastern slopes of the highlands, it is further warmed as a result of subsidence so that the cloud cover disappears and the snowfall ceases (see data for Boston).

187. *Modified cP Air West of the Rockies.* The general west-to-east air movement in middle latitudes, plus the effects of the Rocky Mountain barrier, permit *cP* air only occasionally to invade the Great Basin and the Pacific Coast regions. When, now and then, it does reach the Great Basin it has been considerably warmed as a result of turbulent mixing in the lower layers, which brings down warmer air from aloft. Occasionally *cP* air reaches the Pacific Coast in Washington and Oregon, producing subfreezing temperatures and snow flurries, while very rarely this same weather type may extend southward to coastal California. In those years when *cP* air is more prevalent in the region west of the Rockies, the Pacific Coast may experience relatively severe winters as a result of frequent westward outbreaks of this air mass.

188. *mP* (polar maritime)-Pacific air masses which greatly affect North American weather have as their source region the northern part of the North Pacific Ocean. In winter this region is dominated by the Aleutian Low and its strongly cyclonic circulation. The eastern part of the Pacific in these latitudes is a region of relatively warm surface waters, resembling the situation in the eastern North Atlantic. Surrounding the *mP*-Pacific source region on all sides, except to the south, are *cP* source regions so that most of the air that enters the *mP*-Pacific source region originates in cold continental areas to the north and west and is drawn into the source region by the strong northwesterly flow converging on the Aleutian Low. Heating and humidifying the *cP* air at its base by the warm water transforms it very rapidly from a cold, dry, stable air mass (*cPWs*) into one which is relatively unstable and in which the lower layers at least are comparatively mild and humid (*mPKu*). The instability is the result both of the heating and humidifying of the lower air over an ocean surface which is warmer than the overlying air (*K*) and of the strongly cyclonic circulation which results in a convergence and elevation of the air aloft (*u*).

mPKu air as it arrives on the Pacific Coast of North America is relatively mild with temperatures well above the freezing point, has a steep lapse rate, and is accompanied by low clouds with frequent showers. As this humid, unstable air advances inland, its shower activity is greatly increased as it is forced to ascend over the cooler land air along the coast and also over the coastal ranges. Rain in the lowlands and heavy snowfall in the mountains is characteristic of the winter season. At many stations along the North Pacific Coast the prevailing wind direction in winter is easterly, so that some sort of persistent discontinuity appears to exist in the cool season between the cool easterlies from the interior and the mild unstable *mPKu* air from the Pacific.

189. *Modified mP-Pacific Air East of the Sierra Nevada Mountains.* As the maritime air continues inland over successive mountain ranges and plateaus, the cold land rapidly lowers its surface temperature, while condensation on the highlands causes the air to become drier at low levels. The third type of modification is the increasing stability at upper levels, so that the *u* gradually changes to *s*, as this air is involved in an anticyclonic circulation over the plateau region and also to the east of the Rocky Mountains. Thus the mild, moist, unstable air (*mPKu*) of the west coast has been transformed into a cold, dry, stable continental air mass (*cPWs*) east of the Rockies in central United States. It is not nearly so cold or so dry, however, as is fresh *cP* air from Arctic Canada. The weather associated with this greatly modified *mP* air over the central part of the country is some of the finest winter has to offer—clear skies, light winds, and moderate temperatures—the kind that makes winter sports attractive. On the other hand, along frontal zones where it makes contact with *mT* air from the Gulf, or with fresh *cP* air from Canada, widespread storm conditions may prevail.

190. *mP* (polar maritime)-Atlantic air masses originate over the abnormally cold North Atlantic waters (35 to 40° in winter, and 50 to 60° in summer) off Newfoundland, Labrador, and Greenland. They were originally *cP* air that moved eastward off the continent and was modified over the cold waters acting as a secondary source region. Owing to the prevailing west-to-east air movement in the middle latitudes, the North Atlantic is not an important source region for air masses affecting North America. This is especially true in winter. Normally, this air moves eastward across the Atlantic toward Europe. Two general situations usually account for an invasion of eastern North America by *mP* air. As a *cP* anticyclone moves offshore from eastern Canada, air from its southwestern quadrant passes over the cold waters of the Labrador Current and reaches the North American east coast as a chilly northeast wind. Then again, a strong cyclone in the Ohio Valley or on the Atlantic Coast south of Boston may bring an invasion of *mP* air that travels farther interior. Normally, however, the influence of *mP* air does not extend beyond the Appalachians or south of Cape Hatteras.

In winter, *mP*-Atlantic air is dry and stable aloft as a result of subsidence, while the surface layer is moderately unstable, moist, and chilly. The temperatures are raw rather than bitterly cold. As compared with *mP*-Pacific air at Seattle, the lower levels of *mP*-Atlantic air are colder, drier, and more stable. This is because of both the colder waters in the North Atlantic and the shorter trajectory of *mP*-Atlantic air over the water.

The weather associated with an invasion of *mP*-Atlantic air is distinctly unpleasant. Surface temperatures near freezing or somewhat below, high relative humidity, strong northeast winds, low thick clouds from which light misting rain or light snow flurries are falling—such is the weather of a typical "northeaster" of the New England Coast. Large-scale precipitation is unlikely, owing to the shallow depth of the moist surface layer.

191. *mT*-Gulf and Atlantic air masses which so greatly affect the weather and climate of much of Anglo-America east of the Rockies have as their source region the exceptionally warm ocean surface of the Gulf of Mexico, the Caribbean Sea, and the subtropical western Atlantic. The surface waters of this extensive region are almost uniformly high in temperature, varying from 70° off southeastern United States to over 80° in the Caribbean. Owing to the uniformly warm waters of the source region, *mT*-Gulf air is characteristically warm and humid. Specific humidity and temperature are higher than for any other American air mass in winter. In winter the subtropical high-pressure cell which dominates the *mT* source region is relatively weak and is located farther south so that much of the central and eastern part of the country is controlled by the polar anticyclone and its *cP* air masses. Characteristically the polar front separating *mT*-Gulf and *cP* air lies close to the northern and western portions of the *mT*-Gulf source region. The circulation described above does not favor the easy entrance of *mT* air into eastern and central North America in winter, but when it does enter, it is warmer than the land and as a result it is cooled and stabilized at the surface (*mTW*).

The upper-air properties at this western end of the subtropical anticyclone are in contrast to those at the eastern end. Absence of pronounced subsidence favors a less stable air mass than might be expected in an anticyclonic circulation. Especially when the anticyclonic circulation is drawn toward a front where cyclogenesis is active, the upper levels become definitely unstable ($mTWu$).

In the American South, mT air masses are associated with mild, humid winter days with a good deal of cloudiness of the stratus type, especially at night and in early morning. These clouds usually are dissipated by the sun during the day. As mT air moves northward, the ground strata are cooled by contact with a progressively colder earth, and the surface stability of the air mass is increased. Because of the absence of surface heating and the relative dryness of the upper strata of mT air, convective showers are rare in winter. But, since there is present a marked potential instability, if the northward-flowing mT air, through being drawn into a cyclonic circulation or encountering a relief barrier, is forced to ascend, precipitation may be extremely heavy and widespread. Such rains from mT air in the Appalachian region may cause severe winter floods. Much of the winter rain and snow over central and eastern North America are the result of mT-Gulf air being lifted along fronts in cyclonic circulations. With no obstacle forcing it to rise, northward-moving mT air, through cooling at the surface, frequently develops a dense fog. If the air movement is stronger, turbulence may prevent a ground fog, although a dense mist or fine drizzle may fall so that the visibility is almost that of dense fog, with a ceiling of 100 to 200 meters. In such weather, flying is practically impossible.

192. mT (maritime tropical)-Pacific air masses which affect chiefly extreme southwestern United States and northwestern Mexico originate in the subtropical eastern Pacific Ocean in almost identical latitudes to those in which mT-Gulf air develops. But although the latitudes of their source regions are similar, their other characteristics are not. The eastern subtropical Pacific westward from Mexico and California is dominated by the circulation around the *eastern* end of a subtropical high where upper-level subsidence is strong with resulting marked stability (mTs). A further influence in stabilizing the surface air is the relatively cool coastal waters off the Pacific Coast of Mexico and California. Therefore mTs air which arrives along the North

American Pacific Coast is considerably cooler, drier, and more stable than the mT air which affects southeastern United States.

As mT-Pacific air moves northward along the coast of California, occasionally reaching the latitudes of Oregon and Washington, it is cooled at the surface as it moves over the colder water and is further stabilized, acquiring W characteristics. Fog is often the result. When, as frequently happens, it is drawn into a frontal or cyclonic convergence, its s property changes to u, so that moderate precipitation may result from lifting along fronts or topographic obstacles. Ordinarily it is not as good a rain bringer as is mT-Gulf air, which possesses a more marked conditional instability. In part this may also be due to the smaller temperature and density contrasts along fronts formed between mT and mP air on the Pacific coast than is true of those fronts formed in eastern North America between mT and cP air masses. As mT-Pacific air moves inland aloft over the western states, it continues to give moderate precipitation as it ascends over colder air or over mountains. Rarely can it be identified east of the Rockies.

SUMMER AIR-MASS PROPERTIES IN NORTH AMERICA

193. cP (polar continental) air in summer has approximately the same source region geographically speaking that winter cP air has, but on the other hand the nature of the source region is very different (Figs. 4.6, 4.8). The snow cover, so characteristic of the arctic lands of North America in winter, has entirely disappeared, so that the land surface absorbs considerable heat during the very long summer days. All the surrounding oceans have surface temperatures which are appreciably cooler than the land so that air entering the continent is warmed at the base and given a K characteristic. This is opposite to the situation in winter. Evaporation from rivers, lakes, and vegetation cover adds a fair amount of moisture to the air mass. The weak anticyclonic circulation causes the summer cP air aloft to be mildly stable (s) but not to the degree it is in winter. Surface temperatures are moderately low, but the low

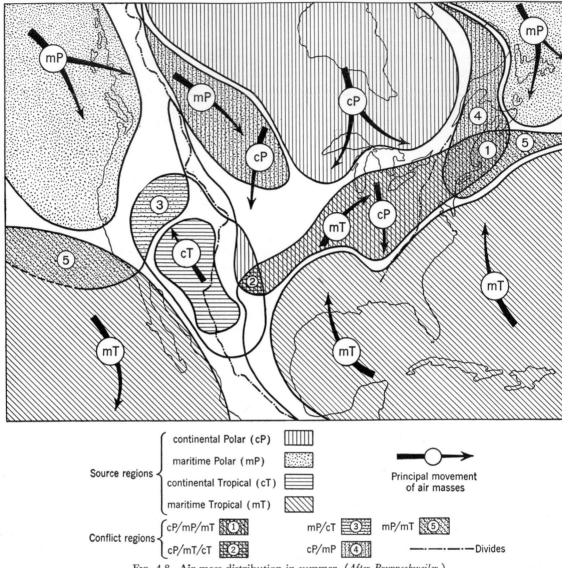

Source regions
- continental Polar (cP) ▥
- maritime Polar (mP) ▨
- continental Tropical (cT) ▤
- maritime Tropical (mT) ▧

⬤➔ Principal movement of air masses

Conflict regions
- cP/mP/mT ①
- cP/mT/cT ②
- mP/cT ③
- cP/mP ④
- mP/mT ⑤

—·—·—·—Divides

Fig. 4.8. Air mass distribution in summer. (*After Brunnschweiler.*)

humidity favors strong insolational heating by day and rapid radiational cooling at night, so that diurnal temperature variations are large. At its source *cP* air is typically cloudless. In spite of its daytime surface instability with resulting convective turbulence, the condensation level is so high that a few scattered high cumulus clouds are the most that can develop. In the northern half of central and eastern United States summer heat waves are normally broken by a southward advance of fresh *cPKs* air which, for a day or

two, substitutes cool, clear weather for the su try or desiccating heat prevailing earlier.

Southward moving outbreaks of summer *c* air into the United States are much less fre quent than in winter and they are also weake or slower moving. As a rule they move eastwar more than southward so that the cool air rarel reaches the southern states. As *cP* air advance southward and eastward from the Canadia border, it is slowly warmed at all levels an some moisture is added at the base but genera

Summer Characteristics of Some North American Air Masses

Air mass	Station	Weather element	Elevation above sea level				
			Surface	1 km.	2 km.	3 km.	4 km.
cP	Ellendale, N.D.	Temp., °F.	66	61	50	39	27
		Sp. humid., g./kg.	6.3	5.6	3.9	3.1	2.9
		Rel. humid., %	42	45	43	44	57
	Royal Center, Ind.	Temp., °F.	63	55	43	36	28
		Sp. hum., g./kg.	8.3	5.8	4.5	2.6	1.4
		Rel. humid., %	68	57	64	43	27
	Pensacola, Fla.	Temp., °F.	73	68	54	45	
		Sp. humid., g./kg.	13.4	9.8	7.2	5.0	
		Rel. humid., %	79	65	67	57	
mP	Seattle	Temp., °F.	63	48	41	34	28
		Sp. humid., g./kg.	7.1	6.3	3.9	2.3	1.7
		Rel. humid., %	62	91	60	42	33
	San Diego	Temp., °F.	64	72	70	57	43
		Sp. humid., g./kg.	10.3	7.7	3.5	3.6	3.4
		Rel. humid., %	79	40	20	27	36
mT	Miami, Fla.	Temp., °F.	75	68	59	48	41
		Sp. humid., g./kg.	17.3	14.9	9.3	6.3	4.3
		Rel. humid., %	93	88	74	58	48
	Royal Center, Ind.	Temp., °F.	84	77	65	51	
		Sp. humid., g./kg.	15.9	13.9	11.5	8.6	
		Rel. humid., %	61				
	Ellendale, N.D.	Temp., °F.	84	81	72	55	
		Sp. humid., g./kg.	16.5	13.3	8.7	5.7	
		Rel. humid., %	66	54	42	43	
cT	El Paso, Tex.	Temp., °F.	75	81	75	64	
		Sp. humid., g./kg.	11.0	9.7	9.9	7.6	
		Rel. humid., %	52	37	43	43	

stability persists except when the cP air enters a cyclonic circulation. When the latter situation occurs, instability develops aloft and scattered light thundershowers may occur in the afternoon.

194. mP (polar maritime)-Pacific air masses in summer have the same source region geographically speaking that they have in winter; yet the properties of the summer and winter mP air masses are very different. During the warm season the waters of the North Pacific are relatively colder than the surrounding lands, so that air entering the source region is chilled at the base and stabilized (W). Of still greater consequence is the fact that most of the eastern Pacific, where in winter the circulation is controlled by the Aleutian Low, in summer is dominated by the Pacific High, so that upper-air subsidence is marked (s). The total effect of the cool waters and the anticyclone is to make summer mP-Pacific air very stable and cool (mPWs) and opposed to the formation of clouds and precipitation.

During the summer, as pressure becomes low over the continent and the strengthened Pacific anticyclone shifts poleward, a marked pressure gradient from sea to land is developed along the whole western coast. This makes for a general and steady transport of cool stable mP air southeastward along the entire Pacific Coast as far southward as California. The movement of cool air from the northwest is so persistent in summer that it practically prevents any mT air from reaching the coast. The result is unusually low summer temperatures along the Pacific littoral. Farther south in subtropical California the extraordinarily cool waters along the coast, caused by upwelling, tend to cool the mP air masses from the northwest even further. As a result, mP air at San Diego has practically the same surface temperatures that it has at Seattle.

After mP air has reached the interior of the country, it is quite impossible to distinguish it from cP. As a result, the designation cP is satisfactory for both mP and cP air in summer in the interior of the continent.

195. mP (polar maritime)-Atlantic air masses are of most frequent occurrence during late spring and early summer, for it is at this season that ocean surface waters are relatively coldest with respect to both the ocean proper and the continent to the west. The ocean region from Cape Cod to Newfoundland in summer becomes a genuine source region for cool air. As cP air moves eastward from the continent over the cold waters, it is chilled and stabilized (W) at the base, while the prevailingly anticyclonic circulation produces upper-level stability (s). The circulation on the southerly side of this high carries chilly mP-Atlantic air in over New England and not infrequently to the coastal areas east of the Appalachians as far south as Cape Hatteras. It has been known to reach as far south as northern Florida, bringing with it drops in temperature of 15 to 25° and at times even 35 to 45°.

Summer mP-Atlantic air was originally cP air that had been chilled over the cool waters. Along the North Atlantic Coast in summer it is associated with weather characterized by low temperatures, clear skies, and good visibility. Because of its dryness, surface fog is absent even over the coastal waters. Thin and broken clouds are relatively frequent at the top of the turbulence layer,

but precipitation never falls from these clouds in summer. Rain is unknown in mP-Atlantic air except in connection with cyclonic activity.

196. mT (tropical maritime)-Gulf and Atlantic air masses largely control the weather of the United States east of the Rocky Mountains during the summer season. Because of the prevailing sea-to-land pressure gradients over eastern United States in summer, mT air is able to enter into the continent much farther at that season than in winter. A strengthening of the Bermuda High over the western Atlantic Ocean and the tendency toward a thermally maintained low over the warm continent produces a relatively persistent monsoonal indraft that flows northward even into Canada. Not only do the mT air masses cover much wider areas in summer than in winter, but they are present a much greater share of the time. They are responsible for the oppressive humid heat that characterizes so much of the summer weather of central and eastern United States. Outbreaks of polar air are comparatively weak and infrequent at this season, so that the belt of maximum frontal activity, or *polar front*, is shifted from its normal winter position somewhere over the northern Gulf of Mexico northward to the Great Lakes or beyond.

As it leaves its source region, summer mT air is relatively similar to winter mT. Over the Caribbean Sea, for example, ocean surface temperatures are only 5 or 6° higher in summer than in winter, although this difference increases to 15 or 20° on the immediate Gulf Coast. Especially in the lower levels the summer air masses are somewhat warmer and more humid, although their vertical structure is not greatly different from that of winter. Although the general circulation in which the mT-Gulf air is involved is anticyclonic in character, it should be emphasized that this is the western end of the cell where subsidence is much less marked. Upper-level instability (mTu) therefore is not uncommon. As summer mT air moves inland over the warm continent the tendency will be for its surface temperature to be increased, with a consequent increase in surface instability ($mTKu$). This is in contrast to the winter condition when a cold continent has the reverse effect. The high relative humidity indicates that only a small amount of vertical lifting is required in order to start active convection. The marked potential instability, plus the added effect of daytime insolational heating of the surface air, is the reason for the development of cumulus and cumulonimbus clouds and numerous local thunderstorms so characteristic of summer mT air masses in the Gulf States.

By the time mT-Gulf air has reached the Upper Mississippi Valley region it has usually lost so much of its moisture in the local thundershowers that ordinary thermal convection is much less effective in causing thunderstorms. Within the air mass in this region only cumulus clouds and mild showers will occur, and some form of frontal activity is usually required to provide the necessary lift for intense thunderstorm development. However, the passage of even a weak cyclone with its accompanying fronts is usually sufficient to lift the lower and intermediate layers of the air mass to the saturation point so that active convection can take place.

In the arid southwestern portions of the United States, the warm season thunderstorms are associated with invasions of mT-Gulf air as it is forced to ascend mountain barriers. These summer showers are frequently intense so that the name "cloudburst" has been applied. They are characteristically localized with respect to mountain masses. On those rare occasions when mT-Gulf air reaches southern California, that region experiences its occasional summer showers. Severe local thunderstorms are likewise characteristic of mT air as it is lifted in passing over the Appalachian Mountains. Such storms may retain their activity for 100 miles or more over the coastal plain.

197. mT (**tropical maritime**) **Pacific air masses** are practically absent along the Pacific Coast of North America during the summer months. With a weak Aleutian Low, and the intensified Pacific High shifted northward and centered at about 35 or 40°, the pressure arrangement is such that mP air dominates west coast weather throughout the warm season.

198. cT (**tropical continental**) **air** in North America is of comparatively little significance. Owing to the marked narrowing of the continent to the south in Mexico and Central America and the prevalence of highlands in those regions, an extensive source region for cT air is lacking. Only in northern Mexico and adjacent parts of western Texas and eastern New Mexico is there provided even a limited source region. In large part cT air probably consists of mT-Pacific air that has stagnated over this secondary source region for several days, thereby becoming greatly heated and desiccated in its lower strata. cT air is a feature of the warm season only. It is absent in winter, for the source region has no distinctive characteristics at that season. Very high daytime temperatures, extremely low humidities, and an almost complete lack of precipitation characterize cT air in summer. Outside its source region cT air is felt chiefly in the southern Great Plains where it is associated with severe drought. It is rarely found east of the Mississippi River or north of Nebraska.

Air Masses of Asia

For much of Asia there are no published materials dealing with air-mass characteristics. Actually little has been accomplished in the way of upper-air soundings that might yield valuable information on air masses. It is chiefly in eastern and southeastern Asia that some progress has been made in describing the source regions and mapping vertically and horizontally the characteristics of air masses. Within this region of southeastern Asia the air masses bear many resemblances to their counterparts in eastern North America.

WINTER AIR-MASS PROPERTIES

199. cP (**polar continental**) **air masses** have their origin chiefly in Siberia and Outer Mongolia. This source region is similar in most respects to subarctic Canada, the source region for North American cP air. They are both characterized by extreme winter cold, and air masses originating in them are intensely cold and dry. In Siberia surface air temperatures in winter usually vary between about 5 and −40°. At Irkutsk in southernmost Siberia winter cP air has a surface temperature of −13° and a specific humidity of 0.4. Relative humidity is close to 80 per cent. Farther north, temperature and humidity are both lower. At the surface, unless winds prevent, a strong temperature inversion is present which persists up to 1 km. or more above the ground.

As cP air surges outward from its source region toward the Pacific Ocean, it is forced to travel great distances over rough terrain before it descends to the plains of China. During this journey, the temperature inversion is destroyed by mechanical turbulence, while the temperature and humidity of the lower strata are increased.

cP air masses enter China by two different routes, a land and a sea route. When the center of high pressure is in Mongolia and North China, the polar air trajectory has been entirely over land; but, if the high-pressure center is located in Manchuria and the Sea of Japan, cP air arrives by the sea route. Since the land and sea surfaces are very unlike in temperature and humidity, the weather in China associated with cP air arriving by these different routes is much in contrast.

A *land* cP air mass in China is much warmer than it was in its source region, surface temperatures being as much as 20 to 35° higher. Winter cP air at Peking has a surface temperature of about 32° with relative humidity of 30 per cent. At Nanking, comparable figures are 45° and 55 per cent. Above 2 km. the air is little modified, having practically all the features of cP air at its source. Land cP air is associated with clear, cold, and often cloudless weather in China. If the outbreak of polar air is unusually strong, it frequently carries with it a large amount of fine dust, which is the source of the extensive loess deposits of North China. Because of the clear atmosphere, large daily ranges of temperature are characteristic of land cP air, and ground fog is common in the early morning. During winter, much of Asia is under the influence of the great Siberian High, so that cP air in modified form invades practically all parts of the continent,

even extending into tropical latitudes. Its character varies, to be sure, with the degree of modification depending upon distance from the source and the kinds of surfaces crossed. In North China and Manchuria winter weather is largely dominated by land cP air masses and consequently is clear and cold. But farther south, where cP is more frequently in conflict with marine air of tropical origin, the weather is more gloomy and wet. India is effectively protected from invasions of genuine cP air by the high mountains and plateaus lying to the north. In this region the dry, cool air masses of the winter monsoon are of local origin or are normal trades.

Winter cP Air at Its Siberian Source
(After Petterssen)

Irkutsk

Elevation, meters	Temperature, °F.	Specific humidity, g./kg.
——	−13	0.40
750	− 6	0.56
1,600	−15	0.46
2,550	−22	0.37
3,600	−31	0.26
4,850	−42	0.18

Winter Land cP Air in China
(After Tu)

Nanking

Elevation, meters	Temperature, °F.	Relative humidity, %	Specific humidity, g./kg.
7	45	54	3.3
500	35	54	2.5
1,000	29	52	2.0
2,000	23	42	1.4
3,000	19	37	1.2
4,000	10	24	0.6

Peking

Elevation, meters	Temperature, °F.	Relative humidity, %	Specific humidity, g./kg.
70.5	32	27	1.1
500	26	29	1.0
1,000	19	31	0.8
2,000	6	37	0.7

Winter Sea cP Air in China
(After Tu)

Nanking

Elevation, meters	Temperature, °F.	Relative humidity, %	Specific humidity, g./kg.
7	48	59	4.5
500	42	58	3.6
1,000	38	55	3.0
2,000	31	41	2.1
3,000	24	36	1.5
4,000	14	35	0.9

Winter mT Air Masses
(After Tu)
Nanking

Elevation, meters	Temperature, °F.	Relative humidity, %	Specific humidity, g./kg.
7	53	74	6.2
500	60	53	6.2
1,000	56	49	5.1
2,000	48	39	3.5
3,000	42	31	2.4
4,000	26	28	1.4

Winter Monsoon Air over India
(After Petterssen)
Agra

Elevation, meters	Temperature, °F.	Specific humidity, g./kg.
———	66	4.3
850	50	4.2
1,800	41	3.5
2,850	34	3.1
4,050	23	1.7
5,400	7	1.2

cP air masses that come to North and Central China after having passed over the sea of Japan, Gulf of Pohai (Chihli), the Yellow Sea, or the Pacific Ocean have been sufficiently modified that they may well be distinguished from true land *cP* air. Such sea *cP* air is produced when the winter anticyclones from Siberia move out over the Pacific Ocean with their centers north of latitude 45°. Air streams from the southern quadrants of these high-pressure centers arrive in China as east and northeast winds. Although these are designated by some writers as *mP* air, Tu insists that they are not, for their marine modification takes place over seas south of latitude 45°. As one might expect, this sea *cP* air is slightly warmer and more humid than land *cP*. It usually gives rise to fine clear weather unless it is associated with fronts. In its lower strata it is convectively unstable, so that, if it is sufficiently lifted by colder air masses or forced to ascend relief barriers, precipitation may occur. When sea *cP* air is undercut by fresh *cP* air from Siberia, precipitation is fairly common.

In winter these cold, dry winter *cP* air masses from the continent come into contact with maritime air masses along the eastern coast of the continent and over southern China, resulting in these areas being a region of important cyclo-

genesis. Japan lies pretty much in the path of these numerous cyclones in winter.

200. *mP* (**polar maritime**) **air masses** play a very minor role in the weather of eastern Asia. It is possible that *cP* air modified over the Okhotsk Sea (*Po*) may affect the maritime provinces of Siberia, Manchuria, and Korea, but it seems to be absent in China proper. Even in Japan, Arakawa failed to detect any genuine *mP* air masses. The strong west to east atmospheric circulation in eastern Asia in winter almost precludes the possibility of *mP* air reaching the coast of Asia south of Korea. In general character, *mP* air in eastern Asia would resemble *mP*-Atlantic air in New England.

201. *mT* (**tropical maritime**) **air masses** are so largely excluded from Asia in winter by the Siberian anticyclone that they play only a minor role in the cool-season weather of that continent. Rarely does *mT* air reach the surface as far north as the Yangtze Valley, although in South China it is much more frequently at the ground. Aloft in cyclones it may be found overrunning colder air of continental origin and producing precipitation. *mT* air masses are warmer and moister than other air masses in winter. As they move northward over the cooler land surface, low stratus cloud and misting rain may occur.

SUMMER AIR MASSES

202. *cP* (**polar continental**) **air masses** in the warm season, because of the changed character of the source region, have properties quite in contrast to those of winter. The snow-free and moderately warm land surface tends to heat the air from below. Eastern and southern Asia are so dominated by *mT* air in summer that *cP* air plays only a minor role in the weather of that region. Any *cP* air that comes to China usually arrives by way of the Sea of Japan and the Yellow Sea, so that its moisture content at lower levels is higher than *cP* air in the United States. As compared with tropical air masses, it is somewhat cooler and drier, and so does not have the sultry and oppressive qualities of the tropical air. Weather conditions associated with *cP* air are usually fine, with rain and thunderstorms rare. Since most of China is dominated by tropical maritime air in summer, invasion of *cP* air is likely to develop fronts with consequent stormy weather.

Summer cP Air Masses in China
(After Tu)
Nanking

Elevation, meters	Temperature, °F.	Relative humidity	Specific humidity, g./kg.
7	80	61	12.4
500	72	67	11.1
1,000	66	65	9.1
2,000	55	55	6.7
3,000	45	46	4.5
4,000	37	28	2.4

Summer mT Air Masses in China
(After Tu)
Nanking

Elevation, meters	Temperature, °F.	Relative humidity	Specific humidity, g./kg.
7	85	76	19.3
500	78	78	17.3
1,000	73	77	14.8
2,000	59	75	10.0
3,000	48	70	7.7
4,000	34	70	4.7

Summer mT Air Masses
(After Tu)
Jakarta (Batavia), Java

Elevation, meters	Temperature, °F.	Relative humidity	Specific humidity, g./kg.
0	80	86	18.7
1,000	74	77	15.9
2,000	69	74	14.2
3,000	59	66	10.2
4,000	49	64	7.8
5,000	39	60	3.6
Nanking			
7	85	79	21.4
500	79	85	18.2
1,000	75	82	17.4
2,000	64	84	13.4
3,000	54	80	10.2
4,000	43	80	7.2
Agra (India)			
(After Petterssen)			
900	82	..	19.0
1,900	70	..	15.0
3,000	59	..	12.0
4,250	43	..	7.5
5,700	30	..	5.0

203. *mP* (**polar maritime**) **air** from the Sea of Okhotsk appears to play a somewhat more important role in the weather of eastern Asia in summer than in winter. Tu and some other writers indicate that north of about 40° latitude the summer monsoon is of maritime polar air, while to the south it is tropical and equatorial in origin. If this is true, Manchuria and eastern Siberia are influenced by *mP* air in summer. According to certain Japanese meteorologists, *mP* air comes southward over Japan in early summer and is there overrun by tropical air. This results in the formation of a semistationary front with associated gloomy drizzly weather (the *Bai-u* season).

204. *mT* (**tropical maritime**) **air masses** pretty much dominate the weather of eastern and southern Asia during the summer season. This is the well-known summer monsoon. These air masses are warm, very moist, and convectively unstable to a marked degree. As observed over the South China Coast, they are almost identical with *mT*-Gulf air over southeastern United States. A lift of only 200 to 600 meters is necessary to saturate the air and bring about precipitation in the form of heavy showers.

As *mT* air moves in over the warm land, its surface temperature is increased, and strong midday convection results. In contrast to *mT*-Gulf air over eastern United States, the tropical air over southeastern Asia almost immediately encounters orographic barriers that provide the lift necessary to saturate the potentially unstable air. In addition it is involved in frontal convergences and cyclonic activity over the continent which result in increased instability and abundant summer precipitation. In spring in South and Central China, and in midsummer in North China and Manchuria, the invading *mT* air meets *cP* air along the polar front, giving rise to active cyclogenesis.

Air Masses of Europe

The air masses that control the weather of Europe are in many respects similar to those of western North America. Thus, *mP*-Atlantic air in western Europe is essentially similar to *mP*-Pacific air in western United States, and *mT*-

Atlantic air in Britain is like *mT*-Pacific air in British Columbia. However, the contrasts in the relief of the two continents make for great differences in the relative importance of marine and continental air masses in Europe and North America. Thus, while the latter continent is bordered along its western margins by high mountains that tend to shut out the marine air, Europe is freely open to invasions of air from the Atlantic.

WINTER AIR MASSES

205. *cP* (**polar continental**) **air masses** influence chiefly the weather of eastern and central Europe, less frequently that of western Europe. The general west-to-east atmospheric circulation

Winter Air Masses of Europe
(After Petterssen)
1. *cP* Air

	Elevation, meters	Temperature, °F.	Specific humidity, g./kg.
Moscow	—	1	1.0
	800	7	1.0
	1,650	3	1.0
	2,600	− 9	0.56
	3,700	−26	0.39
	4,950	−42	0.20
Munich	800	12	1.4
	1,700	1	1.0
	2,650	− 6	0.60
	3,750	−15	0.38
	5,050	−33	0.16

2. *cP* (*arctic*) Air, Modified over the Norwegian Sea

	Elevation, meters	Temperature, °F.	Specific humidity, g./kg.
Berlin	—	36	3.7
	800	28	2.9
	1,700	16	2.0
	2,700	5	1.1
	3,850	− 9	0.56
	5,150	−26	2.26

3. *mP-Atlantic* Air

	Elevation, meters	Temperature, °F.	Specific humidity, g./kg.
Hamburg	—	39	4.4
	850	34	3.5
	1,750	23	2.2
	2,750	14	1.3
	3,950	0	0.8
	5,250	−17	0.5

4. *mT-Atlantic* Air

	Elevation, meters	Temperature, °F.	Specific humidity, g./kg.
Hamburg	—	48	6.2
	850	41	5.4
	1,800	36	3.7
	2,850	25	2.2
	4,000	10	1.4
	5,400	− 2	0.8

in these latitudes tends to prevent, except under certain special pressure arrangements, a reverse east-to-west movement of air so as to give western Europe continental air masses. Moreover, the fact that Europe, in contrast to North America, narrows poleward causes the former to have a less extensive source region for the development of severe *cP* air masses. Most of the *cP* air affecting western and central Europe arrives from Fenno-Scandia and western Russia. Less frequently it arrives from Arctic Russia, and when it does, more severe cold is the result. This latter air mass resembles *cP* in North America and is cold, dry, and stable. By the time it reaches central and western Europe, however, it has been considerably modified so that it does not furnish the counterpart of the severe cold waves of interior North America. A European invasion of severe Arctic Russian *cP* air usually develops in connection with a synoptic condition involving a strong high located over northern Russia and a deep low over Scandinavia. *cP* air from western Russia and Fenno-Scandia, which is associated with less severe cold than that from Arctic Russia, is more frequently experienced in western and central Europe. This *cP* air resembles more the strongly modified *cP* air of North America as it is found in south central United States. Not only is it less severe and of more frequent occurrence than Arctic Russian air, but it also extends over larger parts of the continent.

206. *mP* (**polar maritime**) **air masses** are far more significant in western Europe's weather than are the continental types. Chiefly they comprise air from North America that has been greatly modified over the waters of the North Atlantic, which is the primary source region. As it enters the continent of Europe, it strongly resembles *mP* air along the northwest coast of North America, being relatively mild, humid, and conditionally unstable. Lacking north-south mountain barriers, except in Scandinavia, Europe is relatively open to invasions of maritime air as far east as the Alps, and marine climate is therefore extensive. This is in contrast to conditions in North America. When *mP* air is lifted along surfaces of discontinuity in cyclones, widespread rains develop, and over high-lands rainfall may be heavy.

If the mP air has its origin over the Arctic Ocean east of Greenland and north of Iceland, it may differ considerably in character from the usual mP, the amount of modification depending on the path taken in reaching Europe. If the path is short, it arrives as a cold, stable air mass not greatly different from cP in North America, although somewhat warmer and more humid. In this state it is some of the coldest maritime air found anywhere on the earth. If the path taken is a longer one so that it remains several days over the open sea after leaving the region of arctic pack ice, it takes on more and more of the characteristics of ordinary mP air.

207. mT (**tropical maritime**) **air masses** in Europe have strong resemblance to mT-Pacific air as it is found along the west coast of the United States but are cooler, drier, and more stable than mT-Gulf air in southeastern United States. Coming from the northern and eastern flanks of the Atlantic subtropical high-pressure cell where subsidence is strong, mT air that arrives in Europe, although relatively warm and moist as compared with polar air, is pronouncedly stable. Since leaving its source in the subtropical anticyclone it has had a trajectory over a colder surface that further increases its stability. Ordinarily it yields little or no rain on lowlands except where it is involved in cyclonic systems, under which conditions widespread precipitation is common. Providing the warm-sector air masses in cyclonic storm, mT air is an extensive rain and snow bringer to western and central Europe.

208. cT (**tropical continental**) **air masses** have their origin in the extensive desert lands of North Africa. They are characterized by dryness, moderate warmth, and marked stability aloft. It is this air that provides the heat supply for the Mediterranean cyclones of winter. Good weather with clear skies and high temperatures prevails under cT control. In the Mediterranean regions of Africa, Europe, and western Asia, cT air, when displaced by mP air behind cold fronts, yields a moderate amount of winter precipitation.

SUMMER AIR MASSES

209. cP (**polar continental**) **air** in Europe in summer commonly develops from what previously was mP air and consequently its moisture content is somewhat higher than that of cP air in the United States. While its temperature may not be so different from its North American counterpart, summer cP in Europe nowhere makes contact with strongly contrasting tropical air masses to form well-developed fronts such as form in the Mississippi Valley between sharply contrasting cP and mT air masses. European cP is only slightly cooler than cT in western Europe, while it is warmer than mP. But great air-mass temperature contrasts are lacking; therefore summer weather in western and central Europe is not characterized by great variability.

Summer Air Masses in Europe
(After Petterssen)

	Elevation, meters	Temperature, °F.	Specific humidity, g./kg.
1. cP Air			
Berlin	—	63	9.6
	850	57	7.5
	1,850	46	5.7
	2,900	36	3.9
	4,050	21	2.3
	5,450	7	1.3
2. mP Air			
Hamburg	—	59	8.5
	850	50	6.3
	1,800	39	4.7
	2,850	28	3.1
	4,050	16	1.8
	5,400	1	1.0
3. mT Air			
Hamburg	—	68	8.9
	900	57	7.5
	1,850	48	6.2
	2,900	37	4.6
	4,100	25	3.3
	5,500	12	2.1
4. cT Air (Source Region in Europe)			
Berlin	—	68	9.5
	900	64	8.5
	1,850	52	6.5
	2,925	39	4.6
	4,150	27	2.7
	5,500	7	1.6

mP (*polar maritime*) air in Europe in summer shows considerable variation in character, depending on where it originates within the extensive source region and the length of its sojourn over the ocean. If it originates in the southern part of the source region and reaches Europe after a long trajectory over the water, it is generally stable. This air mass gives rise to cool fair weather and is a rain producer only when it experiences a marked lift along fronts in well-developed cyclones. On the other hand, air that reaches Europe more directly from the northern part of the source region shows mild instability and may give rise to some convective activity. Heavier showers result when this air is lifted along frontal surfaces. mP air is distinctly cooler than the land that it invades, so that its general effect is to give western Europe a cool, marine summer climate.

210. mT **(tropical maritime) air masses** are relatively unimportant in the summer weather of Europe. When they do invade the continent, they arrive only in greatly modified form. The mT air reaching Europe has originated on the northern and eastern side of the Azores High where subsidence is strong so that stability aloft is marked (mTs). In addition, its northward trajectory has caused it to pass over cool ocean waters which have tended to stabilize the surface layers. Such air cannot give rise to the thundery, showery weather so typical of summer mT-Gulf air in southeastern United States. Only when it is forced to rise over topographic obstacles or along fronts of well-developed cyclones can it become an important rain maker.

211. cT **(tropical continental) air masses** that develop over the Sahara and Asia Minor in summer are extremely dry and hot. Under the influence of low-pressure centers over northern Europe, the cT air occasionally flows northward across the Mediterranean Sea and into southern Europe and southwestern Siberia and en route picks up considerable moisture, so that the condensation level is lowered and convective instability increased. Modified cT air masses therefore provide a fair share of moisture for the summer rainfall of southern and eastern Europe and of southwestern Siberia. cT air in Europe has a characteristic opalescent haze, the result of numerous fine dust particles transported from the Saharan region.

cT air of a less extreme type develops over southeastern Europe and adjacent parts of Asia during summer anticyclonic conditions. This air is more stable than the modified cT air from North Africa, and summer thunderstorms are therefore less frequent when it prevails. Usually it is only slightly warmer than cP air in the same region.

In concluding this brief summary of European air masses, it is worth emphasizing that Europe has no air mass comparable in heat, humidity, and instability to mT-Gulf air in the United States. For this reason it has no counterpart to the sultry weather with numerous thunderstorms characteristic of our humid subtropical cotton belt region and of the corn belt.

Air Masses of the Southern Hemisphere

212. General. The network of upper-air soundings in the Southern Hemisphere is so incomplete that anything like a satisfactory survey of its air masses is impossible at the present time. Because of the preponderance of water surface, maritime air masses greatly exceed continental ones in importance. The greater strength and prevalence of the westerlies in the Southern Hemisphere likewise results in much less meridional (north-south) transport of air here than in the Northern Hemisphere. As a result, frontal migration and temperature variability are less. Excepting Antarctica there are no extensive land masses in the middle and higher latitudes so that cP air masses are not known in South America, Africa, and Australia. Only South America extends sufficiently far poleward to be able to produce cP air, but here the narrowness of the continent cancels out the effect of latitude. Antarctica, the one area where cP air does develop, is so well insulated from the other continents by extensive water bodies that air invading from the polar land mass has been transformed into mP by the time it reaches the three other continents.

213. South America. A somewhat tentative description of the arrangement of air masses and fronts in South America has been presented by

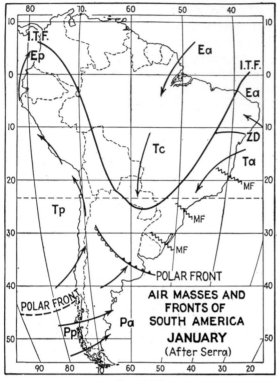

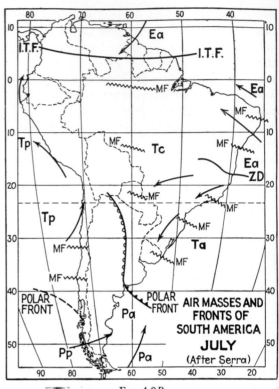

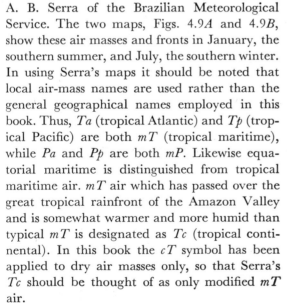

FIG. 4.9A.

FIG. 4.9B.

A. B. Serra of the Brazilian Meteorological Service. The two maps, Figs. 4.9A and 4.9B, show these air masses and fronts in January, the southern summer, and July, the southern winter. In using Serra's maps it should be noted that local air-mass names are used rather than the general geographical names employed in this book. Thus, *Ta* (tropical Atlantic) and *Tp* (tropical Pacific) are both *mT* (tropical maritime), while *Pa* and *Pp* are both *mP*. Likewise equatorial maritime is distinguished from tropical maritime air. *mT* air which has passed over the great tropical rainfront of the Amazon Valley and is somewhat warmer and more humid than typical *mT* is designated as *Tc* (tropical continental). In this book the *cT* symbol has been applied to dry air masses only, so that Serra's *Tc* should be thought of as only modified *mT* air.

In July (winter) equatorial air masses prevail over most of northern South America, equatorial North Atlantic north of the intertropical front (*ITF*) and equatorial South Atlantic to

the south of it. These air masses are warm, very humid, and potentially unstable. They are characterized by towering cumulus clouds and showery thunderstorm weather. Farther poleward are the tropical air masses, *Ta* (tropical Atlantic) on the eastern side of the continent and *Tp* (tropical Pacific) on the west. The latter, being derived from the poleward and eastern flanks of the South Pacific High where subsidence is marked, is cool, dry, and stable. These characteristics are further accentuated as this air moves over abnormally cool water along the coast. The result is the desert of northern Chile and Peru. *Ta* air, on the other hand, from the western and equatorial side of the South Atlantic High is warmer, more humid, and unstable. South of the tropical air masses are those designated as polar, which originate over the high middle latitudes of the South Pacific and South Atlantic Oceans. *Pp* (polar Pacific) air, like its counterpart in North America, is potentially unstable, and ascent over the mountains of southern Chile therefore gives rise to very heavy precipitation. As the polar air moves equatorward against the Tp air, definite fronts (MF) are produced that account for the winter rains of the Mediterranean region of Chile. So strong is the atmospheric circulation in winter that many of the Pp air masses cross the Andes south of latitude 30° and become confused with Pa air. On the eastern side of the continent, the polar air masses move equatorward along two routes, one following the Paraná and Paraguay Valleys, the other the Brazilian Coast. Along both routes, fronts (MF) are formed between the polar and tropical air masses.

In January, the Southern Hemisphere summer, certain significant modifications of the July air-mass arrangement and characteristics occur.

The intertropical front (ITF) has migrated much farther south over the continent, and unstable E and Tc air prevail over a large part of the tropical interior south as far as latitude 20°. This is the rainy season for northern and central Brazil. Ep (equatorial Pacific) air prevails along the west coast north of the equator and Ea in northeastern Brazil. The atmospheric circulations in subtropical latitudes are weaker in summer so that the Pp air does not form fronts with Tp air but moves equatorward with clear skies. On the eastern side of the continent polar air masses move equatorward as far as latitude 15°, forming fronts that are partly responsible for the heavy summer rain of the coast of southern and southeastern Brazil.

SELECTED BIBLIOGRAPHY ON AIR MASSES AND THEIR PROPERTIES

1. General. Willett, pp. 181–196; Byers, pp. 235–254; Petterssen, "Weather Analysis and Forecasting," pp. 138–204; Petterssen, "Introduction to Meteorology," pp. 123–133.
2. North America. Willett, pp. 196–224; Byers, pp. 255–277; Brunnschweiler, Dieter H. The Geographic Distribution of Air Masses in North America. *Vierteljahrsschr. naturforsch. Ges. Zurich*, Vol. 97, pp. 42–49, 1952.
3. Asia. Arakawa, H. The Air Masses of Japan. *Bull. Am. Meteorological Soc.*, Vol. 18, pp. 407–410, 1937; also *Met. Zeit.*, Vol. 54, pp. 169–174, May, 1937; Tu, Chang-Wang. Chinese Air Mass Properties. *Quart. Jour. Roy. Meteorological Soc.*, Vol. 65, pp. 33–51, 1939; Byers, pp. 287–291.
4. Europe. Petterssen, "Weather Analysis," numerous scattered references to European air masses on pp. 138–204; Schinze, G. Troposphärische Luftmassen und vertikaler Temperaturgradient. *Beitr. Physik der frein Atmosphäre*, Vol. 19, pp. 79–90, 1932; Byers, pp. 278–287; Belasco, J. E. Characteristics of Air Masses in the British Isles. *Geophys. Mem.*, No. 87, Meteorological Office, Great Britain, 1952.
5. Southern Hemisphere continents and the tropics. Deppermann, C. E. Outlines of Philippine Frontology. Philippine Weather Bureau, Manila, 1936; Dunn, Gordon E. Cyclogenesis in the Tropical Atlantic. *Bull. Am. Meteorological Soc.*, Vol. 21, pp. 215–229, June, 1940; Frolow, S. La Frontologie aux Antilles, *Ann. phys. du globe de la France d'Outre-Mer.* Vol. 5, pp. 114–117, 1938; see review by John Leighly, *Geog. Rev.*, Vol. 29, p. 155, January, 1939; Hubert, Henry. Les Masses d'air de L'Ouest Africain, *Ann. phys. du globe de la France d'Outre-Mer*, Vol. 5, pp. 33–64, 1938; see review by John Leighly, *Geog. Rev.*, Vol. 29, pp. 154–155, January, 1939; James, Preston E. Air Masses and Fronts in South America. *Geog. Rev.*, Vol. 29, pp. 132–134, January, 1939; Serra, A., and Ratisbonna, L. Air Masses of Southern Brazil. *Monthly Weather Rev.*, Vol. 66, pp. 6–8, 1938; Frolow, S. Synoptic Analysis of Caribbean Weather. *Bull. Am. Meteorological Soc.*, Vol. 22, pp. 198–210, May, 1941; Serra, A. B. The General Circulation over South America. *Bull. Am. Meteorological Soc.*, Vol. 22, pp. 173–178, April, 1941.

CHAPTER 5: *Atmospheric Disturbances and Their Associated Weather Types*

214. Atmospheric Disturbances as Generators of Precipitation. It is a common misconception that air blowing in from the ocean over the land is the immediate and direct cause of rainfall. This is rarely the case except in a minor way, possibly as a result of frictional retardation of the lower air currents with a consequent overrunning and lifting of those aloft. There are plenty of illustrations on the daily weather maps, where air blows in from the sea over flattish land areas with no rainfall resulting. But this is not to say that the land or sea origin of air is of little consequence in affecting the probability of precipitation. On the contrary, it is significant, and for the reason that air from over the sea is likely to have a more abundant supply of water vapor and so has greater potentialities for rain.

But actually to cause condensation on a large scale, with resulting precipitation, there is a further requirement than merely abundant atmospheric moisture. That requirement is some method of causing a large volume of air to be lifted and consequently cooled. Except where orographic barriers are the cause for ascent, atmospheric disturbances, or storms, are the principal local centers of rising air, with the result that storms of various types are the earth's principal generators of precipitation.

A large quantity of moisture in the air is meteorologically significant, not only as a potential reservoir for rainfall, as indicated above, but also because it creates an atmospheric environment conducive to the development and growth of storms. Tremendous amounts of latent energy (heat of condensation) are stored up in

the atmosphere's water vapor, where it is available for the production and growth of storms. Dry air therefore has less potential *storm energy* than humid air. It is especially with rain-producing storms that this chapter deals.

215. Storms as Climatic Phenomena (Secondary Circulation). An observation of the United States daily weather map, or still better a weather map of the entire Northern Hemisphere, impresses one with the fact that the seasonal isobaric and wind-flow patterns as described under the heading of general circulation and shown in Figs. 2.21 and 2.22 are not so readily discernible. This is because there is superimposed on the broader patterns of the general circulation a great variety of wave and vortex disturbances and irregularities, and these are so numerous that they tend almost to mask the major lineaments of the general circulation (Fig. 5.1). On a United States daily weather map, for example, the so-called "prevailing westerlies" are pretty much obscured by a series of large-scale eddy circulations which appear to be converging and diverging circulations about distinct low- and high-pressure centers. It is analogous to a river being so full of disturbances in the form of eddies, whirls, and cross currents that the general downstream flow of the main current is rendered less conspicuous. These week-to-week and day-to-day irregularities and disturbances in the general circulation, called by the meteorologist *the secondary circulation*, are of the utmost importance in understanding temporal and regional weather. Hence, they are of major importance climatically, since climate is but a composite of weather conditions as applied

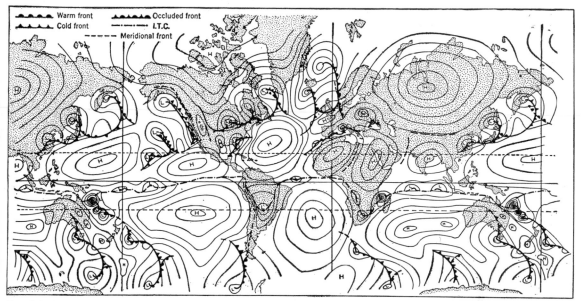

FIG. 5.1. Typical daily weather map of the world in the Northern Hemisphere winter. The most conspicuous features on the map are the very numerous wave and vortex disturbances. This is especially the case in the middle latitudes. (*From M. A. Garbell, "Tropical and Equatorial Meteorology."*)

to a particular region. These short-time disturbances and perturbations as shown on the weather map are the subject for discussion in the present chapter.

The climatologist's interest in atmospheric disturbances, or storms, derives from their effects chiefly upon precipitation and temperature which are the principal weather and climatic elements. As pointed out in an earlier section, to produce large-scale condensation and associated precipitation, it is necessary to cause deep and extensive masses of air to be lifted and adiabatically cooled below the saturation point. Except where orographic barriers are the cause of large-scale ascent of air, storms of various kinds are the principal local centers of rising air over the earth. It follows, therefore, that storms are the principal generators of the earth's precipitation. They likewise cause numerous temperature changes and irregularities. This comes about, in part, as a result of their associated cloud covers which greatly affect incoming and outgoing radiation. Storms also generate the advection of air masses which transport temperature conditions from their places of origin. Thus in part the general monthly and seasonal tem-

perature patterns of the earth are the result of the nature and distribution of storms. It is only the more common, and hence climatically significant, storms, or disturbances, that will receive attention.

Middle-latitude Cyclones and Anticyclones

216. While the pressure and wind irregularities to be observed on the daily surface weather charts are very numerous and have various shapes and patterns, the two most common, and the ones whose effects on weather and climate are of greatest importance, are the so-called cyclone and anticyclone. Middle-latitude weather is characterized by a succession of alternating low- and high-pressure systems moving around the earth from west to east in the stream of the prevailing westerlies. These storms, with their attendant cloud, rainfall, and temperature phenomena, infest the belts of westerly winds and account for the variability and fickleness of weather so characteristic of the middle latitudes. It is in these regions so greatly affected by cyclones and anticyclones that well-developed weather-forecasting services are most essential and also best developed.

Before examining the origin, structure, and attendant weather conditions of these atmospheric disturbances, it may be wise to establish the general picture of them as they appear on the surface weather maps. Since, in all probability, many of the students using this book already have been introduced to the weather map, the discussion here will be in the nature of a short and elementary summary. It should be borne in mind that none of the lows and highs as they appear on the weather maps exactly resemble each other, for there is great variety in size, shape, and degree of intensity. Consequently the generalizations concerning middle-latitude cyclones and anticyclones which follow must not be expected to apply precisely and in all respects to any individual storm. Moreover, these storms differ from one part of the world to another, and even within an area the size of the United States they look and act somewhat unlike in different regions.

217. Nature and Location. As seen on the surface weather map, *cyclones* are areas of relatively low pressure surrounded by concentric closed isobars, while *anticyclones* are areas of relatively high pressure surrounded by closed isobars

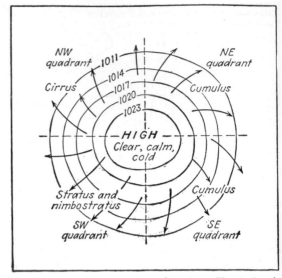

Fig. 5.3. A model anticyclone (Northern Hemisphere).

(Figs. 5.2, 5.3, 5.4). A middle-latitude cyclone, therefore, frequently goes by the name of *low*, *depression*, or *trough* if it is an elongated storm. The anticyclone is called a *high* or, if elongated, a *ridge*. Since its surface pressure is low, the cyclone must be a mass of relatively less dense air as compared with the anticyclone. Cyclones of the type under discussion seem to develop in areas of air-mass conflict or along well-developed fronts. It is for this reason that they are concentrated in the middle latitudes (35 to 65°), which are the zones of convergence and conflict between polar and tropical air masses. Since they develop as waves in the belts of westerly winds, their general movement is from west to east, although the route of an individual storm is frequently far from direct.

218. Shape and Appearance. While the isobars of a low as seen on a weather map are usually concentric, the shapes of individual storms vary greatly. Some have isobars which are nearly circular in form. Others are definitely V-shaped, with the broader portion to the north and the long axis oriented northeast-southwest (Northern Hemisphere). Some are so much elongated that they are in the form of troughs. Storms with well-developed fronts are frequently subangular in shape, the blunt angles being located approximately where the fronts intersect

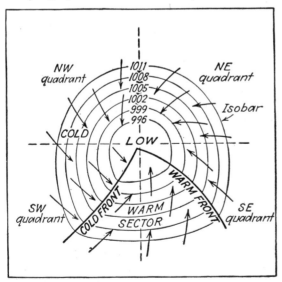

Fig. 5.2. A model cyclone (Northern Hemisphere) showing typical arrangement of isobars, wind system, warm and cold sectors, and surface fronts.

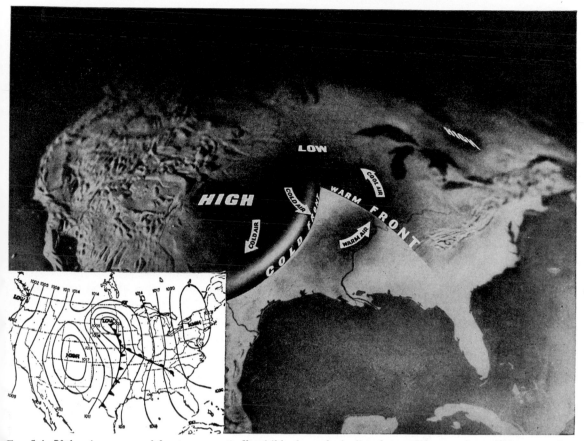

Fig. 5.4. If the air masses and fronts were actually visible the cyclonic disturbance shown on the small inset weather map might appear as shown in the three-dimensional illustration. (*Courtesy of U.S. Weather Bureau.*)

the isobars. The contrast in shape, general appearance, and arrangement of fronts between Northern Hemisphere and Southern Hemisphere cyclones is illustrated in Figs. 5.2, 5.4, 5.12.

In a cyclone, or low, the pressure is lowest at the center and increases toward the margins of the storm. In an anticyclone the highest pressure is at the center. The terms low and high, as applied to pressure in these storms, is not specific, but relative. In other words, no specific amount of pressure separates lows from highs; it is always a relative thing. Normally the pressure difference between the center and margins of a low is 10 to 20 mb., or several tenths of an inch. It is possible for large and well-developed winter lows to show as much as 35 mb., or 1 in., of pressure difference. An intense high may show an equivalent pressure difference between center and circumference, although half that amount is more normal. The winter season has many more large and steep-gradient cyclones and anticyclones than summer, so that the cooler seasons have more variable weather than the warmer periods of the year.

Because the cyclone is a low-pressure storm it is an area of converging winds of moderate velocity. Rarely are they violent or destructive, however. Earth rotation causes the converging winds to approach the low center obliquely so that the surface-wind arrows make an angle of 20 to 40° with the isobars. Because air in a low is converging, it is being lifted so that cloud and precipitation are common. In the Northern Hemisphere such a converging system of winds usually results in a warm sector to the south and east of the center where the winds are from a southerly direction, and a cooler section to the north and west where the winds are northerly.

The surface winds in a high move outward from the center toward the circumference; in other words, it is a diverging system with vertical settling or subsidence feeding the surface currents.

219. Size. There are great variations in the size of these storms, but on the whole they spread over extensive areas, sometimes covering as much as one-third of the United States, or 1,000,000 square miles, although most of them are smaller. They are *extensive* rather than *intensive*. Thus a normal cyclone with a vertical thickness of 6 to 7 miles probably will have a diameter one hundred times as great. Cyclones are inclined to be elliptical or egg-shaped in contour, with the narrow end toward the equator. The long axis, extending in a northeast-southwest direction, is commonly nearly twice the length of the short one (northwest-southeast), so that a typical well-developed winter cyclone might show long and short diameters of 1,200 and 650 miles, respectively. Anticyclones are inclined to be somewhat larger, their diameters averaging roughly 25 per cent greater than those of lows.

220. Direction and Rate of Movement. As noted in an earlier paragraph, lows and highs travel in a general west-to-east direction. This movement results from two causes. In the first place, throughout the troposphere in the middle latitudes winds have a westerly component, so that cyclones and anticyclones are carried along with these currents. Second, according to the wave theory, a cyclone of the wave type would move in such a way that the warmer air is on the right in the Northern Hemisphere and on the left in the Southern Hemisphere. Wave movement therefore also contributes to a west-east propagation. That is not to say, however, that storms always move due eastward. To be sure, they follow different routes, and there are some regions of concentration and others of divergence; but, in spite of their vagaries in direction, as well as in rate of movement, their progress is, in general, eastward. The direction and rate of movement of cyclones are approximately those of the upper winds. It is easy to understand, therefore, why a weather forecaster in the middle latitudes bases his prediction upon

weather conditions to the west, rather than to the east, of his station. Those storms to the east already have gone by; those to the west are approaching. There is a tendency for storms to follow certain general tracks. A more detailed account of world-wide storm movements, and the routes followed, will appear later in the chapter.

Variability in rate of movement is characteristic, both as to season and as to individual storms. In the United States storms move eastward across the country at velocities averaging 20 miles an hour in summer and 30 miles an hour in winter, with the highs somewhat slower than the lows. In summer, when the whole atmospheric circulation is slowed down, storm speeds are reduced, and the contrasts between cyclones and anticyclones are less pronounced. As a consequence, warm-season weather is less changeable, and atmospheric disturbances are less violent. In the winter season a well-developed low characteristically requires 3 to 6 days for the transcontinental journey across the United States.

Just as temperature, pressure, and wind belts shift north and south, following the movements of the sun's rays, poleward in summer and equatorward in winter, so also do the storm tracks. This fact helps to explain the fewer and weaker storms over the middle latitudes in summer as compared with winter.

221. Origin of Cyclones. Middle-latitude cyclones appear to comprise a collection of different kinds of disturbances of which the two most common are (*a*) unstable waves developed along surface fronts and (*b*) surface cyclones which have been formed by the building downward of an upper-air trough. A combination of the processes suggested above is probably of frequent occurrence, and all very strong cyclones seem to have this dual origin. It may be, therefore, that what appears to be a double process is only one after all. One group of meteorologists feels that the first development of a cyclone occurs along fronts near the surface and that the developing disturbance is at a later stage connected with a high-level trough. There is good evidence to support the opposite argument, however, that surface disturbances have their beginnings in the upper atmosphere and that the surface cyclone is the result of a downward propagation of the disturbance aloft. By what process upper-air long waves act to produce surface cyclones is not known. Certain it is, however, that the fully developed extratropical cyclone in the Northern Hemisphere consists of a counterclockwise vortex of air which extends up into an upper-air trough in the westerlies. The connection is there between surface and upper-air phenomena, but which is cause and which is effect is still disputed. The following frontal, or air-mass, explanation of cyclones is the so-called classical one developed by the Norwegian school of meteorologists. Here the emphasis is placed upon low-level origins. The effects of the high atmosphere upon surface-cyclone formation is still largely unknown, although a great deal is suspected.

Extratropical cyclones tend to develop along fronts separating two air masses of unlike temperature, density, and direction of movement. This front may be the polar front or one of the others. Thus, regions where large-scale air currents of contrasting properties converge are called areas of *frontogenesis*. Conversely, regions of horizontal divergence, where fronts are destroyed, are called areas of *frontolysis*. The regions along the east coast of North America and south of Greenland in winter are excellent regions of frontogenesis, as is the region just to the east of Asia. Here the temperature contrasts are great and converging air masses frequent. These same regions are also characterized by well-developed upper-air troughs.

It is possible to have two contrasting air masses in contact along a front with air flow in opposite directions and parallel with the front and yet with no active vertical displacement of the air. Such a front will be stationary and in equilibrium because the air streams parallel to the front. Along such a front, vertical displacement being absent, cloud and precipitation are not formed, and the front would have no practical weather significance. In the vicinity of the front, the cold air underlies the warmer air in the form of a wedge, the inclined boundary surface between the two air masses having a slope of about 1/100. Along this sloping boundary surface the air is moving in opposite directions, with the consequence that there is a strong wind shear. When the wind shear is sufficient, waves are likely to develop along the sloping frontal surface in the same way that waves are formed on a water surface when a wind blows across it. Wave motion on the frontal surface causes it to bulge up and down, with the result that the front at the ground develops a wave, or bulge. This wave on the surface front is the beginning of what may become a mature cyclonic storm. Apparently such waves are formed not alone from the shearing action of two oppositely directed air masses, for at times they seem to develop also as a result of some nearby disturbance in the westerlies, such as may result from the frictional effects along a coast line or the deflective effects of mountain barriers.

Some of the waves which develop along fronts apparently are stable in that they do not grow in magnitude, but are eventually damped out. On the other hand, some are unstable and these grow in size and pass through the several stages of a definite life cycle to become fully developed mature cyclones (Fig. 5.5). Following this climax stage, they begin to wane and eventually become extinct. In the beginning, the air, in adjusting itself to the newly formed frontal wave and seeking again to gain equilibrium, is drawn in toward this bulge, or "weak point," in the front and, under the combined forces of gradient, earth rotation, and friction, develops a characteristic cyclonic circulation. This air movement is such as to cause tropical warm air to advance over colder air in one part of the cyclonic system and cold air to advance against retreating warm air in still another part. Two fronts are thus formed. Vertical displacement of the warm air over the cold frequently leads to condensation and precipitation.

The principal source of energy of the cyclonic system lies in the temperature and density contrasts between the two air masses in the storm. A secondary source, but of considerable importance, is the latent heat of condensation that is released in the rising air. In cyclones which are fed by very warm and moist air, latent heat of

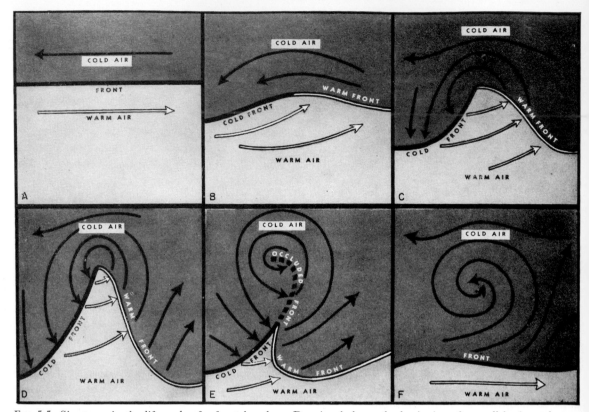

FIG. 5.5. Six stages in the life cycle of a frontal cyclone. Drawing *b* shows the beginning of a small horizontal wave along the front. In drawing *c* the wave development has progressed to the point where there is a definite cyclonic circulation with well-developed warm and cold fronts. Because of the more rapid movement of the cold front, drawing *d* shows a narrowed warm sector as the cold front approaches the retreating warm front. In drawing *e* the occlusion process is occurring, the cyclone has reached its maximum development and the warm sector is being rapidly pinched off. In drawing *f* the warm sector had been eliminated, the cyclone is in its dying stages and is represented by only a whirl of cold air. (*Courtesy of U.S. Weather Bureau.*)

condensation may become the more important source of storm energy.

222. Stages in the Life History of Cyclones. Figure 5.5 illustrates the stages in the life history of a middle-latitude frontal cyclone. Figure 5.6 is the fully developed storm. Figure 5.5*a* shows an equilibrium front before the beginning of a wave disturbance. A westerly current of warm air lies next to an easterly current of cold air. The front is stationary, for the air currents are parallel to the front. The cold air underlies the warm air in the form of a wedge with an inclination of about 1:100. There is no vertical displacement of the warm air, however, and as a result there is no condensation or precipitation. Along the inclined frontal surface separating the

two oppositely moving air masses, there is likely to be a strong wind shear, and this may form waves on the frontal surface. The wave motion causes the frontal surface to bulge up and down, and this in turn causes the front at the ground to oscillate in the form of a wave. Figure 5.5*b* shows the formation of such a wave on the surface front. Stippled areas indicate where precipitation is falling as a result of vertical displacement of the warm air by the cold. Such a slight wave disturbance may develop no further than the stage shown in Fig. 5.5*b*, and if so it travels along the front for a distance and finally flattens out and dies. On the other hand, if the wave is unstable and continues to increase in amplitude (Fig. 5.5*c*), within about 12 to 24 hr.

it probably will have developed to the stage represented by Fig. 5.6. Following this mature stage the cold front begins to overtake the warm front, Fig. 5.5*d*, and occlusion commences. This process of the cold air masses pinching out the warm air at the surface continues (Fig. 5.5*e*) until finally the cyclone becomes a large whirl of relatively homogeneous air (Fig. 5.5*f*). It appears that the cyclonic circulation develops at the poleward ends of the tongues of warm air or at the crest of the wave, with the line of surface discontinuity separating the unlike air masses passing through the center of the storm.

223. The Cyclone Model. The fully developed cyclone is shown in Fig. 5.6. The middle portion of the figure represents the cyclone as it appears on the weather map at sea level (Fig. 5.7). The upper portion of the figure is a *vertical* cross section through the cyclone to the north of the center, while the lower portion is a similar vertical cross section to the south of the center. In the cross section *AB* to the north of the storm center, the warm air does not reach the earth's surface, but it is present aloft. It is the lifting of the warm air aloft that produces the precipitation shown. South of the center warm air does reach the earth's surface, and the vertical cross section shows two surface fronts.

It is clear from the preceding discussion and from Figs. 5.6 and 5.7 that a cyclone consists of two essentially different air masses separated from one another by fronts. To the south and

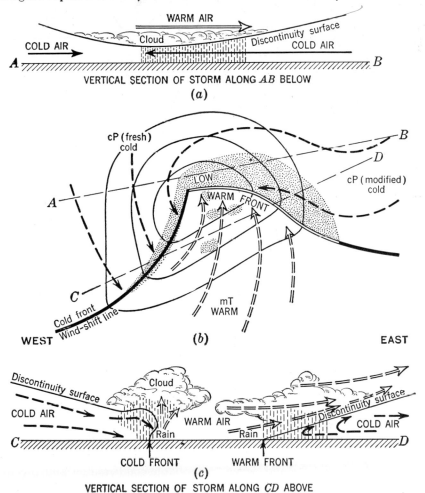

FIG. 5.6. The cyclone model. Ground plan and vertical sections of a fully developed wave cyclone.

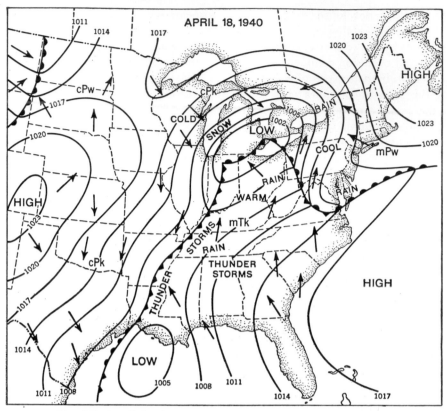

FIG. 5.7. A well-developed wave cyclone over eastern United States.

east is a poleward extension of warm humid tropical air, called the *warm sector*, which is enveloped on its western, northern, and northeastern sides by colder, drier air of polar origin. The nature of this polar air varies with different locations and source regions. In North America east of the Rocky Mountains the polar air to the west and northwest is usually fresher and colder than that to the east and northeast which has been considerably modified by several days travel over the middle latitudes. The discontinuity surface separating the polar and tropical air masses may be classified into warm and cold fronts, depending on whether the warm or the cold air is the aggressor. Where warm air leaves the earth's surface and actively moves upward over a wedge of cold air, as it does ahead of the eastward-advancing tongue of tropical air, a *warm front* develops. On the other hand, when moving cold air, acting as the aggressor, nndercuts and brings about forced ascent of warm air,

as it does to the rear, or west, of the warm sector, a *cold front* originates. Warm fronts in central and eastern United States are most commonly developed as a consequence of *mT*-Gulf air overrunning a barrier formed by modified polar air returning poleward on the rear of a retreating anticyclone.

224. *Warm Fronts.* The inclination of the surface of discontinuity in a warm front is relatively gentle, usually of the order 1:100 to 1:400. In other words, a person flying at an elevation of 5,000 ft. above the ground and in a direction at right angles to the front should cross the boundary separating the two air masses 100 to 400 miles ahead or east of the front (Fig. 5.8). As the warm air moves up the gently inclined surface of the cold-air wedge, its pressure is decreased, resulting in adiabatic cooling, and probable condensation and precipitation. Frictional drag tends to thin out and flatten the wedge of retreating cold air near the surface

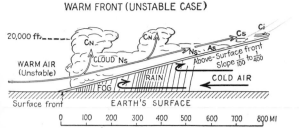

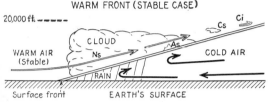

FIG. 5.8. The contrasting activity of stable warm air and unstable warm air along warm fronts.

front. This, together with the mixing that occurs with the advancing warm air, tends to blend the two air masses along the contact zone so that it is difficult to locate the warm front at the surface. The change in temperature and wind direction is transitional rather than abrupt.

The west-to-east movement of the cyclone plus the arrangement of fronts within it makes it evident that warm-front weather phenomena will be the first indications of an approaching cyclonic storm. Since the discontinuity surface has such a mild inclination, its influence may be seen in terms of certain high-level cloud forms as far as 1,000 to 1,500 miles ahead of the surface front where the wedge of cold air may be 15,000 to 20,000 ft. deep. The first clouds heralding the approaching storm are the high cirrus and cirrostratus, the latter forming the familiar halos around sun and moon. If the overrunning warm air is unstable, cirrocumulus will be present, giving the well-known "mackerel sky" recognized by old sailors as a harbinger of the storm. As the front approaches and the cold wedge becomes thinner, the cloud deck becomes lower and thicker. Altostratus and altocumulus deepen into stratocumulus and finally nimbus. Precipitation usually begins with the altostratus and continues until the surface front has passed. Soon after the rain starts, clouds and fog usually begin to form within the cold air mass below the

discontinuity surface. These result largely from evaporation from raindrops and surface water. The suddenness with which these lower clouds and the fog form makes them a genuine hazard to air navigation.

The character of the weather activity at the warm front depends to a considerable degree upon the nature of the overrunning warm air. If it is dry and stable, considerable ascent will be necessary to produce condensation forms, and precipitation will be light if it occurs at all. On the other hand, if the warm air is conditionally or convectively unstable, ascent over the cold wedge may be vigorous enough to produce showery conditions and thunderstorms (Fig. 5.8). To the observer at the ground the rain appears to be coming from the cold air. Most of it, however, has its origin in the overrunning warm air aloft. Because of the cold air at the surface, the rain is likely to be chilly and the weather disagreeable with low visibility. Such weather the New England poet had in mind when he wrote

> The day is cold and dark and dreary;
>   It rains and the wind is never weary.
> The vine still clings to the moldering wall,
>   And with every gust the dead leaves fall,
> And the day is dark and dreary.

Because of the slight inclination but great horizontal extent of the surface of discontinuity, warm-front precipitation is inclined to be steady, long continued, and of wide extent, but not excessively heavy, unless of course the ascending air is markedly unstable so that convection results from the initial lift along the front. The variable intensity of warm-front rain sometimes noted may be due in part to the wavy nature of the surface of discontinuity with the wave crests parallel to the surface front. Along such an irregular surface, ascent will be more vigorous in some places than in others, with consequent variations in quantity of precipitation.

With the passage of a warm front at the surface and the shifting of the observer from the cold air mass into the warm one, the following weather changes are likely to be noted: (a) a marked clearing of the weather; (b) an abrupt

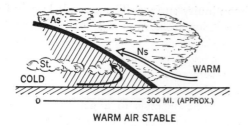

WARM AIR STABLE

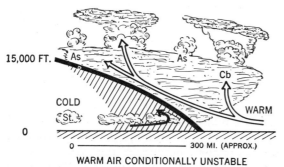

WARM AIR CONDITIONALLY UNSTABLE

FIG. 5.9. The contrasting activity of stable warm air and unstable warm air along slowly moving cold fronts.

temperature rise; (c) a rapid increase in specific humidity; (d) a slight barometric trough; (e) a slight shift in wind direction, usually about 45°.

225. *Cold Fronts.* In this type of discontinuity the warm air above the cold wedge is forced to rise by the aggressive action of the moving wedge of cold air (Fig. 5.9). Along such a front cold air replaces warmer air. When cold fronts are well developed, they are easily recognizable on the weather map by their marked wind discontinuities, which are known as wind-shift lines. Under normal conditions the slopes of cold-front surfaces of discontinuity are considerably greater than those of warm fronts, the values for the former being of the order 1:25 to 1:100. The slope, therefore, is roughly four times steeper in the cold than in the warm front. This difference is largely due to the contrasting effects of frictional forces which, along the warm front, through a drag effect upon the retreating wedge of cold air, tend to thin it out and reduce its slope. Along the cold front, on the other hand, the advancing cold air at the ground is held back by friction so that it tends to push forward aloft, thereby increasing the slope.[1] Characteristically

[1] B. C. Haynes, A Density Channel for Illustrating

the forward edge of a rapidly moving cold front takes the form of a squall head, as shown in Fig 5.6. Here the cold air aloft pushes out ahead of the front at the ground, obviously creating a highly unstable condition. This overrunning by the cold air may on the average amount to 25 miles, and, at a maximum, 100 miles. The elevation of the advanced portion of the cold tongue is usually about 1,500 ft. above the surface. Where movement of the front is slow, there is less overrunning and no pronounced squall head.

Since the surface of discontinuity slopes upward away from the direction of storm movement, the approach of the cold front is not heralded by cloud forms or other weather phenomena. Moreover, the zone of bad weather associated with rising air is much narrower at the cold than at the warm front and passes more rapidly. This is because the former has a greater speed of movement and a steeper slope and because the direction of its motion causes the warm air to retreat from the front rather than slide actively up over the surface of discontinuity. If the front moves rapidly and steadily, clearing takes place quickly after it has passed. If it is retarded for any reason, cloudy conditions may prevail for some time.

The nature of the weather along the cold front depends in a large degree upon the structure of warm air that is being displaced. If it is dry and stable, such as *mP*-Pacific air east of the Rocky Mountains, the front may be accompanied only by broken clouds and no precipitation. On the other hand, if it is warm humid *mT*-Gulf air, cumulonimbus clouds and frontal thunderstorms are likely. On the whole, however, owing to the blunt nose of the rapidly advancing wedge of cold air, the upthrust of warm air along the cold front is more vigorous than along the warm front, resulting in more tumultous weather and pelting rains than usually occur at the warm front, although their duration is shorter. A well-marked cold front thus is often marked by brief but violent precipitation and by cumulonimbus cloud forms.

Fronts and Occlusions, *Bull. Am. Meteorological Soc.*, Vol. 20, pp. 37–38, February, 1939. Contains photographs of laboratory-produced fronts in tanks.

In some cases most of the precipitation occurs in advance of the front; in others it is behind the front in the cold air.

If an unusually cold and vigorous air mass back of a cold front passes over a warmer water surface, the addition of heat and moisture in the lower layers often leads to the development of *secondary fronts* with associated snow flurries. This phenomenon is most common in late fall and early winter when contrasts in temperature between air and water are most marked. Similar secondary fronts and snow flurries may occur over land areas where the latter are distinctly warmer than the southward-advancing cold air mass.

With the passage of a cold front and the shifting of the observer from the warm to the cold air mass, the following weather changes are characteristic: (*a*) a marked clearing and improvement in the weather, usually fairly rapid; (*b*) an abrupt fall in temperature; (*c*) a well-marked barometric trough; (*d*) a pronounced decrease in specific and relative humidity; and (*e*) a marked wind shift of 45 to 180°.

226. Occluded Fronts. In normal cases the cold front of a cyclone travels faster than the warm front, so that it gradually catches up with and eventually overtakes the warm front. When contact between the two cold air masses, one on the front and the other on the rear of the warm sector, has been made and the intervening wedge of warm air has been lifted above the earth's surface, an *occlusion* is said to have taken place. This is a normal development in the life history of middle-latitude cyclones. Occlusion begins at the apex of the warm sector near the center of the storm and gradually progresses equatorward until the warm sector has been completely obliterated at the surface. The cyclone is thus partly occluded during the major part of its life history. Actually the cyclone usually reaches its maximum intensity 12 to 24 hr. after the beginning of the occlusion process. Although the two polar air masses involved in the occlusion may have had a similar origin, their life histories and trajectories have usually been enough different since leaving the source region that their temperatures, humidities, and densities are no longer

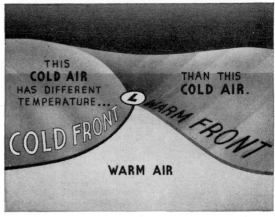

A

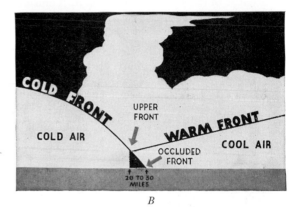

B

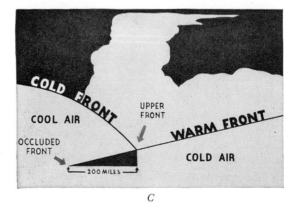

C

Fig. 5.10. Types of occlusion. *A* shows the warm and cold fronts preceding occlusion. *B* is a cold-front occlusion in which the fresh colder air to the west is undercutting the cool air to the east. *C* is a warm-front occlusion in which the cool air to the west is rising up over a wedge of colder air to the east. (*Courtesy of U.S. Department of the Navy.*)

the same. Consequently, as the cold front overtakes the warm front, a new discontinuity—this one between the two polar air masses—is created. When the air behind the cold front is colder than that ahead of the warm front, which is usually the case in central and eastern United States, the resulting discontinuity will resemble a new cold front (Fig. 5.10B). On the other hand, if the air ahead of the warm front is colder than the air behind the cold front, the occlusion will be of the warm-front type at the surface (Fig. 5.10C). In either case the warm air is lifted, but the cold air mass that is displaced vertically will vary, depending upon whether the occlusion is of type A or type B.

Because of the variations possible in occlusions it is difficult to be specific regarding the weather associated with them. In a general way the sequence of weather in warm-front occlusions resembles that in the ordinary warm front. The weather that accompanies the cold-front occlusion is of a composite type. Because of the warm

front aloft, there is normally widespread precipitation and cloud *ahead* of the surface front, although this area of bad weather is not so extensive as with a true warm front. Along the occluded cold front and behind it, weather is relatively similar to that associated with a true cold front (Fig. 5.11).

Precipitation along occluded fronts results from both the continued lifting of the warm air and the vertical displacement of the less dense of the cold air masses. As occlusion continues, the depth of cold air along the occluded front increases, and the warm air is crowded upward until it is high enough to spread out laterally over the cold air masses enclosing it. When this happens, further lifting of the warm air ceases, and that air mass plays no further part in cloud and rain production. From this point on the weather conditions are governed by the contrasts in the characteristics of the two cold air masses, one on either side of the occluded front.

In their later stages of occlusion cyclones be-

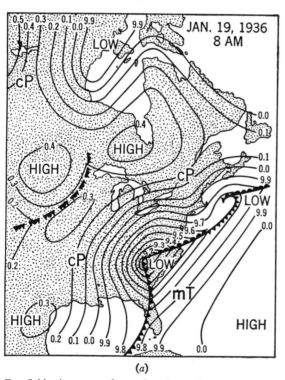

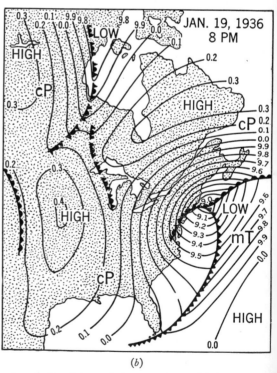

(a)   (b)

FIG. 5.11. A wave cyclone of moderate intensity deepening and occluding into an intense cyclone with heavy snow and gales over northeastern United States. In the later stages of occlusion, cyclones wane in intensity and do not yield abundant precipitation. (*After George and Elliot, Bull. Am. Meteorological Soc., March,* 1939.)

come less intense and precipitation is much less abundant than in the earlier stages of the storm's life cycle. The temperature and density contrasts between the cold air masses comprising the cyclone are not marked, and the heat of condensation derived from lifting the cool air is not great, so that the storm's energy sources are greatly reduced. There may be an extensive cloud cover but usually the clouds are not thick and the precipitation is light. Lifting of the cool air mass does not ordinarily result in heavy rains, for the moisture content is relatively low and the air mass is likely to be stable. Regions with a predominance of occluded cyclones, such as western Europe, are characterized by a great deal of low cloud, only modest amounts of precipitation, and small nonperiodic temperature changes.

227. Families of Cyclones. Toward the end of the occlusion process, when the original depression has practically disappeared, it is not uncommon for a secondary cyclone to develop to the south and west (Northern Hemisphere) of the parent storm. This new secondary depression goes through a life history similar to that of the original depression. There may actually be a whole family of these cyclones, each progressively smaller than the preceding one, and each developing farther equatorward. Such a train or family of cyclones seems to correspond with the long waves in the upper atmosphere, with each member of the cyclone family corresponding with a minor wavelike perturbation superimposed upon the pattern of a long wave at the 500-mb. (18,000 ft.) level.

228. Cyclones and Anticyclones as a Principal Method of Heat Exchange. It bears reemphasizing that middle-latitude cyclones and anticyclones are in the nature of traveling disturbances in the zonal westerlies. They represent a breakdown in the zonal circulation of the atmosphere by which means there is facilitated a latitudinal exchange of polar and tropical air. Through this exchange the imbalance in radiation between low latitudes and high latitudes is corrected. Consequently moving cyclones and anticyclones as observed on the daily weather map may be thought of as a surface expression of the mechanism by which the heat balance of the earth is maintained.

229. Kinds and Origins of Middle-latitude Anticyclones. As indicated in an earlier section, the anticyclone is an extensive area of high pressure with which there is associated a diverging system of surface winds.

Two kinds of anticyclones are recognized: (*a*) the rapidly moving cold anticyclone composed of air originating in high latitudes and usually located to the rear of a middle-latitude cyclone and (*b*) the warm anticyclone composed of air originating in subtropical latitudes and moving very slowly or not at all. Not infrequently the cold anticyclone is converted into a warm anticyclone by heating in the lower middle latitudes. In this process it slows down or even becomes stationary. The cold anticyclone develops as a result of the cooling of the surface air which loses its heat to the underlying cold surface by radiation and conduction processes. The cold, dense surface layer is only a few kilometers deep so that the cold anticyclone is a relatively shallow phenomenon. The cooling and vertical shrinking of the surface layer of air results in a lowering of the isobaric surfaces aloft with a consequent inflow of air at higher levels, thus creating higher barometric pressure at the surface.

A satisfactory explanation of warm, deep anticyclones has not yet been given. They are associated in origin with the high-pressure cells of the subtropics, which in turn are related to the long waves in the upper westerlies.

WIND SYSTEMS IN CYCLONES

230. Not Destructive Storms. Among laymen the terms *cyclone* and *tornado* often are used synonymously, but incorrectly, to represent any violent and destructive windstorm. While such is the nature of hurricanes and tornadoes, it is not the character of most intermediate-zone cyclones, which are a quite different type of storm. Occasionally there are winter cyclones and anticyclones accompanied by boisterous winds which produce blizzard conditions and raise heavy seas on the oceans and large lakes, but even these are not violently destructive. By far the larger number of lows and highs are accompanied by winds of only moderate velocity. It is the structure, or system, of winds in these middle-latitude storms that is distinctive, not their velocities.

231. A Converging Wind System. Because the cyclone is a low-pressure system with the gradient directed toward the center, it is to be expected that at the surface there will be a flow of air from the circumference of the storm toward its center (Fig. 5.2). It is, in the first place, therefore, a *converging* system of winds. Such a converging system makes necessary the escape of the inward flowing air by ascent and outflow aloft. This upward flow of air in a cyclone is not to be thought of as an uprush of vertically ascending air such as occurs in a thunderstorm. Much more frequently it is a relatively slow lifting of the air along mildly sloping surfaces of discontinuity. Cloud types associated with cyclones are not characteristically cumulus in character, a type which is associated with vertical convection. Instead they are of the flattish, or sheet, type.

On a rotating earth, however, a direct flow of air toward the central low pressure of the storm is impossible. Coriolis force plus surface friction tend to modify the simple convergence so that the air moves toward the center as a counter-clockwise whirl (Northern Hemisphere) with the *surface* wind arrows crossing the isobars at an angle of 20 to 40°. A more correct picture of the cyclone's wind system, therefore, is that of a vortex movement with the winds spiraling in obliquely toward the low-pressure center. This general horizontal convergence of an indirect

type is characteristic of the friction layer of the closed vortex, or up to about 1 km., or 3,500 ft.

But such a simple circular cyclonic vortex as described above cannot exist at all levels. The Coriolis force is not the same in the northern and southern parts of the vortex, and the results are that the wind will be stronger in the southern part as compared with the northern. As a consequence there will be net air transport across a north-south median wall from the western to the eastern half of the cyclone. Above the friction layer, therefore, there is general horizontal convergence and lifting of air toward the front or east of the center and horizontal divergence to the rear or west. This contrast in the wind system of the eastern as compared with the western half of the cyclone is of unusual importance in understanding the distribution of cloud and precipitation in such a storm.

However, the simple inward-spiraling wind system of the cyclone's surface air as described above and observable on a weather map requires still further modification. In the first place the cyclone is not a stationary thing as shown on the weather map but is actually moving at the rate of 500 to 1,000 miles a day. Moreover, in any converging system of winds in the middle latitudes air of very different temperatures and densities must be pulled into the vortex in its northern and southern parts. The actual wind system of a moving cyclone in the middle latitudes is more accurately, although still very diagrammatically, represented in Fig. 5.13. In it the convergence of air flow is still conspicuous, but the simple inward-spiraling system is considerably modified. Most significant is the fact that there are two contrasting air masses, a warmer one to the south, usually of tropical or subtropical origin, and a colder one of polar origin to the north, west, and northeast. The cold air appears to enter the moving cyclone along the warm front, circles the wave apex, and turns southward to invade along the cold front. Fresh polar air enters from the northwest. The warm air of tropical origin enters the cyclone from the southwest with a speed which is only slightly greater than that of the cyclone in its eastward movement. As it reaches the warm

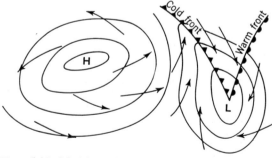

Fig. 5.12. Model cyclone and anticyclone in the Southern Hemisphere. Here the cyclonic circulation is clockwise and that of the anticyclone, anticlockwise.

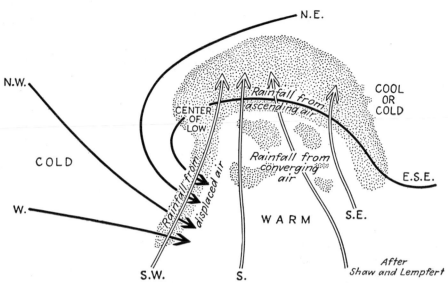

FIG. 5.13. Representation of the wind system and precipitation areas (stippled) in a middle-latitude cyclone.

front, it climbs the retreating wedge of modified polar air.

As a result of the converging system of surface air flow about a cyclonic center, winds on the *front* of the center (east, or direction storm is traveling) are from a general easterly direction, northeast in the northeastern quadrant and southeast in the southeastern quadrant. These easterly winds on the front of the cyclone can be either polar or tropical air, depending on the directional trend of the warm front. One cannot be certain of the primary origin of the air merely by observing wind direction, for the modified polar air on the front of a cyclone is frequently to be observed as a southeasterly current. This is polar air that was brought southward in a preceding anticyclone and has had a relatively long trajectory over the middle latitudes.

It is obvious that all these easterly winds on the front of a cyclone are opposite in direction to the general current of westerly winds in which they exist and likewise opposite to the direction of storm movement. Thus, while the storm travels from west to east, the winds on its front blow from east to west. This characteristic of a cyclone, which in many respects is an eddy or whirlpool of air in the westerlies, finds a counterpart in the whirlpool of a river. The whirlpool of water is carried downstream by the major current just as the storm is carried eastward by the westerlies, but on its downstream side the water flows into the whirl in a direction opposite to that of the general current and likewise opposite to the downstream movement of the whirlpool itself.

It is evident, then, that a cyclone is the meeting place of two very contrasting masses of air: a colder, drier, and heavier one arriving from higher latitudes on the poleward and rear sides of the storm; and a milder, more humid one from lower latitudes on the equatorward and front side.

232. Wind Shift with the Passing of a Cyclone. When a cyclonic center approaches and passes by an observer, the latter will experience general easterly winds as long as the low center is to the west of him, or, in other words, as long as he is on the front of the storm. As the center passes by, leaving him in the western, or rear, half of the low, the winds shift to the west. Easterly winds, therefore, often indicate the approach of a cyclone with its accompanying rain and cloud, while westerly winds more often foretell the retreat of the storm center and the coming of clearing weather.

In many cyclones this shift from easterly to westerly winds is rather gradual and lacking in abruptness. In others, and especially those storms with a marked equatorward elongation, so that the isobars are roughly in the form of the letter V, the wind shift is likely to be abrupt (Fig. 5.31A). Along the wind-shift line, which is approximately a line joining the apexes of the V-shaped isobars south of the center, winds of contrasting temperature, humidity, and density meet at a sharp angle, and violent storms and turbulent weather conditions often are the result. This wind-shift line is the cold front described in section 225.

233. *Veering and Backing Winds.* If the center of a cyclone passes to the north of the observer, so that he is in the southern quadrants of the storm, the succession of winds experienced will be southeast, south, southwest, and finally west and northwest (Fig. 5.14). This is called a *veering wind shift.* On the other hand, if the storm center passes south of the observer, so that he is on the north side of the cyclone, he will experience in succession northeast, north, and finally northwest winds. This is known as a *backing wind shift.* The following note regarding *wind-barometer indications* associated with a passing cyclone formerly appeared on the United States daily weather map.

"When the wind sets in from points between south and southeast and the barometer falls steadily, a storm is approaching from the west or northwest, and its center will pass near or north of the observer within 12 to 24 hr. with wind shifting to northwest by way of southwest and west. When the wind sets in from points between east and northeast and the barometer falls steadily, a storm is approaching from the south or

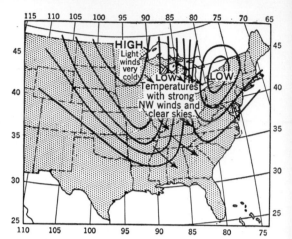

Fig. 5.15. A winter anticyclone advancing southeastward as a mass of cold polar air.

southwest, and its center will pass near or to the south or east of the observer within 12 to 24 hr. with wind shifting to northwest by way of north. The rapidity of the storm's approach and its intensity will be indicated by the rate and the amount of the fall in the barometer."

Backing and veering winds have important climatic significance. In a veering wind shift tropical air and one or more fronts are likely to be encountered, while with a backing wind shift the observer will be continuously in air of polar origin and surface fronts are less likely. Therefore regions which prevailingly lie on the equatorward sides of passing cyclones and experience veering winds are likely to have relatively higher average temperatures, greater variability of temperature, stronger convection, and more cumulus clouds than if they are located on the poleward sides of passing cyclones. Backing winds are associated with generally lower temperatures, less variability of temperature, a more continuous cloud cover, and greater likelihood of snow in winter.

234. Wind System of an Anticyclone. The term *anticyclone* was invented to designate the outflowing, or diverging, system of winds about a center of high pressure (Fig. 5.3). Deflection due to earth rotation causes the outflow of air about a high to develop something of a clockwise whirl (Northern Hemisphere). Since surface air in the high is constantly spreading outward from the center, it follows that there

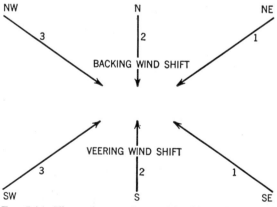

Fig. 5.14. Illustrating veering and backing wind shifts.

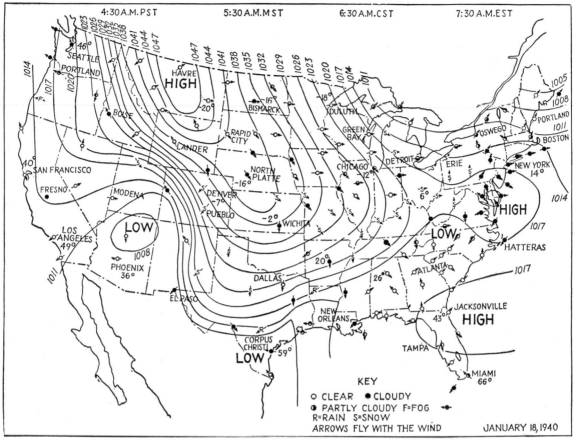

FIG. 5.16. United States daily weather map. A great polar continental (*cP*) air mass had advanced into the United States as a high-pressure system from the arctic plains of Canada. St. Joseph, Mo., had a minimum temperature of 21° below zero, and Galveston, Tex., on the Gulf of Mexico, 15° above zero. Ten inches of snow fell at Birmingham, Ala., and at Atlanta, Ga. (*Courtesy of U.S. Weather Bureau.*)

must be a compensatory feeding in of air at higher elevations, and subsequent settling of it, in order to maintain the high. The wind systems about highs and lows, therefore, are opposite (*a*) in direction of gradient-induced flow, (*b*) in direction of spiral deflection, and (*c*) in the kind of vertical movement at the centers.

Anticyclonic wind systems are usually less well developed than those of cyclones so that no characteristic wind shift is forecast as they pass by. In general, however, winds on the front (east) of an eastward advancing cold high are westerly, while those on the rear are easterly (Figs. 5.15, 5.16). Since lows and highs often alternate with one another as they move across the country, it is evident that the westerly winds on the front of a high and the rear of a low have

a similar origin and are much alike in character. Pressure gradients are usually less steep, and wind velocities lower, in anticyclones than in cyclones. Weak pressure gradients are particularly conspicuous toward the centers of highs where there is much light wind and calm. The strongest winds are likely to be found on the front margins of advancing cold highs where there is a merging with the preceding low. In this location between the cyclonic and anticyclonic systems the isobars tend to become nearly parallel straight lines trending in a general north-south direction. A strong horizontal pressure gradient from west to east is thereby developed, which is a consequence of combined westerly wind gradients and storm gradients, vigorous west and northwest winds

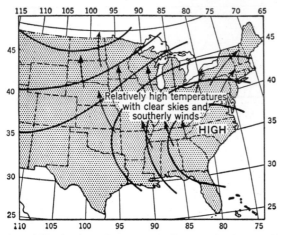

FIG. 5.17. A relatively warm, stagnant anticyclone over southeastern United States producing unseasonably warm weather over the central and eastern parts of the country.

being the result. Cold waves and blizzards over central and eastern North America are associated with these strong outpourings of cold air in the transition areas between the rears of lows and the fronts of cold highs.

Warm highs, of subtropical origin, normally have weaker pressure gradients and less well-developed wind systems than the cold highs and their movement is likely to be much slower (Fig. 5.17). They are inclined to remain stagnant over an area for days at a time.

PRECIPITATION IN CYCLONES AND ANTICYCLONES

235. Cyclones and Anticyclones Opposite in Precipitation Characteristics. As a general rule, the convergent air movement typical of cyclones is conducive to condensation, so that commonly they are accompanied by large areas of cloud and often by precipitation as well. Not every cyclone, to be sure, is associated with rainfall, but on the other hand many of them are. Anticyclones, still maintaining their opposite nature in precipitation as well as in pressure and winds, are inclined to be fair-weather areas with clouds much less prevalent and rainfall meager. These differences are not unexpected, since in lows there is a general convergence of contrasting air currents toward the center of the

storm with a consequent development of fronts. Lifting of the converging air masses and subsequent cooling due to expansion is the result. On the other hand, the slowly settling and warming air in anticyclones, as well as the diverging character of the surface air currents, is distinctly antagonistic to cloud and rainfall. As pointed out in an earlier section, subsidence, which is characteristic of anticyclones, tends to decrease the lapse rate, therefore increasing the stability of the air. In addition, the diverging nature of the anticyclone's air makes a conflict of contrasting air masses unlikely, and active fronts are therefore not to be expected.

It is not correct to assume, however, that shower activity is never associated with anticyclones. The tongues of anticyclonic air derived from the western ends of the subtropical highs where subsidence is less marked may be relatively humid if they have had a trajectory over warm ocean surfaces and under certain conditions they may be responsible for considerable rainfall. For example, the moist tongues of anticyclonic air from the western end of the North Atlantic subtropical anticyclone which enter the United States from the Gulf of Mexico in summer account for much of the summer shower activity in eastern Arizona, New Mexico, and parts of Colorado and in the Gulf and South Atlantic States as well. Similar situations should prevail in a number of the world's subtropical continents, more especially their eastern margins, where mT air masses enter from the western limbs of high-pressure cells.

236. Precipitation in Cyclones. Most of the cool-season precipitation of lowlands in the middle latitudes is cyclonic, or frontal, in origin. Winter snowfall on plains in these latitudes is almost exclusively associated with the fronts of cyclonic storms. The fewer and weaker lows of the warmer months yield a smaller percentage of that period's rainfall, since in summer convection and thunderstorms are likely to be more prevalent. Yet, even a considerable part of the warm-season convection, and many of the thunderstorms, are associated with cyclonic storms. Although cyclonic rain is the result of rising air, normally it does not rise because of local heating but rather because of forced ascent resulting from (*a*) a convergence of great masses of air toward a center, (*b*) the underrunning and lifting of warmer and lighter air masses by cooler, heavier ones, and (*c*) the ascent of warm currents over colder ones (Fig. 5.13). Unlike conditions in a thunderstorm, where rapid vertical ascent is characteristic, the lifting of air in cyclones, as noted earlier, is more often a gliding of warm, moist air up a mild slope formed by the upper surface of a colder, denser mass of air. Cooling is slower in the latter case, and rainfall less heavy. Cyclonic precipitation therefore inclines toward being light or moderate in rate of fall, but, because of the greater areal extent of the storm, it is of relatively longer duration than that of thunderstorms. Dull, gray, uniformly overcast skies, with steady precipitation, are typical of cyclonic weather. It should be stressed that precipitation in any storm would be minor in amount and of short duration if it were not that new supplies of water vapor are constantly being imported by winds to any area where rain is falling.

Neither the expectancy of precipitation nor its nature and origin are the same in all parts of a low. In general, the front, or eastern half, is more cloudy and rainy than is the rear, or western half, although the latter is not completely lacking in precipitation. Clouds extend much farther to the front of the center than to the rear. The reason for the asymmetrical arrangement of cloud and precipitation about a cyclonic depression is partly to be explained by the condensation associated with fronts to be described in the following sections. In part, however, it is related to the very important fact that the front or eastern half of a low is an area of horizontal convergence of air quite disassociated from fronts. On the other hand the rear half of a cyclone is an area where divergence and downward movement of air predominates. In well-developed winter lows, snow is more common in the cooler northeastern part, while rain occurs more frequently in the warmer southeastern quadrant. Heavy snows over the central and eastern part of the United States usually arrive when storms travel the more southerly routes,

so that the central and northern states are on the poleward sides of the cyclones.

237. Regions of Precipitation within a Cyclone. Three general regions of precipitation within a low may be distinguished. As a general rule the rain areas are associated with vertical displacement of less dense marine and tropical air masses. The cold polar air masses usually act only in the capacity of barriers over which the warmer air is lifted, although a small amount of the cyclonic precipitation may be derived from the polar air itself.

a. Warm-front Rain. The largest area of precipitation is covered by warm-front rain. To the north, northeast, and east of the storm center the warm, humid southerly air masses meet the colder drier air of polar origin. Because the latter is more dense, the warm air flows up over the gently inclined wedge of colder air, is cooled by expansion, and widespread cloud and precipitation are the result (Figs. 5.8, 5.13). Chilly, gray, overcast days, with long-continued steady rain, are typical of weather in this part of the storm. In the colder months this is also the region of heavy snowfall. Since the warm air is rising over the cold wedge along a gently inclined plane whose angle of slope is between 1:100 and 1:400, its increase in elevation is slow, so that the resulting precipitation is likely to be only light or moderate in rate of fall, although, because of its long duration, the total amount may be considerable. It is not unusual for warm-front rains to continue steadily for 24 hr. and more without letup. Such drizzly rain is ideal in some respects, for it comes slowly enough for the ground to absorb most of it, and surface runoff and destructive slope wash and gullying are reduced to a minimum. Low evaporation under such conditions of weather likewise increases the effectiveness of the precipitation. Cool overcast weather with rain is ideal for the growth of forage crops and pasture but less so for a crop like corn, which benefits from sunshine and higher temperatures. It should be kept in mind that it is not from the cold surface air that most of the rain is coming but rather from the southerly currents aloft which are rising over the cold northerly air.

When the air aloft ascending over the cold wedge is warm, humid and unstable, showery weather with intermittent heavy rains and thunderstorms may result (Fig. 5.8).

b. Cold-front Rain. To the south and southwest of the storm center is still another region of forced ascent. Here the cold west and northwest currents of polar origin meet and underrun the warm southerly currents, forcing them upward, sometimes with much vigor (Figs. 5.9, 5.13). The cold-front rain belt is best developed in storms with a marked southward looping of the isobars, *i.e.*, a V-shaped cyclone, for under these conditions the contrasting air masses meet at a sharp angle with resulting vigorous overturning. In storms with more circular shape this is less likely to be the case. The cold front may be a region of great atmospheric turbulence, with associated severe thunderstorms and squall winds. Because of the rapid lifting and overturning of the warm air along the cold front, the accompanying rain is likely to be in the form of heavy showers but not of long duration. This cloud and rain belt, therefore, is usually much narrower than that along the warm front.

c. Nonfrontal or Air-mass Precipitation. The previously described upward movement of warm air along frontal surfaces with associated precipitation should be thought of as superimposed upon the more general pattern of vertical movement involving ascent in the eastern part and descent in the western part of a cyclone. This general upward movement on the front of a cyclone may be sufficient to cause precipitation in areas of the storm not associated with upgliding along frontal surfaces. Within the warm sector, where southerly winds predominate, nonfrontal rain is especially prominent (Fig. 5.13). This may be the result of the humid southerly currents being forced upward as a result of general convergence in the eastern half of the depression. A part of it may be showery convective precipitation resulting from surface heating of the unstable tropical air. A small amount may be drizzle falling from low clouds formed by the cooling of warm, moist air flowing over cold surfaces, chiefly oceans.

Within the warm sector of some cyclones, extending in a line roughly parallel with the cold front and usually between 100 and 300 miles ahead of it, are showers and thunderstorms which are associated with what is called the *prefrontal squall line.* It is only recently that the reality of prefrontal squall lines as independent phenomena has been widely accepted and even yet their structure and origin are not well understood (Fig. 10.14).

It should be stressed here that not all these three rainfall types or areas are present in each storm, nor are they always distinct from each other. There are numerous mergings, modifications, and intermediate conditions. Nevertheless, all three types are sufficiently common and distinct in cyclones to warrant their recognition.

TEMPERATURE IN CYCLONES AND ANTICYCLONES

238. It is difficult to make significant generalizations regarding temperature contrasts between lows and highs. It is not true, as is sometimes stated to be the case, that, disregarding the season of the year, cyclones are always areas of high temperature and anticyclones of low. In themselves they are neither hot nor cold, but, depending upon (*a*) the nature of the air masses that comprise them, (*b*) the season of the year, and (*c*) the humidity of the air and the per cent of cloudiness, they may be either or both. *An analysis of surface temperatures in cyclones and anticyclones chiefly resolves into a study of the air masses that comprise the storms,* for, to a large extent, the prevailing temperature is the result of advection and of heat exchange with the ground.

239. Temperatures in Anticyclones. Certainly in the winter season a vigorous, well-developed high, advancing rapidly toward central and eastern United States from northern Canada (Figs. 5.15, 5.16), progresses as a mass of cold, dry polar continental air with clear skies. Such a cold anticyclone accounts for the *cold waves* and bitterest winter weather (Fig. 5.16). This type of high is cold for two reasons: (*a*) because it advances southward from the Arctic regions where it originated, as a mass of cold polar air, accompanied by strong northwest winds, and (b) because its dry clear air provides ideal conditions for rapid terrestrial radiation during long winter nights. An anticyclone composed of polar Pacific air brings much less severe winter weather to the interior of the country. Even in summer, a well-developed high approaching rapidly as a mass of polar air from higher latitudes gives low temperatures for the season, providing several days of clear, cool, delightful weather. It is not unusual in middle latitudes, then, for highs to have come to be associated with low temperatures for any particular season.

However, when in summer a large, relatively stagnant warm high composed of air of subtropical or tropical origin spreads slowly eastward over the south-central part of the country, excessively high temperatures, called *hot waves*, are likely to result over central and eastern United States (Fig. 5.17). The same clear skies and dry air that make for rapid terrestrial radiation during the long winter nights are conducive to maximum receipts of strong solar radiation during long summer days. Moreover, as the tropical air from this anticyclone moves northward over the country, the south winds carry with them the heat absorbed in the lower latitudes. Clear mild days in the cooler seasons likewise are usually associated with these same stagnant warm highs over the south-central part of the country. Of this origin is the much-cherished Indian summer weather in October and November.

In summary, then, it may be stated that, since highs may be composed of either polar or tropical air masses, they may in turn be responsible for either cold or warm weather. Vigorous moving cold highs arriving from higher latitudes are likely to bring lower than normal temperatures, especially in winter, while weak stagnant warm highs, especially in summer, are associated with abnormally high temperatures.

240. Temperatures in Cyclones. Well-developed cyclones, accompanied by an extensive cloud cover and precipitation, are likely to bring higher than average temperatures in winter, and somewhat lower than average temperatures in summer—just the opposite from those induced by the anticyclone. During the long winter nights the cloud cover and humid air of the cyclone tend to prevent rapid loss of earth heat, while these same conditions in summer, when days are long and sun stronger, tend to weaken incoming solar radiation.

241. *Temperature Contrasts within Different Parts of a Cyclone.* The foregoing general rule concerning lows and seasonal temperatures cannot be accepted too literally, however, for a cyclone usually has marked temperature contrasts within its several parts, or quadrants, depending upon the air masses that are represented. Thus the south and southeast part of a low, which is the warm sector of tropical air, is considerably warmer than the north and west portion where the air movement is from cooler, higher latitudes. The effect of these temperature importations is to cause the isotherms in cyclones to trend north-northeast by south-southwest instead of the usual east-west direction, the south winds of the warm air mass on the front of the storm pushing them poleward, and the northwest winds of the cold air mass on the rear pushing equatorward (Fig. 5.18). To the east and north of the storm center, where the air mass is of a modified polar character and therefore colder than the tropical air but less severe than the fresh *cP* air to the rear, the isotherms more closely follow the parallels.

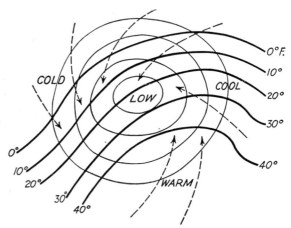

Fig. 5.18. Characteristic arrangement of isotherms in a winter cyclone over central and eastern United States. The rear, or west side, of the storm is usually colder than the front, or east.

In general, the average rise of temperature above seasonal normal in front of a winter storm in eastern United States is not far from 10°, although it may reach 20 or 30°. Between the front and rear of a well-developed winter cyclone in eastern United States, the temperatures may differ by as much as 30 to 40° or even more. If the temperature of the center of a low is taken as a standard, the average departures of the four quadrants of well-developed winter cyclones in eastern United States are as follows: northwest, −8.7°; northeast, −5.6°; southeast, +6.3°; southwest, +2.6° (Ward). Stations on the southern side of a passing low therefore experience a greater *change* in temperature than do those to the north of the center, even though the temperatures are not so low.

242. Summary of Weather Changes with the Passing of a Well-developed Cyclone and a Following Cold Anticyclone over Eastern United States. The essence of cyclonic control in weather is its irregularity and undependability. Averages of the weather elements by days, months, or years give only a lifeless picture of the actual weather experienced, for such averages tend to mask the nonperiodic storm control. Rapid and marked weather changes are characteristic of regions and seasons where cyclones and anticyclones are numerous and well developed, as they are, for instance, over eastern United States in winter. Temperature changes with passing storms are especially marked in winter, when latitudinal temperature gradients are steepest and importations by winds consequently most severe. In summer, with the poleward migration of the storm belt (frontal zones), cyclones are fewer and weaker, temperature gradients milder, and sun control, with its daily perio-

dicity, is more influential. In that season, then, weather changes are more regular and diurnal, and less marked.

It is incorrect to conceive of cyclonic control as identical in different parts of the earth. Even within the United States storms act differently over the Pacific Coast or the western plateaus from the way they do in eastern United States. Northwest winds on the rear of a cyclone obviously cannot import very low temperatures if they come from over the open ocean, as they do most of the time in northwestern Europe or the Pacific Coast of the United States. Storms differ in character with the regions and the seasons, although they all conform to the same general laws. Following is a description of a series of weather changes during the passage of a well-developed cyclone and a following anticyclone over eastern United States (Figs. 5.19, 5.20, 5.21).

As the cyclone approaches from the west and the barometer falls, there is a gradual clouding up in front of the storm. Far out in front of the center, as the first evidence of ascent along the warm-front surface of discontinuity, the sky becomes covered with fine veils, or films, of cirrus and cirrostratus clouds, which produce circles around the moon or sun. These distant heralds of the storm are associated with the warm-front discontinuity surface as much as 1,000 to 1,500 miles ahead of the surface warm front where the inclined wedge of cold air may be 3 to 4 miles thick. Contemporaneous with the appearance of the cirrus and cirrostratus clouds the wind sets in from an easterly direction and continues easterly until the surface warm front has passed. As the surface warm front approaches closer and the cold wedge becomes thinner, the clouds gradually thicken, darken, and become lower in elevation. Precipitation usually begins several hundred miles ahead of the surface warm front and continues until that front has passed. Temperature increases somewhat as the surface warm front draws nearer, but since the air on the front of the storm may be modified polar in character, there is no abrupt temperature rise until the warm front at the surface passes. The passage of the warm front at the surface, with an associ-

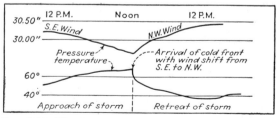

Fig. 5.19. The barograph and thermograph record of the approach and retreat of a middle-latitude cyclone.

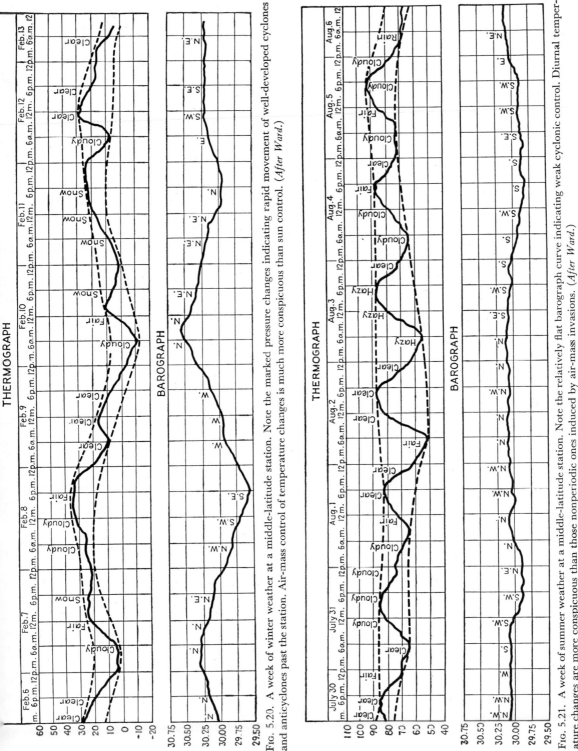

FIG. 5.20. A week of winter weather at a middle-latitude station. Note the marked pressure changes indicating rapid movement of well-developed cyclones and anticyclones past the station. Air-mass control of temperature changes is much more conspicuous than sun control. (*After Ward.*)

FIG. 5.21. A week of summer weather at a middle-latitude station. Note the relatively flat barograph curve indicating weak cyclonic control. Diurnal temperature changes are more conspicuous than those nonperiodic ones induced by air-mass invasions. (*After Ward.*)

ated shift from polar to tropical air, is marked by a number of weather phenomena, including (a) a slight wind shift, usually about 45°, the wind becoming more southerly as the warm air mass is entered; (b) a distinct rise in temperature; (c) a clearing in the weather conditions; and (d) a rapid increase in the amount of moisture in the air.

Within the warm air mass weather conditions may vary considerably, depending on the nature of the air and the season of the year. In summer if the air is from the Gulf of Mexico hot sultry weather with local showers and thunderstorms is common. If the air is from a drier source, the heat will be less oppressive but more desiccating. In winter this tropical air mass gives rise to mild weather and rapid thaws, often associated with fog.

The passage of the cold front at the surface with an accompanying shift from the warm to the cold air mass is frequently associated with strong turbulence, particularly if the cold front is well developed. In summer severe thunderstorms with strong squall winds are common. Other associated weather phenomena are (a) a marked rise in barometric pressure, (b) an abrupt drop in temperature heralding the arrival of the cold air, (c) well-marked shift in wind direction amounting to from 45 to 180° (southerly to westerly), (d) heavy rains at the front but fairly rapid clearing and improvement in the weather conditions following its passage, and (e) a marked decrease in both specific and relative humidity. The advancing anticyclone moving southeastward as a mass of cold polar air with northwest winds continues to reduce the temperature until its center has passed. Toward the center of the high, winds are light and calms are prevalent, and in winter extremely low temperatures are likely to prevail. As the anticyclone retreats, the cycle is complete, winds again become easterly, and another approaching cyclone begins a new sequence.

Obviously there are considerable variations from the above description. These variations depend upon the nature of the air masses generating the storms as well as upon the routes the storms take with respect to the observer. For example, the poleward side of a cyclone is characterized by northerly winds and by prevailingly lower temperatures than in the area south of the center; by a backing instead of a veering wind shift; by the absence of a warm sector and frequently of surface fronts; and by a greater likelihood of snowfall in winter.

243. Paths of Cyclonic Storms. All parts of the middle latitudes, and likewise the adjacent margins of the low and high latitudes, are affected by moving cyclones and anticyclones of the westerlies. All parts, however, are not affected to the same degree, for while there is no rigid system of clearly defined *storm tracks*, there are, nevertheless, certain broad belts over which storm centers travel more frequently than elsewhere. Of course the effects of a storm are felt far beyond the path of its center. Figure 5.22 shows in a generalized way the principal cyclonic tracks of the world. This figure should be compared with Figs. 4.3 and 4.4, which show locations of the principal frontal zones. Although the fronts are shown as single lines, it must be kept in mind that these are only mean locations of fronts that oscillate within wide limits, depending on the season and the actual wind distribution.

In the Southern Hemisphere, as a result of a very stable and intense cold source over the Antarctic Continent throughout the year, there is great year-round vigor of cyclonic storms, in summer as well as winter. These storms appear to follow the subpolar low-pressure trough, but the poleward parts of all the Southern Hemisphere continents are affected by their northerly margins, especially in the low-sun season. The Cape Horn region of South America, extending as it does nearly to latitude 55°S., is a stormy area at all times of the year. Winter cyclones are likewise relatively numerous over the Pampa of Argentina.

244. *Northern Hemisphere Tracks.* The less vigorous (except in winter), and likewise less persistent, continental anticyclones forming over the arctic and subarctic regions provide the principal southward gushes of cold polar air for the formation of Northern Hemisphere storms. The arctic and subarctic anticyclones are relatively weak in summer, which accounts for the poleward migration of the storm tracks as well as for the general weakening of cyclonic control over the whole Northern Hemisphere in that season. In winter, on the other hand, when the arctic and subarctic high-pressure centers are much better developed, and therefore are able to provide the necessary southward surges of cold air, storms are both numerous and vigorous in the middle latitudes.

Middle-latitude cyclones characteristically originate as waves along the western parts of the principal fronts. Thus the common regions of cyclogenesis are the pressure troughs and zones of convergence along the east coasts of middle-latitude continents where there are marked temperature contrasts between the cold high over the winter continent and the warm subtropical air over the ocean. This same type location appears to be a region of concentration of a long upper-air trough in the westerlies. Young cyclones formed on this location travel northeastward and eastward along the polar front toward the subpolar centers of low pressure over the oceans.

In Fig. 5.22 the two principal cyclogenesis areas, as shown by the concentration of storm tracks, are the frontal zones off the east coasts of North America and Asia (Fig. 2.46). This is particularly true in the cooler seasons. The polar fronts in these two areas oscillate considerably in location, and as a result the areas of frontogenesis do as well. Actually continental North America east of the Rocky Mountains, which is freely open to the invasion of polar and tropical air masses, is an important region of cyclonic origin and concentration. The storms that originate in the North American zone of frontogenesis travel northeastward toward the Icelandic Low, which is an unusually stormy area in winter. As they progress eastward, they occlude, so that most of the storms arriving in northwestern Europe are in the occluded stage of the life cycle. The cyclones of the Pacific Ocean which originate chiefly on the frontal zone off the east coast of Asia travel northeastward toward the Aleutian Low, most of them reaching the west coast of North America, usually as occluded storms. Occasionally these storms cross the western highlands and reach central and eastern United States where they may regenerate. A secondary region of cyclogenesis and

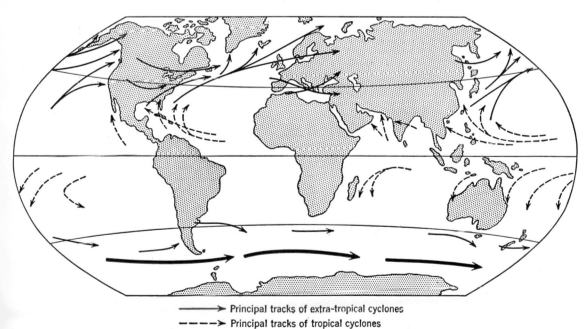

———————> Principal tracks of extra-tropical cyclones
– – – – –> Principal tracks of tropical cyclones

FIG. 5.22. The cyclone tracks here shown are greatly simplified. (*After Petterssen.*)

storm track concentration is the Mediterranean Basin. This front is active in the cooler seasons only.

The United States, without doubt, is the world's most cyclonic continental area. This unique distinction derives from the numerous and strong secondary fronts which form east of the Rockies where extensive lowlands reaching from Arctic to tropics permit a free clash of contrasting air masses. There appears to be a general bunching of cyclonic storm tracks in the northwestern and northeastern parts of the country, with a spreading and southward looping of them over the interior (Fig. 5.23). The northeastern and northwestern sections of the country in winter obviously must have much changeable weather with abundant cloud and precipitation. Most storms follow the northern rather than the southern routes across the country, a fact of utmost importance in understanding American weather. Polar air-mass anticyclones, one group from the North Pacific (*mP*) and the other from the arctic plains of Canada (*cP*), enter the United States at two far separated points and travel in general southeasterly courses across the country (Fig. 5.23).

TROPICAL DISTURBANCES

245. Classification of Tropical Storms. The literature on tropical meteorology suggests to the reader that there is a considerable variety of atmospheric disturbances capable of developing cloud and rainfall in those parts of the low latitudes where humidity is abundant. At the same time this literature is far from clear in distinguishing and classifying the various types of disturbances, noting their distinctive and characteristic weather types, and describing their geographical distributions. Most types of tropical disturbances appear to be relatively mild phenomena as far as pressure gradients and winds are concerned. Their principal climatic significance is that they generate clouds and precipitation, and hence they are noteworthy chiefly as affecting one climatic element, *viz.*, rainfall. In the low latitudes temperature changes and variations associated with storms are relatively inconsequential, and hence they have little or no part in this discussion. Unfortunately, as far as the climatologist is concerned, it is the violent and spectacular tropical storm of the hurricane type which has been studied most intensively. Yet these violent storms

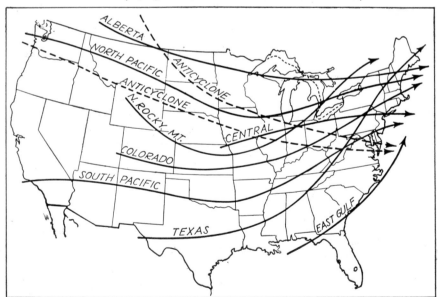

FIG. 5.23. Solid lines show principal tracks of cyclones; broken lines are the principal tracks of anticyclones. Note how the cyclone tracks converge on the northeastern part of the United States. Anticyclones moving south from northern Canada (*cP* air) bring severe cold in winter; those from the Pacific northwest (modified *mP* air) bring only moderate cold.

are relatively few compared with the milder types, and they are characteristic of much more restricted areas within the tropics so that their climatic significance is much less. Genuine hurricanes cannot develop over, or even invade for any distance, extensive land masses, so that it is exclusively the weaker storms which affect the weather of the interiors of tropical continents.

In the United States the following classification of tropical storms, based upon their degree of intensity, has received general acceptance.

a. Tropical Disturbance. One or no closed isobars, wind circulation poorly developed, and velocities weak. This is the most widespread of the tropical disturbances, for it is common throughout both the wet tropics and the subtropics.

b. Tropical Depression. One or more closed isobars, wind force equal to or less than Beaufort 6 (up to about 25 to 30 miles per hr). Most common in the region of the equatorial or intertropical convergence and less frequent in the trades. Much the larger number of tropical disturbances and depressions never reach the hurricane stage although most hurricanes appear to develop out of one of these milder forms of cyclones.

c. Tropical Storm. Closed isobars and a wind force between Beaufort 6 and 12 (under 75 miles per hr.).

d. Hurricane or Typhoon. Wind force Beaufort 12 (75 miles per hr.) or more.

246. Weak Tropical Lows. The shallow tropical disturbances and depressions which seem to be common throughout the humid low latitudes are relatively inconspicuous on the surface weather map, for their isobars are few and their pressure gradients weak. Their wind systems are poorly developed and velocities are usually light. The movement of such weak storms is erratic and usually slow, and there is a tendency for them to hover in one spot for days. Direction of movement is not the same in all parts of the tropics. In India and tropical northern Australia where they are best known, their tracks and directions of movement are confusing. The weak summer depressions of India reach a maximum development at the height

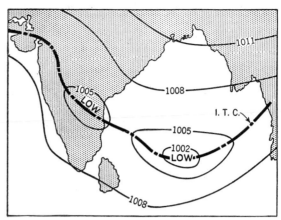

Fig. 5.24. Weak tropical lows of the summer-monsoon period developed along the *ITC* over India.

of the southwest monsoon (Fig. 5.24). They appear to develop near the head of the Bay of Bengal and then progress slowly westward and northwestward across the country. In northern tropical Australia in summer the depressions also appear to travel principally westward.

It is in the rainfall element that these weak storms become particularly conspicuous and significant, for frequently they are productive of beneficial rainfall, not always supplied in sufficient amount by the simple convectional showers typical of these regions. When these same weak disturbances remain nearly stationary over a limited area for several days, the rainfall may even become excessive, resulting in damaging floods. Without doubt too large a percentage of tropical rainfall has been ascribed to local convection resulting from surface heating, and too little to the effects of these weak tropical lows which certainly are more numerous, as well as more beneficial, than are the better known hurricanes. Compared with thunderstorm rainfall, that associated with weak tropical lows is much more extensive, usually is not so vigorous but is of longer duration, and falls from skies that are more uniformly overcast.

The origin of these shallow tropical disturbances and depressions which so greatly affect the weather of the humid low latitudes is a much disputed question. Until recently there was a tendency to associate them with zones of convergence and fronts. Now, with doubt being cast upon the reality of genuine temperature fronts in the tropics, the whole matter of origin of tropical disturbances is very controversial. Without doubt many of them do develop in convergence zones, even where significant temperature contrasts are not present. On the other hand, there are others that do not appear to be related to convergences which are observable at least at the surface. Perhaps there are multiple origins so that those of one region are dissimilar in their beginnings to those of another.

Weak cyclones, resembling those of the tropics are not unknown in humid subtropical parts of middle latitudes as well, although there they are confined to the warm season. They are best known perhaps in South China and over the southern half of Japan. In the latter country they give rise to an unpleasant and depressing rainy season extending from about mid-June to mid-July, during which the sky is overcast much of the time, and more or less rain falls nearly every day. The air is so damp that walls and pavements remain wet, and furniture and clothes become moldy. These *Bai-u* rains (meaning plum rains) are highly important for the rice crop, for they come at the time of transplanting when the rice fields need to be soaked.

247. *Other Weak Rain-bringing Tropical Disturbances.* Within recent years it has been discovered that there exist in the deep easterly currents of the tropics, and independent of fronts or convergence zones, pressure waves of small amplitude which move steadily from east to west. They are known as *easterly waves*.[1] These disturbances are easier to detect through perturbations in the wind field than in the pressure field and they are more conspicuous aloft than at the surface (Fig. 5.25). Winds are northeast (Northern Hemisphere) ahead of the trough and southeast behind it. Ahead of the wave there is positive divergence, the tradewind inversion is low, and the weather is fine, with few clouds and little precipitation. Behind the trough there is a convergence of air, the trade inversion is high or absent, and the weather is frequently squally and showers are numerous. A few of the waves develop into small but violent hurricanes. The easterly waves were first discovered in the Caribbean region where these disturbances follow tracks which correspond with the main hurricane routes. More recently they have been identified in West Africa, the western Indian Ocean, and the southern North Atlantic and North Pacific (Fig. 5.26). No widely accepted explanation for the origin of easterly waves exists.

Other types of wave disturbances in the tropics clearly not associated with surface fronts or convergences have recently been detected. In New Guinea disturbances in the speed field of the easterly current near the equator are revealed through maxima and minima of speed which travel downstream in the wind field. These are sometimes called *Freeman waves* after the person who made the discovery. It is possible that these disturbances may be the result of the orographic and locational peculiarities of New Guinea, for it is recognized that many local subsidiary convergences are of this origin. In the lower parts of the easterlies in the Caribbean there are in the winter season disturbances which on the surface weather map in some ways resemble the

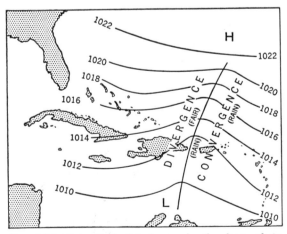

FIG. 5.25. A tropical disturbance in the form of an easterly wave. (*After Riehl.*)

[1] G. E. Dunn, Cyclogenesis in the Tropical Atlantic, *Bull. Am. Meteorological Soc.*, Vol. 21, pp. 215–229, 1940; H. Riehl, Waves in the Easterlies and the Polar Front in the Tropics, Department of Meteorology, University of Chicago, *Miscellaneous Report* 17, 1943; C. E. Palmer, Tropical Meteorology, "Compendium of Meteorology," pp. 868–872; Reid A. Bryson, On Disturbances in the Easterlies, Ph D. dissertation, University of Chicago, 1948.

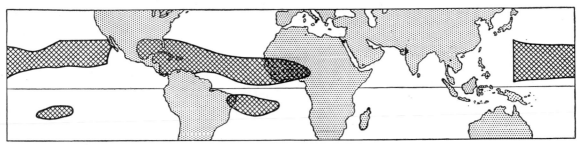

FIG. 5.26. General areas where easterly waves have been observed or suspected. (*After Berry, Bollay, and Beers.*)

easterly waves of summer. However, these cool-season disturbances in the trades move from west to east against the surface winds rather than with the general surface circulation as do the easterly waves. Thus the recent discovery of several different kinds of rain-bringing disturbances in the low latitudes opens up a relatively new field as far as origin of clouds, precipitation, and weather types in the tropics is concerned.

248. Tropical Cyclones of the Hurricane and Typhoon Variety. While meteorologically of great importance, these often violent and destructive storms of the low latitudes are of much less significance climatically, since they are not of frequent occurrence and are characteristic of only restricted areas within the tropics. Moreover, since the hurricane type of storm develops and matures over water bodies only, the land surfaces which feel their fury are limited to coastal areas and islands.

These storms of the low latitudes in some respects resemble the middle-latitude cyclones, as, for instance, in the central area of low pressure, the cyclonic system of winds, and a relatively widespread area of cloud and rain. In other ways, however, the hurricane differs from its less intense counterpart of the middle and higher latitudes. Some of the more important features that distinguish it from the middle-latitude cyclone are as follows: (*a*) The isobars of the tropical storm are more symmetrical and more nearly circular (Fig. 5.27). Pressure gradients also are steeper, so that winds are much stronger. To be a genuine hurricane, wind velocities in the storm must reach at least 75 miles an hour. (*b*) Rains are inclined to be more torrential and somewhat more evenly distributed about the center, although this latter character-

istic is more common in nearly, or quite, stationary storms than in moving ones. (*c*) Temperature distribution around the center is relatively similar in every direction. There are no fronts as in the middle-latitude low and contrasting air masses are absent. (*d*) There are no sharp wind shifts, the winds developing a more perfect spiral whirl, with strong vertically ascending currents around the vortex, or core. (*e*) They are most numerous in the warm season, rather than in winter. (*f*) Hurricanes have relatively calm, rainless centers, 5 to 30 miles in diameter. This is called the "eye" of the storm. (*g*) The tropical hurricane has no anticyclonic companion. (*h*) Hurricanes move from east to west with the prevailing trades and the circulation around the western ends of the subtropical anticyclones over the oceans. (*i*) Their source of energy is latent

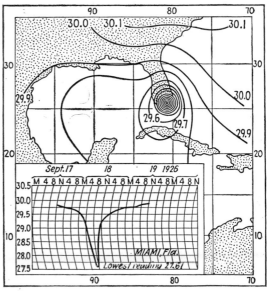

FIG. 5.27. A West Indies hurricane.

heat of condensation and air-mass density contrasts appear to play no part.

The hurricane type of storm varies greatly in size, but in general it is smaller and more intense than the low of middle latitudes. The total diameter of the whirl may be from 100 to 400 miles (Fig. 5.27). Wind velocities are not always violent, but on the other hand they may reach such destructive speeds as 90 to 130 miles per hr. Tremendous damage to shipping and coastal settlements, with accompanying loss of life, is by no means rare. A considerable part of the property destruction, and loss of life from drowning, is due to the great avalanches of sea water piled up and driven onshore by the gale winds and to the excessive rainfall and associated floods that accompany the storm.

The inundation by sea water is of two kinds, the *hurricane wave* and the *hurricane tide*. The hurricane wave is the lifting of the sea water near the calm center of intense storms, the average height being 10 to 20 ft. It is not in the form of individual waves, but instead is a rapid uplift of a great mass of water. While its origin is not entirely clear, it is thought to be caused by the damming effect of the strong winds forward of the calm center upon the current generated by the violent winds from the opposite direction on the rear side of the center. The hurricane tide is the rise in water level along a coast line due to the current generated by the winds in an approaching hurricane. It is most striking in a somewhat enclosed body of water where the concave coast does not readily permit the escape of the advancing water, with the consequence that it is piled up on the shore. On concave coasts the height of storm tides is usually from 3 to 10 ft. The rise in water level along the shore may begin when the storm is as much as 500 miles distant and will continue until the storm passes beyond the area.

249. *Origin.* The intense hurricane type of storm will develop only over relatively warm water, probably 82°F. or higher. There is no generally accepted theory as to their origin, although it is clear that their development requires a very special set of circumstances. Some of them develop in the equatorial convergence zone when it is displaced some distance from the equator, so that appreciable Coriolis force is present to initiate the cyclonic wind system. However, it does not appear necessary to have real air-mass density contrasts for their development. Others have their origin in easterly waves and occasionally they develop in the equatorial portions of old polar troughs which have entered the tropics.

250. *Regional Distribution and Frequency of Hurricanes.* Although all parts of tropical oceans in both hemispheres probably experience tropical storms, there is no record of one of hurricane intensity in the South Atlantic Ocean or the eastern South Pacific. None have been observed within 5° of the equator, where the Coriolis force is absent. There are at least six general regions of their origin and concentration (Fig. 5.22). These are noted below, together with special areas and seasons of occurrence, and the average number of storms per year. The figure in parentheses is the number reaching hurricane intensity, but for some areas these data are not known.

1. South, and especially the southwestern, portion of the North Atlantic Ocean: 7.3(3.5).
   a. Cape Verde Island area—August and September. Possibly these storms do not attain hurricane intensity until they reach the western part of the ocean.
   b. East and north of the West Indies, including Florida and the South Atlantic coast of the United States—June through October.
   c. Northern Caribbean Sea—late May through November.
   d. Southwestern Caribbean Sea—principally June and October.
   e. Gulf of Mexico—June through October.
2. North Pacific Ocean off the west coast of Mexico—June through November: 5.7 (2.2).
3. Southwestern North Pacific Ocean, especially the China Sea, the Philippine Islands and southern Japan, chiefly May through December: 21.1. Here the tropical cyclones are known as typhoons.

4. North Indian Ocean:
   a. Bay of Bengal—April through December: 6.0.
   b. Arabian Sea—April through June and September through December: 1.5.
5. South Indian Ocean:
   a. Madagascar eastward to 90°E.—November through April: 0.9.
6. South Pacific Ocean eastward from Australia to about 140°W.—December through April.

It can be noted there is a distinct concentration of these storms in the warm season, the maximum occurring in late summer and early fall. The region of greatest frequency of tropical cyclones, and perhaps the one having storms of the greatest intensity, is the typhoon area of the Philippines and the China Sea. On the other hand, the best-known hurricane region is the Caribbean and western North Atlantic region where there are numerous inhabited islands, and a relatively important ocean traffic, so that observational data are abudant.

251. *Weather Elements in the Hurricane.* After a tropical depression has intensified to Beaufort 6 or 7, deepening takes place rapidly, and maximum deepening usually occurs within 3 to 5 days. If the storm remains over water, little change then occurs until it has recurved around the western end of the subtropical high and enters the lower middle latitudes. At that period in its development it begins to take on extratropical characteristics. Central pressure begins to rise, the pressure gradients are less steep, and the isobars are less circular as contrasting air masses and fronts develop. The lowest barometric reading ever recorded in a tropical hurricane storm is 26.185 in. in a typhoon near the Philippines. Readings between 27.00 in. (914.3 mb.) and 27.50 in. (931.3 mb.) are not uncommon. Steepness of pressure gradient increases with the depth of the barometric minimum and may vary from 0.025 to 0.06 in. per mile. Mean pressure fall in a hurricane depends both on the barometric gradient as well as upon the rate of movement of the storm. A pressure fall of 0.4 to 0.8 in. per hr. is fairly common. Pressure falls of over an inch in 30 min. have been recorded.

Winds blow counterclockwise around and slightly toward the center of the storm. The wind velocities are usually highest to the right of the center in the Northern Hemisphere. Thus hurricane winds extend somewhat more to the right of center than to the left. The dimensions of the hurricane winds vary considerably from one storm to another and also in various stages of the same storm. In large storms in the western North Atlantic, the diameter of the hurricane winds may exceed 100 miles. In the central calm area, or "eye" of the storm, the wind velocity drops suddenly to 15 miles per hr. or less, the sky may clear, and the rain ceases. On the average, these calm centers are 12 to 15 miles in diameter.

The total rainfall in a hurricane varies greatly in amount, but perhaps averages 5 to 10 in. In special instances where topographic conditions are favorable, 30 to 40 in. have fallen. Due to the violent winds, the loss of rain from rain gauges may amount to 50 per cent. In Baguio in the Philippines, one typhoon gave 76 in. in 24 hr., and at Silver Hill, Jamaica, 96.5 in. were recorded in 4 days with the passing of a hurricane.

Thunderstorms

252. General Characteristics and Structure. A thunderstorm, as the name indicates, is a local storm characterized by the presence of lightning and thunder. These two elements, however, are the result rather than the cause of the storm and are only incidental to the processes going on within it. The thunderstorm resembles an ordinary convectional shower except that it is accompanied by thunder and lightning. And since the development of lightning seems to be associated with relatively intense convection in humid air, it can be said that a thunderstorm is the most violent type of instability shower. Fundamentally the thunderstorm is a thermodynamic machine in which the potential energy of latent heat of condensation and fusion in moist conditionally or convectively unstable air is rapidly converted into the kinetic energy of violent vertical air currents with associated torrential rain, hail, gusty surface squall winds, lightning, and thunder. The intensity of the storm depends upon the supply of latent energy and the rate at which this available energy is expended. A thunderstorm is therefore an intense instability outbreak.

A thunderstorm is characterized by "chimneys" of vigorously ascending warm air with compensating areas of cooler downdrafts. It is typically a cellular type of vertical circulation, with several convectional cells comprising the mature thunderstorm. In its beginning, or cumulus, stage it is characterized by an updraft throughout the cell. In its mature stage it is characterized by both updrafts and downdrafts, while in its dissipating stage weak downdrafts prevail throughout. In fact, the thunderstorm owes its origin to vertical updrafts of warm, moist air, for a thunderstorm is only a complex cumulonimbus cloud with all its attendant phenomena of lightning, thunder, and squall winds. This characteristic turbulence is very evident in the seethings and convulsions that one sees taking place in a great thunderhead cloud (Fig.

5.28). Rapid vertical upthrusts of air are commonly associated with high surface temperatures and vigorous convectional overturning, so that it is not unexpected to find thunderstorms most prevalent in the warmer latitudes of the earth, in the warmer seasons of middle latitudes, and in the warmer hours of the day. It is obvious that heat, particularly humid heat, and thunderstorms are closely related, although high temperatures do not provide their exclusively favorable environment. Many thunderstorms appear to originate along density fronts in cyclonic storms, while convergent zones in general are their preferred areas.

253. Conditions Favorable for Thunderstorms. The prerequisites for thunderstorms may be briefly stated as follows:

a. Warm, moist, unstable air. An adequate supply of moisture is required to provide the necessary energy to maintain the storm. Normally the relative humidity of the air mass must exceed 75 per cent. The lapse rate must be conditionally or convectively unstable to or above the 14°F. isotherm. Ordinarily the degree of in-

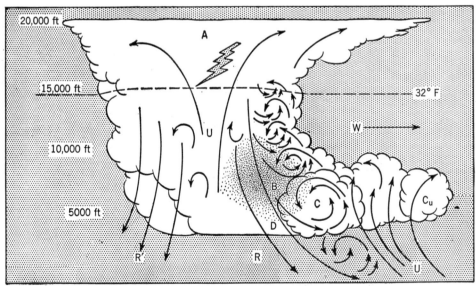

Key to diagram of cumulonimbus cloud

A – Anvil top
B – Dark area
C – Roll cloud
C_u – Advance cumulus clouds
D – Down drafts

U – Up drafts
R – Primary rain area
R' – Secondary area
W – Wind direction

Fig. 5.28. Vertical section through a local heat thunderstorm and its cumulus cloud.

stability determines the intensity of the storm. Through a lifting agent, conditionally or convectively unstable air may be given a condition of actual instability, after which, other conditions being favorable, thunderstorms may occur.

b. An appreciable cloud thickness between condensation level (cloud base) and icing level. Ordinarily this thickness exceeds 10,000 ft. In middle latitudes at least, there is little thunderstorm activity until the rising air reaches the freezing or icing level. It seems as though latent heat of fusion and ice crystals are necessary for the sudden release of abundant precipitation that produces the electrical phenomena and violent convection currents accompanying thunderstorms. The higher the freezing level above the cloud base, and therefore the thicker the cloud, the more intense the convective activity. This would explain the infrequency of thunderstorms in winter in middle latitudes and their greater prevalence and intensity in lower latitudes.

c. An agent to set off the activity by rendering the air unstable at some level.

254. Precipitation in Thunderstorms. As indicated in an earlier article, rainfall in thunderstorms is likely to be more vigorous while it lasts, but of shorter duration than that associated with cyclones. One speaks of *thundershowers* rather than *thunder rains*. This downpour type of precipitation is related to (a) the more rapid vertical ascent of air in thunderstorms (at least 2,400 ft. per min. must often occur) than in most cyclones and (b) the higher temperature and, therefore, higher specific humidity of the air in the summer season when thunderstorms are prevalent. The vigorous nature of convectional rainfall, together with the fact that in middle latitudes it is concentrated in the growing season, has important economic consequences. The rainfall pattern in a thunderstorm is closely associated with the arrangement of the cells and their stages of development. The heaviest rain occurs under the core of a cell and decreases toward its margins. The duration of the heavy rain from a single cell varies from a few minutes in weak ones to upwards of an hour in large and very active cells. In eastern and southern United States the duration of thunderstorm rain at an individual station is about 25 min., although it is highly variable.

255. *Hail.* Occasionally hail, the most destructive form of precipitation, is developed in very intense thunderstorms. Fortunately it occurs in only a few, and usually it falls in only restricted areas or belts within any individual storm. It appears to be associated only with particular cells within the thunderstorm rather than with the entire storm. On first thought, it may appear peculiar that these relatively large globules of layered ice and snow should be a form of precipitation almost confined to the warm season of the year. That is because they are associated with vigorous convectional systems such as are typical principally of the warmer season. The growth of a hailstone is through the collection of supercooled water as it falls through the cloud. Its onion-like, or layered, structure is the result of the nonhomogeneous character of the turbulent cumulus cloud. The process of hail formation resembles the accretion of ice on aircraft, where a layered structure is also commonly observed. Hailstones occasionally grow to be as large as golf balls and, in rare instances, even larger.

When the strong currents of uprushing air are temporarily weakened, the hailstones fall to earth, often doing serious damage to crops, to structures such as greenhouses, and occasionally even killing livestock in the fields. The regional and local variations in the frequency of hail and in the amount of hail damage are startling. It should be noted that hail frequency and thunderstorm frequency do not show the same distribution. Hail is practically unknown in the tropics where thunderstorms are most numerous. Within the United States thunderstorms are most frequent in the subtropical southeastern part, especially in Florida and the Gulf Coast, but this is a region of almost no hail. Hail frequency is greatest over the interior of the country, more particularly over portions of the Rocky Mountains and the Great Plains where newly formed intense showers are relatively frequent.

Of all the weather hazards to growing crops, hail is the only one which is extensively insured by private insurance companies. Locally the variation in hail frequency and damage are very great. For example, the rate charged for crop hail insurance in extreme eastern Nebraska is only one-sixth what it is in the western part.

256. Lightning, Thunder, and Squall Winds. Three other common phenomena of thunderstorms need brief comment: *lightning*, *thunder*, and the *squall wind*. Lightning results from the splitting up of large raindrops, and the consequent development of strong charges of static electricity in rapidly ascending air currents. Like hail, therefore, lightning is a feature of vigorous convectional storms which are most numerous in warm seasons and warm regions. As raindrops in a storm grow larger and larger, they eventually reach such a size (about 4 mm.) that their limit of cohesion is past, and they begin to break up, the larger portions of the drops remaining near the base of the cloud in the region of the rapidly ascending currents, while the smaller particles and the water vapor detached from the drops are carried upward and outward into the other portions of the cloud.

The raindrops before disruption carry positive and negative charges of electricity in equal amounts so that they are neutral in character. But with the splitting of the drops by the strong convectional currents, the negative and positive drops with their electric charges become concentrated in particular sections of the cloud mass. In this manner great differences in electric potential between cloud and earth, or between different parts of the cloud, are generated (Fig. 5.29). In its mature stage at least, the thunderstorm has a positively charged upper portion and a negatively charged lower portion. When the electric-potential gradient becomes too great, a lightning discharge takes place, approximately 65 per cent of them entirely within the cloud or from one cloud to another. The discharge from cloud to earth fortunately is less frequent. Thunder is produced by the violent expansion of the air caused by the tremendous heat of the lightning. It is due wholly to an explosive type of expansion consequent upon an extremely sudden and great rise in temperature.

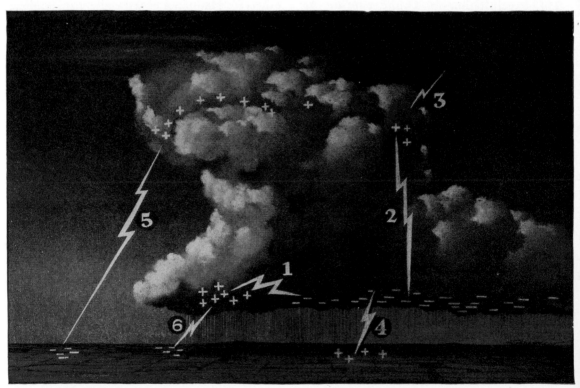

Fig. 5.29. Electric charges and lightning in a cumulonimbus cloud. (*Courtesy of Weatherwise.*)

257. *Winds in a Thunderstorm.* In the beginning, or cumulus, stage of a thunderstorm the surface winds are mildly convergent. As the cell grows and the downdraft develops, the cold divergent outflow from the downdraft is strong and gusty. The cold dome of outflowing downdraft is asymetrically developed, extending out much farther on the downwind side, or the front, of the storm. This is the so-called *thundersquall.* It is associated with the squall cloud, an onrushing dark-gray boiling arch or roll of cloud which is the forward projection of the lower portion of the storm cloud. The velocity of the squall wind at times attains hurricane violence, so that it may do serious damage. The force of the squall is due in part to the cool air that has been brought down from aloft with the mass of falling rain. Being denser than the warm surface air, it spreads out in front of the storm, underrunning the warm air. In part its velocity is due also to the onrushing motion of the storm mass itself, so that forward and outward motions are combined.

THUNDERSTORM TYPES

258. Thunderstorms result from a steepening of the lapse rate in very moist air. Hence thunderstorms may be classified according to the process which causes a steepening of the lapse rate. In the classification here employed the two principal classes of thunderstorms, (*a*) *air mass* and (*b*) *frontal*, are based upon the weather map conditions with which they are associated, while the subtypes are designated according to the process which causes a steepening of the lapse rate and produces the instability. None of these processes will produce thunderstorms if the air is very stable or unless the air is very moist. It is not unusual for several of these processes to exist in combination.

Types of Thunderstorms
- *A.* Air-mass types
  1. Local or heat
  2. Orographic
  3. Advective
- *B.* Frontal types
  1. Cold front
     - *a.* Prefrontal
  2. Warm front

Air-mass thunderstorms are those which occur within relatively homogeneous air masses and do not appear to be associated with any frontal activity. Frontal types, as the name indicates, occur in connection with the boundary surfaces between air masses.

Air-mass Thunderstorms

259. The local, or heat, thunderstorm is the most common type (Fig. 5.28). Since this type of storm is thermally induced, being due to radiation heating at the ground, it should be most prevalent in the warm parts of the earth, in the warm seasons of the year, and in the warm part of the day. In the United States it occurs most frequently in hot, humid *mT*-Gulf air when barometric gradients are relatively weak. The heat, humidity, and convergent movement characteristic of the doldrums appear to furnish ideal conditions for the development and growth of such thunderstorms. They are local in character and seldom cover a great area. Usually they occur as isolated storms or groups of storms. Reaching their maximum development in the late afternoon or evening, they usually dissipate during the late evening when the cooling ground ceases to supply the necessary sustaining energy. The intensity of the storm is directly related to heat characteristics of the surface over which it is passing. These storms tend to intensify over cities where the buildings give off large quantities of heat. They are weaker over wooded areas than over plowed fields. Passage of the storm over a cool body of water tends to dissipate it, since active convection is lacking. It is this feature of a heat thunderstorm which led to the old saying, "a thunderstorm will never cross a river."

An unstable condition results from insolational heating of the quiet humid surface air, so that convection and towering cumulus clouds are often the result. If the latter grow to cumulonimbus size, they may give rise to a thundershower. Steep lapse rate and high specific humidity are the conditions most conducive to the development of the local cumulonimbus cloud. Such scattered local storms may travel in almost any direction, although usually in the middle latitudes they move toward the east, which is the average direction of the wind in intermediate altitudes. Literally hundreds of these ephemeral thundershowers may dot southern and eastern United States on a hot summer day. It is impossible to forecast the exact time or place of their occurrence. They are of great economic significance, for they produce a considerable part of the summer precipitation in the interiors of middle-latitude continents and probably a still larger part of that which falls in tropical latitudes.

Less commonly, local thunderstorms may occur in cold air masses whose surface layers have developed a steep lapse rate and have become unstable as a result of passing over a relatively warm surface such as warm ocean currents or lakes. Such storms are usually mild in character, for high moisture and heat content are lacking within the air mass. They are most common in winter and spring when the upper air layers are still relatively cold. This advectional contact heating accounts for many thunderstorms which develop over oceans.

Willis I. Milham gives the following excellent description of a local thunderstorm:

"It has been a hot sultry, oppressive day in summer. The air has been very quiet, perhaps alarmingly quiet, interrupted now and then by a gentle breeze from the south. The pressure has been gradually growing less. The sky is hazy; cirrus clouds are visible; here and there they thicken to cirro-stratus or cirro-cumulus. The temperature has risen very high, and the absolute humidity is very large, but owing to the high temperature the relative humidity has decreased somewhat. The combination of high moisture and temperature and but little wind has made the day intensely sultry and oppressive. In the early hours of the afternoon, amid the horizon haze and cirro-stratus clouds in the west, the big cumulus clouds, the thunderheads, appear. Soon distant thunder is heard, the lightning flashes are visible, and the dark rain cloud beneath comes into view. As the thundershower approaches, the wind dies down or becomes a gentle breeze blowing directly toward the storm. The temperature perhaps drops a little as the sun is obscured by the clouds, but the sultriness and oppressiveness remain as before. The thundershower comes nearer, and the big cumulus clouds with sharp outlines rise like domes and turrets one above the other. Perhaps the loftiest summits are capped with a fleecy, cirrus-like veil which extends out beyond them. If seen from the side, the familiar anvil form of the cloud mass is noticed. Just beneath the thunder-heads is the narrow, turbulent, blue-drab squall cloud. The patches of cloud are now falling, now rising, now moving hither and thither as if in the greatest commotion. Beyond the squall cloud is the dark rain cloud, half hidden from view by the curtain of rain. The thunderheads and squall clouds are now just passing overhead. The lightning flashes, the thunder rolls, big, pattering raindrops begin to fall or perhaps, instead of these, damage-causing hailstones. The gentle breeze has changed to the violent outrushing squall wind, blowing directly from the storm, and the temperature is dropping as if by magic. Soon the rain descends in torrents, shutting out everything from view. After a time, the wind dies down but continues from the west or northwest, the rain decreasing in intensity; the lightning flashes follow each other at longer intervals. An hour or two has passed; it is growing lighter in the west; the wind has died down; the rain has almost stopped. Soon the rain ceases entirely; the clouds break through and become fracto-stratus or cirriform; the temperature rises somewhat, but it is still cool and pleasant; the wind has become very light and has shifted back to the southwest or south. Now the domes and turrets of the retreating shower are visible in the east; perhaps a rainbow spans the sky; the roll of the thunder becomes more distant; the storm has passed, and all nature is refreshed."[1]

260. Orographic thunderstorms are produced by the mechanical lifting of a conditionally or convectively unstable air mass by a relief obstacle such as a mountain range or a plateau front (Fig. 5.30). Such upward deflection furnishes the trigger effect necessary to release large reserves of latent energy in air masses already conditionally unstable. It follows, therefore, that thunderstorms are more numerous in hilly and mountainous regions than they are where the terrain is flat. They are common in summer over the mountainous regions of our West and Southwest and over the Alleghenies. In many ways this type resembles the local thunderstorm except that there is greater intensity of action over larger areas. Because their formation is governed

[1] W. I. Milham, "Meteorology," pp. 321–322, The Macmillan Company, New York, 1912.

FIG. 5.30. The development of an orographic thunderstorm.

to a great extent by the local terrain, orographic thunderstorms have individual peculiarities of time, occurrence, intensity, and location, which make them an easy type to forecast. A unique characteristic of many orographic thunderstorms is their tendency to remain almost stationary, probably because the upward thrusts of air that feed them are distinctly localized. This feature explains their tendency to produce cloudburst precipitation.

261. Advective Thunderstorms. Such storms may be due either to warm-air advection at low levels or cold-air advection aloft. If warm air is advected at lower levels, while the air aloft does not have its temperature changed, the lapse rate may be sufficiently steepened to produce strong convection. Nighttime thunderstorms which are common on the Great Plains are frequently the result of warm-air advection at levels between 3,000 and 6,000 ft. Cold-air advection aloft similarly steepens the lapse rate.

Frontal Thunderstorms

262. Cold-front thunderstorms are those that originate as a direct result of cold-front activity. They are characteristically formed along the wind-shift lines of well-developed V-shaped summer cyclones (Figs. 5.31, 5.32). The wind-shift line, or cold front, marks the abrupt meeting place of warm, humid, southerly currents (usually *mT*) on the front and south of the cyclone, with the cooler, drier, and denser

polar air masses on the rear. Thunderstorms may form a nearly continuous series of active centers hundreds of miles long, the individual storms strung out along the cold front like beads on a string. When the cool and relatively dense polar air from the west and northwest strikes the side of the warm southerly currents along the cold front, they either underrun it like a

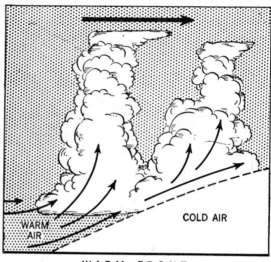

WARM FRONT
(A)

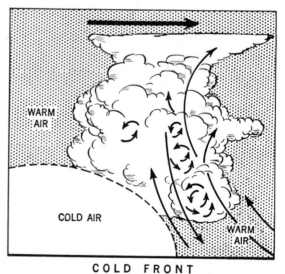

COLD FRONT
(B)

FIG. 5.31. Thunderstorm development along warm and cold fronts. Cold-front thunderstorms are usually more severe. Heavy arrows at top indicate direction of movement.

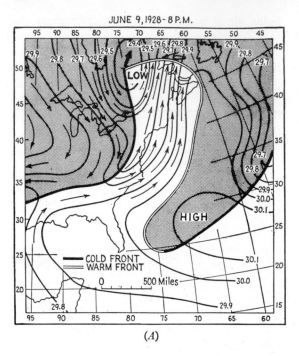

JUNE 9, 1928 - 8 P.M.

(A)

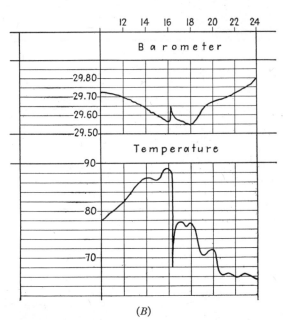

(B)

Fig. 5.32. (A) A V-shaped summer cyclone with a well-developed cold front and associated severe thunderstorms. Regions covered by air of polar origin are shaded; those covered by air of tropical origin are left unshaded. (B) Record of pressure and temperature at the Naval Air Station, Anacostia, Washington, D.C., during the approach and passage of the cold-front storm shown in Fig. 5.32A. Hours indicated at top.

blunt wedge or, owing to surface friction, overrun a portion of the warm air and entrap it (Fig. 5.13). In either case violent overturning and mechanical upthrust of the warm air take place, with resulting turbulence and associated development of thunderstorms. Occasionally tornadoes, those most violent of all windstorms, likewise develop at or near the wind-shift line of V-shaped cyclones. Since the cold-front variety of thunderstorm is associated with a frontal zone, it must of necessity travel with the latter, and its approach and passage can therefore be forecast with a considerable degree of accuracy. In general, a cold-front storm can be distinguished from the local heat variety by the following criteria: (a) The cold-front storm is commonly more severe although by no means always so. (b) It is not confined to any particular time of day, for its origin does not depend entirely upon local surface heating. It may arrive at any time of day or night. Local convectional storms, on the other hand, are more concentrated in the warmer hours of the day. Even cold-front thunderstorms are more numerous during the warmer hours of the day, for the steeper lapse rate at that time causes the warm air mass to be in its most favorable state for thunderstorm development once the "trigger action" of the cold front goes into effect. (c) The cold-front thunderstorm is usually followed by a shift of wind from southwest, south, or southeast to northwest and by a consequent drop in temperature as the observer shifts from the tropical to the polar air mass (Fig. 5.32B). The local heat thunderstorm gives only very temporary relief from the heat during the period of cloud cover and rain and is likely to be followed by the same kind of hot, humid weather that preceded it. (d) Cold-front thunderstorms may occur at almost any season of the year, provided the air mass being displaced is conditionally unstable. Since instability is most pronounced in the warmer seasons, it is to be expected that summer will show a maximum of such storms; yet they occur much earlier and later in the warm season than the intra air mass type.

The action at the cold front is due to several causes. In part it is due to lifting by the cold air but convergence and cold-air advection aloft ahead of the front are also involved. All these processes are at a maximum at the advanced edge of the cold air, so that the area of greatest turbulence extends almost vertically above the surface front. The intensity of this type of storm increases in direct proportion to the following:

a. As the instability of the warm air is increased.

b. As the horizontal temperature gradient across the front increases.

c. As the wind direction in the cold sector approaches an angle of 90° to the front.

d. As the velocity of the front increases.

263. *Prefrontal thunderstorms* are often developed 200 to 300 miles in advance of a cold front. They are usually arranged in belts or lines roughly parallel to the cold front (Fig. 10.14). Sometimes there are several roughly parallel lines of thunderstorms rather than a single well-developed squall line. Their origin is not entirely understood. Prefrontal thunderstorms can occur at all hours of the day or night, although they are most frequent in late afternoon and early evening. They have the general characteristics of an intense cold-front storm. Both hail and severe line squalls are common. Usually, however, the prefrontal squall is less extensive and does not present a continuous wall of activity for hundreds of miles as does the cold front.

264. Warm-front thunderstorms are not nearly so common as are those associated with cold fronts, the reason being that the vertical movements associated with the warm-front discontinuity surface are not so marked. These storms almost always occur in mT air high in heat and humidity and very unstable. The "trigger action" necessary to release the abundant storm energy is the upward deflection of the warm, conditionally unstable air over the retreating cold wedge. In addition, convergence and cold-air advection play only minor roles compared with their action at the cold front. Such storms show less diurnal periodicity and on the whole are less severe than other frontal types. Much of their action takes place aloft, above the cloud deck formed along the surface of discontinuity, so that the characteristic cumulus cloud forms may not be obvious. They are definitely a high-level type, so that turbulence does not extend down to the earth's surface.

Many thunderstorms likewise occur along occluded fronts. In a general way the thunderstorm conditions along an occluded cold front resemble those along a cold front, and the same is true for warm-front occlusions and warm fronts.

265. Distribution of Thunderstorms. Since in the inner tropical area in the vicinity of the equator, with its convergent wind system, constantly high temperatures and high humidity, are to be found relatively ideal conditions for thunderstorm formation, it is not surprising that equatorial regions should have the maximum number of days with such storms. There is a general decrease in their frequency from equator toward the poles but with some variations (Figs. 5.33, 5.34). Normally, the latitudes of the subtropical highs show up as interruptions in the general decrease poleward of thunderstorm frequency. At first thought one might expect to find an even greater decrease than actually does occur in the latitudes of the subtropical highs, because in these latitudes the tropical deserts are concentrated. But it must be remembered that by no means are all longitudes in the subtropics dry. Beyond latitudes 60 or 70° thunderstorms are very few. The general latitudinal decrease poleward of thunderstorms is evidence of the importance of high temperatures in the production of strong convection. In parts of the equatorial latitudes thunderstorms occur on 75 to 150 days and there are a few places recording more than 200. Most of these are scattered local storms which develop as a result of radiation surface heating. In places, however, they appear to have a genuine pattern of arrangement and seem to concentrate along lines of convergence or in association with highlands. The low-latitude deserts have fewer than 5 days with thunderstorms.

The seasonal profiles as well as the charts showing percentage frequency of thunderstorms exhibit the latitudinal displacement of the belts

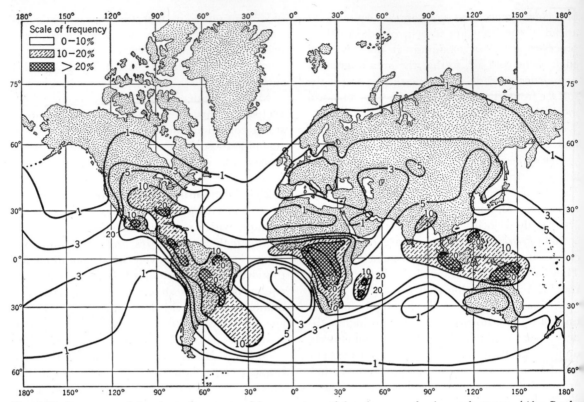

Fig. 5.33. Frequency of thunderstorms expressed in percentage of days in a year having such storms. (*After Brooks, Geophys. Mem., Vol.* 3, *No.* 24, 1925.)

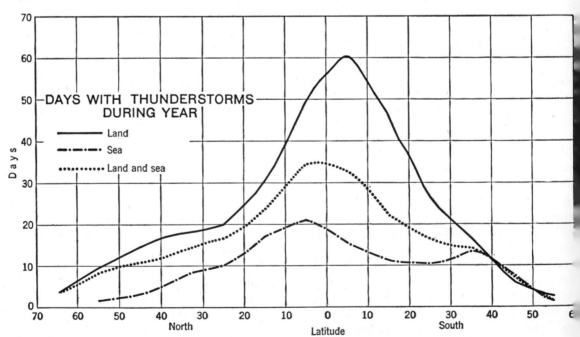

Fig. 5.34. Zonal distribution of days with thunderstorms during the year. (*After Brooks.*)

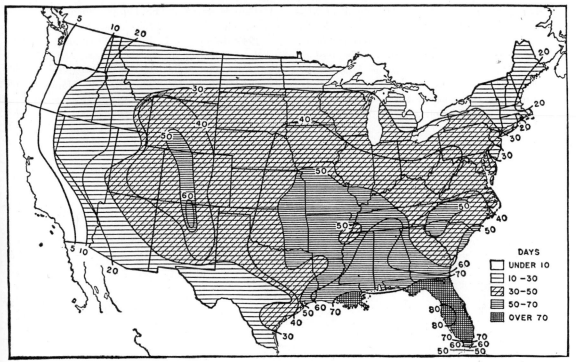

FIG. 5.35. Average annual number of days with thunderstorms.

of maximum and minimum occurrence following the shifts in insolation. Since thunderstorms are commonly the consequence of thermal convection, it is expected that they will be at a maximum in the summer hemisphere. Land areas, with their high summer temperatures, show a greater number of thunderstorms in the warm season than do the oceans.

In the United States the fewest days with thunderstorms are characteristic of the Pacific Coast states which are dominated by stable *mP* air in summer (Fig. 5.35). There appear to be two regions of maxima: (*a*) the southern and southeastern states, more especially the Gulf Coast, and (*b*) the Rocky Mountain area. The eastern Gulf Coast region of the United States is the most thundery area outside the tropics, there being 70 to 90 days a year with thunderstorms. Here heat, humidity, and atmospheric instability combine to produce an environment conducive to strong convectional activity. The number decreases to the north and west, the central tier of states having 40 to 50 such days and the northern tier 30±.

SELECTED REFERENCES FOR FURTHER STUDY OF TOPICS CONTAINED IN CHAPTER 5

1. Middle-latitude cyclones and anticyclones. Byers, 309–339; Willett, 225–256; Petterssen, "Introduction to Meteorology," 134–190; Petterssen, "Weather Analysis," 274–350; "Yearbook of Agriculture, 1941," 579–598; Blair, 157–173; "Compendium of Meteorology," 577–629.
   a. Special weather types in the United States. Ward, Robert De C. "The Climates of the United States," pp. 359–418, Ginn & Company, Company, Boston, 1925.
2. Tropical disturbances.
   a. Hurricanes. Tannehill, Ivan R., "Hurricanes, Their Nature and History." Princeton University Press, Princeton, N.J.; Byers, 417–448; Willett, 165–182; "Compendium of Meteorology," 887–913; Garbell, 77–92.
   b. Weaker disturbances. "Compendium of Meteorology," 868–872, 875–878, 887; Riehl, H. Waves in the Easterlies and the Polar Front in the Tropics. *Miscellaneous Report* 17, Department of Meteorology, University of Chicago, 1943; Garbell 183–185; Berry, F. A., Bollay, E., and

Beers, Norman R., eds., "Handbook of Meteorology," pp. 767–775; Ramanathan, K. R. and Ramakrishnan, K. P. The Indian Southwest Monsoon and the Structure of Depressions Associated with It. *Mem. Indian Meteorological Department*, Vol. 26, Part II, 1933; Rau, N. S. S. Atmospherics during the Monsoon Period. *Proc. Indian Acad. Sci.*, Vol. 17, No. 3, Sec, A. pp. 83–105, March, 1943.

3. Thunderstorms. "The Thunderstorm," Report of the Thunderstorm Project, U.S. Weather Bureau, 1949; Brooks, C. E. P. The Distribution of Thunderstorms over the Earth, *Geophys. Mem.*, No. 24, British Meteorological Office, 1925; Byers, 559–581; Willett, 266–271, 275–279; Haurwitz and Austin, 97–100, Plates xiv–xv; "Compendium of Meteorology," 681–693; Blair, 201–210; Ward, "Climates of the United States," pp. 317–342.

PART TWO

The World Pattern of Climates

Climatic Types and Their Distribution

CHAPTER 6: *Classification of Climates and the World Pattern*

266. The Composite Climate of an Earth Region. In the preceding chapters comprising Part I of this book the individual elements out of which climates are composed have been analyzed as to their nature and origin, and their distributions over the earth's surface have been described. Variations in the amount, intensity, and seasonal distribution of these elements, as determined by the climatic controls, resulting in changeful combinations of the elements, are the reason for the existence of the variety of climates, the description and explanation of which is contained in Part II.

The climate of any locality or region is not determined by a single climatic element but rather by the combinations of climatic elements and of weather types prevailing there. Although it is the composite climatic picture which is sought, this is not to be attained apart from an analysis of the individual climatic elements and weather types and of the interrelations which exist between them. This might seem to suggest that the student who has labored over the elements and weather types described in Part I already has acquired understanding of the composite climate of any region. In a general way this is true. On the other hand, it was the broader *world* distribution patterns and relationships that were emphasized in Part I, and while his knowledge has fundamental value it requires further refinement and detail when applied to individual localities and regions. Also lacking in the method of treatment followed in Part I was the close regional integration of the several climatic elements. This leads to the conclusion that it is difficult to create a satisfactory composite of climate for a locality or region from treatment of the climatic elements individually in terms of their general world patterns. A sharper focus is required.

267. Climatic Elements and Weather Types. In the introduction to Part I it was suggested that there are two complementary methods of presenting the regional climatic picture, *viz.*, (*a*) by an analysis of the individual climatic elements from data resulting from instrumental observation and (*b*) from an analysis of the prevailing weather types as revealed through a study of the daily weather map. Ward puts this forcefully when he writes, "Anyone who seriously attempts to study the climatology of the United States should have a series of weather maps in one hand and a set of climatic charts of the country in the other." The first method, and the one most commonly employed, recommends itself because it permits of a quantitative expression of climatic character in terms of degrees of temperature and depth of rainfall based upon carefully gathered instrumental data. Since these data are based upon periodic time units, the most fundamental of which is the solar-determined day of 24-hr. duration, they fail to reveal in precise form the effects of nonperiodic or storm control which is so much in evidence on the synoptic weather chart. Neither statistical averages of the climatic elements nor an analysis of regional weather types is adequate in itself as a method of climatic synthesis. Both are required for a complete and satisfactory treatment. Unfortunately a satisfactory quantitative method has not yet been developed for adequately portraying the nonperiodic storm control. The number of cyclonic storms within a specified time interval which affect a region is valuable information, but since storms vary greatly in intensity, in air-mass characteristics, in speed of propagation, and in associated weather features, other supplementary data concerning storms are needed. The weather accompanying individual storms varies widely.

268. Classification of Climates. Classification is a process basic to all sciences. It consists of recognizing individuals having certain important characteristics in common and of grouping these individuals into certain classes or types. By noting the similarities between numerous individuals, and then by recognizing these individuals as forming a class, the many are reduced to one. Thereby simplicity and order are introduced into what at first may have been a bewildering multiplicity of individuals. Classification thereby aids in establishing general truths from numerous individual instances.

Since the climate of any locality or region is composed of a great variety of elements, it is nearly impossible for two places to have identical climates. It is this almost limitless number of individual climates on the earth which requires a grouping into classes and types. It should be noted that all classifications of climates are manmade and are not naïvely given. There is no divine plan which is being sought. There can be a variety of ways of classifying earth climates, each of which has merit. It follows that there are a number of good classifications of climate. There is no one which is best, for some are better for one purpose and some for another. They all have the same goal, however, *viz.*, the reduction of innumerable locality climates to a relatively few groups or classes having important characteristics in common.

269. Classification by Temperature Zones. Perhaps the broadest and most general classification of climates is the one devised by the ancient Greeks, who divided each hemisphere into three broad belts, or zones. Thus in the low latitudes is the *winterless* tropical region where temperatures are high throughout the year. Similarly in the high latitudes, in the vicinity of the poles, are the *summerless* polar regions, where there is a general prevalence of low temperatures. Between these two extremes, which are the tropical and the polar parts of the earth, are broad intervening belts where seasonal contrasts in temperature are marked, one season usually being warm or hot and the other cool or cold. These are the *intermediate*, or *middle*, *latitudes*, sometimes designated as the "temperate zones," although obviously that name is not well chosen.

270. Climatic Regions and Climatic Types. This threefold classification of the earth's climates into tropical, middle-latitude, and polar groups emphasizes chiefly one element, temperature. It fails to take into consideration that other primary element, precipitation, and in addition many less important elements, since within both the low and the middle latitudes there are very wet as well as very dry climates. It is obvious that the geographer and climatologist require not only a more detailed and refined classification but also one in which the climatic subdivisions are based upon precipitation as well as upon temperature characteristics. Such a subdivision of the land areas of the earth into climatic types and climatic regions is presented on Plates I, II, and III.

Any portion of the earth's surface over which the climatic elements, and therefore the broad climatic characteristics, are similar (not necessarily identical) is called a *climatic region*. But it will be noted that not all the subdivisions on Plates I, II, and III differ from one another climatically, for areas with similar climates are found in widely separated parts of the earth, although often in corresponding latitudinal and continental locations. Frequent approximating of climates in roughly corresponding positions on the continents suggests that there is order and system in the origin and distribution of the climatic elements. It likewise makes possible the classification of the numerous *climatic regions* into a relatively few principal *climatic types*. The climatic region is a subdivision of the climatic type, and hence the type is composed of numerous regions.

It will be observed in the latitudinal and continental arrangement of climatic regions and types that there is a recognizable world pattern of climates. This is to be expected, since the greatest controls of climate are to be found in the distribution of solar energy and the general circulation of the atmosphere which in themselves have clearly defined world patterns. The general features of world distribution of climates is illustrated by Fig. 6.4 which purports to show climatic arrangement as it might appear on a hypothetical continent of relatively low and uniform elevation. That there are numerous modifications of, or deviations from, any idealized scheme of world climatic distribution suggests the operation of other controls, some of which are not entirely understood. For this reason not all the facts of climatic distribution are at present capable of being explained. One of the most fertile fields of climatic investigation is the searching for explanations for the numerous departures from what is thought of as the normal world pattern. In this book, however, little attention is given to individual climatic regions or to the uniquenesses of different continental climatic patterns, important as those topics are. The emphasis here is upon the general climatic types, their over-all characteristics, and their global distribution.

271. Systems of Climatic Classification. As indicated previously, the number of different classifications of climate is numerous. Among those which are better known and most widely used are Hettner's,[1] de Martonne's,[2] Köppen's,[3] and Thornthwaite's.[4] The latter two probably are most familiar to American geographers. Köppen's and Thornthwaite's classifications are particularly noteworthy because, unlike some others, they are quantitative systems which use numerical values for defining the boundaries of climatic groups and types. Where specific values of temperature and precipitation are employed to limit individual climatic types, the boundaries

[1] Alfred Hettner, "Die Klimate der Erde," B. G. Teubner, Leipzig, 1930.

[2] Emmanuel de Martonne, "Traité de géographie physique," 7th ed., Vol. I, Librairie Armand Colin, Paris, 1948.

[3] Köppen-Geiger, "Handbuch der Klimatologie," Vol. I, Part C, Gebrüder Borntraeger, Berlin, 1936.

[4] C. Warren Thornthwaite, The Climates of North America According to a New Classification, *Geog. Rev.,* Vol. 21, pp. 633–655, October, 1931; The Climates of the Earth, *Geog. Rev.,* Vol. 23, pp. 433–440, July, 1933; An Approach toward a Rational Classification of Climate, *Geog. Rev.,* Vol. 38, pp. 55–94, January, 1948.

are subject to checking and revision as new data become available. Many of the numerical values used to establish climatic boundaries have been selected because they appear fairly to coincide with certain significant landscape boundaries, particularly those of native vegetation.

272. Köppen's classification of world climates was devised by Dr. Wladimir Köppen of the University of Graz (Austria). First published in 1918 and subsequently changed and modified a number of times, the latest *world* map appears in Köppen's book, "Grundriss der Klimakunde," Berlin, 1931. Still more recent and detailed maps, but covering only individual continents or parts of continents, are contained in Volumes II to V of the Köppen-Geiger, "Handbuch der Klimatologie" (see reference list, p. 237). Volume I, Part C (Köppen, "Das geographischen System der Klimate," 1936) of the above handbook contains the latest analysis of the classification. See Appendix A for a detailed presentation of the Köppen classification, together with a world map showing distribution of his climatic types.

The classification is based upon annual and monthly means of temperature and precipitation. Native vegetation is looked upon as the best expression of the totality of a climate so that many of the climatic boundaries are selected with vegetation limits in mind. Köppen recognizes that the effectiveness of precipitation upon plant development and growth depends not alone upon amount of precipitation but also upon the intensity of evaporation which causes large losses of water from soil and plants. That part of the rainfall which is evaporated is of no value in vegetation growth. Köppen's method of indicating evaporation intensity, and hence precipitation effectiveness, is to combine precipitation and temperature. Thus the same number of inches of rainfall falling in a hot climate, or concentrated in a hot season where evaporation is great, is less effective for plants than the same amount falling in a cooler climate. While useful, it must be admitted that this method of measuring precipitation effectiveness is not entirely satisfactory.

A unique and distinctive feature of the

Köppen system is the employment of an ingenious symbolic nomenclature in designating the climatic types. This makes unnecessary the coining of cumbersome descriptive terms. Each type of climate is described by a formula consisting of a combination of letters, each one of which has a precise meaning. Thus the formula *Af* may be translated as follows: *A*: constantly hot, average temperature of the coldest month above 64.4°; *f*: constantly wet, no month of the year having on the average less than 2.4 in. of precipitation.

The Köppen classification has been criticized by geographers from various points of view.[1] Some feel that the dearth of meteorological observations for large parts of the world makes a climatic classification with rigid boundary criteria unsatisfactory. They point out that this too often leads to pronounced discrepancies between climatic subdivisions and the features of the natural and cultural landscapes. To include, as Köppen does, the humid Puget Sound region with its splendid Douglas fir forests in the same climatic type (Mediterranean, *Cs*) with central California obviously indicates a weakness in the classification. Others have pointed out that, while some of the Köppen climatic boundaries have been chosen with certain natural landscape features in mind, others have been purely arbitrary choices. It has been suggested also that Köppen has erred in applying to higher altitudes his formulas derived for lowland climates. In any classification such as Köppen's which recognizes only a few principal types of climate it must be true that along climatic boundaries where one type gradually merges

into another the climatic designations often seem unsatisfactory. This situation could be improved, of course, by increasing the number of climatic types and regions. But such a multiplication of subdivisions, while it permits of greater accuracy, adds greatly to the complication of the basic system. It seems preferable for the individual worker to create subdivisions of the few basic types as his needs require.[1]

Admittedly the Köppen classification of climates has shortcomings, but its merits as a teaching device so far outweigh its deficiencies that it has been widely accepted in this country and abroad by geographers and climatologists. As a tool for presenting the general world pattern of climates, and of suggesting some of the more important deviations from this pattern, it has substantial merit. It is an empirical classification in the sense that its types and boundaries have not been selected with genesis in mind. Yet on the other hand a considerable number of the Köppen types coincide reasonably well with certain broad features of the atmospheric circulation and are to be explained in terms of them.

273. Thornthwaite's Classifications of Climates. Two classifications of climate developed by Thornthwaite need to be distinguished apart, one dated 1931 and 1933 and the other dated 1948. Superficially the two systems appear relatively similar, although their author quite rightly insists that they are fundamentally different. A world map showing distribution of climates according to the earlier classification is available but this is not true for the 1948 system.

274. *The* 1931 *Thornthwaite Classification of Climates.* The earlier Thornthwaite classification followed the Köppen principle that the plant is in the nature of a meteorological instrument which is capable of measuring all the integrated climatic elements. Under this system climatic types are identified and their boundaries determined empirically through noting vegetation,

[1] See C. Warren Thornthwaite, The Climates of North America According to a New Classification, *Geog. Rev.*, Vol. 21, pp. 633–655, 1931, reference on pp. 633–634; S. B. Jones, Classifications of North American Climates, *Econ. Geog.*, Vol. 8, pp. 205–208, 1932; and Edward A. Ackerman, The Köppen Classification of Climates in North America, *Geog. Rev.*, Vol. 31, pp. 105–111, January, 1941 (the last reference contains a revised map of the climates of North America); F. Kenneth Hare, Climatic Classification, Chap. 7 in "London Essays in Geography," edited by L. Dudley Stamp and S. W. Wooldridge; Stephen B. Jones, What Does Geography Need from Climatology? *The Professional Geographer*, N.S., Vol. 2, No. 4, pp. 41–44, 1950.

[1] For sample studies to illustrate this method, see R. J. Russell, Climates of California, *Univ. Calif. Publications in Geography*, Vol. 2, pp. 73–84, 1926; Climates of Texas, *Ann. Assoc. Am. Geographers*, Vol. 35, pp. 37–52, 1945.

soil, and drainage features. Precipitation effectiveness for furthering plant growth is determined by dividing total monthly precipitation by total monthly evaporation (called the P/E ratio), and the sum of the 12 monthly P/E ratios is called the P/E index. Theoretically this may be a somewhat more refined method for determining precipitation effectiveness than that employed by Köppen. However, in practice it is not so satisfactory since actual evaporation data are available for only small portions of the earth. As a result a P/E ratio formula was developed from temperature and precipitation relationships as observed at 21 stations in southwestern United States. This formula developed and tested for one local area is then applied to the rest of the earth.

Based upon the P/E index Thornthwaite distinguishes five humidity provinces each of which appears to be associated with a characteristic vegetation type (Fig. 6.1).

Humidity Province	Characteristic Vegetation	P/E Index
A, wet	Rainforest	128 and above
B, humid	Forest	64–127
C, subhumid	Grassland	32–63
D, semiarid	Steppe	16–31
E, arid	Desert	Under 16

The five principal humidity provinces are subdivided into four subtypes based upon seasonal concentration of precipitation:

r = rainfall abundant at all seasons
s = rainfall deficient in summer
w = rainfall deficient in winter
d = rainfall deficient in all seasons

Based upon thermal efficiency six temperature provinces are recognized:

Temperature Province	T/E Index
A′, tropical	128 and above
B′, mesothermal	64–127
C′, microthermal	32–63
D′, taiga	16–31
E′, tundra	1–15
F′, frost	0

Theoretically 120 combinations of the three elements, precipitation effectiveness, seasonal

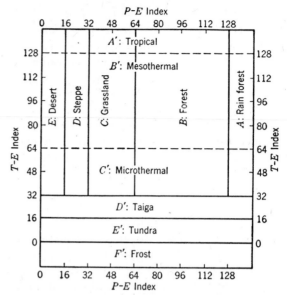

FIG. 6.1. Temperature and humidity provinces according to the Thornthwaite system of climatic classification. (*After Thornthwaite, Geog. Rev., Vol. 21, p. 649, 1931.*)

concentration of rainfall, and thermal efficiency are possible. Nowhere near all these combinations actually occur, and on his world map Thornthwaite only recognizes 32 climatic types (see Appendix A, Plate III).

Thornthwaite's 1931 classification of climates is like Köppen's, not only in being quantitative, but likewise in that it employs a shorthand system of letter combinations to designate individual climates. It differs from Köppen's classification in that, instead of employing simple temperature and precipitation values as limiting boundaries, the new concepts, temperature efficiency and precipitation effectiveness, cannot be expressed in ordinary climatic values, and consequently the boundaries are less easily comprehended. This is the principal handicap of the Thornthwaite classification for classroom use. Moreover, the number of different climatic types appearing on the world map reaches a total of 32, approximately three times the number of Köppen types. On the other hand, the number of symbolic letters is few and their combinations are simple and easy to remember. The climatic types have no descriptive names, so that they can be designated only by their letter formulas.

275. *Thornthwaite's* 1948 *Classification.* As in the earlier classification, this later one also employs the same three climatic indices, precipitation effectiveness, seasonal concentration of rainfall, and thermal efficiency. But they are used in a contrasting way in differentiating and locating climatic boundaries. While in the 1931 classification the plant was viewed as a meteorological instrument for measuring climatic character, in this second one vegetation "is regarded as a physical mechanism by means of which water is transported from the soil to the atmosphere; it is the machinery of evaporation as the cloud is the machinery of precipitation." The combined loss through evaporation from the soil surface and transpiration from plants is called "evapotranspiration." Unfortunately no instrument has been invented which will measure loss of moisture from earth to atmosphere, so that Thornthwaite is obliged to compute it as a function of temperature.

In the older classification the climatic subdivisions are really vegetation regions climatically determined. In the 1948 system climatic boundaries are determined rationally by comparing precipitation and potential evapotranspiration. Thus the climatic classification is developed independently of other geographic factors such as vegetation, soils, and land use. Climatic boundaries are determined from the climatic data and these alone. When the annual march of potential evapotranspiration and of precipitation for a station are plotted as smooth curves and the two curves superimposed (Fig. 6.2), one is able to determine whether precipitation exceeds evapotranspiration or whether the opposite is true. Also it can be noted at what periods of the year one is in excess of the other. Thus definite break points are revealed in the climatic series so that there are distinctive points which serve as climatic boundaries. This fact according to Thornthwaite provides the basis for a *rational* classification of climates.

Owing, in part, to inadequacy of data for computing potential evapotranspiration for large areas of the earth no map of world climates

based upon this newer rational classification has been produced. Moreover, up to the present time no rational method has been discovered for delimiting temperature efficiency regions.

276. Genetic Classification of Climate. There are those who are dissatisfied with the kinds of climatic classifications as represented by Köppen's and Thornthwaite's systems and urge instead that a dynamic climatology with a classification based upon origin or genesis be emphasized. The classifications previously described, and designated as empirical or rational, define the climatic types and their boundaries in terms of the effects of climate on vegetation (Köppen, Thornthwaite, 1931) or in terms of the climatic data themselves (Thornthwaite, 1948). They make no pretense of relating climatic types with distinctive geographic locations or of associating them with particular wind, air-mass, or pressure systems. They depend upon observation alone and no rationalization of location is attempted. Flohn of Germany has recently come out strongly as opposed to a strictly descriptive climatology and in favor of a more dynamic treatment of the subject, including a genetic classification based upon the physical causes of climates, more especially the general atmospheric circulation. He argues with some validity that modern climatology, which is preponderantly descriptive, is in the unenviable position of an auxiliary science to other fields of learning, such as geography, agriculture, medicine, and geology, and has failed to develop as an independent science with a fundamental interest in causes as well as distributions. Certain it is that much climatological literature is wearisome and lacking in zest because of its pedestrian description with little or no attempt at explanation.

No purely genetic classification of climates has yet been devised. Indeed it is doubtful whether such a classification based exclusively on genesis would be satisfactory to geographers, biologists, and agriculturists, since it would be inclined to include more than one rational or empirical type within a genetic group. Nevertheless it might be possible to combine in one classifica-

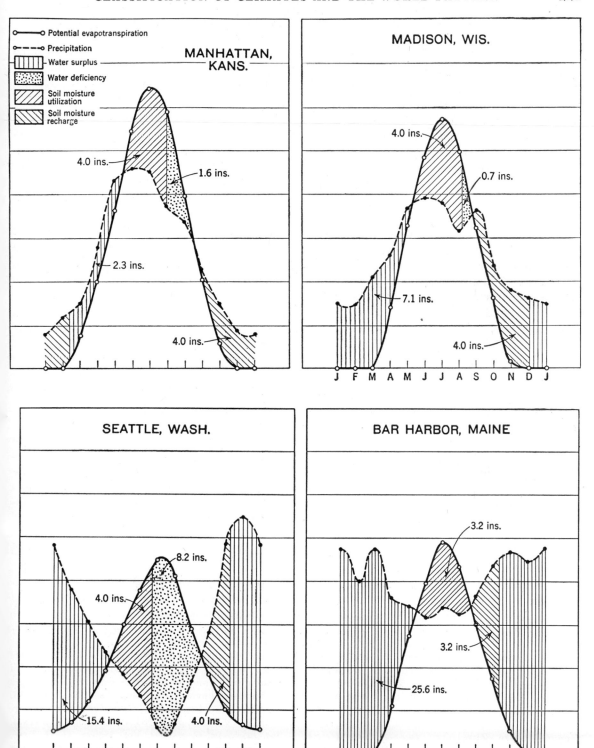

Fig. 6.2. Precipitation and evapotranspiration curves for selected stations. (*After Thornthwaite, courtesy of the Geographical Review.*)

tion some of the valuable attributes of both the empirical-rational and the genetic systems.

Flohn has made some interesting suggestions relative to a semigenetic classification of climatic zones, and has shown the location of these zones or types on a hypothetical continent (see table, p. 231).[1] No world climate map has yet resulted. Seven zones of climate are differentiated, and for each of these the corresponding pressure and wind belts are indicated as well as the prevailing winds in the extreme seasons. An attempt is made to relate each of the seven zones to the appropriate Köppen types and to suggest the typical vegetation forms. Four of the zones remain within one wind belt throughout the year; the others experience alternations of wind belts with the seasons. Flohn refers to the first group as *constant climatic zones* and to the second group as *alternating climatic zones*. In the genetic classification proposed by Flohn and outlined in the following table, p. 231, it will be observed that precipitation plays the major role in differentiating the seven climatic zones. Temperature is considered to be a more general element which changes only gradually.

277. Present Scheme of Climatic Classification. The general scheme of climatic classification employed in this book is one designed for use in a first course in climatology where the goal of instruction is the development of the world pattern of climates. The needs of geographers are made paramount. Such a classification should be kept simple, and consequently it should recognize only a relatively few principal climatic types. Increasing the number tends to obscure the elemental features of the climatic pattern. Where further detail is required than that provided by the major climatic types, this

can be readily secured by adding as many second-order and third-order subdivisions within a climatic type or region as are required for the purpose at hand. Such a method has the merit of flexibility in that it retains the great advantage of a relatively few primary climatic types as comprising the principal elements of the world system, while at the same time allowing for any degree of detail desired.[1] It is believed there is great value in orienting all climatic description with respect to the framework of a standard and recognized classification of climates.

Since the needs of geographers provide the essential focus for this book, it is believed that an empirical type of classification is the most appropriate scheme for presenting the main lineaments of climatic distribution. For those, such as geographers, biologists, or agriculturists, who need to understand and use the climatic environment for their own purposes, the facts of climate must be presented realistically and without forcing them into any preconceived genetic structure or any scheme of type location. First and foremost one must be guided by the observed data.

On the other hand, description without resort to genesis or origin, leading to explanation, soon becomes dull and tiresome, features which, unfortunately, characterize much of the regional climatic literature. A recognition of the importance of genesis not only whets interest and adds to the scientific quality of climatic analysis but also gives insight and understanding which increases the quality of the description. One cannot observe the arrangement of world climates as developed under any good empirical classification without being conscious that there is order and system in the distribution. In other

[1] H. Flohn, Neue Anschauungen über die allgemeine Zirkulation der Atmosphäre und ihre klimatische Bedeutung, *Erdkunde*, Vol. 4, pp. 155–159, 1950; John Borchert, Regional Differences in the World Atmospheric Circulation, *Ann. Assoc. Am. Geographers*, Vol. 43, pp. 14–26, March, 1953; H. Flohn, Grundzüge der atmosphärischen Zirkulation, *Deutscher Geographentag Frankfurt*, Vol. 28, pp. 105–118, 1952; A. Austin Miller, Air Mass Climatology, *Geography*, Part 2, Vol. 38, pp. 55–67, 1953.

[1] For examples of detailed regional studies of climate which have followed the principle suggested above of creating subdivisions within the recognized world types of standard climatic classification, see R. J. Russell, Climates of California, *Univ. Calif. Publications in Geography*, Vol. 2, No. 4, pp. 73–84, 1926; Climates of Texas, *Ann. Assoc. Am. Geographers*, Vol. 35, pp. 37–52, June, 1945. See also John Kesseli, The Climates of California According to the Köppen Classification, *Geo. Rev.*, Vol. 32, pp. 476–480, 1942.

Atmospheric Climatic Zones of the Earth
(After Flohn)

Zone	Precipitation	Pressure belt and wind belt	Winds*		Typical climate, Köppen	Typical vegetation forms
			Summer	Winter		
Inner tropical zone	Constantly wet, mostly heavy rains	Equatorial west-wind zone† >8 months	T	T	Af, Am	Tropical rainforest, monsoon forest
Outer tropical zone (tropical margins)	Summer rain (zenithal rain)	Equatorial west-wind zone† <8 mo., alternating with trades	T	P	Aw, in part Cw	Savanna with galeria forest, dry forest
Subtropical dry zone‡	Prevailingly dry (infrequent downpours)	Trade or sub-tropical high	P	P	BS, BW	Steppe, desert-steppe, semidesert, true desert
Subtropical winter-rain zone‡	Winter rain, in part equinoctial rain	Summer subtropical high, winter-middle-latitude westerlies	P	W	Cs	Hardleaf woods
Moist temperate zone	Rain in all seasons	Middle latitude westerlies	W	W	Cf, in part Cw	Broadleaf and mixed forest
Boreal zone§	Rainfall predominantly in summer, winter snow cover	Middle-latitude westerlies, in part polar easterlies	W	E	Df, Dw	Coniferous forest and birches
Subpolar zone	Meager rain throughout the year	Polar easterlies and west winds (subpolar low)	W	E	ET	Tundra
High polar zone	Meager snowfall throughout the year	Polar easterlies	E	E	EF	Cold desert (ice)

* *T* = equatorial westerlies and doldrums.
  P = tropical easterlies (trades) and subtropical high.
  W = middle latitude westerlies.
  E = polar easterlies.
† Or doldrums.
‡ Absent on east side of continent.
§ Only on the continents; absent in southern hemisphere.

words, there is a recognizable world pattern in many of the larger features of climatic distribution. This fact suggests genesis. To be sure there are numerous and important deviations from the world pattern, but these departures equally urge the necessity of explanation. Therefore it is believed that the empirical classification of climates should be supplemented in every way possible by genetic classification to the end that explanation of the qualities and distribution of climates shall be suggested.

In its fundamentals the classification of climates employed in this book is a modified form of the Köppen system, the description of which is presented in Appendix A. It is recognized that some instructors do not regard the structure and

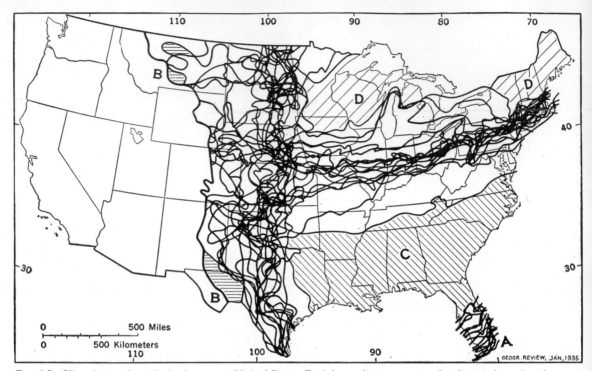

Fig. 6.3. Climatic year boundaries in eastern United States. Each heavy line represents the climatic boundary between *B* and humid climates, or between *C* and *D* climates for a single year. It becomes clear that climatic boundaries shift position from one year to the next and that their locations as drawn on a general map of climatic types is simply a mean of the different locations for a large number of individual climatic years.

boundary details of the Köppen system as essential to an undergraduate course, and this is one reason for omitting such a discussion from the main body of the text. Certainly caution is necessary to avoid putting so much emphasis on boundaries and their definitions that the true nature, meaning, and cause of the core climates within the boundaries are concealed or slighted. The Köppen system has been criticized as a tricky puzzle, but it does not need to be. The boundary definitions are useful, but they need not be turned into a feat of memorization. A climatic boundary as it appears on any small-scale map of climates represents only the mean position of numerous climatic-year boundaries which often depart widely in location from the mean position (Fig. 6.3).[1] Too great emphasis

in memorizing the exact location of a mean boundary which shifts its position from year to year can scarcely be defended. To those who prefer to use the unmodified Köppen system, or those who desire a more complete outline of the structure of the Köppen system as a background for better understanding the modified Köppen system here employed, reference is made to Appendix A. Only a general outline of the present classification and of its deviations from the standard Köppen system are presented at this point.

Following Köppen, five great groups of climate are recognized. In the low latitudes near the equator, there is a winterless region of constantly high temperatures with adequate rainfall (*A*). This is the humid tropics. Within this group

[1] See R. J. Russell, Dry Climates of the United States, Part II, Frequency of Dry and Desert Years 1901–1920, *Univ. Calif. Publications in Geography*, Vol. 5, No. 5, pp. 245–274, 1932; R. J. Russell, Climatic Years, *Geog. Rev.*, Vol. 24, pp. 92–103, 1934; Henry Madison Kendall,

Notes on Climatic Boundaries in Eastern United States, *Geog. Rev.*, Vol. 25, No. 1, pp. 117–124, 1935; Jack Richard Villmow, The Position of the Köppen *Da/Db* Boundary in Eastern United States, *Ann. Assoc. Am. Geographers*, Vol. 41, No. 1, pp. 76–97, 1952.

two climatic types, based upon rainfall contrasts, are identified, the constantly wet type (*Af*) and the tropical wet-and-dry type with its summer, or zenithal, rains and its low-sun dry season (*Aw*). The former type (*Af*) reasonably well coincides with the zone of equatorial convergence (*ITC*, doldrums, equatorial westerlies) and is dominated by convergence throughout most of the year. The *Aw* type alternately is under the influence of the *ITC* for a part of the year (high sun) and of the drier trades, characterized by subsidence, for the remainder.

Poleward from the *A* group and extending beyond the tropics far into the middle latitudes are the dry climates (*B*). The *B* group is subdivided into an arid, or desert, type (*BW*) and a semiarid, or steppe, type (*BS*). Further subdivision separates the *hot* tropical and subtropical deserts and steppes (*BWh, BSh*) from the cold middle-latitude deserts and steppes (*BWk, BSk*). The *h/k* boundary separating hot, dry climates from cold, dry climates is the 0°C., or 32°F., isotherm for the coldest month. The hot dry climates reasonably well coincide with the subtropical anticyclones and poleward parts of the trades where atmospheric subsidence and divergence are characteristic. The cold dry climates have locations leeward of high mountains or in the interiors of large continents far from sources of moisture and where cold anticyclones with subsidence prevail in winter.

The humid middle latitudes, with their seasonal contrasts in temperature, are divided into two climatic groups, the mesothermal in which the winters are mild and short (*C*), and the microthermal in which they are severe and long (*D*). Within the *C* group three types of climate are recognized: subhumid dry-summer subtropical (*Cs*), humid subtropical with hot summers (*Ca*), and middle-latitude marine with cool summers (*Cb*). Why these subdivisions of the *C* group depart from the standard Köppen classification will be explained later. The *Cs* group with its winter rainfall and summer drought is alternately influenced by middle-latitude westerlies and their cyclonic storms in winter and the subtropical high in summer. The *Ca* type, also in the subtropics, is affected by the

unstable western margin of the subtropical anticyclone in summer and the westerlies and their cyclonic storms in winter. *Cb*, poleward of the subtropics and characteristically on the windward side of the continent, is affected by the cyclonic westerlies throughout the entire year.

Within the microthermal group *D*, the principal types are based upon temperature contrasts. This is a further departure from the standard Köppen system. This group of boreal climates is associated with large land masses in relatively high middle latitudes so that they alternately feel the effects of the westerlies in summer and the polar winds in winter. The humid continental types (*Da* and *Db*) are differentiated on the basis of summer temperatures, *Da* having warm summers (warmest month over 22°C., or 71.6°F.) and *Db* cool summers (warm month under 22°C., or 71.6°F.). The subarctic type (*Dc, Dd*) is characterized by very short cool summers and long severe winters (*c* = less than 4 months over 10°C. or 50°F.; *d* = coldest month below −38°C., or −36.4°F.).

Finally, in the higher latitudes are the summerless polar climates (*E*). These are dominated by polar winds throughout the year. Two subdivisions are recognized, *ET*, or tundra, where the warmest month is above 0°C., or 32°F., and *EF*, or ice cap, where all months are below 0°C., or 32°F.

The outline of principal climatic groups and their subdivisions into types, together with their appropriate letter symbols, appears in the table on p. 234. Also an attempt has been made to suggest significant relationships of the individual climatic groups and types to features of the atmospheric circulation and to characterize their seasonal rainfall regimes. Some of the more important Köppen symbols and their definitions are provided in a footnote to the following table. Definitions of other Köppen symbols are provided in footnotes throughout the text, where they may be useful. Further details of the Köppen system are to be found in Appendix A.

278. Summary of Departures of Present Classification from the Standard Köppen System. *a.* In the *B* climates Köppen has used

Types of Climate*

| Groups of climate | Types of climate | Pressure system and wind belt | | Precipitation |
		Summer	Winter	
A. Tropical rainy	Af (Am), tropical wet	ITC, doldrums, equatorial westerlies	ITC, doldrums, equatorial westerlies	No dry season
	Aw, tropical wet and dry	ITC, doldrums, equatorial westerlies	Trades	High-sun wet (zenithal rains) low-sun dry
B. Dry	BS, semiarid (steppe)			
	BSh, tropical and subtropical	Subtropical high and dry trades	Subtropical high and dry trades	Short moist season
	BSk, middle latitude		Continental winter anticyclone	Meager rainfall, most in summer
	BW, arid (desert)			
	BWh, tropical and subtropical	Subtropical high and dry trades	Subtropical high and dry trades	Constantly dry
	BWk, middle latitude		Continental winter anticyclone	Constantly dry
C. Humid mesothermal	Cs, dry summer subtropical	Subtropical high (stable east side)	Westerlies	Summer drought, winter rain
	Ca, humid subtropical	Subtropical high (unstable west side)	Westerlies	Rain in all seasons
	Cb, Cc, marine climate	Westerlies	Westerlies	Rain in all seasons, accent on winter
D. Humid microthermal	Da, humid continental, warm summer	Westerlies	Westerlies and winter anticyclone	Rain in all seasons, accent on summer; winter snow cover
	Db, humid continental, cool summer	Westerlies	Westerlies and winter anticyclone	Rain in all seasons, accent on summer; long winter snow cover
	Dc (Dd) subarctic	Westerlies	Winter anticyclone and polar winds	Meager precipitation throughout year
E. Polar	ET, tundra	Polar winds	Polar winds	Meager precipitation throughout year
	EF, ice cap	Polar winds	Polar winds	Meager precipitation throughout year
H. Undifferentiated highlands				

Types of Climate*.—(Continued)

* A = temperature of coolest month over 18°C. (64.4°F.)
   B = evaporation exceeds precipitation
   C = coldest month between 18°C. (64.4°F.) and 0°C. (32°F.)
   D = temperature of coldest month under 32°F. (0°C.); warmest month over 10°C. (50°F.)
   E = temperature of warmest month under 10°C. (50°F.)
   a = warmest month over 22°C. (71.6°F.)
   b = warmest month below 22°C. (71.6°F.)
   c = warmest month below 22°C. (71.6°F.); less than four months above 10°C. (50°F.)
   d = coldest month below −38°C. (−36.4°F.)
With A climates:
   f = no dry season; driest month over 6 cm. (2.4 in.)
   s = dry period at high sun or summer; rare in A climates
   w = dry period at low sun or winter; driest month under 6 cm. (2.4 in.)
With C and D climates:
   f = no dry season; difference between rainiest and driest months less than in s and w; driest month of summer
       over 3 cm. (1.2 in.)
   s = summer dry; at least 3 times as much rain in wettest month of winter as in driest month of summer; driest
       month less than 3 cm. (1.2 in.)
   w = winter dry; at least 10 times as much rain in wettest month of summer as in driest month of winter

the mean annual isotherm of 64.4°F. (18°C.) as the boundary separating Bh from Bk, *i.e.*, the hot dry from the cold dry. In the modified system here employed the 32° isotherm for the coldest month has been accepted as the h/k boundary. For the United States at least, the 32° January isotherm is more significant than the 64.4° mean annual.

b. Köppen uses the coldest month isotherm of 26.6°F. (−3°C.) as the boundary between C and D climates. In the present modified system 32°F. (0°C.) for the coldest month is substituted for the above. This is identical with the h/k boundary in the dry (B) climates. In North America, Europe, and Asia the 32° January mean temperature is much more significant than 26.6° for January.[1]

c. In the humid mesothermal group of climates (C) Köppen distinguishes three principal climatic types, the basis for the differentiation being seasonal distribution of rainfall: Cs, summer dry; Cw, winter dry; and Cf, no dry season. From the standpoint of logic, this method of differentiation is sound, but it is the author's belief that it does not differentiate the three principal climatic types in so far as their effects upon soils, vegetation, and culture are concerned. Köppen's Cw type is found not only in

[1] For an elaboration of this point, see *Geog. Rev.*, Vol. 31, pp. 108–111.

lower middle latitudes where there is a strong monsoon influence, but also in tropical uplands where altitude reduces the temperature of at least one month below 64.4°, which is the A/C boundary. These two very unlike type locations of Cw, plus certain fundamental contrasts in the climates they represent, have led the author to discard the type. Moreover, most Köppen Cfa regions have a summer maximum of precipitation, and whether the wettest summer month has somewhat more or less than ten times the precipitation of the driest winter month does not seem very consequential. In southern China, where both Cfa and Cwa are represented, there appear to be no significant differences between them in native vegetation, soils, or culture.

Within the C group of climates seasonal rainfall appears to be the critical differentiating factor in only one type, Cs. In other C regions summer temperatures stand out as of greater consequence than the season of rainfall. Therefore, in the modified Köppen system employed in this book, the second and third subdivisions of the C group are $Ca(f, w)$ and $Cb(f, w)$, one having warm summers such as the cotton belt of the United States, and the other cool summers such as western Europe. Surely there is more reason for differentiating climatically between southern China (Ca) and the British Isles (Cb) than between Cw and Cf in southern China.

d. In the humid microthermal group of climates (*D*) Köppen again differentiates the principal types based upon season of rainfall: *Dw*, winter dry; *Df*, no dry season. *Dw* occurs only in eastern Asia where a strong moonsoon wind system prevails; yet on the other hand most of the *D* regions of the world have a pronounced summer maximum, even though they cannot qualify as *Dw*. Based upon observations

in eastern Asia, it is the author's conviction that *Dw* and *Df* climates in that region do not differ so fundamentally in vegetation, soils, and culture as do *Da*, *Db*, and *Dc* climates, where summer temperature is employed as the differentiating element. In the present classification, therefore, the subdivisions of the *D* group are based primarily upon summer temperatures.

e. Köppen attempts to differentiate the vari-

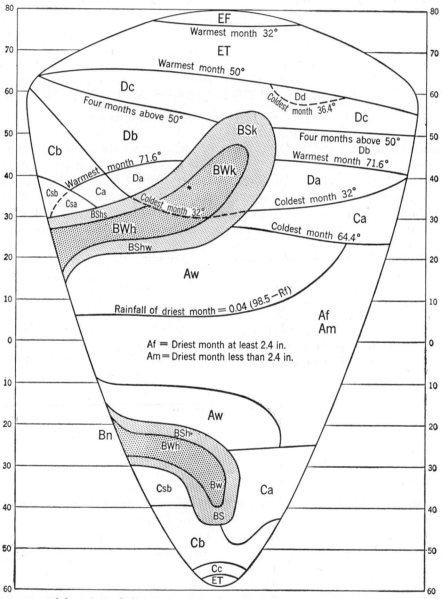

FIG. 6.4. Arrangement of the principal climatic types on a hypothetical continent of relatively low and uniform elevation together with certain boundary criteria.

ous climates within highland areas, employing the same boundary criteria used for lowland climates and with somewhat unsatisfactory results. Owing to the relatively few climatic data that are available for most highland regions, and also because of the great complexity of climates within mountains, this differentiation has usually not been attempted here. In the tropics populated uplands of low or moderate elevation have been indicated by stippling.

279. Distribution of Climates on a Hypothetical Continent. In studying the text materials on types of climate to follow, constant reference should be made to Plate I, which shows distribution of the types over the land areas of the earth. In conjunction with the analysis of actual distribution as exhibited on Plate I, careful attention likewise should be paid to Fig. 6.4, which is designed to show the typical positions and arrangements of the climatic types and their boundaries as they would appear on a hypothetical continent of low and uniform elevation, the shape of which corresponds roughly to that of the actual land masses. In other words, on this hypothetical continent one is able to see the climatic types as they probably would be, with the modifications and complications resulting from varying shapes, sizes, positions, and elevations of the land masses eliminated. Here the world pattern of climates is most clearly revealed. The strong resemblances between Fig. 6.4 and Plate I are obvious.

REFERENCES FOR PART II

Ackerman, Edward A. The Köppen Classification of Climates in North America. *Geog. Rev.*, Vol. 31, pp. 105–111, 1941.

"Atlas of American Agriculture." Part II, Climate. 3 sec.: Frost and the Growing Season; Temperature, Sunshine and Wind; Precipitation and Humidity. Government Printing Office, Washington, D.C. Contains excellent and detailed maps of the climatic elements.

Blair, Thomas A. "Climatology, General and Regional." Prentice-Hall, Inc., New York, 1942.

Brooks, Charles F., Connor, A. J., and others. "Climatic Maps of North America." Harvard University Press, Cambridge, Mass., 1936.

Clayton, H. H. World Weather Records. *Smithsonian Miscellaneous Collections*, Vol. 79, 1927, Vol. 90, 1934, and Vol. 105, 1947, Smithsonian Institution, Washington, D.C. A compendium of climatological data for the various parts of the world.

"Climate and Man." Yearbook of Agriculture. 1941. United States Department of Agriculture, Washington, D.C. Contains abundant climatic data on the United States and on foreign countries as well.

Hann, Julius. "Handbook of Climatology." Part I, English trans. by Robert De C. Ward. The Macmillan Company, New York, 1903. 4th rev. German ed. by Karl Knoch, J. Engelhorn's Nachfolger, Stuttgart, 1932. Parts II and III (untranslated) deal with regional climates.

Hare, F. Kenneth. Climatic Classification, Chapter VII in "London Essays in Geography," L. Dudley Stamp and S. W. Woolridge, eds., Harvard University Press, Cambridge, Mass. 1951.

Haurwitz, Bernhard, and Austin, James M. "Climatology." McGraw-Hill Book Company, Inc., New York, 1944.

Hettner, Alfred. "Die Klimate der Erde." B. G. Teubner, Leipzig, 1930.

Kendrew, W. G. "Climatology" (3d ed. of "Climate"), Clarendon Press, Oxford, 1949.

Kendrew, W. G. "Climates of the Continents." 3d ed., Oxford, University Press, New York, 1941. The discussion is regional, but unfortunately no climatic classification is employed. Contains numerous climatic data for each of the continents.

Knoch, K., and Schulze, A. Methoden der Klimaklassifikation. Erganzungsheft N 249, *Petermanns' Geograph. Mitt.*, 1952.

Köppen, W. "Grundriss der Klimakunde." Walter de Gruyter Company, Berlin, 1931. Contains a relatively complete analysis of the Köppen scheme of climatic classification.

Köppen, W., and Geiger, R. "Handbuch der Klimatologie." Gebrüder Borntraeger, Berlin, 1930 and later, 5 vols; not completed. Vol. I covers the field of general climatology; the other four are on regions. Those parts dealing with the United States, Mexico, West Indies, Central America, Australia, New Zealand, and parts of eastern Africa are in English; the other parts in German. The most complete and up-to-date compendium of information on general and regional climatology. Contains abundant climatological data, and the latest maps showing distribution of Köppen's climatic types. The following sections are the most valuable in the fields of climatic classification and regional climates:

Knoch, K. "Klimakunde von Südamerika." Vol. 2, Part G, 1930.

Sapper, K., "Klimakunde von Mittelamerika." 1932.

Ward, Robert De C., and Brooks, Charles F. "Climatology of the West Indies." Vol. 2, Part I, 1934.

Birkeland, B. J., and Föyn, N. J. "Klima von Nordwesteuropa und den Inseln von Island bis Franz-Josef-Land." Vol. 3, Part L, 1932.

Alt, E. "Klimakunde von Mittel- und Südeuropa." Vol. 3, Part M, 1932.

Braak, C. "Klimakunde von Hinterindien und Insulinde." Vol. 4, Part R, 1931.

Taylor, G. "Climatology of Australia," and Kidson, E., "Climatology of New Zealand," Vol. 4, Part S, 1932.

Robertson, C. L., and Sellick, N. P. "The Climate of Rhodesia, Nyasaland, and Moçambique Colony." Vol. 5, Part X, 1933.

Ward, Robert De C., and Brooks, Charles F. "Climatology of the West Indies," Vol. 2, Part I, 1934.

Ward, Robert De C., and Brooks, Charles F. "The Climates of North America; The United States, Mexico, Alaska." Vol. 2, Part J, 1936.

Köppen, W. "Das geographische System der Klimate." Vol. I, Part C, 1936.

Sverdrup, H. U.; Petersen, Helge; Loewe, Fritz. "Klima des kanadischen Archipels und Grönlands." Vol. 2, Part K, 1935.

Connor, A. J. "The Climates of North America, Canada," Vol. 2, Part J, 1938.

Schott, G. "Klimakunde der Südsee-Inseln," Vol. 4, Part T, 1938.

Meinardus, W. "Klimakunde der Antarktis," Vol. 4, Part U, 1938.

Köppen, W. "Klimakunde von Russland," Vol. 3, Part N, 1939.

de Martonne, Emmanuel. "Traité de géographie physique," 7th ed. Librairie Armand Colin, Paris, 1948.

Meyer, Alfred H. An American Adaptation of the Köppen Classification of Climates. *Papers of the Michigan Academy of Science, Arts and Letters*, Vol. 23, pp. 361–366, 1937.

Miller, A. Austin. "Climatology." 7th ed., Methuen & Co., Ltd., London, 1950.

Thornthwaite, C. Warren. The Climates of North America According to a New Classification. *Geog. Rev.*, Vol. 21, pp. 633–655, 1931.

Thornthwaite, C. Warren. The Climates of the Earth. *Geog. Rev.*, Vol. 23, pp. 433–440, 1933.

Thornthwaite, C. Warren. Problems in the Classification of Climates. *Geog. Rev.*, Vol. 33, pp. 232–255, 1943.

Thornthwaite, C. Warren. An Approach toward a Rational Classification of Climate, *Geog. Rev.*, Vol. 38, pp. 55–94, 1948.

U.S. Weather Bur. Bull. W: Climatic Summary of the United States, Government Printing Office, Washington, D.C. Contains the most complete summary of surface climatic data of the United States.

U.S. Weather Bureau, Climatological Data for the United States by Sections. Surface data for individual months by states.

U.S. Weather Bureau, Climatological Data, National Summary. Surface and above-surface data for individual months and years.

Ward, Robert De C. "Climate." 2d ed., G. P. Putnam's Sons, New York, 1918.

Ward, Robert De C. "Climates of the United States." Ginn & Company, Boston, 1925.

CHAPTER 7: *The Tropical Rainy Climates* (A)

280. Type Location and Boundaries. The humid tropics comprise a somewhat interrupted and irregular "belt" 20 to 40° wide around the earth and straddling the equator (Fig. 6.4, Plate I). This region is distinguished from all other humid regions of the earth by reason of the fact that it is constantly warm; in other words, *it lacks a winter*. Throughout the tropical rainy climates temperature differences between day and night considerably exceed the differences between the warmest and coolest months of the year (Fig. 7.1). In the humid tropics summer heat is a less important factor than a season of coolness, during which there is some relief from high temperatures. As a consequence, the poleward boundary of the tropical rainy climates, except where they come in contact with the dry climates, is, according to Köppen, approximately the isotherm of 18°C., or 64°F., for the *coolest month*.[1] Stated in a different way, within this climatic group there is no month with an average temperature of less than 64°. This temperature was selected because it was found to coincide reasonably well with the poleward limit of certain plants, such as the various palms, which grow only in the warmest regions and cannot tolerate marked seasonal changes in temperature. This is the realm of that great group of plants known as *megatherms*, plants that require continuously high temperatures together with sufficient precipitation. The chief interruptions of the belt of humid tropical climates over the continents are caused by mountains and plateaus, these elevated lands, even though near the equator, having temperatures too low to permit them to be classed as

[1] Some upland savannas, therefore, could not be included if the definition were strictly applied.

typically tropical. In the immediate vicinity of the equator the *A* climates prevail up to elevations of about 3,000 to 3,500 ft.

The *A* climates are by far the most widespread of any of the great climatic groups, occupying, according to Hermann Wagner, about 36 per cent of the entire earth's surface. Nearly 20 per cent of the earth's land surface, and approximately 43 per cent of the ocean surface, lie within the *A* group.

Normally the tropical rainy climates have their greatest latitudinal spread in the eastern parts of the continents (Fig. 6.4). In other words they extend somewhat farther poleward in the central and eastern parts of the land masses than they do toward their western margins where they are somewhat more restricted in latitudinal extent. It will be noted also that toward the eastern sides of the lands the *A* climates are bounded on their poleward margins by humid subtropical climates *Ca*, one of the milder types of the middle latitudes. Both *A* and *Ca* climates are humid, so that the *A/C* boundary is defined in terms of the temperature of the coolest month, 18°C., or 64.4°F. By contrast, toward the interiors and western sides of tropical continents the *A* climates are bounded on their poleward sides by the dry climates *B* (Fig. 6.4). Instead of low temperatures in winter the limiting factor here is increasing aridity, and this aridity usually reaches its maximum equatorward extent along the west coasts of the land masses.

This somewhat asymmetrical development of the *A* climates, and of the contrasting climates and boundaries which limit them in their eastern and western parts, is largely explainable in terms of certain features of the atmospheric

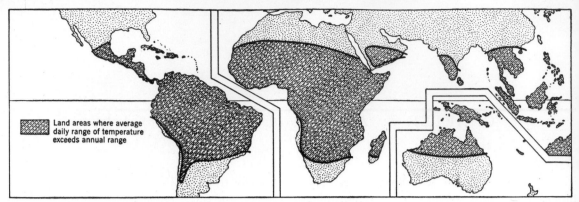

Land areas where average daily range of temperature exceeds annual range

FIG. 7.1. A distinctive feature of climates in the low latitudes is the fact the average daily range of temperature exceeds the average annual range. (*After Troll.*)

circulation. The western margins of the sub-tropical anticyclones which affect the eastern sides of tropical continents are characterized by neutral or unstable maritime air masses. Here subsidence is weak or absent and the trade-wind inversion absent or very high so that deep convectional overturning is possible. In this unstable air all kinds of rain-bringing atmospheric disturbances, including thunderstorms, easterly waves, and cyclones of all degrees of intensity, find an environment conducive to their development. In addition, the easterly side is prevailingly the windward side of the continent so that there is an onshore movement of humid air from over warm ocean currents. Any orographic lifting of this air is likely to produce heavy precipitation. Western sides of continents in low latitudes, except close to the equator, are more likely to be affected by the stable eastern margins of the subtropical anticyclones where subsidence is strong and the inversion layer low. In some continents, especially western South America and Africa south of the equator the drying effects of the anticyclones thrust the *B* climates to within about 5° of the equator (Plate I). The anticyclonic subsidence, with perhaps some aid from the prevailing cool ocean currents, produces a stable atmosphere which is opposed to the development of rain-bringing atmospheric disturbances.

281. Precipitation. Rainfall is relatively abundant, rarely lower than 30 in., and usually it is well over that amount. The precipitation is multiple in origin. Much of it falls as heavy intermittent showers of convectional origin associated with thunder and lightning. More extensive disturbances in the form of waves and cyclones producing general rains of longer duration are likewise numerous and are responsible for a moderate proportion of the total precipitation. Unlike the uniform temperature conditions, rainfall is more variable in amount and in both seasonal and areal distribution. The two principal climatic types within the humid tropics are distinguished from each other on the basis of their seasonal distribution of precipitation, one type, *Af*, having ample rainfall throughout the year, while in the other, *Aw*, there is one wet and one dry season. Since throughout much of the humid tropics rainfall is associated with the *ITC* and its unstable air masses, it is not unexpected that precipitation will reach a maximum at the time of high sun when the *ITC* prevails. It is well said, therefore, that in the tropics rainfall follows the sun.

The intensity of sunlight, both direct and reflected, is a noteworthy feature of *A* climates. Speaking of the intensity of light in regions near the equator, Maud D. Haviland writes:

"Except in the very deepest jungles, some sunlight filters to the forest floor through chinks in the foliage canopy overhead. These shafts of light strike as bright and hot as the rays from a burning glass; and as they move over the leaves, small invertebrate life creeps out of their way. I once watched such a sunbeam searchlight overtake a party of ants who were

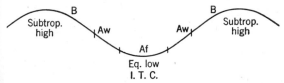

FIG. 7.2. Type location of *Af* and *Aw* climates on the meridional profile of sea-level pressure.

devouring the decomposing body of a caterpillar. Within half a minute they fled helterskelter and the remains of their meal shrivelled up as if before a furnace."[1]

282. The Subdivisions of Tropical Rainy Climates.[2]

Within the *A* group of climates rainfall contrasts cause two principal types and one subtype to be recognized: These are (1) *Af*, tropical wet, or tropical rainforest, climate, in which there is no dry season, all months having more than 6 cm., or 2.4 in., of precipitation; (2) *Am* monsoon rainforest climate, a subtype of *Af*, in which unusually heavy rainfall compensates for a short dry season; (3) *Aw*, wet-and-dry climate, in which the dry season is longer and more severe than in *Am* and the rainfall of the wet period is insufficient to compensate for the drought (Fig. 7.2). A dense broadleaf evergreen forest is characteristic of *Af* climate. *Am* climate also supports an evergreen rainforest, although the forest may not be so dense, and, where rainfall is not so heavy, some of the trees may be deciduous in character. Lighter deciduous forest, thorn forest, and tall grasses characterize *Aw*. Figure 7.3 shows diagrammatically the boundaries of the types of *A* climates. The *Af* boundary is self-explanatory and does not vary. The *Am/Aw* boundary is variable, depending upon the total amount of the annual rainfall and the amount that falls during the driest month. If the total yearly rainfall is 100 in., one month can be completely dry, and still the region will have

[1] Maud D. Haviland, "Forest, Steppe, and Tundra," pp. 37–38, Harvard University Press, Cambridge, Mass., 1926.

[2] For an analysis of health and acclimatization problems in the wet tropics, see Robert G. Stone, *Health in Tropical Climates*, "Yearbook of Agriculture, 1941," United States Department of Agriculture, Washington, D.C., 1941; and Grenfell A. Price, *White Settlers in the Tropics*, *Am. Geog. Soc. Special Publication* 23, New York, 1939.

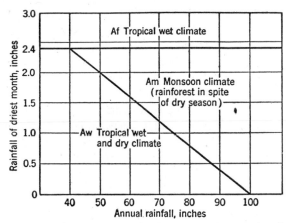

FIG. 7.3. Graphical representation of the boundaries of the *Af*, *Am*, and *Aw* climates. (*After Köppen.*)

an *Am* climate. As rainfall declines in amount, the driest month must have more rainfall, *i.e.*, the amount of rain in the driest month varies inversely with the total annual rainfall. With an annual total of 80 in., the driest month must have at least 0.74 in.; with 60 in., 1.55; with 50 in., 2.

Af, Tropical Wet Climate[1] (Tropical Rainforest)

283. Type Location. (*a*) Uniformly high temperatures and (*b*) heavy precipitation distributed throughout the year, so that there is no marked dry season, are the two most distinguishing characteristics of tropical wet (rainforest) climate. When typically located, this climate is found astride the equator and extending out 5 or 10° on either side. This latitudinal spread may be increased to 15 or even 25° along the windward margins of the continents. *Af* is associated with the equatorial trough of low pressure and with the intertropical convergence of trades, doldrum conditions, and equatorial westerlies which prevail in that general low-pressure zone. It may at times be encroached upon by the trades at the time of their maximum equatorial migration but never

[1] Temperature and precipitation data for representative stations are included for each type of climate. Supplementary climatic data can be found in Appendix B.

to the extent that a drought season associated with upper-level subsidence prevails. Characteristically *Af* climate passes over into *Aw* (or *Am*) along the poleward margins, the boundary between them being 6 cm., or 2.4 in., of rainfall for the driest month (Fig. 6.4). On the wetter eastern margins of continents *Af* climate may extend poleward until it meets a middle-latitude climate, *Ca*, the poleward limit here being the presence of a cool season (18°C., or 64.4°F., for the coolest month).

TEMPERATURE

284. Annual and Seasonal Temperatures. Lying as it commonly does athwart the equator and consequently in the belt of maximum insolation, it is to be expected that temperatures in the *Af* climate will be uniformly high, the yearly averages usually lying between 77 and 80°+ (see data, pp. 250, 384). Since the sun's noon rays are never far from a vertical position, and days and nights vary little in length from one

MANAOS, BRAZIL
3° 1′ S

FIG. 7.5. Thermograph of an *Am* station. (*After Hartshorne.*)

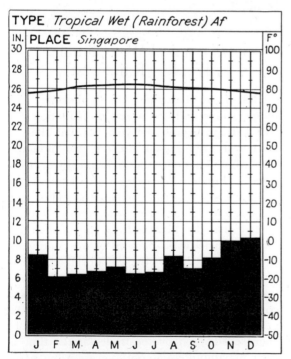

FIG. 7.4. Average monthly temperatures and precipitation for a representative station with a tropical wet (*Af*) climate. Monthly temperatures are much more uniform than monthly amounts of precipitation.

part of the year to another, not only are the annual temperatures high, but there is likewise little seasonal variation (Figs. 7.4, 7.5, 7.6). The annual temperature range, or difference between the warmest and coolest months, is usually less than 5°. Thus Belém and Iquitos in the Amazon Valley have annual ranges of 3 and 4°, respectively, Coquilhatville in central Africa 2+°, and Singapore in southern Malaya 3°. Over the oceans in these low latitudes ranges are even less, Jaluit in the Marshall Islands in mid-Pacific recording only 0.8° difference between the extreme months. It becomes evident from the very small temperature ranges that it is not the excessively high monthly averages but rather the *uniformity* and *monotony* of this constant succession of hot months, with no relief, that characterizes the tropical rainforest climate. Thus the average July temperatures of many American cities, such as Charleston with 82°; Galveston, 83°; and Montgomery, 82°; may equal, or even exceed by a few degrees, those of the hottest months at stations near the equator. The hottest month at Belém (Amazon Basin) is only 80°, and at Akasa (Niger delta) 80°. The slight temperature contrasts between the warmest and coolest months are determined not so

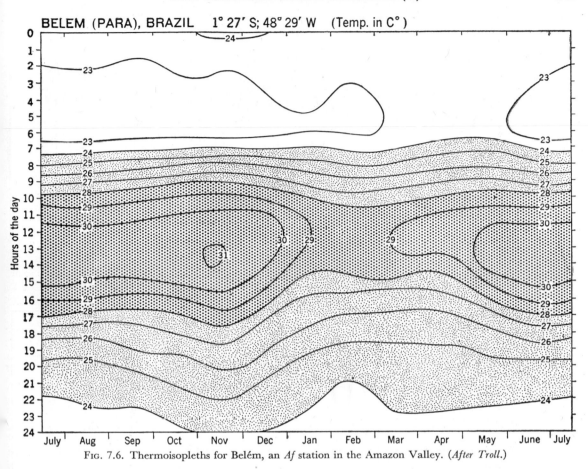

FIG. 7.6. Thermoisopleths for Belém, an *Af* station in the Amazon Valley. (*After Troll.*)

much by the position of the sun as by the amount of cloudiness and precipitation, the highest temperature usually occurring during the seasons of least rain and clearest skies.

285. Daily Temperatures. The daily, or diurnal, range of temperature (difference between the warmest and coolest hours of the day) is usually 10 to 25°, or several times greater than the annual range. For example, at Bolobo in the Belgian Congo, the average daily range is 16°, while the annual range is only 2°. During the afternoons the thermometer ordinarily rises to temperatures varying from 85 to 93° and at night sinks to 70 or 75° (Figs. 7.7, 7.8). It is commonly said, therefore, that night is the winter of the tropics. Even the extremes of temperature are never very great, the average of the daily maxima at Belém being only 91°, and the average of the daily minima 68°. The highest

temperature ever recorded at Santarem (Amazon Basin) is 96°, while the lowest is only 65°. This absolute maximum of 96° may be compared with 109° for Chicago and 110° for St. Louis. Although the day temperatures may not be excessively high, the heat, together with slight air movement, intense light, and high relative and absolute humidity, produces an atmospheric condition with low cooling power. It is oppressive and sultry so that one's vitality and energy are sapped. *Sensible temperatures* are, therefore, excessively high, although the thermometer readings may not indicate abnormal heat.

Even the nights give little relief from the oppressive heat. Yet to the poorly clad and none too vigorous natives, who are sensitive to even the slightest drop in temperature, the humid night air may appear even chilly. Fires are often

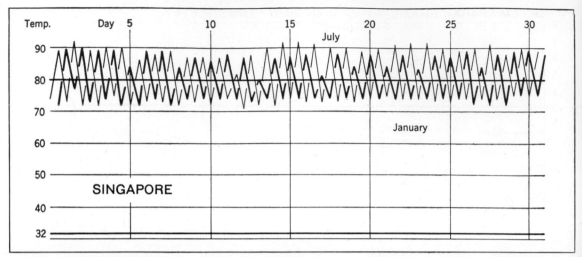

FIG. 7.7. Daily maximum and minimum temperatures for the extreme months at a representative *Af* station. Solar control is almost complete as shown by the regular daily rise and fall of temperature. (*After Jefferson.*)

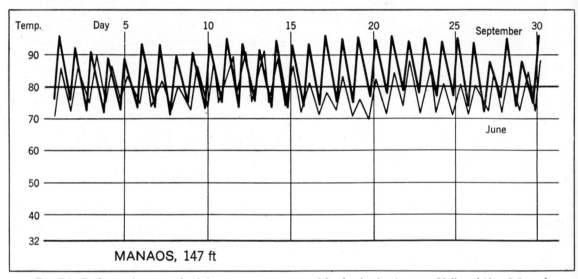

FIG. 7.8. Daily maximum and minimum temperatures at Manáos in the Amazon Valley. (*After Jefferson.*)

lighted at night if the temperature drops below 70°. Certain Negro groups in central Africa have heated sleeping quarters which they use during the coolest season when the average temperature is about 66°. Rapid nocturnal cooling is not to be expected in regions of such excessive humidity and abundant cloudiness. It is often sufficient, nevertheless, to cause condensation in the near-saturated air, so that lowland fogs and heavy dews are common. The periods of least rainfall and clearest skies have the lowest

night temperatures, the thermometer on rare occasions falling below 60°.

286. Daily March of Temperature. Figures 7.7, 7.8 show the daily march of temperature for the extreme months at representative stations within the tropical wet (*Af*) climate. The graphs illustrate a temperature regime in which sun is almost completely in control. There is a marked diurnal regularity and periodicity about the changes, temperatures rising to about the same height each day and falling to about the same level each night, so that one 24-hr. period almost duplicates every other. Daily oscillations are extremely periodic. Irregular invasions of warm and cold air masses, of the type so common in the middle latitudes, are practically unknown. This absence of nonperiodic and erratic temperature variations results from (a) the great width of tropical zone, making invasions of cold air relatively impossible; and (b) the general lack of vigorous, well-developed, moving cold anticyclones, which are the instigators of many of the great nonperiodic temperature changes of middle latitudes.

PRECIPITATION

287. Amount and Distribution. Rainfall is both heavy and distributed throughout the year, there being no distinctly dry season (Fig. 7.4; see data, p. 250). Taken as a whole, *Af* climate is coincident with the world's heaviest belt of precipitation. Ward estimates the average rainfall of the doldrum belt to be in the neighborhood of 100 in., with less over the continents and more over the oceans. Because of the abundant precipitation, surface ocean waters in the doldrums are less salty than in the trades. The largest amount of rainfall in the *Af* climates, and the greatest known for any place on the earth, is on the windward side of a low mountain on the island of Kauai in the Hawaiian group where the average amount is over 450 in. At Debundja near the foot of Cameroon Peak in Nigeria, Africa, the annual rainfall averages 400 in. Cherrapunji, an *Am* station in the Khasi Hills of northeastern India, receives annually 426 in. In all these stations, however, the excessive precipitation is associated with orographic effects. Such amounts of rain are unknown over extensive lowlands.

In this region close to the equator conditions are ideal for rain formation. Of fundamental importance in causing the heavy rainfall is the fact that in these equatorial latitudes there is a convergence of the tropical air masses with associated lifting of the air. Supplementing the item of horizontal convergence are the features of high temperature and abundant humidity, with the nearly saturated condition prevailing

throughout a deep atmospheric layer. The reservoir of atmospheric moisture for producing precipitation is therefore unusually great. In this warm, humid, and highly unstable air only a slight amount of original lifting is required to trigger off strong local convection with associated heavy showers.

Cloudiness, much of it cumulus in character, is moderately high in *Af* climates, averaging in the neighborhood of 60 per cent. At Manáos, in the Amazon Valley, cloudiness varies between $\frac{6}{10}$ and $\frac{7}{10}$ for each month. At Belém it is $\frac{4}{10}$ in the driest month and $\frac{8}{10}$ in the rainiest.[1] Completely clear days are almost unknown. Considering the fact that the *Af* climates are the rainiest of the earth, it may seem strange that the percentage of cloudiness is not as great near the equator as it is in the higher middle latitudes where rainfall is much less. This is related to the fact that a larger proportion of the clouds in equatorial latitudes is convective clouds of the cumulus type and heavy convective showers predominate. Such clouds and showers are local in character and the clouds cover a small proportion of the sky and persist for shorter periods of time than is true of frontal clouds of the middle latitudes. On the other hand, frontal rain is less intense and lasts for longer periods of time. Cloudiness in the *Af* climates has a distinct diurnal periodicity with a maximum being reached in the warmer hours of the day when convectional ascent is at a maximum. Nights and early morning hours are characteristically clearer (see data for Belém).

Diurnal March of Cloudiness at Belém
(In tenths of sky covered)

6 A.M.	3.6	2 P.M.	5.7
8 A.M.	3.8	4 P.M.	6.0
10 A.M.	5.5	10 P.M.	5.2

288. Nature of the Rainfall. Without a doubt the rainfall is predominantly convectional in origin, falling in hard showers from towering cumulonimbus clouds. This reflects the prevailingly unstable character of the atmosphere. Sky conditions are lively and full of animation as the

[1] Cloudiness is here expressed in terms of the part of the total sky covered.

upward-surging air currents give rise to clouds full of motion and variable in form and color. The maximum precipitation usually occurs during the warmer hours of the day when local heating, and therefore convectional ascent, are at a maximum. Early mornings are often relatively clear, but, as the sun climbs toward the zenith and temperature increases, cumulus clouds begin to appear, growing in number and size with the heat of the day, until by afternoon ominous thunderheads are common. Several thunderstorms, accompanied by thunder and lightning, in a single afternoon are not unusual, and the rain may continue on into the evening, although there is a tendency for the skies to become clearer as the heat wanes. The cloud cover and downpour of rain accompanying the storm temporarily cool the air, but with its passing and the appearance of the sun again, the usual oppressive conditions are reestablished. Within the equatorial region thunderstorms reach their maximum development for any latitude of the earth, there being on the average 75 to 150 days with such storms during the course of the year. Tropical thunderstorms, although local in extent, are of extreme intensity. The great thickness of the heated and humidified air in these latitudes is assurance of an abundance of storm energy. These paroxysms of nature, with their fierce lightning, crashing thunder, and deluges of rainfall, are awesome spectacles. One traveler[1] writes as follows concerning the heavy convectional showers in the tropical wet climate:

"The force of the downpour is another factor in the oecology of the forest. In the wet season thunderstorms of great violence are frequent, and the rain descends with a suddenness and volume unknown outside the tropics. The sun is shining, the forest glitters with a million lights, birds are on the move, and insects hum and dance from leaf to leaf. All at once a shadow is drawn over the sun, and all activity of bird and beast ceases as the sound of rushing rain rapidly approaches. An avalanche of water then crashes down, blotting out surrounding objects and, as it seems, sweeping the very breath from the nostrils, bewildering and benumbing the senses. Every twig and leaf is bent and battered, and in a few seconds

[1] Haviland, *op. cit.*, p. 39.

streams pour down the paths and the world seems changed into a thundering cataract. Then, as suddenly as it came, the storm passes, and the sun blazes out again before the roar of the storm sweeping over the treetops has died away in the distance. Even before the leaves have ceased to drip, or the land-crabs, tempted forth by the teeming water, have scuttled to cover again, the life of the forest is resumed. It is almost incredible how some fragile forms escape destruction under such terrific bombardments. . . . "

Days with continuous overcast skies and steady rain are less common in the tropics than in the middle latitudes where well-developed fronts and cyclonic storms are more frequent. Nevertheless, such weather types are by no means uncommon and very likely are more numerous than is now realized. Although little mention is made of them in the climatic literature dealing with the low latitudes, especially the wetter portions, there are in the wet tropics numerous atmospheric disturbances of wave and vortex types which are abundant rain bringers. Such mild disturbances appear to reach their maximum frequency in the vicinity of the inter-tropical convergence zone. Their movement is usually slow and in a general east-to-west direction although their tracks are indefinite. They are without winds of high velocity and they produce no significant temperature changes. Their chief importance as a weather type is that they produce irregular spells of relatively long-continued rain, covering extensive areas, which may not be accompanied by lightning and thunder. They stand in contrast, therefore, to the convectional showers and thunderstorms which are local in extent and diurnal in their periodicity. Knox, in describing the Ivory Coast of tropical Africa, speaks of the relatively continuous rains in the wet season when it "sometimes does not stop for 40 hr." These nonperiodic disturbances appear to be most numerous at the periods of heaviest rainfall. The hurricane type of storm is never a feature of *Af* climates which lie close to the equator. It is chiefly characteristic of littoral and insular *Af* locations along rainy east coasts poleward of 5 or 10°.

289. Seasonal Distribution of Rainfall. While it is true that there is no genuinely dry season in the tropical wet climate, it should not be inferred that the rainfall is, therefore, evenly distributed throughout the year. By comparison with the rainiest periods, there are others that may be called drier, but since there is no period without rain, they scarcely can be called dry (see data for Belém, p. 250). They might more properly be referred to as less wet. It is often stated that the annual rainfall curve of regions close to the equator shows two periods of maximum rainfall and two corresponding periods of minimum rainfall, the two maxima and the two minima being relatively symmetrical. Theoretically this should be the case, the seasons of heaviest rains roughly coinciding with, or following somewhat, the zenithal positions of the sun, and the periods of lighter precipitation coinciding with, or following, the solstices, when the trades advance closest to the equator. Actually the ideal does not prevail, for the rainfall curve by no means closely parallels the symmetrical insolation curve. It is possible to find stations with two well-proportioned maxima and minima in yearly rainfall, but they are rare. Emphasis, therefore, needs to be placed upon the characteristic lack of a dry season instead of upon a typical seasonal regime of rainfall.

*Average Amount of Precipitation and Number of Rainy Days at Belém in the Amazon Valley**

	Rainfall, Inches	Rainy Days
January	12.68	26.8
February	13.90	26.1
March	13.91	28.2
April	13.07	26.4
May	9.45	22.6
June	5.87	20.5
July	5.24	18.5
August	4.72	16.2
September	3.70	15.4
October	3.35	12.6
November	2.13	10.3
December	5.98	19.5
Year	94.03	243.1

* C. M. Delgado de Carvalho, "Météorologie du Brésil," pp. 205, 216, John Bale Sons and Danielson, Ltd., London, 1917.

290. Rainy Days. During the rainier season or seasons, precipitation falls on a large majority of the days, although there are always a few without any. During the drier periods, not only are there fewer rainy days, but the amount per day is also less. Thus at Belém, March, which is the wettest month, has six and one-half times as much rain as November, which is the driest (see preceding table); but even in November there are 10+ rainy days with a total of more than 2 in. of precipitation. On the other hand, March has nearly 14 in. of rain, falling on 28+ days. Thus 91 per cent of the days in the wettest month are rainy, and only 34 per cent of those in the driest month. No hint of a double maximum is evident in the data of the station. Following are the diary entries of a British army officer concerning weather conditions during September, an average month, in southern Nigeria:[1]

"Sept. 2 Raining hard most of day
"   3 Rain most of day but not so bad as on Sept. 2
"   4 Cloudy afternoon
"   7 Rain most of day
"   8 Fine most of day
            . . . .
"Sept. 21 Fine most of day
"   22 Raining hard
"   23 Raining hard
"   24 Fine
"   25 Raining hard all day
"   26 Raining during most of day
"   27 Fine
"   28 Raining hard
"   30 Fine"

From the above descriptions it is clear that there are rainy spells in the drier seasons and dry spells even in the rainy seasons. This comes about partly as a result of fluctuations in the positions of the intertropical convergence, fluctuations which are not only seasonal in character but which also vary considerably and irregularly within short periods of time. The tropical easterlies, or trades, are constantly advancing and retreating, so that *ITC*, doldrums,

[1] Knox, Alexander, "The Climate of the Continent of Africa," p. 136, Cambridge University Press, New York, 1911.

and equatorial westerlies shift positions frequently. The more general and continuous rains of the wet season indicate the close proximity of the *ITC* and doldrums, while rainy spells even in the drier months probably denote a temporary reestablishment of these controls. The less rainy seasons and the drier spells indicate a greater prevalence of dry tropical air masses at those times.

291. *Rainfall Variability.* In spite of the heavy rainfall characteristic of this climate, there may be considerable variations from year to year in total amount, although usually they are not enough to be serious. Certainly annual fluctuations of rainfall are much greater than those of temperature. Variability in precipitation is more especially a characteristic feature of subhumid and dry climates, but, strange as it may seem, droughts occasionally do occur in the humid climates near the equator. Infrequently they may even jeopardize crops. This does not necessarily mean that the rainfall is excessively meager in an absolute sense even in the driest years—only relatively so. In these low latitudes where temperatures are constantly high, evaporation is excessive, and, moreover, the crops grown are of a kind that require abundant precipitation. Consequently a total that might be judged as very adequate in the middle latitudes could be deficient to the point of being injurious in the wet tropics.

Rainfall Variability at Two Tropical Stations, * *Inches*

	Driest Year	Wettest Year	Average
Colombo, Ceylon	51.6	139.7	83.8
Singapore	32.7	158.7	92

* Stephen S. Visher, Variability versus Uniformity in the Tropics, *Sci. Monthly*, Vol. 15, No. 1, pp. 22–34 (29), July, 1922.

292. Winds. The feeble temperature gradients beget only weak pressure gradients, so that air movement is prevailingly slight. The whole region is poorly ventilated, and this, in conjunction with high temperatures and excessive humidity, makes for physical discomfort. Temporary relief may be brought by the strong squall winds associated with thunderstorms. Occasionally the trades advance far enough equatorward, especially in the drier periods, to bring spells of desiccating weather. This wind, known as the *harmattan* along the Guinea Coast of Africa, is usually described as a cool wind, especially at night, probably owing to its great evaporation.

Sea breezes are important climatic phenomena along coasts in the low latitudes. The importation of cooler air from the sea during the heat of the day is a great boon to residents along the littoral, causing tropical coasts to be much more livable than are the interiors. Ordinarily the effects of the sea breeze reach inland only 30 to 60 miles.

293. Weather in *Af* **climates** strongly reflects sun control and consequently is largely a diurnal phenomenon. In the descriptions of the various climatic elements of *Af* climates which has preceded, the daily regularity of their change has been strongly emphasized. Temperature, for example, rises to about the same maximum each day and falls to about the same minimum each night (Figs. 7.7, 7.8). There is scarcely any appreciable deviation from this diurnal sun-controlled monotony in the form of irregular nonperiodic invasions of either abnormally hot or abnormally cool air masses, a feature which is so characteristic of weather in middle latitudes (see Figs. 10.19, 10.21). The weak temperature gradients in the tropics, the great latitudinal width of the tropical zone, and the infrequency of strong and extensive atmospheric disturbances in equatorial latitudes, all contribute to the weakness of the nonperiodic weather element in *Af* climates. It is chiefly where *Af* climates extend abnormally far poleward along the eastern sides of continents that they experience irregular indrafts of cool air from the middle latitudes as brought by cold anticyclones.

The following description by an eye witness, of daily weather conditions in the Amazon Valley, may serve to synthesize and vivify the previous description:

"The heat increased rapidly toward two o'clock (92° and 93° Fahr.), by which time every voice of bird or mammal was hushed; only in the trees was heard at intervals the harsh whir of a cicada. The leaves, which were so moist and fresh in early morning, now become lax and drooping; the flowers shed their petals. Our neighbors, the Indian and Mulatto inhabitants of the open palm-thatched huts, as we returned home fatigued with our ramble, were either asleep in their hammocks or seated on mats in the shade, too languid even to talk. On most days in June and July a heavy shower would fall some time in the afternoon, producing a most welcome coolness. The approach of the rain-clouds was after a uniform fashion very interesting to observe. First, the cool sea-breeze, which commenced to blow about 10 o'clock, and which had increased in force with the increasing power of the sun, would flag and finally die away. The heat and electric tension of the atmosphere would then become almost insupportable. Languor and uneasiness would seize on every one; even the denizens of the forest betraying it by their motions. White clouds would appear in the east and gather into cumuli, with an increasing blackness along their lower portions. The whole eastern horizon would become almost suddenly black, and this would spread upwards, the sun at length becoming obscured. Then the rush of a mighty wind is heard through the forest, swaying the tree-tops; a vivid flash of lightning bursts forth, then a crash of thunder, and down streams the deluging rain. Such storms soon cease, leaving bluish-black motionless clouds in the sky until night. Meantime all nature is refreshed; but heaps of flower-petals and fallen leaves are seen under the trees. Toward evening life revives again, and the ringing uproar is resumed from bush and tree. The following morning the sun again rises in a cloudless sky, and so the cycle is completed; spring, summer, and autumn, as it were, in one tropical day. The days are more or less like this throughout the year in this country. . . . It is never either spring, summer, or autumn, but each day is a combination of all three. With the day and night always of equal length, the atmospheric disturbances of each day neutralising themselves before each succeeding morn; with the sun in its course proceeding midway across the sky, and the daily temperature the same within two or three degrees throughout the year —how grand in its perfect equilibrium and simplicity is the march of Nature under the equator!"[1]

There is not, however, the same degree of diurnal regularity in the cloud and precipitation

phenomena that there is in the temperature element. To be sure there is a build-up of cumulus clouds in the warmer hours of the day, while nights in general have less cloudiness, and there is also a relatively strong daytime maximum of rainfall which is associated with afternoon convectional overturning, so that diurnal regularity is much more striking than in the middle latitudes where moving atmospheric disturbances are more numerous and likewise stronger. Nevertheless, it is these tropical storms, in the form of traveling atmospheric waves, weak depressions, and even occasional hurricanes in a few poleward locations, which cause a moderate degree of nonperiodic weather irregularity in the rainfall element of *Af* climates. There are spells of weather when it continues to rain steadily at night as well as day and the rainfall is far from being local.

294. Representative Regions. The Amazon Valley in South America and the Congo Basin in Africa are the two largest contiguous areas with a tropical wet (*Af*) climate. The East Indies, Philippines, and some of the coast lands of tropical Asia are likewise included. In addition, there are more isolated areas of *Af* in eastern Central America, parts of the windward sides of some islands in the West Indies, western Colombia, the coastal lowlands of eastern Brazil and the Guianas, eastern Madagascar, and sections of the Guinea coast of Africa. Of the two large interior regions, the Amazon and Congo Basins, the former possesses the more severe rainforest climate, having, on the whole, heavier rainfall. Equatorial and tropical air masses find relatively free entrance into the Amazon Valley through the opening between the Brazilian and the Guiana Highlands, and likewise by way of the Orinoco Valley, carrying with them enormous supplies of moisture which are precipitated as rain in the interior. Unlike the Amazon Valley, whose elevation is low, the Congo Basin averages 1,000 to 1,600 ft. in elevation. Moreover, it is shut off from the sea on the east by a relatively high plateau, which prevents entrance of the moisture-bearing easterly winds. As a result, the rainfall is 10 to 20 in. less than in the Amazon Valley.

[1] Henry Walter Bates, "The Naturalist on the River Amazon," pp. 31–32, John Murray, London, 1910.

Climatic Data for Representative Tropical Wet (Af) Stations

Singapore, Straits Settlements (Malaya)

	J	F	M	A	M	J	J	A	S	O	N	D	Yr.	Range
Temp.	78.3	79.0	80.2	80.8	81.5	81.1	81.0	80.6	80.4	80.1	79.3	78.6	80.1	3.2
Precip.	8.5	6.1	6.5	6.9	7.2	6.7	6.8	8.5	7.1	8.2	10.0	10.4	92.9	

Belém, Amazon Valley

	J	F	M	A	M	J	J	A	S	O	N	D	Yr.	
Temp.	77.7	77.0	77.5	77.7	78.4	78.3	78.1	78.3	78.6	79.0	79.7	79.0	78.3	2.7
Precip.	11.6	12.9	14.9	12.1	9.4	6.7	6.2	4.5	3.5	2.8	2.6	6.0	93.2	

Nouvelle Anvers, Belgian Congo

	J	F	M	A	M	J	J	A	S	O	N	D	Yr.	
Temp.	79.2	80.1	79.2	78.1	79.2	78.4	76.5	76.3	77.0	77.4	77.9	78.1	78.1	3.8
Precip.	4.1	3.5	4.1	5.6	6.2	6.1	6.3	6.3	6.3	6.6	2.6	9.3	66.9	

MODIFIED TROPICAL WET TYPES

295. *Am*, **Monsoon Rainforest Climate.** This subtype is somewhat intermediate in character between *Af* and *Aw*, having the heavy rainfall of the former and the seasonal precipitation distribution of the latter. Characteristically *Am* is found along tropical coasts backed by highlands along which during a portion of the year, usually the high-sun period, there is a strong onshore movement of *mT* air. These seasonal winds, commonly but not always of monsoon origin, are the cause of the strongly seasonal precipitation distribution. A portion of the precipitation is

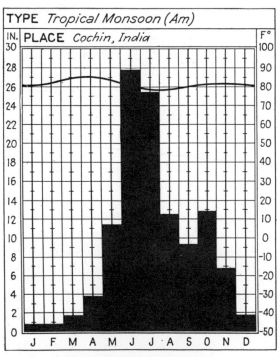

FIG. 7.9. Average monthly temperatures and precipitation amounts for a tropical monsoon (*Am*) station.

either directly or indirectly of orographic origin. The rainfall of the wet season is so great that in spite of a short dry season the subsoil is not dried out sufficiently to prevent the growth of an evergreen rainforest. Not infrequently the total annual rainfall is heavier than the average for *Af* climates. On the other hand, the dry season ordinarily is neither so dry nor so long as in the *Aw* climates. The temperature difference between the warmest and coolest months may be somewhat higher than in *Af* climates, annual ranges occasionally reaching 12 to 14° in those *Am* regions located farthest from the equator. Temperatures usually reach a maximum during the period of clearer skies just before the season of heaviest rainfall and cloud, even though the latter is the period of highest sun (see Fig. 7.9 and data for Calicut). Köppen recognizes this peculiarity of seasonal temperature distribution by adding the letter *g* to the climatic symbol, which signifies a Ganges type of annual march of temperature where the hottest month precedes the solstice and the summer rainy season.

This subtype is best developed in southeastern Asia where the monsoon wind system is particularly well developed. Within this large region, the Malabar Coast of western India, the Ganges-Brahmaputra delta section of the same country, the Arakan Coast of Burma, the east coast of Indo-China (Vietnam), and northern Philippines are representative *Am* sections. The type is also found along the western Guinea Coast of Africa, the eastern Amazon Valley and the Guiana coastlands in South America, and portions of the West Indies.

296. The Eastern Littorals. From the map of climatic regions (Plate I) it is evident that rainforest climate extends farther poleward along the

Climatic Data for Calicut, India, a Representative Am Station

	J	F	M	A	M	J	J	A	S	O	N	D	Yr.	Range
Temp.	77.8	79.8	81.6	83.6	83.1	78.5	76.7	77.4	78.3	79.1	79.5	78.3	79.5	6.9
Precip.	0.3	0.2	0.6	3.2	9.5	35.0	29.8	15.3	8.4	10.3	4.9	1.1	118.6	

eastern margins of some continents than it does along the west coasts or in the interiors (Fig. 6.4). Witness, for example, such cases as the east coasts of Central America, Brazil, the Philippines, and Madagascar. In such locations the heavier rainfall, compared with that of interiors and west coasts, is partly the result of orographic and hurricane precipitation being added to that resulting from convection and disturbances common to these latitudes. In consequence, rainforest vegetation characteristically is carried poleward 15 to 20° on either side of the equator along these windward tropical coasts. In such marine, windward locations typical *Af* conditions are slightly meliorated (Fig. 7.10). Gray skies and steady, long-continued rains are more common, especially during the low-sun period when the trades are strong-

est. Since this subtype extends out into somewhat higher latitudes than is true of rainforest climates in general, its poleward margins are likely to have slightly more variable weather conditions. In winter, especially, it occasionally may feel the effects of passing cyclones and anticyclones in the lower middle latitudes. Thus the equatorward-advancing polar air masses in central and eastern United States sometimes continue southward across the Gulf of Mexico to the Caribbean coasts of Mexico and northern Central America, where they produce relatively cool, drizzly weather. Temperature differences between the warmest and coolest months may be slightly greater than in typical *Af* climate. This slightly modified form of *Af* climate is not designated by a special symbol on the climatic regions map (Plate I.)

Climatic Data for Belize, British Honduras, a Representative Eastern Littoral Af Station

	J	F	M	A	M	J	J	A	S	O	N	D	Yr.	Range
Temp.	74.8	76.8	79.2	79.2	81.9	82.4	82.6	82.6	82.0	79.3	76.1	73.6	79.3	9
Precip.	5.1	2.6	1.6	1.5	4.1	9.1	9.6	8.5	9.4	11.0	10.2	6.3	79.0	

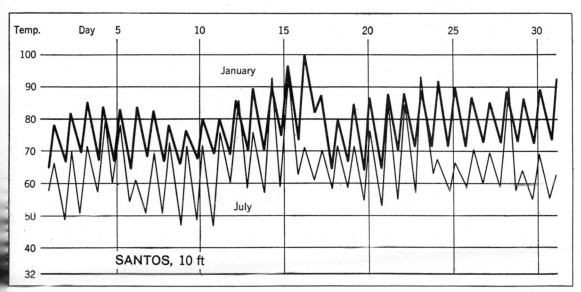

FIG. 7.10. Daily maximum and minimum temperatures for an *Af* station located on the east coast of Brazil 24° south of the equator. Note the somewhat greater nonperiodic temperature changes as controlled by air-mass variations.

ASSOCIATED FEATURES OF THE PHYSICAL EARTH IN THE TROPICAL WET (*Af, Am*) CLIMATE

297. Climate and the World Pattern. The individual physical elements (climate, surface configuration, native vegetation, soils, drainage, etc.) that cause earth regions to differ from one another do not exist separately and apart from each other in spite of the fact that they are usually so studied. For any portion of the earth these physical elements exist and develop together, not only in an areal sense but likewise as interrelated elements of a region, the parts of which are geared together so that they are interdependent, each element reacting upon all the others and in turn being reacted upon by them. The soil of a region, for example, can scarcely be thought of as having a separate existence apart from the bedrock, landforms, climate, vegetation, and drainage, all of which have influenced its evolution and character. The bonds of interrelationship among the several natural elements or features of a region are extremely complicated. The total assemblage of interrelated natural features within a region is called its *natural landscape.*

298. *Climatically Induced Natural Landscapes.* The complex of *natural* features that characterizes any part, or the whole, of the earth's surface is the result of two sets of forces and their associated processes acting upon the solid, liquid, and gaseous earth materials. One of these two sources of energy is the forces residing within the earth; the other is provided by the sun. The interior, or tectonic, forces and processes (gravitational, volcanic, and diastrophic) are the cause, for instance, of variations in earth materials and likewise in many of the larger aspects of surface configuration from one part of the earth to another. The nature of these forces resident within the earth's interior is not so well known, and the distribution of types of surface features (mountains, plateaus, plains) resulting from them does not seem to follow any repeated world distribution pattern, as do climatic and soil types, for instance. Plains, plateaus, or mountains may occur at the pole as well as at the equator and along the eastern or the western

sides of continents. Mineral deposits, likewise, seem to follow no apparent repeated world distribution patterns.

Solar energy, the second of the two great forces fashioning the earth's surface, expresses itself most directly through climatic processes and indirectly through a great variety of physical and chemical reactions, two of the most important being the weathering of rocks and the growth, death, and decay of plants. The gradational agents (streams, waves, wind, glaciers) likewise are principally of climatic and gravitational origin. Here, then, in a vast laboratory, composed of the thin outer shell of the solid earth and the adjacent lower layers of atmosphere with which it is in contact, is the focus of an unbelievably complicated set of reactions, where sun-induced processes are acting upon earth materials and major surface forms of tectonic origin to produce the present patternful array of natural features with which the earth's surface is adorned.

299. *Mature Natural Landscape.* The very name (weathering) of the processes by which solid rock is broken down into the mantle rock or regolith cover emphasizes the role of such atmospheric conditions or elements as temperature, moisture, oxygen, and carbon dioxide in rock destruction. Temperature and moisture conditions are likewise primary in determining the nature of the vegetation cover, while climate and climatically induced vegetation play significant roles in soil formation and quality. Many of the drainage features, and some of the landform features as well, are the result of weathering and gradational agents, stemming indirectly from climatic energy. The regolith cover, composed of both inorganic and organic materials, and the vegetation cover develop in a region together, both responding to the conditions imposed by climate, and each in turn modifying the character of the other. It becomes evident, therefore, that within any particular region the climatic forces peculiar to it, if undisturbed over a long period of time, will produce a layer of mantle rock the depth and quality of which represent a state of balance between the rate of weathering and the rate of removal. This regolith is, in turn, covered by a mantle of vegetation, nourished by the soil layer underneath but likewise in harmony with the temperature and rainfall conditions surrounding it. Through the character and intensity of gradational forces, minor landform features and drainage conditions, in a somewhat lesser degree, likewise are brought into step with the atmospheric environment, so that the whole landscape complex bears the stamp of the regional climate. Landforms, which are so much influenced by tectonic forces, character of earth materials, and stage of development, usually bear this stamp of climatic environment much less conspicuously than do vegetation and soils, for instance. Within a large region of relatively uniform climate, there is a tendency, nevertheless, for many of its natural features, each adjusted to and in balance with all the others, to develop a considerable degree of similarity throughout. When that state of balance has been reached, the region may be said to have a *mature* natural landscape.

300. *The Three Great Patterns.* It has been emphasized in an earlier section of this book that (*a*) climates tend to remain relatively uniform over extensive areas and (*b*) similar climates are repeated on the land masses in characteristic latitudinal and continental locations. There is a definite and repeated world pattern in the distribution of climatic elements which permits of classifying climates into a relatively few major types. It now becomes apparent that these extensive, and often far separated, regions included within the same type of climate are also likely to possess similarities in certain other natural features as well.

Three great patterns dominate the earth—the pattern of climate, the pattern of native vegetation, and the pattern of soils. If the three patterns are placed one upon the other, the remarkable coincidence between their boundaries is striking. This is because climate is a fundamental dynamic force shaping the other two. The schematic representation of the three patterns is shown in Fig. 7.11. Generalized maps showing world distributions of vegetation formations and soil groups (Figs. 7.12 and 7.13) should be compared with Fig. 6.4 and also with Plate I, Climates of the Earth.

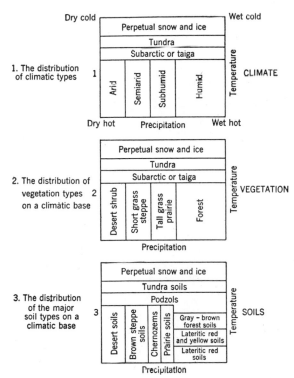

Fig. 7.11. Schematic representation of the distribution of climatic, vegetation, and soil types. (*Modified from Blumenstock and Thornthwaite.*)

Since the character of the bedrock, the size and quality of mineral deposits, and the nature of tectonic landforms are chiefly the result of interior earth forces, these features usually do not fit harmoniously into a world pattern based primarily upon climatic imprint.

301. Native Vegetation. Typical of the *Af* climate is the tropical rainforest, or *selva*, the earth's most vigorous and luxuriant vegetation growth (Fig. 7.12). In external aspect it presents a richly varied mosaic of many shades, gray, olive, brown, and yellow tints being more common than the fresh green of middle-latitude woodlands. No other forest equals it in richness of species, and these are intricately intermingled so that a few kinds of trees do not strongly predominate, as is usually the case in forests of middle latitudes. Pure stands of a species are practically unknown. Tropical rainforest is evergreen broadleaf in character, there being no general dormant period, each tree shedding its foliage imperceptibly as the new leaves grow. Just as

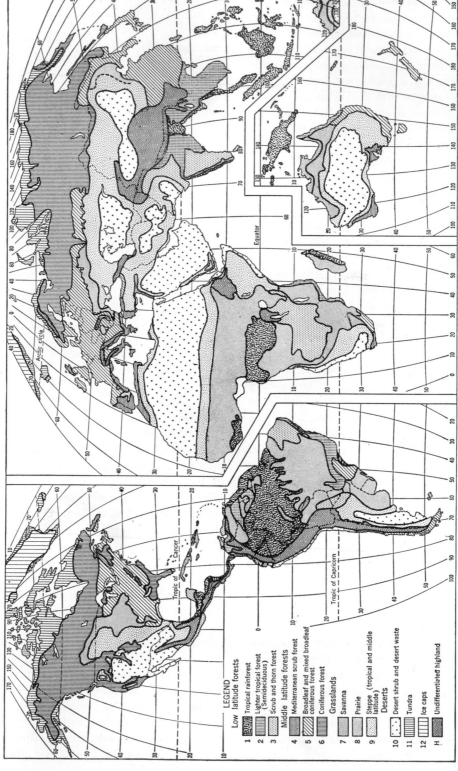

FIG. 7.12. World distribution of the principal vegetation formations. (*Courtesy of the Yearbook of Agriculture, 1941.*)

LEGEND
Low latitude forests
1   Tropical rainforest
2   Lighter tropical forest (Semideciduous)
3   Scrub and thorn forest
Middle latitude forests
4   Mediterranean scrub forest
5   Broadleaf and mixed broadleaf coniferous forest
6   Coniferous forest
Grasslands
7   Savanna
8   Prairie
9   Steppe (tropical and middle latitude)
Deserts
10 Desert shrub and desert waste
11 Tundra
12 Ice caps
H   Undifferentiated highland

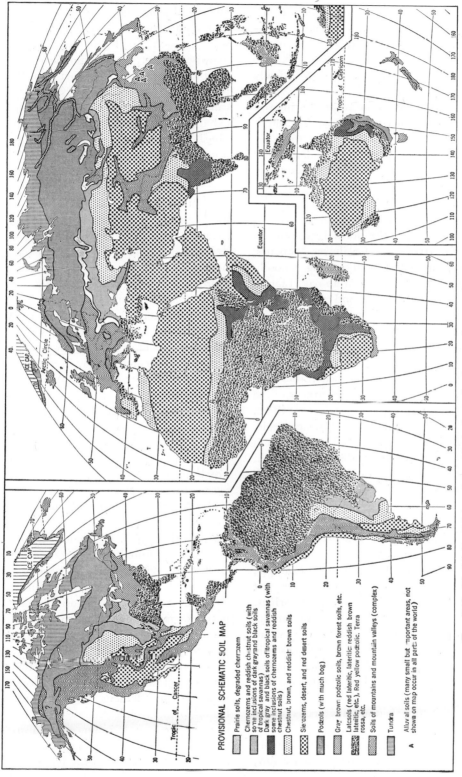

PROVISIONAL SCHEMATIC SOIL MAP

Prairie soils, degraded chernozem

Chernozems and reddish chestnut soils (with some inclusions of dark gray and black soils of tropical savannas)

Dark gray and black soils of tropical savannas (with some inclusions of chernozems and reddish chestnut soils)

Chestnut, brown, and reddish brown soils

Sierozems, desert, and red desert soils

Podzols (with much bog)

Gray brown podzolic soils, brown forest soils, etc.

Latosols (red lateritic, lateritic reddish brown lateritic, etc.), Red yellow podzolic. Terra rossa, etc.

Soils of mountains and mountain valleys (complex)

Tundra

A   Alluvial soils (many small but important areas, not shown on map occur in all parts of the world)

FIG. 7.13. World distribution of the principal zonal soil types. (*Courtesy of U.S. Department of Agriculture.*)

the climate is without seasonal rhythm, the vegetation is likewise. As a result of the continuousness of the addition and fall of leaves the forest is never bare and without foliage. Needle trees are largely absent, leaves characteristically being broad and thin.

An internal view shows the tropical rainforest to be composed of tall trees (often 150 ft. high) with large diameters, growing close together. It is not a single-storied forest, an understory of smaller trees being characteristic. The result is a dense canopy of shade with very subdued light underneath. In the Congo forest Shantz found that the time required for a photograph was twenty thousand times the normal exposure in the open. The trees have few lower branches, their trunks characteristically being smooth, resembling a conifer more than an oak. Lianas, climbing plants, epiphytes, and parasites are relatively abundant. This mass of vines and creepers appears almost to suffocate the trees that are its supports. Within the forest the tall, branchless trunks resemble gigantic dark columns supporting an almost impenetrable canopy, composed of the interlocking crowns of the trees and the vines and creepers that cover them. In the virgin forest, because of deep shade, undergrowth is not unusually dense although often sufficient to obstruct distant views. In regions of deepest shade only a thick mat of herbs or ferns covers the floor, so that one can proceed in all directions without following paths or even chopping new ones. Typical *jungle* conditions, with a thick and impenetrable undergrowth, mainly are characteristic of sections where light reaches the forest floor, for example, along rivers and coasts, on precipitous wet slopes, and in abandoned agricultural clearings.

302. Zonal Soils. Lateritic red soils, one of the earth's least productive soil groups, are characteristic of *Af* regions where climatic energy is most lavish and vegetation growth most vigorous (Fig. 7.13). The constant heat and humidity permit intense chemical weathering so that the regolith cover is unusually deep and the mature soil likewise.

While the depth of the mature soil is usually great, the amount of mineral plant foods is low, for these same factors of high temperature, abundant rainfall, and slightly acid ground water which accelerate rock decomposition, likewise intensify the leaching processes whereby soluble minerals are dissolved from the soil and removed by drainage waters. As a result, the rainforest laterites and lateritic soils are quickly exhausted when subjected to continuous cropping. Their striking porosity permits them to absorb much water, so that destructive runoff is reduced from what it would be in regions of more impervious soils.

In humus content, as well as in mineral plant foods, virgin rainforest soils are remarkably deficient, and this in spite of having the earth's densest vegetation cover. It must be remembered, however, that leaves are scarcely of first rank as sources of humus. Moreover, in this climatic environment, where destructive oxidation of organic matter takes place very rapidly, little humus is incorporated into the soil, while considerable amounts of the organic matter are dissolved and carried away in solution. The coffee-colored water of rainforest rivers is not always due to sediment held in suspension, but quite as often to dissolved organic matter carried in solution.

As a result of their coarsely granular structure, tropical rainforest red soils are friable, break up readily, and form fair seedbeds. However, this soil structure deteriorates rapidly under cultivation. Although they are receptive to fertilizer, it is only temporarily effective, disappearing quickly under the prevailing climatic conditions and porous soil structure. Even the virgin soils are so poor as not to be well suited to commercial agriculture. When cleared, the soil is almost immediately in need of fertilization and, without persistent and careful attention, will not endure continuous cropping.

In estimating the production potentialities of the tropical rainforest realm, it becomes obvious that the infertile soils are a critical offsetting factor to the prolific climate and the abundant vegetation cover. It is almost a truism, as far as this earth is concerned, that bountiful climates are seldom associated with highly fertile soils.

The reason is twofold: (1) continuous warmth and heavy rainfall lead to abundant leaching of soils and rapid destruction of organic material, while (2) forest vegetation, which is commonly associated with humid climates, does not usually provide an abundance of high-grade raw material out of which humus can be developed. Moreover, leaves decompose on *top* of the ground rather than *in* it, as do grass roots. Reflecting the infertility of rainforest soils is the characteristic shifting type of native agriculture, known by such names as milpa, chena, and fang. In this realm, as in several others having characteristically infertile mature soils, it is the young, unleached, and frequently rejuvenated soils of deltas and floodplanes that are the principal centers of crop production. Young slope soils are likewise more fertile.

303. Landforms and Drainage. Since the original framework of surface configuration within a region is largely the result of interior forces, there is no reason for expecting that there will be any general likeness in the tectonic features throughout the realm. However, since constantly high temperatures, one of the essential elements of the tropical rainforest climate, are confined to relatively low elevations, it is obvious that mountains and high plateaus are immediately ruled out as common surface features of the realm. On the whole, lowlands predominate, although hill country is well represented.

304. *The Gradational Agents and Processes.* Running water is the dominant gradational agent throughout the wet tropics. The heavy, well-distributed rainfall gives rise to an unusual abundance of full-flowing streams, both large and small, which characteristically develop a complete and intricate drainage pattern. Intensity of precipitation is likewise marked, leading to rapid soil removal on slopes from which the vegetation mantle has been removed as a preliminary to cultivation. The degradational processes are not only vigorous but they also continue active throughout the entire year. In most parts, the dense vegetation cover, providing through its roots anchorage for the soil, retards active slope wash and gullying, but these

processes are disastrous on cleared hillside farms. The removal of the regolith cover on steep forest-covered slopes more often takes place by mass movement under the influence of gravity, either in the form of slump and landslides or by the movement of mud beneath the root mat. Numerous travelers have described the enormous landslides of wet tropical regions, the scars of which are conspicuous at a distance of several miles. It is even possible for removal by slump and slide to be so rapid on steep slopes that the underlying bedrock remains exposed.

Differential weathering and erosion are less marked in the tropical rainforest realm than in any other climate, so that sharp ridges or ledges of exposed rock are not common. Both the deep regolith and the forest cover tend to make surface irregularities less conspicuous through their mantling effects. River-aggraded features are both widespread and extensive. Valleys have conspicuous depositional features, in part composed of slump and landslide materials. Broad floodplains, their surfaces a confused association of active and abandoned channels, the latter in various stages of fill, and of levees and back marshes, are characteristic. Natural levees are unusually prevalent, the streams appearing to flow *on*, rather than *in*, the floodplain.

Tropical Wet and Dry Climate (*Aw*)

305. *Aw* climate differs in two principal respects from *Af* climate: (*a*) it usually has less precipitation; and (*b*) rainfall is unevenly distributed throughout the year, there being a distinctly wet and a distinctly dry season. These climatic contrasts result in the dense rainforest, typical of areas near the equator, being replaced by tree-studded grasslands in the *Aw* regions. It is this widespread occurrence of tall tropical grass (called savanna) which commonly has led to the designation of *Aw* as savanna climate, although the name may not be so appropriate since pure savannas, without trees, seem to be the exception rather than the rule.

306. Type Location and Boundaries. In Fig. 6.4, showing the distribution and characteristic locations of types of climate on a hypothetical continent, *Aw* is bounded by *Af* climate on its equatorward side and by dry climates (*B*) and humid subtropical climate (*Ca*) on its poleward side (Fig. 7.2). Its equatorward boundary coincides with the transition zone separating a climate with no dry season (*Af*) from one with an emphatic dry season (*Aw*). Köppen has suggested 6 cm., or 2.4 in., of precipitation in the driest month as defining this boundary. As a usual thing *Aw* on its poleward side is bounded by dry climates in the interiors and western parts of continents and by humid *Ca* climate toward the eastern sides. Thus it is a rainfall deficiency, determined by the rainfall-evaporation ratio, which locates the *B/Aw* boundary, and a temperature deficiency which locates the *Ca/Aw* boundary. *A* climates grade into *C* climates where the temperature of the coolest month falls below 10°C., or 64.4°F. The reason why *Aw* climate grades into dry climate on the western side of a continent and into humid climate on the eastern side is associated with the contrasting nature of subtropical anticyclones along their eastern and western margins. This has previously been explained in the general discussion of *A* climates.

The typical latitudinal location of *Aw* is from about 5 or 10° to 15 or 20° (Figs. 6.4, 7.2). On the generalized profile of sea-level pressure *Aw* is therefore located between the equatorial low-pressure trough and the subtropical highs. Thus on a mean wind chart it would be found in the tropical easterlies, or trades, and somewhat toward their humid equatorial margins. This position places *Aw* in an intermediate, or transitional, location between the humid unstable air masses associated with equatorial convergence zone and doldrums on one side, and the stable subsiding air masses of the subtropical anticyclones on the other. During the course of a year, with the north-south shifting of the insolation belts, and as a consequence pressure and wind migration, *Aw* latitudes are alternately encroached upon by the wet *ITC* and doldrums (convergent) at the time of high sun and by the drier parts of the trades and subtropical anticyclones (divergent) in the low-sun period. The result is rainy "summers"

and dry "winters." In a genetic sense *Aw* may be classed as one of the "alternating" climates, since the most distinctive characteristic of a wet and a dry season is closely associated with its dominance by contrasting elements of the general circulation in the opposite seasons. Since *Aw* is intermediate between dry climates on their poleward sides and wet climates on their equatorward sides, it is to be expected that within an *Aw* region there will be a gradual change in climatic character from the wetter equatorial margins toward the drier poleward margins. The dry season becomes increasingly longer and more severe toward the poleward side. These latitudinal contrasts are less marked toward the eastern sides of continents.

307. Geographical Location. It becomes evident from a scrutiny of Plate I that many, if not most, of the large *Aw* areas do have the type locations just previously described and shown in Fig. 6.4. This is true of the two extensive *Aw* areas in South America, one to the north of the Amazonian *Af*, in Venezuela, Colombia, and the Guianas, and the other to the south of the *Af*, in south central Brazil and adjacent parts of Bolivia and Paraguay. It is equally true in Africa where there is the extensive Sudan *Aw* north of the equator and the equally large veld *Aw* area to the south. Less characteristic is the presence of *Aw* in eastern Africa in equatorial latitudes. A large part of the *Aw* in eastern and southern Africa is somewhat atypical because of the presence of plateaus where altitude reduces the temperature below that which is normal for *Aw*. The same is true for parts of southeastern Brazil. The *Aw* of northern Australia and that of southern Asia in India, Burma, Thailand, and Indo-China also are relatively typical in location. Some may want to call the Asiatic *Aw* a monsoon savanna and argue that the rainy season is the result of precipitation associated with the onshore summer monsoon winds. This is not seriously objectionable, provided one realizes that the so-called monsoon is in the nature of southwest winds (equatorial westerlies?) blowing toward the *ITC* which has migrated abnormally far north due to the heat of the land mass. In this sense the Asiatic *Aw* is little different in its origin from that of the others. Smaller or less contiguous areas of *Aw* are to be found in western Madagascar, insular and peninsular areas in the Caribbean area, and the western lowlands of Central America.

TEMPERATURE

308. The temperature elements in *Aw* and *Af* climates are not greatly unlike. Constantly high temperatures are still the rule, for the noon sun is never far from a vertical position, and days and nights change little in length from one part of the year to another. In general, however, yearly ranges are somewhat greater (although still small) than in typical *Af* regions, usually over 5° but seldom exceeding 15° (Figs. 7.14, 7.15). These larger ranges may result both from the high-sun months being slightly hotter and from the low-sun months being slightly cooler than is typical for regions nearer the equator.

It is significant that the hottest month or months many times do not coincide with the time of highest sun but usually precede it somewhat and thus occur before the height of the rainy period at which time the more persistent cloud cover and heavier precipitation tend to lower the temperature. Thus March, April, and possibly May are likely to be hotter than June or July which are the rainiest periods for Northern Hemisphere *Aw*. In some *Aw* regions the inhabitants recognize three temperature periods: (*a*) the cooler dry season at the time of low sun, (*b*) the hotter dry season just preceding the rains, and (*c*) the hot wet season during the rains. Temperatures may rise again very slightly just after the rainy period as a result of the clearer skies and drier atmosphere (see temperature data following).

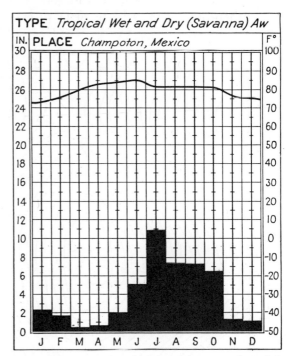

FIG. 7.14. Average monthly temperatures and precipitation amounts for a representative tropical wet-and-dry (*Aw*) station, (19°21′N., 90°43′W.).

During the so-called *cooler dry season* (period of lowest sun), day temperatures are still high, with afternoon maxima between 80 and 90° and occasionally above 90°, but the humidity is low so that the heat is not oppressive (Figs. 7.16, 7.17). Nights at this season are inclined to be pleasantly mild, the thermometer usually going below 70° and not infrequently below 60°, for the dry air and clear skies are conducive to rapid terrestrial radiation.

During the *hot dry period*, which usually begins about the time of the spring equinox, increased intensity and duration of solar radiation cause

Climatic Data for Representative Aw Stations
Timbo, French West Africa (10°40′N.)

	J	F	M	A	M	J	J	A	S	O	N	D	Yr.	Range
Temp.	72	76	81	80	77	73	72	72	72	73	72	71	74	9.7
Precip.	0.0	0.0	1.0	2.4	6.4	9.0	12.4	14.7	10.2	6.7	1.3	0.0	64.1	

Calcutta, India

	J	F	M	A	M	J	J	A	S	O	N	D	Yr.	Range
Temp.	65	70	79	85	86	85	83	82	83	80	72	65	78	21
Precip.	0.4	1.1	1.4	2.0	5.0	11.2	12.1	11.5	9.0	4.3	0.5	0.2	58.8	

Cuiabá Brazil (15°30′S.)

	J	F	M	A	M	J	J	A	S	O	N	D	Yr.	Range
Temp.	81	81	81	80	78	75	76	78	82	82	82	81	80	6.6
Precip.	9.8	8.3	8.3	4.0	2.1	0.3	0.2	1.1	2.0	4.5	5.9	8.1	54.6	

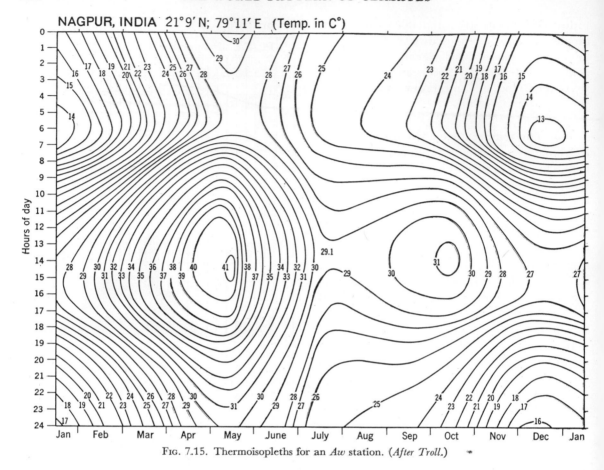

FIG. 7.15. Thermoisopleths for an *Aw* station. (*After Troll.*)

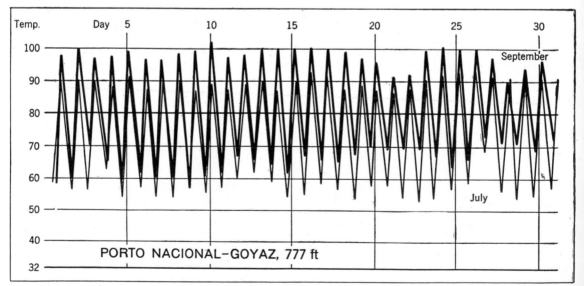

FIG. 7.16. Daily maximum and minimum temperatures for the extreme months at a representative *Aw* station in Brazil. Solar control is dominant. (*After Jefferson.*)

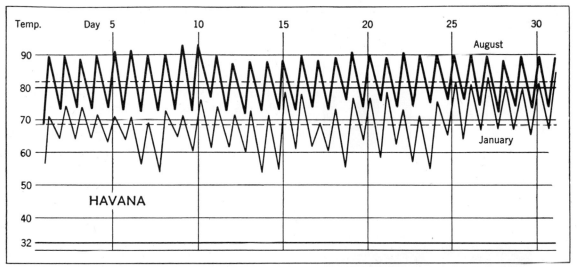

FIG. 7.17. *Aw* station with a marine location. There is evidence of some weak nonperiodic air-mass control in January. (*After Jefferson.*)

the daily maxima to rise well above 90° and often over 100° (Figs. 7.16, 7.17). With the beginning of the rains, however, temperature conditions resemble very much those of the tropical wet climate. The diurnal range becomes somewhat less, and while the heat is not so intense as in the hot dry season, the higher humidity causes it to be much more oppressive and sultry.

PRECIPITATION

309. Amount of Rainfall. Since temperatures are not greatly different within the tropics, rainfall becomes the more critical element in setting apart the several climatic types of the low latitudes. Characteristically, the total amount of rainfall of the *Aw* is less than that of the *Af* climate, 40 to 60 in. being more typical of the former. But since the *Aw* type usually occupies transitional belts between the constantly wet and the constantly dry climates, it naturally follows that there will be considerable contrast between the amounts of rainfall on its two margins.

310. Rainfall Regime. It is the seasonal distribution, rather than the amount of precipitation, however, which chiefly distinguishes the two climates of the humid tropics, for the *Aw* type has a distinctly wet and a distinctly dry season (Fig. 7.14). This contrast between the two types is principally due to their latitudinal

locations, for while *Af* is almost constantly within the humid equatorial *ITC* air where convergence, ascent, and heavy rainfall prevail, *Aw* is on the equatorial margins of the trades and, therefore, in an intermediate position between the rainy *ITC* on the one side and the drier poleward margins of the trades and associated subtropical anticyclone on the other (Fig. 3.20).

The Sudan *Aw* of northern Africa may be used as a concrete example to clarify further the mechanics of the *Aw* rainfall regime. As the sun's vertical ray moves northward from the equator after the spring equinox, their thermal effects cause pressure and wind belts to shift in the same direction, although lagging a month or two behind in time. As the convergent *ITC* belt of heavy rains gradually creeps northward, thunderstorms begin to appear in March or April over the Sudan, and the rainfall continues to increase in amount until July or even August, when the *ITC* reaches its maximum northward migration. With the southward retreat of the *ITC*, following the sun, the rains decline in amount, until by October or November the dry, subsiding air masses again prevail over the Sudan, and drought grips the land. The length of the wet and the dry seasons is variable, depending upon distance from the equator.

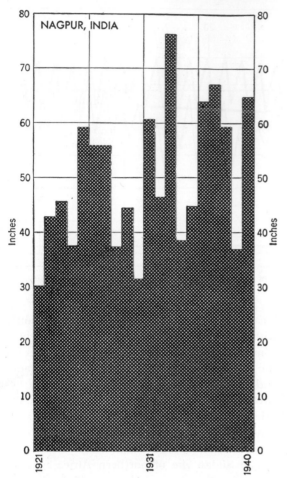

FIG. 7.18. Variations in amount of annual rainfall over a 20-year period at Nagpur, India, an *Aw* station. Large annual variations in rainfall are characteristic of *Aw* climates.

There is no abrupt boundary between the constantly wet *Af* and the wet-and-dry *Aw* climates, but a very gradual transition from one to the other. Thus, on the equatorward margins of the *Aw*, the rainy season persists for almost the entire year. In such locations there may be even a slight depression at the crest of the precipitation curve, this falling off of the rains occurring in the short interval of time between the northward and southward migrations of the *ITC* (Fig. 3.21, Zungeru). The farther poleward one travels in the Sudan the shorter is the period of *ITC* control and the longer that of the subsiding air masses, so that

the dry season increases in length while the wet period shrinks. For the sake of emphasis, it bears repeating that the rainy season in *Aw* closely coincides with the period of high sun, while the dry season is identified with the period of low sun. Most emphatically, rainfall follows the sun. This rule holds for either hemisphere, although one should keep in mind that December to February is the period of high sun (summer) south of the equator and June to August the period of low sun (winter). It is obvious, therefore, that, when a Northern Hemisphere savanna is having its rainy season, a similar region south of the equator is experiencing drought, and vice versa.

311. Rainfall Reliability. Not only is *Aw* rainfall less in total amount, and more seasonal in its distribution throughout the year, as compared with *Af*, but it is likewise less reliable, there being wider fluctuation in the amounts from year to year. One year may bring such an abundance of rain as to flood the fields, rot the crops, and increase the depredations of injurious insects and fungi, while the following year may witness even more severe losses from drought. In northern Australia the average rainfall variation from the normal is as much as 25 per cent (Fig. 7.18).

312. Seasonal Weather. During its rainy season the weather of *Aw* climate closely resembles that of *Af* at its worst. This period usually is ushered in and out by violent thunderstorms and severe squall winds, which in Africa are called "tornadoes." In these transition periods the weather is very trying, "violent short deluges of rain and intensely hot sunshine alternating." As the rainy season advances, sunny days become rarer, and precipitation assumes a more regular aspect. During the height of the rains, violent thunderstorms appear to be less frequent than they are at the transition periods, while on the other hand, heavy, long-continued, and more general rains reach their maximum at that time. These latter probably originate in atmospheric disturbances of the wave and weak-cyclone types identical with those described previously for *Af* climates. The Australian Weather Bureau states that most of the mid-rainy-season precipitation of northern Australia is from these tropical lows. Similarly, much of the *Aw* rain of India occurring during the height of the monsoon is received from weak depressions which form over the head of the Bay of Bengal and move slowly in a northwesterly direction across India.

In the low-sun, or dry, season the weather is like that of the deserts. In spite of the aridity, the dry season is welcomed after the humid, oppressive heat of the rainy periods. Occasional showers may occur during the months of drought, the number depending upon which margin of the *Aw* is being considered. On the dry margin the period of absolute drought may be of several months' duration, while on the rainy margin, where it makes contact with *Af* climate, there may be no month absolutely without rain. *The fact should never be lost sight of that none of these climatic boundaries is sharp, there being very gradual transitions from one type to another.* During the dry season the savanna landscape is parched and brown, the trees lose their leaves, the rivers become low, the soil cracks, and all nature appears dormant. Smoke from grass fires and dust fill the air, so that visibility is usually low.

The following quotation is a description of the seasonal weather and related landscape changes in an *Aw* region. It should be emphasized, in order to avoid confusion, that the region described is Zambezia, Africa, which is *south* of the equator. As a result of Southern Hemisphere location, the months included within the several seasons are exactly opposite from what they are in *Aw* regions north of the equator.

"The winter months, or dry season, extend, with a slight variation, from April to November. They are, as I have said, pleasant and healthy in the extreme. Now the traveller and hunter of big game make their appearance; the deciduous trees are leafless; the grasses dry, yellow, and ready for the chance spark or deliberate act which, with the aid of a steady breeze, will turn vast expanses of golden grasslands into so many hideous, bare deserts of heat-tremulous black. All nature seems to be at a standstill, hibernating. The rivers are low. Where, but a few short months since, wide, watery expanses rushed headlong toward the sea . . . there now remain but tranquil, placid channels, flowing smilingly at the bottom of steep, cliff-like banks. . . .

"With October the heat becomes very great. Vast belts of electrically charged, yellowish clouds, with cumulus, rounded extremities, begin to gather and at the close of day are seen to be flickering in their murky centres with a menacing tremor of constant lightning. This may go on for a week or more, and then Nature arises like a strong man in anger and looses the long pent-up voice of the thunder and the irresistible torrents of the early rains. The first manifestation may come at evening and is a soul-moving display of natural force. . . .

"After such a disturbance as the one I have just described, rain is fairly continuous for some time, and the effect of this copious irrigation makes itself felt in every branch of animal and vegetable life. Within a few days the change is startling; the paths and roadways choke themselves with a rich clothing of newly sprung grasses, whilst the trees, the extremities of whose twigs and branches have been visibly swelling, now leap into leaf and blossom. The mosses, which for months past have looked like dry, bedraggled, colourless rags, regain once more their vivid, tender green. Now the forest throws off its puritanical greyness and, with an activity and rapidity beyond belief, decks itself in flowers of a thousand gorgeous shades of colour, from chrome-yellow and purple to grateful mauve.

"The birds now put on their finest feathers, the animals appear in their brightest hues. Colour and warmth run riot in the brilliantly clear air now washed clean from the mist and smoke which for so many months have obscured it. The clear verdant green of rapid-springing grasses and opening fronds clothes the landscape, and the distant peaks of the mountains lose their pale, bluey-grey haziness and stand boldly out in the light of the sun. The months succeed each other, bringing with them new and strange beauties, for summer is now at its height, and trees and flowers at their most perfect period. . . . April comes, and suddenly Nature holds her hand. The swollen rivers and inundated plains shake themselves free from the redundant waters. The grasses have now reached a formidable height. The rains now cease, and the land begins to dry up. Rich greens turn to copper, and brown, and yellow, and little by little, with the advent of May, the winter returns with its sober greyness."[1]

[1] R. C. F. Maugham, "Zambezia," pp. 383–388, John Murray, London, 1910.

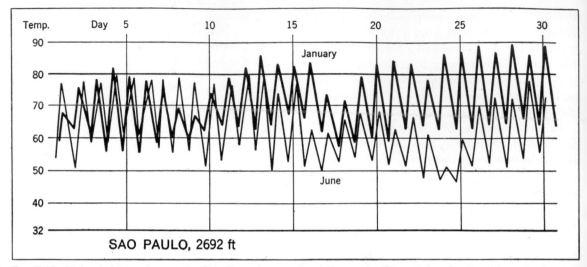

FIG. 7.19. Upland *Aw* station on the Brazilian plateau. According to the Köppen classification this station has a *C* climate, for several months has average temperatures below 18°C. (64.4°F.). While solar control is dominant, some nonperiodic air-mass control is to be observed. (*After Jefferson.*)

313. Upland *Aw* (Including *Cw*).[1] In tropical latitudes on several of the continents, but especially Africa and South America, there are extensive upland areas, possessed of many of the normal *Aw* characteristics but differing chiefly in their lower temperatures (Fig. 7.19). Within

On Plate I these somewhat atypical tropical uplands continue to be designated as *Aw*, even though some parts actually are *Cw*. Extensive upland *Aw-Cw* regions are distinguished by a light overshading on Plate I. (For climatic modifications imposed by altitude see Chap. 11).

Climatic Data for a Typical Upland Aw-Cw Station
Sao Paulo, Brazil (23°33′S.) 2,690 ft.

	J	F	M	A	M	J	J	A	S	O	N	D	Yr.	Range
Temp.	69	69	68	65	60	59	58	59	62	63	66	68	64	11.0
Precip.	9.1	8.5	6.2	3.0	2.9	2.2	1.3	2.1	3.4	4.5	5.2	7.6	56.0	

these upland areas in low latitudes, there are stations so located that altitude may cause the average temperature of some months to be slightly below the minimum required for an *A* climate (18°C., or 64.4°F). Other stations at somewhat lower altitudes may have no month with an average temperature below 18°C. and still throughout the year temperatures may be lower than is normal for a typical *Aw* climate.

[1] According to the Köppen classification, *Cw* climates appear in two characteristic locations: (*a*) tropical uplands, where because of altitude the temperature is lowered below that of the surrounding lowlands (*Aw*); and (*b*) mild subtropical monsoon lands such as exist in parts of southern China. It is the first group that is here being classified as the subtype *upland Aw*. The other group is included within the humid subtropical climates (*Ca*) of the lower middle latitudes.

ASSOCIATED FEATURES OF THE PHYSICAL EARTH IN THE *Aw* CLIMATES

314. Native Vegetation. Because the climate is transitional in character, the native vegetation is likewise, and consequently it changes in character and appearance from the humid (*Af*) to the dry (*B*) margins of the type as the number of humid months becomes fewer. Throughout *Aw* regions grass and trees usually are intermingled. The dominant vegetation element, which was almost lacking in *Af*, is coarse grass and it is from this element that the name savanna is derived.[1] While pure grasslands without trees are not unknown in *Aw*, especially in Africa,

[1] Waibel and others have expressed the opinion that open tropical grasslands were originally thinly wooded and that the trees have disappeared through constant

this form of vegetation cover seems to be less common than grasslands with low trees and shrubs in stands of varying density. Clumps of trees dotting the grasslands give them a park-like appearance, and in some parts the trees become numerous enough to give the appearance of a woodland. Where the dry season is relatively short, and the rainy season is of 7 to 9+ months duration, a relatively lush *moist tree savanna* characterized by tall grasses and numerous trees prevails. As the wet season becomes shorter, a *dry tree savanna* with somewhat shorter grasses and shorter and fewer trees is characteristic. This passes over into a *thorn savanna* as the rainy season declines to 3 to 4 months in length, but with grasses and trees still intermingled. In this driest of the savannas the stunted thorny trees are especially well equipped to endure drought.

The tall and unusually coarse savanna grasses grow in bunches or tufts, the latter separated by intervals of bare soil. They spring up rapidly at the beginning of the rainy season and may within a few months reach heights of 4 to 12 ft. Seldom do savannas have the verdant, refreshing tints of humid meadows but instead are dull green in color with yellowish or brownish tints. Blades are stiff and harsh, especially when dry, so that they are practically inedible. In the drought season the grasses become sear and brown so that they burn readily. No natural hay is provided by the brittle, unpalatable dead grasses, and the wild herbivorous animals and domesticated cattle must, in the drought season, rely on the tender new shoots along rivers or the receding margins of ponds or lakes. Where tree growth is relatively luxuriant, the vegetation may be classed as lighter tropical forest. Typically it is more open in character than the *Af* rainforest, so that grasses and a denser undergrowth of shrubs occupy the less shaded forest floor. Climbing vines and epiphytes may be numerous. The trees of the savanna, in addition

to being more widely spaced, are smaller in size and usually deciduous in character, although not all the trees may be leafless during the dry season. It is during the drought season, nevertheless, that contrast with the rainforest is most marked. Throughout the tropical savannas dense galeria forests characteristically follow the stream courses, coinciding with the flood plains where water is abundant.

315. Zonal Soils. Little seems to be known with assurance concerning the mature soils of the tropical savannas and tree savannas. It is probable that they belong to the general lateritic red and yellow soil group, and therefore in many respects they resemble the infertile leached soils of *Af* regions. There is some indication that tropical forest soils are superior to those of the tropical grasslands.[1] If this is true, it is a reversal of the situation which usually prevails in the middle latitudes where the grassland soils are higher grade than those which develop under forests. A serious handicap of the soils of tropical wet and dry climates is the presence of a hard surface crust which makes tillage with hand tools difficult. As in most regions of infertile or stubborn mature soils, it is the fresh new-alluvium surfaces of floodplains and deltas that provide the most attractive sites for cultivation in the *Aw* regions.

316. Landforms and Drainage. Paralleling the rainfall regime, the streams likewise show a remarkable seasonal fluctuation in volume. This stands in contrast to the year-round, full-flowing drainage channels of the *Af* regions where a genuine dry season is absent. During the drought period the parched and relatively unprotected ground likewise suffers from wind erosion. As the streams increase in number and volume with the advance of the rainy season, their channels, clogged with silt, are unable to carry away the waters sufficiently fast. As a result they overflow their banks and, where lowlands prevail, inundate large areas of the then verdant countryside. As precipitation diminishes with the

burning. If this is true, the term "savanna climate" is scarcely defensible. See Leo Waibel, Vegetation and Land Use in the Planalto Central of Brazil, *Geog. Rev.*, Vol. 38, pp. 529–554, 1948.

[1] Waibel, *op. cit.*, p. 554. See also Leo Waibel, Place Names as an Aid in the Reconstruction of the Original Vegetation of Cuba. *Geog. Rev.*, Vol. 30, pp. 392–393, 1943.

advance of the dry season, rivers gradually lose volume and velocity and return to their narrower channels, leaving large expanses of alluvial flats to dry in the sun. Their loads of silt are deposited in the stream beds, resulting in numerous sand bars and a maze of braided channels. A large number of the rivers are intermittent in character, their courses being entirely without water during the dry season.

Because of the periodic fluctuation of streams, aggradational surfaces, in the form of flood-plains and deltas, are extraordinarily well developed. Owing to the inability of the channels, clogged by the deposits of the preceding dry season, to carry off the flood waters of the rainy season, streams characteristically overflow their banks, produce a maximum of lateral cutting, and develop extensive valley flats. Under similar conditions of surface configuration, probably in no other realm is the width of floodplain so great in proportion to the size of the stream. Levees are likely to be conspicuous features.

CHAPTER 8: *The Dry Climates (B)*

317. Definition of Dry Climate. The essential feature of a dry climate is that potential evaporation from the soil surface and from vegetation shall exceed the average annual precipitation. In other words, during a normal year the capacity of the atmosphere to acquire water evaporated from the soil surface and transpired from plants is greater than the water added to the soil through precipitation. In such a climate there is a prevailing water deficiency and a constant ground-water supply is not maintained, so that permanent streams cannot originate within such areas. It may be possible, however, for permanent streams to cross areas with dry climates, as do the Nile, the Colorado, and the Indus, for instance, provided they have their sources in more humid regions. Where water deficiency exceeds the water need, the climate is dry. Where precipitation is in excess of the water need, the climate is moist.

318. Boundaries of Dry Climates. Since water deficiency in any area depends not only upon the quantity of rain that falls but also upon the rate at which it is lost through evaporation and transpiration, called "evapotranspiration," it is clear that no specific *amount* of rainfall can be accepted as the boundary of dry climates in general. It is not possible to determine whether a climate is moist or dry by knowing only the precipitation. It must be determined whether the precipitation is greater or less than the water needed for evapotranspiration. But to discover which quantity is greater is no easy matter, for while the rain gauge measures precipitation with a fair degree of accuracy so that it is known how rainfall varies from place to place on the earth and how it varies throughout the year, no instrument has been perfected for measuring

evapotranspiration, or water loss, from earth to atmosphere. As a consequence little of significance is known about the distribution of actual or potential evapotranspiration over the earth.

Because actual measurements of evapotranspiration are lacking, the only alternative is to discover a relationship between potential evapotranspiration and other climatic factors for which abundant data do exist. Since the rate of evaporation depends upon the vapor-pressure difference between the surface and the air immediately above, and also upon turbulence which carries the moistened air upward, it has been determined that there is a fairly close relationship between temperature and potential evapotranspiration. For example, potential evapotranspiration is higher in southern United States than in northern, and it is higher in summer than in winter. Various attempts have been made to construct formulas for measuring evaporation based upon monthly or annual temperatures and by this means to arrive at an index of aridity. None seem to be entirely satisfactory or universally acceptable. All of them recognize that in the warmer lower latitudes where the losses due to evapotranspiration are great, less of the total rainfall is effective for plant growth than in the cooler middle latitudes. It is quite possible, then, that an amount of precipitation sufficient to produce a humid climate in regions with moderate temperatures might be classed as dry in a region of great heat. Paris, France, has an annual rainfall of only 23 in.; yet in that cool marine climate it produces a distinctly humid landscape. The same amount in tropical Africa would result in semiarid conditions. Moreover, if a large amount of the total annual rainfall comes in the

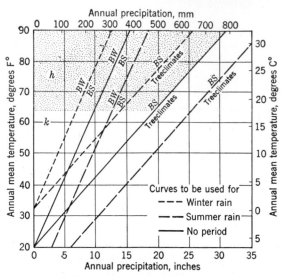

FIG. 8.1. Boundaries between dry and humid climates according to the Köppen classification. (*After Haurwitz and Austin.*)

warmer months, much more is lost through evapotranspiration than if it is evenly distributed over the 12 months, or concentrated in the cool season (Fig. 8.1). It should be obvious, then, that the boundary separating humid from dry climates is determined by a combination of rainfall and temperature conditions, and not by rainfall alone.

Köppen's method for determining the amount of annual precipitation (r) defining the boundary between dry and humid climates is expressed by the following formulas:

(1) $r = 0.44t - 8.5$ when rainfall is evenly distributed

(2) $r = 0.44t - 3$ when rainfall is concentrated in summer

(3) $r = 0.44t - 14$ when rainfall is concentrated in winter

In these formulas r = annual rainfall in inches; t = average annual temperature in degrees Fahrenheit.[1] From the formulas it is obvious that the amount of rainfall (r) defining the humid boundary of dry climates will be large where mean annual temperatures are high, and hence losses through evapotranspiration great, and

[1] A. Austin Miller has proposed the formula, $r = t/3$, as defining the dry/humid boundary.

low where the temperatures are low. Also r will be highest where rainfall is concentrated in the warm season (formula 2), and least where the maximum is in winter when evapotranspiration is least (formula 3). From the table below it becomes clear that while in a climate with a

Boundary between Humid and Dry Climates According to the Köppen Classification

Temp., F°	50	60	70	80	90	100
Precip., in.	13.5	17.9	22.3	26.7	31.1	35.5

mean annual temperature of 50° (rainfall well distributed seasonally) a yearly rainfall of only 13.5 in. or over is required to produce a humid climate, where the annual temperature is 80° the comparable figure is just about double that, or 26.7 in.

319. Desert and Steppe. Two subdivisions of dry climates are commonly recognized: (*a*) the arid, or desert, type and (*b*) the semiarid, or steppe, type. In general, the steppe is a transitional belt surrounding the real desert and separating it from the humid climates beyond. The boundary between arid and semiarid climates is a relatively arbitrary one, but by Köppen it is defined as one-half the amount separating steppe from humid climates. For example, if in a particular region 19 in. of rainfall marks the outer, or humid, boundary of dry climates in general, then 9½ in. may be taken as the boundary between steppe and desert for that same region. Thus the three Köppen formulas given previously for determining the boundary of steppe and humid climates must have the right-hand side of each equation divided by 2 in order to represent the boundary between desert and steppe. A. Austin Miller who has suggested the formula $r = t/3$ as representing the boundary between steppe and humid climates proposes $r = t/5$ as defining the boundary between desert and steppe.

Dry climates are the most extensively developed over the land surface of the earth of any of the great climatic groups, occupying, according to Köppen, 26 per cent of the continental area. Of this total, 14 per cent is steppe and 12 per cent is desert. As would be expected, dry climates occupy a much smaller proportion of the earth's water surface, probably between 4 and 5 per cent.

320. Temperature. Since dry climates exist in a wide variety of latitudes and continental locations, few significant general comments on their annual temperatures can be made. On the whole, however, because of characteristic interior and leeward locations on the continents, and because of clear skies and dry atmosphere, they tend to be severe for their latitude, having relatively extreme seasonal temperatures and consequently large annual ranges.

More marked, however, are the large daily ranges, clear cloudless skies and relatively low humidity permitting an abundance of solar energy to reach the earth by day but likewise allowing a rapid loss of earth energy at night. Large diurnal ranges in deserts also are associated with the meager vegetation cover, which permits the barren surface to become intensely heated by day. The surface of dry ground may reach a temperature of 200°F. It is a physical law that the higher the temperature of a body, the more rapid is its loss of heat by radiation, and consequently the more rapid its reduction in temperature.[1] Deserts, therefore, not only acquire but also lose heat rapidly. In humid regions with a relatively complete vegetation cover, more of the solar radiation is utilized in transpiration to change water from plants into vapor. Much of the heat consumed in evaporation must come from the plant itself. Transpiration, therefore, is a heat regulator, preventing excessively high temperatures both in plants and in air. As a consequence, regions with a vegetation cover are unlikely to have extreme ground and air temperatures like those of deserts. Where vegetation is abundant, water vapor is likely to be also, so that night cooling is retarded.

321. Precipitation and Humidity. Rainfall in the dry climates is always meager. In addition it is extremely variable from year to year so that the average is not to be depended upon (Fig. 3.2). It is a general rule, worthy of memorization, that dependability of precipitation usually decreases with decreasing amount. Two handicaps, therefore, (a) meagerness and (b) unreliability of rainfall, seem to go together. No part of the earth is known for certain to be absolutely rainless, although at Arica, in northern Chile, the rainfall over a period of 17 years was only 0.02 in. During the whole 17 years there were only three showers heavy enough to be measured.

Relative humidity is (with a few exceptions) low in the dry climates, 12 to 30 per cent being usual for midday hours. Conversely potential evaporation is extremely high. But absolute humidity, on the other hand, is by no means always low, for hot desert air usually contains a considerable quantity of water vapor, even though it may be far from being saturated. The amount of sunshine is great, and cloudiness small. Direct as well as reflected sunlight from the bare, light-colored earth is blinding in its intensity.

322. Winds. Dry regions are inclined to be windy places, there being little frictional retardation of the moving air by the lowly and sparse vegetation cover. In this respect they are like the oceans. Moreover, the rapid daytime heating of the lower air over deserts leads to strong convectional overturning, this interchange of lower and upper air tending to accelerate horizontal surface currents during warm hours when convection is at a maximum. "In the desert the wind is almost the only element of life and movement in the domain of death and immobility. A journey in the desert is a continuous strife against the wind charged with sand and, in moments of crisis, a painful physical struggle" (Gautier). Nights are inclined to be much quieter, which is a partial explanation of the rapid nocturnal cooling of surface air in dry regions. Because of the strong and persistent winds, desert air is often murky with fine dust which fills the eyes, nose, and throat, causing serious discomfort. Much of this dust is carried beyond the desert margins to form the loess deposits of bordering regions. The heavier, wind-driven rock particles, traveling close to the surface, are the principal tool of the wind in sculpturing desert landforms.

[1] The amount of heat radiated by a body is directly proportional to the fourth power of its absolute temperature.

In the classification of climates here employed, four principal subdivisions of dry climates are recognized. Using rainfall as the critical element, the twofold subdivision into desert and steppe is the result. Based upon temperature contrasts, on the other hand, the subdivisions are (a) the dry climates of the low latitudes, or the *hot* steppes and deserts; and (b) the dry climates of the middle latitudes, or the *cold* (in winter) steppes and deserts.[1] Not infrequently the low- and the middle-latitude dry climates are continuous with each other, the latter occupying the far interiors of the middle-latitude continents, and the former the interiors and western (leeward) margins of land masses in the latitudes of the dry trade winds and the subtropical highs. Although on Plate I the primary subdivisions are recognized as steppe and desert, for the sake of convenience and brevity the textual materials are grouped under the headings of tropical dry climates and middle-latitude dry climates.

Tropical and Subtropical Dry Climates (*BWh* and *BSh*)

323. Type Location. The heart of the tropical dry climates (Fig. 6.4) is in the vicinity of latitudes 20 or 25°N. and S., with the average positions of their extreme margins at approximately 15 and 30. They are fairly coincident with the dry, subsiding air masses of the subtropical anticyclones. Subsidence and drought are by no means confined to the centers of the anticyclonic cells, for these same characteristics extend out onto the equatorward slopes of the highs into the trade winds. Ordinarily the dry climates do not extend to the eastern margins of the continents, humid climates characteristically taking their places on these windward margins. It will be recalled, also, that in the earlier discussion of the subtropical atmospheric circulation, it was pointed out that the air masses derived from the western margins (eastern sides of

[1] Köppen uses the mean annual isotherm of 18°C., or 64.4°F., as the boundary between the two principal latitudinal subdivisions of dry climates (see Plate II). In the modified Köppen classification employed in this book the January isotherm of 32°F. has been used (see Plate I)

continents) of the subtropical cells are much less stable and somewhat warmer and consequently much better rain makers than those originating along the eastern margins (west coasts), where upper level subsidence and stability are more marked. Tropical hurricanes also add to the rainfall of some of these east coasts. Along west coasts in these latitudes, on the other hand, dry climates extend down to the sea margins and even far beyond over the oceans (Fig. 3.19). Here, without doubt, the principal drought-producing control is subsidence in the subtropical anticyclone. The cool ocean currents which characteristically parallel these subtropical and tropical west coasts may act to further intensify the aridity. It appears to be a general rule, then, that humid tropical climates extend unusually far poleward along the eastern (windward) sides of the continents (eastern Brazil, eastern Central America, eastern Madagascar), while dry climates are carried equatorward beyond their normal latitudes along the western littorals (western Peru and western Angola in southwestern Africa). The low-latitude dry climates are characteristically bounded by *Aw* climates on their equatorward sides and by middle latitude *C* (usually *Cs*) and *B* climates on their poleward and interior margins (Fig. 6.4, Plate I).

BWh LOW-LATITUDE DESERT

324. Type Locations. The low-latitude deserts, dominated as they are by the subtropical anticyclones, probably are the most nearly rainless regions of the earth. Next to the deserts of snow and ice on the polar ice caps, they are also the most hostile to life. Since they occupy regions of dry, stable, settling and diverging air masses, conditions are unfavorable for the development of convectional showers in spite of the intense heat. This same horizontal divergence is opposed to the development of fronts and atmospheric disturbances. Even when the intense surface heat of summer develops seasonal low-pressure centers over some of the low-latitude deserts, these convergent cyclonic circulations in the lower air are relatively shallow, and anticyclonic circulation continues to prevail aloft dampening any tendency toward a large-scale lifting of air. Too far equatorward to be reached by the equatorward advance of middle-latitude fronts and cyclones on the poleward side, too far poleward to be affected by the *ITC* advancing from the low latitudes, and too far interior from eastern littorals to be affected by the humid onshore winds and the disturbances in the western oceanic trades, these low-latitude deserts are outside the realms of the usual rain-bringing winds and storms (Fig. 6.4). As pointed out in a preceding section, the asymmetrical development of the low-latitude deserts on the land masses is associated with (*a*) the greater instability of the air masses in the western as compared with the eastern parts of the subtropical anticyclones, (*b*) the better development of atmospheric disturbances along the western parts of tropical oceans or the eastern coasts of tropical continents, and (*c*) the general humidity contrasts between windward and leeward coasts in the tropical easterlies. Arid conditions extend not only down to the coast on the western sides of continents but even out over the adjacent oceans as well. Some of the more extensive low-latitude deserts, particularly the Sahara and the Australian desert, are important source regions for tropical continental air masses.

Precipitation and Humidity

325. Annual Rainfall. Although no exact amount of rainfall can be accepted as defining the outer or humid margins of the hot deserts, the figure usually lies somewhere between 10 and 15 in. Over much of the Sahara precipitation is under 5 in., a condition true, as well, of large parts of the other low-latitude deserts, *viz.*, Kalahari in South Africa, Atacama-Peruvian desert in western South America, Australian desert, Thar in northwestern India, and Sonora in northwestern Mexico and southwestern United States. At Cairo, Egypt, the annual rainfall averages 1.2; at Lima, Peru, 2; William Creek, Australia, 5.4; Yuma, Ariz., 3.3; and Port Nolloth in southwestern Africa, 2.3 in. In parts of northern Chile rain may not fall for 5 or 10 years in succession. At Calama in northern Chile, located back of the Coastal Range, no

rain has ever been recorded. However, averages are of little value in giving a correct impression of desert rainfall, for not only is it small in amount, but it is likewise erratic and uncertain in its time of fall. Over most of the low-latitude deserts the rainfall variability shows a 40+ per cent departure from the normal (Fig. 8.2). It is, therefore, almost impossible to speak of a *typical* rainfall curve, or an *average* annual rainfall, for desert stations. As an illustration: At Iquique in northern Chile, during a period of 4 years, no rain fell. Then in the fifth year one shower gave 0.6 in., which made the "average" annual rainfall for the 5-year period 0.12 in. On another occasion 2.5 in. of rain fell in a single shower.

326. Desert Downpours. General, widespread rains are almost unknown over large parts of the *hot* deserts, most of the precipitation coming in violent convectional showers which cover no very extensive area. Seven single storms brought nearly one-quarter of the total rain (30.7 in.) that fell at Helwan in the Egyptian Sahara in a 20-year period. In one of these storms 1.8 in. of rain fell, causing torrents to sweep down the wadies and do much damage to buildings and crops. At Doorbaji, in the desert of Thar in northwestern India, where the annual rainfall is only 5 in., as much as 34 in. has fallen in 2 days (Kendrew).[1] These sudden and heavy downpours may be disastrous in their effects, causing more damage than good. The wadies, entirely without water during most of the year, after one of these flooding rains may become torrents of muddy water filled with much debris. Kendrew states that army regulations forbid French troops in the Sahara from pitching their overnight camps in the bottoms of dry wadies because of the danger of sudden floods, and this in spite of the fact that the high banks of the wadies offer a distinct protection against the disagreeable winds. Settlements suffer; roads, bridges, and railways may be injured; and irrigation systems are often clogged with debris after a serious desert flood. Because of the violence of tropical desert rains and the sparseness of the vegetation cover, temporary local

[1] "Climate," p. 148.

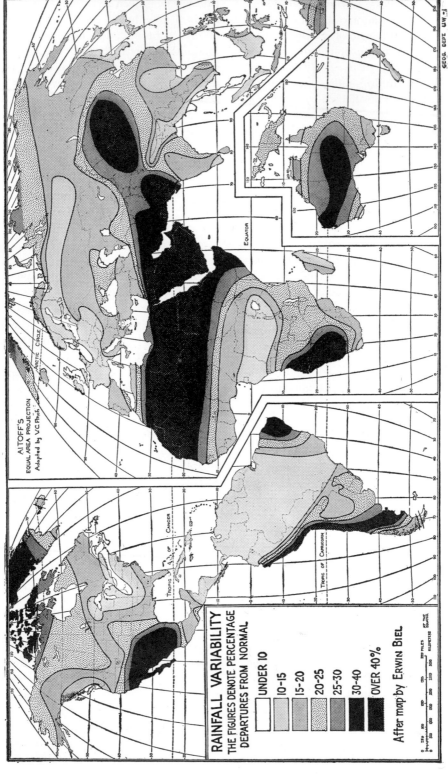

FIG. 8.2. Rainfall variability is characteristically greatest in the earth's dry and subhumid regions. (*After Biel.*)

runoff is excessive, and consequently less of the total fall becomes effective for vegetation or for the crops of the oasis farmer. This "dash" character of hot-desert showers, plus their local nature and their erratic seasonal distribution, makes them of little direct use for agriculture, so that no immediate dependence is placed upon them as a source of water. Much of the precipitation that reaches the earth is quickly evaporated by the hot, dry, desert air, but some sinks in to replenish the underground water which appears at the surface in the form of springs or artesian flows. On the *poleward* margins of low-latitude deserts there are occasional widespread rains of a less violent nature. These are usually associated with the fronts of middle-latitude cyclones and are largely confined to the low-sun period.

327. Cloudiness and Sunshine. Skies are prevailingly clear in the low-latitude deserts so that sunshine is abundant. In the Sonoran Desert of the United States and Mexico 75 ± per cent of the possible sunshine is experienced in winter, and 90 ± per cent in the other seasons. Yuma, Ariz., receives for the year 88 per cent of the possible sunshine: 95 per cent in May, 97 per cent in June, and 78 per cent in January. Over much of the Sahara December and January have a cloudiness of only $\frac{1}{10}$, while from June to October it drops to about $\frac{1}{30}$. The pitiless glare of sunlight in the tropical deserts is such an essential characteristic of their landscapes that the occasional dark or rainy day, being so unusual, is said to be particularly depressing. Strong surface heating, due to the intense insolation and the nearly bare ground, must give rise to vigorous surface convection currents, but the stability associated with subsidence aloft, and the low relative humidity prevent the heated surface air, except infrequently, from rising high enough to reach condensation level and beyond to produce thunderheads. Dark cumulonimbus clouds do form occasionally, sometimes accompanied by thunder and lightning, but the streamers of rain that can be seen descending from them usually are evaporated in the arid atmosphere before they reach the earth. But even though the air may be *physio-logically dry* and have unusual evaporating power (high temperature and low relative humidity), there is usually a moderate amount of moisture in the atmosphere. All that is lacking is a way to cause it to be condensed and precipitated. Thus the air at Yuma, Ariz., contains nearly as much moisture in July, and double as much in January, as does that at Madison, Wis., in the same months. However, the relative humidity at Yuma (January, 47 per cent; July, 34 per cent— 8 P.M. readings) is only two-thirds to one-half as great in either season. In spite of the low relative humidity, nocturnal surface cooling in the deserts frequently is sufficient to produce valley fogs and dew.

328. *Evaporation*, due to the high temperature and low relative humidity, is excessive, often being twenty or more times the precipitation. At Yuma the average evaporation during the hot months is 55 in., while the average rainfall during the same period is not quite 1 in. Relative humidities as low as 2 per cent, with temperatures of over 100°, have been recorded in the Egyptian Sahara. It was the excessively dry air which allowed the Egyptians to mummify their dead.

Temperature

329. Annual and Diurnal Temperatures. Annual ranges of temperature in the low-latitude deserts are larger than in any other type of climate within the tropics, 20 to 30° being usual (Fig. 8.3). Aswan, in the Sahara, has mean temperatures of 61° in January and 95° in July, resulting in an annual range of 34°. Such ranges, which even exceed those of some middle-latitude climates, reflect not only the clear skies, bare earth, and low humidity, but also the higher latitudes of the deserts and somewhat greater seasonal extremes of insolation, as compared with most of the *humid tropics.* It should be emphasized that it is the excessive "summer" heat, rather than the "winter" cold, which leads to the marked differences between the seasons. This is one of the tropical climates where annual may occasionally equal daily ranges. The latter, however, usually are larger, averaging 25 to 45° and in rare instances even reaching 60 or 70°.

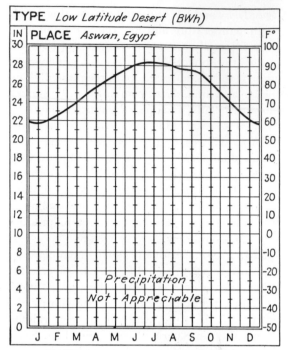

FIG. 8.3. Average monthly temperatures.

The same conditions—dry air, cloudless skies, and bare, dry earth—that make for relatively large temperature differences between the extreme months are likewise conducive to wide differences within the diurnal period. On Dec. 25, 1878, at Bir Milrha, south of Tripoli in the Sahara, a minimum temperature of 31° and a maximum of 99° were recorded on the same day.

330. The Hot Season. During the high-sun period, scorching, desiccating heat prevails. Hot-month temperatures average between 85 and 95° (Yuma 91°; Timbuktu 94.5°; Nullagine, Australia, 90°), and midday readings of 105 to 110° are common at this season. In the western part of the Australian Desert temperatures have exceeded 100° on 64 consecutive days and 90° on 150 consecutive days. At Yuma, in 1914, the daily maxima exceeded 100° for 80 consecutive days, except for one day (Fig. 8.4). At this time of the year, although the lower night temperatures are a distinct relief by contrast with the days, they are by no means cool. At Phoenix, Ariz., the midsummer daily maxima usually exceed 100°, and the minima are close to 75 or 76°. In the northern Sahara average daily maxima of 99° are followed by minima approximating 71°. At Azizia, 25 miles south of Tripoli, 136.4° has been recorded, this being the highest air temperature in the shade ever registered under

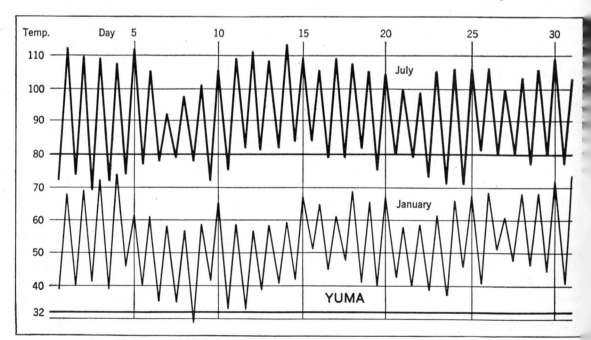

FIG. 8.4. A representative station in a low-latitude desert (*BW*) in Arizona.

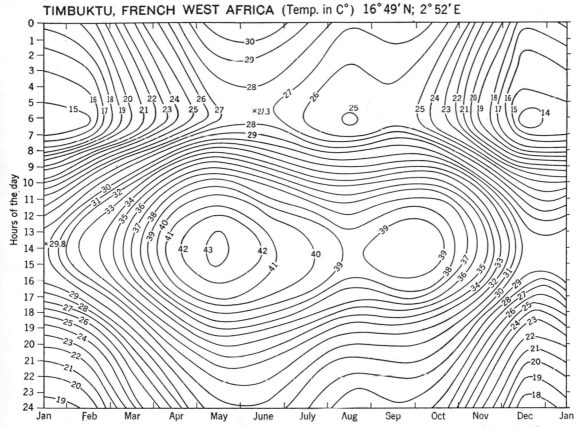

TIMBUKTU, FRENCH WEST AFRICA (Temp. in C°) 16° 49′ N; 2° 52′ E

FIG. 8.5. Thermoisopleths for a representative *BW* station in the Sahara of North Africa. (*After Troll.*)

standard conditions. The highest official air temperature ever recorded in the United States is 134°, in Death Valley in the California desert.

331. The Low-sun Period. During the period of low sun the days still are warm, with the daily maxima usually averaging 60 to 70° and occasionally reaching 80° (Figs. 8.4, 8.5). Nights are distinctly chilly at this season, with the average minima in the neighborhood of 50±°. Insalah, in the Sahara, during January has average daily maxima of about 70° and minima of 40°. The average annual extremes are 29.5 and 121.8°, and the temperature has been known to go as high as 124° and as low as 26°. There are, therefore, occasional light frosts experienced in these tropical deserts. A Saharan traveler gives the following vivid description of the cool season in that arid region:

"In truth the days are generally very trying, for there is either a blazing sun which burns through the thin cotton [clothing], or a bitter wind which pierces every bone in one's body. Sometimes there were both together, and then one side of one is frozen and the other baked! One's skin split and blistered under this treatment, but there was only one hour I shall never be able to forgive the desert. This was the moment when, at 5 A.M., one crept shivering out of one's warm flea-bag into pitch darkness, placed one's feet gingerly on icy cold sand, fumbled with numb fingers for a candle and matches, and proceeded to drag on cold, stiff garments from each of which fell a shower of sand."[1]

332. Daily Weather. As is true of the rest of the tropics, so within the low-latitude deserts the sun very much controls the weather, resulting in a great deal of sameness between successive days. This is especially true of the summer season. On their poleward margins, however,

[1] Rosita Forbes, "The Secret of the Sahara: Kufara," pp. 168–169. Doubleday & Company, Inc., New York, 1921.

Climatic Data for Representative Stations in Low-latitude Deserts

Jacobabad, Pakistan

	J	F	M	A	M	J	J	A	S	O	N	D	Yr.	Range
Temp.	57	62	75	86	92	98	95	92	89	79	68	59	79	41
Precip.	0.3	0.3	0.3	0.2	0.1	0.2	1.0	1.1	0.3	0.0	0.1	0.1	4.0	

William Creek, Australia

	J	F	M	A	M	J	J	A	S	O	N	D	Yr.	Range
Temp.	83	83	76	67	59	54	52	56	62	70	77	81	68	30.5
Precip.	0.5	0.4	0.8	0.4	0.4	0.7	0.3	0.3	0.4	0.3	0.4	0.3	5.4	

which lie close to the middle latitudes, there are occasional invasions of polar air with associated fronts and cyclonic storms, which may now and then cause "spells of weather," particularly during the winter season when the westerlies and the cyclone belt are farthest equatorward. The daily march of temperature at Yuma, Ariz., clearly indicates these nondiurnal oscillations of temperature in winter (Fig. 8.4). On the front of the cyclone, southerly winds of tropical origin import higher temperatures, to be followed by several days of cooler weather as the winds swing around to the north and produce the polar air masses on the rear of the low. Occasional gray days with some rain may result from a few of the cyclones whose centers usually pass by rather well beyond the poleward margins of the deserts. Although these cool-season showers are absent throughout most parts of tropical deserts, the low-latitude margins experience occasional thundershowers during the high-sun period when the *ITC* is farthest poleward.

BWn-BSn, THE COOL WESTERN LITTORALS[1]

333. Temperature in *BWn* Regions. The usual characteristics of tropical deserts—high temperatures, low relative humidity, and little cloud—are modified to a considerable degree along the littorals (usually western) of several of the low-latitude deserts, where cool ocean currents parallel the coasts (Fig. 8.6). The presence of cool currents is especially marked along the desert coasts of Peru and northern Chile from about latitude 4 to 31°S., and the west coast of South Africa from 8 to 32°S., but their influence

[1] In the Köppen symbol, *n* = frequent fog (Nebel); *n'* = high relative humidity and therefore low visibility, but not actual fog.

is also felt along the Atlantic coasts of the Moroccan Sahara from Casablanca to Senegal, Somaliland in eastern Africa, and northwestern Mexico. Some of the regions noted are steppes rather than true deserts. The low temperatures of the ocean waters are partly the result of importations from higher latitudes, as the currents are driven equatorward by the spiraling winds about the eastern ends of the subtropical highs. In part, also, they are due to upwellings of colder subsurface water along these coasts. The land margins adjacent to the cool waters are themselves unusually cool, with temperatures 10° or more lower than normal for the latitude (Fig. 8.7). Thus Callao, on the Peruvian Coast, has an annual temperature of only 67°, and Mollendo 65°, while Bahia on the east coast of Brazil, in a similar latitude, averages 77°. The hottest month at Callao is only 71° (similar to July at Madison, Wis.), while the coldest is 62.5°. At Port Nolloth, a coastal desert station in southwestern Africa, a region paralleled by the cool Benguela Current, temperatures of the warmest and coldest months are 59 and 53°, respectively, while at Durban, across the continent on the east coast, comparable figures are 76 and 64°.

From the temperature data given above, it may be noted that the annual ranges of temperature are unusually small, the temperature difference between the extreme months being only 8.5° at Callao, Peru, and 6° at Port Nolloth in southwestern Africa. These ranges should be compared with a 34° range at Aswan, Egypt, and 40° at Jacobabad, Pakistan. Diurnal ranges are also very small in these cool marine deserts of the low latitudes (Fig. 8.8). *BWn* regions are thus characterized by (*a*) lower-than-average annual temperatures, (*b*) distinctly cooler summers, (*c*) slightly milder winters, and (*d*)

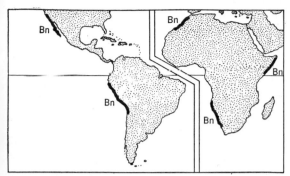

FIG. 8.6. Distribution of cool, tropical dry climates (*Bn*) with a high percentage of fog. Characteristically this subtype of dry climates is located along coasts paralleled by cool ocean currents.

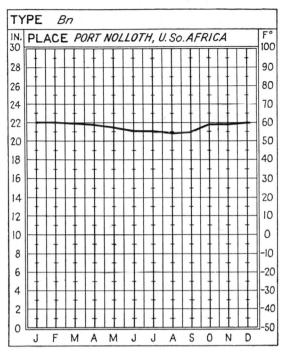

FIG. 8.7. Average monthly temperatures for a representative desert station located on a cool-water coast (*Bn*). Note the abnormally low temperatures for a tropical station and also the small annual range of temperature.

smaller annual and diurnal ranges than are normal for most low-latitude dry climates.

334. Precipitation and Fog in *BWn* Regions. Although along these cool coasts rainfall is extremely low (2.3 in. at Port Nolloth, 1.18 in. at Callao), and the drought conditions may extend to within a few degrees of the equator, they are on the other hand regions of high relative humidity and abundant fog. The intensified aridity is chiefly attributable to the prevalance of the very stable air of the eastern side of the subtropical anticyclone which is strongly developed along these tropical and subtropical west coasts. Perhaps the cool coastal waters have a further stabilizing effect upon the

mT air and hence may be an auxiliary cause for the decreased precipitation. In Peru, this cool, stable air mass must be forced upward along the

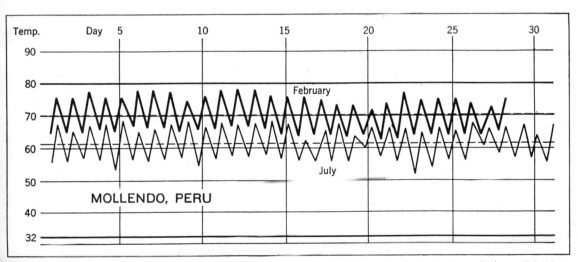

FIG. 8.8. Daily maximum and minimum temperatures for a coastal station in a low-latitude desert (*Bn*) paralleled by a cool ocean current. Note the abnormally low temperatures and small daily range. (*After Jefferson.*)

flanks of the Andes to an altitude of about 5,000 ft. before the zone of annual rains is reached. The fog, so characteristic of these cool-water coasts, is of the advection type. It is formed as a result of cooling the lower strata of sea air as they move over the cool coastal current. The Peru coastal current, for example, is 50 to 100 miles wide, so that fog begins to form at some distance from the coast. The formation of the sea fog actually aridifies the air that comes in over the coasts, since the lower layers of air have lost a good deal of moisture. Usually the fog over the land is confined to the coastal sections, for as the cool foggy air moves inland over the warm land the suspended water particles are quickly evaporated. At Swakopmund (Southwest Africa) fog is recorded on 150 days in the year. Sea breezes along these coasts, intensified by the cool ocean water offshore, are extraordinarily strong.

coast, the grip of the intense aridity is temporarily slackened and heavy rains and high temperatures typical of *Af* climate prevail for a short period. But with the return of anticyclonic control the warm El Niño retreats northward, the cool Peruvian current reestablishes itself, and desert conditions once again prevail.[1] This occasional replacing of *BW* by *Af* climate along the coast of Peru is one of the world's unique climatic phenomena. The Peruvian desert extends northward to about Cape Blanco where there is an abrupt change in coastline trend. To the north of Cape Blanco humid tropical climates begin, and midway along the Pacific coast of Colombia excessively heavy rainfall (300 in.) is encountered. The coastal region from northern Peru to Colombia has one of the steepest rainfall gradients at sea level anywhere on the earth.

Climatic Data for a Representative Desert Station on a Cool-water Coast (BWn)

Lima, Peru

	J	F	M	A	M	J	J	A	S	O	N	D	Yr.	Range
Temp.	71	73	73	70	66	62	61	61	61	62	66	70	66	12.8
Precip.	0.0	0.0	0.0	0.0	0.0	0.2	0.3	0.5	0.5	0.1	0.0	0.0	1.8	

In Peru the heavy fog, or "wet mist," is sufficient to make for a meager showing of vegetation on the coastal hills.[1] Darwin, in his book "The Voyage of the Beagle," describes these Peruvian mists as follows:

"A dull heavy bank of clouds constantly hung over the land, so that during the first sixteen days I had only one view of the Cordillera behind Lima. It is almost become a proverb that rain never falls in the lower part of Peru. Yet this can hardly be considered correct; for during almost every day of our visit there was a thick drizzling mist which was sufficient to make the streets muddy and one's clothes damp; this the people are pleased to call 'Peruvian dew.' "

At intervals of several years when the subtropical anticyclone weakens and withdraws poleward and seaward, at the same time permitting a warm current (El Niño) from the north to replace the cool Peruvian current along the

---

[1] An excellent description of the fogs of the Peruvian Coast is to be found in Isaiah Bowman, "The Andes of Southern Peru," pp. 121–156, Henry Holt and Company, Inc., New York, 1916.

BSh LOW-LATITUDE STEPPE

335. Type Location. It is again necessary to emphasize the fact that low-latitude steppe climates characteristically surround the low-latitude deserts, except possibly on their western sides (Fig. 6.4), and are, therefore, transition belts between *BW* and the humid climates on the north, east, and south. Because *BS* is less at the heart and more on the margins of dry settling tropical air masses associated with the subtropical high-pressure cells, and is therefore one step closer to the humid climates than are the deserts, the steppe lands are encroached upon for a short period of the year by rain-bearing winds and their associated storms. It is this brief period of seasonal rains which causes them, although still having a dry climate, to be semi-arid rather than arid.

In the case of North Africa, which may be taken as a fairly typical example, there are two

---

[1] Robert C. Murphy, Oceanic and Climatic Phenomena along the West Coast of South America during 1925, *Geog. Rev.*, Vol. 16, No. 1, pp. 26–54.

large and separate areas of tropical steppe, each occupying a representative location (Plate I). (a) One borders the Sahara on the *north* and lies between it and the dry-summer subtropical (*Cs*) climate, one of the milder and less rainy types of the middle latitudes. This steppe region is encroached upon by fronts associated with cyclonic storms in winter, the time of their maximum equatorward migration. Other tropical steppes of this same type location are to be found in southern Australia; Mesopotamia, Arabia, and southern Iran in western Asia; and in northwestern Mexico and adjacent parts of southwestern United States. (b) The second steppe region of North Africa lies along the *equatorward* margins of the Sahara and between *BW* and *Aw* types. This steppe receives its meager rainfall at the time of high sun from the poleward-displaced *ITC*. The semiarid regions in northern Australia, much of dry southwestern Africa, and northwestern India largely belong to this group. In Australia these two typical belts of steppe, one on the poleward and the other on the equatorward margins of the tropical desert, are connected by a crescentic belt of steppe along the eastern side of the arid area. It is only on the western sides of the continents, therefore, that the tropical deserts extend down to the sea margins and have no semiarid transition belts.

336. Precipitation and Humidity. Rainfall in the steppes, like that in the deserts, is not only meager but also variable and undependable

who have ventured too far beyond the safety line. Only where irrigation water supplements the normal rainfall is agriculture safe, so that the grazing of animals becomes a more widespread form of land use.

337. *Steppes with Low-sun Rainfall (BShs).*[1] Those belts of steppe lying on the poleward sides of tropical deserts, and close to *Cs* climate, have nearly all their rain in the cool seasons. Like the *Cs* climates on whose margins they lie, these steppes receive their rain from fronts associated with cyclonic storms, which, following sun migration, travel more equatorward routes in winter than in summer. During most of the year, however, they are dominated by dry settling and diverging air masses associated with the subtropical high-pressure cells. Because rainfall is concentrated in the cool season, evaporation is less, and consequently the small amount that falls is relatively effective for plant growth. At Bengasi, in the steppe region north of the Sahara, three of the midsummer months, June, July, and August are absolutely rainless, while December and January are the rainiest months, and the total for the year is slightly less than 12 in. The mean annual precipitation of 12 in. is, however, derived from such relatively divergent figures for single years as 22 in., 24 in., 6.8 in., and 7.1 in., all of which occurred within a span of 7 years. Variability is not so great, however, as in those steppes having a high-sun rainfall maximum (see Fig. 6.4, Plate I).

Climatic Data for a Representative Low-latitude Steppe Station with Low-sun Rainfall (BShs)

Bengasi, Libya

	J	F	M	A	M	J	J	A	S	O	N	D	Yr.	Range
Temp.	55	57	63	66	72	75	78	79	78	75	66	59	69	24
Precip.	3.7	1.8	0.7	0.1	0.1	0.0	0.0	0.0	0.1	0.3	2.1	3.1	11.9	

Fig. 8.2). This characteristic is perhaps even more dangerous in the semiarid than in the arid lands, for in the latter precipitation is never enough to tempt settlers to make agricultural conquest other than at oases, while occasional humid years in the steppe may be sufficiently wet to lure inexperienced persons to attempt it. But humid years are invariably followed by dry ones, and with these comes disaster to settlers

In steppe lands with a low-sun rainfall spells of weather associated with the air masses and fronts of passing cyclonic storms are not unusual in the winter season. Not only cloud and rainfall are involved, but changes in temperature as well, air of tropical origin with higher temperatures preceding the low center, and the reverse importation and temperature change following the

[1] The letter *s* indicates summer drought.

storm. It is obvious that these regions are far enough poleward to feel the effects of modified polar air masses. In spite of winter being the rainiest season, it is, nevertheless, prevailingly sunny, the precipitation coming in showers of rather short duration. Occasionally gray, overcast days with rain do occur, however.

338. *Steppes with High-sun Rainfall BShw.*[1] Those tropical steppe lands lying on the equatorward margins of the deserts, and therefore between them and the *Aw*, are likely to have a very brief period of relatively heavy rains at the time of high sun, when the *ITC* is farthest poleward. Rainfall periodicity is like that of the *Aw* except that the dry season is longer and the total precipitation less. At Gorée, Senegal (French West Africa), 5 months, December to May inclusive, are absolutely dry, 90 per cent of the rain falling, principally in convectional showers, during July, August, and September. Since the rainfall arrives in the hot season when evaporation is at a maximum, less of it is effective for vegetation, and consequently these steppes bordering the savannas usually are characterized by a greater total rainfall than are their poleward counterparts described in Art. 337. Rainfall variability is also greater. In addition they have much less frontal, or cyclonic, weather, with its associated erratic temperature changes, which are characteristic of the steppes with low-sun rainfall. Temperatures are not greatly different from those of the adjacent desert. In the data for Kayes, a station with abnormally high temperatures, the time of greatest heat precedes the rainy season when cloudiness is greatest, and therefore does not coincide with the time of highest sun.

of location within particular pressure and wind belts as are those of low latitudes. Dry climates in the middle latitudes usually are found in the deep interiors of the great continents, far from the oceans, which are the principal sources of the atmosphere's water vapor (Fig. 6.4). Further intensifying the aridity of the deep continental interiors is the fact that in both Eurasia and North America these locations are commonly surrounded by highlands that block the entrance of humid maritime air masses and of rain-producing storms. Where high mountains closely parallel a coast, as, for instance, in western United States, arid climates may approach relatively close to the sea. Asia, the greatest land mass in middle latitudes, has the largest area of dry climates, while North America is next in order.

Although tropical deserts characteristically extend down to the ocean margins on the leeward (western) sides of continents, the leeward (eastern) sides of land masses in the westerlies are far from dry. Witness, for example, eastern North America and Asia. This shifting of middle-latitude dry climates interior from the leeward coasts is associated with the presence of monsoons and cyclonic storms along the eastern sides of land masses in the westerlies. Owing to an unusual combination of circumstances, dry climates do reach the east coast in Patagonia (Argentina), but this is the exception. There the land mass is so narrow that all of it lies in the rain shadow of the Andes, where descending air masses make for drought conditions. This same small land mass also precludes monsoon development and the principal paths of cyclonic storms are to the north and to the south of the

Climatic Data for a Representative Low-latitude Steppe Station with High-sun Rainfall (BShw)

Kayes, French West Africa

	J	F	M	A	M	J	J	A	S	O	N	D	Yr.	Range
Temp.	77	81	89	94	96	91	84	82	82	85	83	77	85	19.2
Precip.	0.0	0.0	0.0	0.0	0.6	3.9	8.3	8.3	5.6	1.9	0.3	0.2	29.1	

Middle-latitude Dry Climates (*BWk* and *BSk*)

339. Type Location. The middle-latitude steppes and deserts are not primarily the result

area in question. Moreover, those storms that do cross the high Andes temporarily are so disrupted that they are unable to bring much rain to the Patagonian uplands. With the exception of South America, none of the other Southern Hemisphere continents extends into suffi-

[1] The letter *w* indicates winter drought.

ciently high latitudes to permit the development of very extensive middle-latitude steppes and deserts. Patagonia is the one extensive region with dry climates where the 32° isotherm for the coolest month (July) is not significant as the *h/k* boundary separating tropical-subtropical dry climates from those of middle latitudes. This arises from the fact that Patagonia is neither hot nor cold but is exceptional in being a marine type of desert. No month has an average temperature below 32° and so, by strict application of the definition, it cannot be *Bk*. On the other hand, since summer-month temperatures do not reach 60°, it is under no circumstances a tropical or subtropical desert. So, although it belongs to the middle latitudes, on Plate I small letter *k* is omitted. The precedent for this procedure is Köppen's omission of the *h* in the climatic symbols for those tropical dry climates along cool-water coasts.

340. Temperature. While dry continental climates of middle latitudes duplicate the arid and semiarid climates of the tropics in their meager and undependable rainfall, they differ from them in having a season of severe cold, which is of course absent in the low latitudes. On the other hand, they are like the *humid continental* climates of comparable latitudes in their temperature and weather characteristics, but unlike them in that they receive less rainfall.

The interior locations of most middle-latitude dry climates assure them of having relatively severe seasonal temperatures and consequently large annual ranges. Because they have such a wide latitudinal spread (15 or 20° in both North America and Asia) it is difficult to speak of *typical* temperature conditions. For example, southernmost Colorado and southern Alberta are included within the dry climates of middle latitudes; yet one is crossed by parallel 37°, while the latter is mostly poleward of 50°. It is obvious that their temperature characteristics must be greatly different, and yet for the particular latitude in which each lies it is relatively severe. Summers are inclined to be warm or even hot, while winters are correspondingly cold. Tashkent in U.S.S.R. at 41°N. ranges from 32° in January to 81° in July, while

for Urga, Mongolia, at 48°N. the comparable figures are −16 and 63°. As a result of the prevailing dryness of the ground, the arrival of spring is relatively sudden, so that the warm season advances rapidly. The quick rise in spring temperatures is much greater than in more humid climates, where a large part of the sun's energy is expended in melting the snow and evaporating the water, rather than in heating the ground and the air. Diurnal ranges are inclined to be large, and for the same reasons as noted in the discussion on tropical steppes and deserts (Fig. 8.10).

341. Precipitation. Two factors chiefly account for the meager precipitation of middle-latitude dry climates: (*a*) They are either in the deep interiors of large continents or separated from the ocean by mountain barriers. (*b*) A well-developed seasonal anticyclone is characteristic of all but their subtropical margins in winter. The regions of most severe aridity have the further contributing factor of being located in basins surrounded by highlands. Unlike the dry climates of the tropics, those of middle latitudes receive a portion of their precipitation in the form of snow, although the amount is characteristically small, and the winter snow cover is not deep.

342. Seasonal Distribution. It is not easy to generalize concerning seasonal distribution of precipitation in the dry climates of middle latitudes. In the more interior and continental locations, however, summer is usually the period of maximum precipitation (see data for Urga and Williston). This is related to the higher surface temperatures and associated convectional overturning, greater specific humidity, and inblowing system of monsoonal winds in summer. In winter the low temperatures and the anticyclonic circulation are antagonistic to abundant condensation. Most of interior Asia and the Great Plains region of the United States are dry lands with a distinct summer maximum in their precipitation curves. Urga, Mongolia, for example, receives 84 per cent of its 7.6 in. of rainfall in the three summer months. Middle-latitude dry climates having a summer maximum of precipitation greatly predominate.

On the other hand, those dry climates which approach and lie not far removed from *Cs* climate are likely to have dry summers and wetter winters (see data for Lovelock, Nev.). This is the typical Mediterranean regime of rainfall and is particularly characteristic of west margins of continents in the lower middle latitudes. The continental anticyclone is largely absent here in winter, so that cyclonic storms of the westerlies are able to bring precipitation. In summer such regions lie south of the cyclonic belt and are under the influence of subtropical highs and other controls that are not conducive to precipitation. The dry lands of southern Turkistan in U.S.S.R. and of the Great Basin in the United States are representative of this type. These dry climates of middle latitudes with a winter precipitation maximum are but poleward extensions of the tropical steppes with a low-sun rainfall regime.

343. *Winter.* The dominant influence in this season in the higher middle latitudes is the continental anticyclone with its settling air and diverging winds. Much clear sky and cold weather are the result. On the whole, winds are not strong at this season. Only with the passing of an occasional cyclone, or during an anticyclonic surge from higher latitudes are pressure gradients steepened so that violent winds result. This latter weather type is known on the North American plains as the *blizzard.* Low temperatures, high wind velocity, and blinding, wind-driven snow make such storms dangerous to human beings as well as to livestock. On the whole, however, the irregular weather element, as brought by moving cyclones and anticyclones, is not unusually well developed in these dry climates. Toward the subtropical and western margins of the dry regions, as indicated in the previous paragraph, this infrequency of winter cyclones is not so characteristic.

344. *Summer.* Summer heat tends to develop a seasonal low over the dry interiors of the continents. This "center of action" generates the inflowing winds of general monsoonal character. Because the great continental lows are the goals of the landward-moving sea winds in summer, one might, on first thought, expect them to be

regions of relatively abundant precipitation. This is unlikely, however, because the size of Asia and North America compels the inflowing air to travel great distances over heated land masses before it arrives at its goal. As a consequence it has already lost much moisture through precipitation en route, while its relative humidity has been greatly reduced through warming. Moreover, portions of both these continents are basin-like in structure, being surrounded by highland rims, so that the incoming air is further heated and dried by descent.

The warm season is characterized by strong winds, particularly during the daylight hours when convection is at a maximum. Huntington remarks on the extraordinary strength and constancy of the winds in eastern Iran during the hot months, where they have been named "The Wind of One Hundred and Twenty Days." He states: "Double-pegged tents which withstand the blast make a noise like that of a rigging of a ship in the wildest storm. The continual hum, clap, clatter, rattle, bang make mental work almost impossible." Of the Gobi in Central Asia, Younghusband writes: "The daily winds were often extremely disagreeable. It was with the greatest difficulty that we could keep our tents from being blown down, and everything used to become impregnated with the sand, which found its way everywhere, and occasionally we had to give up our march because the camels could not make any head against the violence of the wind."

MIDDLE-LATITUDE DESERTS *BWk*

345. Because of their generally lower temperature, and therefore reduced evaporation rate, the humid boundaries of the middle-latitude deserts have lower rainfalls than those of tropical deserts. This does not mean that they are necessarily more arid. In fact, the opposite is probably true, for some precipitation, no doubt, falls in middle-latitude deserts every year, so that they are not so completely rainless as are certain of their tropical counterparts. Characteristically, this subtype of the middle-latitude dry climates occupies the depressed or basin-like areas in the continental interiors. Tarim and

Climatic Data for Representative Stations in Middle-latitude Deserts (BWk)

Santa Cruz, Argentina

	J	F	M	A	M	J	J	A	S	O	N	D	Yr.	Range
Temp.	59	58	55	48	41	35	35	38	44	49	53	56	47.5	24
Precip.	0.6	0.4	0.3	0.6	0.6	0.5	0.7	0.4	0.2	0.4	0.5	0.9	6.1	

Turfan, Sinkiang, China (−56 Ft.)

	J	F	M	A	M	J	J	A	S	O	N	D	Yr.	Range
Temp.	13	27	46	66	75	85	90	85	75	56	33	18	56	77
Precip.			No. data.											

Lovelock, Nevada

	J	F	M	A	M	J	J	A	S	O	N	D	Yr.	Range
Temp.	30	36	43	50	58	66	74	72	62	51	40	31	51.2	44.7
Precip.	0.7	0.5	0.4	0.4	0.4	0.3	0.2	0.2	0.3	0.4	0.3	0.4	4.5	

Turkistan in Asia are surrounded, in part at least, by highland rims, and such is likewise the case with the principal desert area in the United States, which practically coincides with the Great Basin. As a result, these are regions of rain shadow with descending currents, so that excessive aridity is the result. A further consequence of enclosure, when combined with low elevation, is the excessively high summer temperatures, with warm-month averages in some instances even approaching those of tropical deserts. At Turfan, in the Turfan depression of Sinkiang, China, the July average is 90°, while the daily maxima for that month often rise to 110° and more, although this is an extreme case. At this same station, where 118° has been recorded, the January mean is only 13°.

Patagonia, in Argentina, does not correspond in some respects to the description given above for middle-latitude deserts. Being a narrow land mass, with cool waters offshore, temperatures are more marine than continental, summer temperatures being unusually low. Winters are likewise mild, considering the latitude. Thus Santa Cruz at 50°S. has a January (hottest month) temperature of only 59°, while July is 35°.

MIDDLE-LATITUDE STEPPES BSk

346. Middle-latitude steppes, like their counterparts, the semiarid lands of the tropics, occupy transitional, or intermediate, positions between deserts and the humid climates (Figs. 8.9, 8.10). The general characteristics of these continental steppes have already been analyzed. Because of the greater precipitation than in deserts, the steppes are somewhat better fitted for human settlement, but this, together with the unreliable nature of the rainfall, also

makes them regions of greater economic catastrophe (Fig. 8.11). A succession of humid years may tempt settlers to push the agricultural frontier toward the desert, but here also drought years are sure to follow, with consequent crop failure and ensuing disaster. Over a considerable part of the American semiarid country, in 30 to 40 per cent of the years, rainfall is less than 85 per cent of the average. During the period 1892–1930, at Minot, N.D., whose average annual precipitation is 15.7 in., there was one year with rainfall as high as 24.3 in. and another as low as 7.2.

A unique feature of the North American steppe lands east of the Rocky Mountains, from

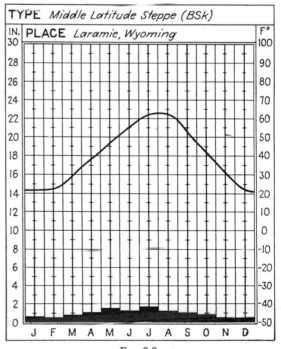

FIG. 8.9.

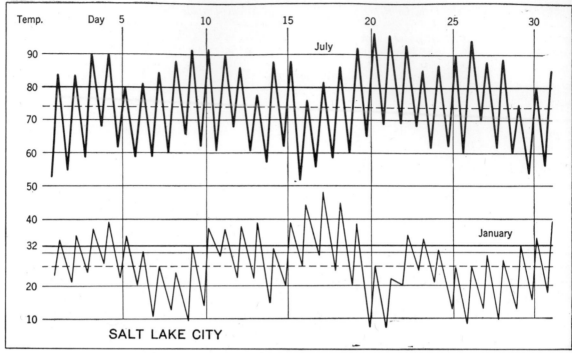

FIG. 8.10. Daily maximum and minimum temperatures for a middle-latitude steppe station (*BSk*).

Alberta to Colorado, is the frequency and strength of chinook winds. Rapid changes in temperature over short periods of time and large variations in the mean winter temperatures of different years are the result.

most widespread and universal resource, while the grazing of domesticated and semidomesticated livestock upon this sparse vegetation cover is the most characteristic and universal form of dry-land utilization (Fig 7.12).

Climatic Data for Representative Stations in Middle-latitude Steppes (Bsk)

	J	F	M	A	M	J	J	A	S	O	N	D	Yr.	Range
				Williston, North Dakota										
Temp.	6	8	22	43	53	63	69	67	56	44	27	14	39.2	62.7
Precip.	0.5	0.4	0.9	1.1	2.1	2.3	1.7	1.7	1.0	0.7	0.6	0.5	14.4	
				Ephrata, Washington										
Temp.	25	33	43	52	61	68	77	75	64	53	39	29	31.7	46.3
Precip.	0.93	0.77	0.42	0.39	0.54	0.77	0.26	0.44	0.53	0.64	1.03	0.96	7.68	
				Urga (Ulan Bator), Mongolia (3,800 Ft.)										
Temp.	−16	−4	13	34	48	58	63	59	48	30	8	−17	28	79
Precip.	0.1	0.1	0.0	0.0	0.3	1.7	2.6	2.1	0.5	0.1	0.1	0.1	7.6	

ASSOCIATED FEATURES OF THE PHYSICAL EARTH IN THE DRY CLIMATES

347. Native Vegetation. The meager and erratic precipitation in the *B* climates, together with a high evaporation rate and an associated low ground-water table, results in a relatively scant vegetation cover. In spite of its scantiness, however, it is, over the dry lands as a whole, the

348. *Deserts.* In the arid phase of *B* climates, vegetation is particularly meager. It is likewise composed of many forms that are unpalatable and inedible to most of the domestic animals, so that its grazing value is small. Considerable variations in vegetation do exist, however, even within deserts. There are large areas, although they do not predominate, which are barren wastes of moving sand dunes or loose rock fragments. These are practically devoid of perennial plants. Such regions, of course, have no grazing value whatever. The Libyan Desert, west of the Nile River, and the Great Arabian Desert are illustrations of this extreme type. But even in these sandy and rocky wastes, seeds of rapidly growing annuals may be present. These burst quickly into life after the occurrence of a rare shower, their brilliant flowers making for a transient show of color. These annuals are not drought-resistant; they simply evade the drought. Even more completely bare of all plant life are the hard, smooth, level floors of dry playas.

But, as stated previously, such wastes are the exception in deserts, for most arid lands have a fairly conspicuous cover of widely spaced, fleshy and woody shrubs, which have an appreciable, although low, grazing value. As a rule, their colors are not a bright green, and during most of the year the greater number of shrubs look perfectly dead. Individual plants are widely spaced so that much bare soil shows between them. The density of the shrub cover is the expression of the amount of water available for plant growth. The succulent plants *resist* drought by the storage of large supplies of water in their fleshy stems and leaves, while other perennials are physically equipped to *endure* the drought. In the slightly more humid parts, a meager amount of short desert bunch grasses is interspersed with the shrubs. They occur only in isolated bunches and, although dry for the greater part of the year, are relatively good, although very meager, forage. In localities whose soils are high in harmful alkali, a salt desert shrub vegetation prevails, consisting of rather rich green, fleshy-leaved plants capable of growing in moist saline soil. These areas have little value as grazing land.

349. *Steppes.* Relatively low-growing, shallow-rooted grasses predominate throughout the semiarid lands. Sometimes it is a relatively even short-grass cover, while in other parts rather widely spaced bunch grasses prevail. Scattered small thorny trees or bushes are in places interspersed with the grasses. Because of the usual prevalence of grass over shrubs, and likewise because the grass cover is more complete, steppes have far greater value as grazing lands than have the deserts. Within the United States, The Great Plains, with their characteristic cover of high-grade short grass, represent one of the most extensive and finest of the earth's semiarid natural grazing lands. Part of this region of short grasses has been brought under the plow, chiefly through dry-farming methods, but this development has taken place principally in the more humid eastern portions, and even there crop failures are frequent. Low and erratic rainfall will no doubt continue to keep the larger part of the world's steppe areas out of cultivation

FIG. 8.11. Fluctuations in the location of the boundary separating dry and humid climates, over a period of 5 years, for the region east of the Rocky Mountains. See also Fig. 6.3. (*After Kendall.*)

and in grass, which is the greatest resource of those regions.

Tropical steppes appear to provide less palatable forage than do similar semiarid regions in the middle latitudes, although there is considerable variation from region to region. On the whole, their grasses are less tall and coarse, and therefore more edible, than are those of the wetter savannas, but during the dry season the tropical steppe grasses too, are not highly palatable, so that wild game and cattle at such times rely largely on the tender fresh grasses along water courses. Where steppe grasses are finer and shorter, they provide better year-round grazing. In South Africa, the coarse-grass steppes are designated as "sour veldt," while, where finer, more palatable ones prevail, "sweet veldt" is the name. Tropical steppes supported large herds of wild game and provided good hunting until the animals were destroyed or driven out.

350. Zonal Soils. *Desert Weathering and Regolith.* The weathering of solid rock is a slower process in dry climates than in wet ones, so that the residual regolith cover is likely to be thin. This is especially true in the most arid parts where the vegetation cover is meager and regolith removal by water and wind therefore vigorous. Slow formation and relatively rapid removal both appear to be involved.

351. *Desert Soils.* In an inventory of the resource potentialities of deserts, the residual soils are of very minor importance. This results from the fact that, no matter how fertile or how poor they may be, the niggardly rainfall largely precludes their use. Oasis agriculture, which is practically the only type of crop development within deserts, characteristically utilizes young, water-transported soils of deltas, floodplains, and alluvial fans, which may have little resemblance to the genuine residual product. Gray color (with tinges of yellow, red, and brown), near absence of humus, coarse texture, and practically unleached mineral content are almost universal features of desert soils (Fig. 7.13).

The most characteristic and extensive arid land soil is a veneer of coarse, stony, pebbly debris—the well-known desert pavement. Loose shifting sand, often in the form of dunes, covers small portions of the dry lands, but this material scarcely constitutes a soil in the scientific sense of the word. It should be emphasized that, although, because of a minimum of leaching, desert soils are usually high in mineral plant foods, most of them are not objectionably alkaline. That condition is usually restricted to those sections where drainage waters temporarily concentrate or where ground water comes close to the surface.

352. *Steppe Soils.* Under semiarid, as compared with arid, conditions, residual soils are much superior. The short-grass cover, even though it is not heavy, provides a fair to good amount of humus, so that steppe soils are characteristically dark (brown, chestnut, or even black) rather than gray in color. The grasses not only provide humus, but they also tend to reduce the removal of small clay and silt particles by wind and water. Moreover, steppe lands are often the recipients of large amounts of fine dust or loess blown out of the drier and less well protected deserts. For all these reasons, typical steppe soils are not injuriously coarse and stony as are those of most deserts. In fact, the upper surface may be a loose, structureless dust mulch. Meager rainfall prevents serious leaching so that mineral plant foods are usually abundant. On the whole, soil structure is good, being roughly granular in character, so that cultivation is easy. What little is known about the mature soils of *tropical* steppes would seem to indicate that they are lower in humus and poorer in structure than their counterparts in middle latitudes.

It becomes evident that semiarid grasslands, particularly those of middle latitudes, are equipped with soils which, in physical and chemical properties, are highly productive. Yet, because of the low and variable rainfall in which they develop, and to which they largely owe their quality, they are not extensively used for crop production. It is the old story of fruitful soils and prolific climates seldom being areally coincident.

353. *Runoff and Soil Erosion.* In the *B* climates runoff is relatively greater in amount and more important in its consequences than in humid regions. The pelting rains of short duration place water on the soil faster than it can be absorbed. On all dry soils of fine texture "puddling" takes place as soon as the rain begins, again retarding penetration. The sparse vegetation cover, and, in the drier portions, the presence of soil crusts and the lack of a humus layer, all tend to aggravate the situation further. The ready runoff is responsible for the short-lived torrents which fill dry-land drainage channels after a downpour. The result is a twofold loss, for not only is the much-needed water not retained by the soil, but in addition active soil erosion becomes a genuine menace.

Throughout the world's steppe lands which consistently are being either grazed or cultivated, drought conditions are being intensified by soil erosion. As a result of overgrazing and burning, the annual return of humus to the soil is decreased, and its water retentiveness likewise. This so changes conditions for plant growth that desert shrubs and weedy plants invade the grasslands, greatly reducing their carrying capacity for grazing animals. Farmers in South Africa speak of this invasion by the desert shrub as "The Creep of the Karoo." As the vegetation cover gradually becomes thinner, and the soils less retentive of moisture, erosion becomes more serious.

354. Drainage and Landforms. *Drainage.* On the whole, there is little water to be taken care of in the dry realm, so that rivers are scarce, and the drainage pattern is relatively coarse and poorly developed. Since evaporation exceeds precipitation, permanent streams do not originate within the dry realm, although the violent convectional showers may produce temporary vigorous torrents capable of rapid corrasion. These native intermittent streams customarily evaporate and disappear on the desert floor, or flow into interior basins, forming playas, whose dry beds are exposed most of the time. In many deserts drainage tends to be interior or centripetal in character, each local depression acting as the center or focus for one or more of these withering native streams. Exotic streams, having their sources in rainier regions, often highlands, occasionally cross portions of the dry realm and

finally reach a sea, but they are greatly reduced in volume en route. Few tributaries and much-braided channels with numerous sand bars are characteristic. The floodplains of these exotic streams, whose permanent water supply makes them particularly attractive for settlement, are characteristic sites for dense agricultural populations.

355. *Desert Landforms.* Among the several realms there is no other which approaches the dry realm in the distinctiveness of its gradational landforms. The climatic stamp appears to be more indelibly impressed upon the surface features of deserts than it is elsewhere in the world.

It is to be expected that the pattern and association of landforms in the desert will differ markedly from those developed under more humid conditions. In the latter, because of the damper earth and heavier vegetation mantle, wind action is practically nil. Arid lands, on the other hand, where opposite conditions prevail, are sometimes designated as the "realm of the wind." The erosive work of this agent has two aspects, abrasion and deflation. By the latter process heavier materials, such as sand, are rolled along the surface and heaped up into dunes, while the finer dust may be carried well beyond the confines of the desert. Wind abrasion is certainly not a factor of much importance in fashioning the most striking and conspicuous landform features of deserts, although it is capable of producing certain peculiar and characteristic minor features. Deflation appears to be much more important and is a major factor in lowering the floors of desert basins.

Permanent streams in abundance, occupying a most intricate and dense network of channels, are the dominant gradational agent in most humid regions. In arid lands, on the other hand, rivers are relatively abnormal features, sporadic in distribution, possessed of few tributaries, temporary in flow, but nevertheless vigorous in action. Odd as it may seem, it is these sporadic desert torrents which are responsible for the larger and more conspicuous gradational features in arid lands. The protective and anchoring effects of a complete vegetation cover are absent, so that the heavy downpours result in rapid runoff which, on the bare surface, quickly accumulates into small drainage channels. The short-lived desert torrents are capable of extraordinarily rapid corrosion and removal, so that they quickly scar a land surface with deeply incised drainage channels. Rarely do these debris-laden streams reach the sea, but instead they deposit their loads in the form of conspicuous fans at the base of the slopes, or spread it out on the desert floor. In humid regions permanent streams carry the rock debris to the sea, but in deserts only the winds and an occasional exotic stream are able actually to *remove* materials from the area.

Processes of desert erosion are highly selective in their action upon rocks. They search out the weak strata and quickly remove them, while more resistant ones stand out in harsh outline with angular profiles. On slopes the disintegrated rock is quickly removed by wind and slope wash, so that the softening effect of a deep regolith cover is absent. Moreover, the few scrubby bushes provide no effective mantle for hiding the surface forms as is done so completely by the tropical rainforest. The whole landscape has a stark and naked appearance, and all details of surface are boldly revealed. Because of the clarity with which earth structures are disclosed, deserts are the geologist's paradise. The characteristic association of desert landforms varies with earth materials, structure, and stage. In plateau regions composed of horizontal sedimentary rocks of varying resistances, flattish, tableland surfaces tend to develop on the more resistant strata. Mesas or buttes, precipitous near the top, and with their lower flanks buried in rock fragments broken from the cliff face, are characteristic. Valleys cut by torrential native streams or by the larger exotic ones often are canyon-like in cross-sectional profile. Steep-walled gorges, character-istic of plateau deserts, are genuinely severe obstacles to communication.

Other desert lands have surfaces composed of detached ranges of hills separated by detritus-floored basins called *bolsons*. V-shaped ravines and gorges incised by torrential streams stand out in sharp relief along the bare hill slopes. Spreading out from the mouth of each ravine and encroaching upon the bolson are conspicuous fans, a number of them often joining to form a piedmont alluvial belt. In the lower central part of the basin a temporary shallow lake may accumulate after a heavy rain, but it soon evaporates, leaving behind the perfectly flat, whitish, salt-encrusted playa. It is doubtful whether any other topographic features of the earth's surface equals the playa in flatness. It is so level that a sheet of water 1 ft. deep may completely cover a plain 5 miles in diameter.

356. *Steppe Landforms.* Being transitional between humid and arid lands in rainfall and vegetation characteristics, the climatically induced gradational landform features are transitional as well. Although native permanent streams are still lacking, in spite of the heavier precipitation, the intermittent ones are somewhat more numerous. The more complete protective cover of grasses, however, permits of less rapid soil removal, so that the regolith cover is characteristically deeper. Rounded contour of elevated landform features is consequently more obvious than it is in the deserts, but there is progressively increasing angularity as the rainfall diminishes. Of further importance in increasing the depth of mantling regolith in many steppe lands is the loessial material swept in from the adjacent deserts and anchored by the grasses. This is more particularly true of steppes that lie on the leeward sides of deserts. Many arid land features, such as gorgelike valleys, large alluvial fans, and playas, are present likewise in some semiarid country.

CHAPTER 9: *The Humid Mesothermal[1] Climates (C)*

357. General Character and Type Locations. Lacking the constant heat of the tropics, and the constant cold of the polar caps, middle-latitude climates are characterized by a very definite seasonal rhythm in temperature conditions, the amplitude of the ranges reaching a maximum for the earth in the north intermediate zone. Thus temperature becomes coequal with rainfall in determining the various types of middle-latitude climates. In the tropics seasons are distinguished as wet and dry since seasonal temperature contrasts are small; in the middle latitudes they are called winter and summer, and the dormant season for plant growth usually is one of low temperatures rather than drought.

In the intermediate zones the changeableness of the weather is a striking characteristic. This results from the fact that the middle latitudes are the realm of conflict between contrasting air masses expelled from polar and tropical source regions. As a consequence fronts and cyclonic storms with their associated weather changes are numerous. The science of weather forecasting is best developed and most useful in the intermediate zones where irregular and nonperiodic weather changes are the rule.

Within the humid middle latitudes (excluding the B climates) two large groups of climate are recognized: the less severe mesothermal group (C) and the more severe microthermal group (D). Although snow falls in both groups, the total snowfall is much less in C, and it does not remain on the ground for a very appreciable length of time. The heavier snowfall in the D group, because of the colder winters, forms a

[1] Meso-, from the Greek word *mesos*, middle. Mesothermal, therefore, refers to "middle," or moderate, temperatures.

durable snow cover for a month or longer during winter. Köppen has selected the −3°C., or 26.6°F., isotherm for the coldest month as defining the approximate southern limit of a durable winter snow cover and as the boundary between the C and D groups. In the present classification the 0°C., or 32°F., cold-month isotherm is substituted. The mesothermal group of climates is thus bounded by the D group on its poleward and interior sides. Toward the equator C makes contact with B climates on the western side of a continent and with A climates on the eastern side. The A/C boundary it will be recalled is the 18°C., or 64.4°F., isotherm for the coolest month.

Since winter temperatures in the mesothermal group are relatively mild, C climates are found only in those type locations which preclude severe and long-continued low winter temperatures and hence a prevalent snow cover. They are, therefore, restricted to either (a) the equatorward parts of the intermediate-zone continents where latitude prevents severe winter weather or (b) to marine locations, usually on the windward or western sides of continents, farther poleward (Figs. 6.4, 9.1).

Within the mesothermal group three distinct climatic types are recognized. Two of these are subtropical types and are located in the lower middle latitudes closest to the equator. One of these, Cs, or *dry-summer subtropical*, is distinguished because of its unique seasonal rainfall consisting of dry summers and humid winters. It is subhumid in character. The other subtropical type, *humid subtropical (Ca)*, is not only wetter than Cs but it has no dry season, although there is usually some accent upon summer. The third type, *marine climate (Cb)*, has a cool sum-

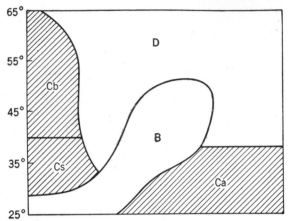

FIG. 9.1. Type locations of the three mesothermal (*C*) climates.

mer, and rainfall is distributed throughout the year. It is the one mesothermal type which extends into the higher middle latitudes, being found as far poleward as 60° or more, but characteristically only on the windward or western sides of the middle-latitude continents (Fig. 9.1).

Cs, Dry-summer Subtropical (Mediterranean) Climate

358. General Features. In its simplest form this climate is characterized by three principal features: (*a*) a concentration of the modest amount of precipitation in the winter season, summers being nearly or completely dry; (*b*) warm to hot summers and unusually mild winters; and (*c*) a high percentage of the possible sunshine for the year and especially in summer. Quite deservedly this climate, with its bright, sunny weather, blue skies, few rainy days, and mild winters, and its usual association with abundant flowers and fruit, has acquired a glamorous reputation. The *Cs* type is strongly marked in its climatic characteristics, these being duplicated with notable similarity in the five regions where it occurs, *viz.*, the borderlands of the Mediterranean Sea, central and coastal southern California, central Chile, the southern tip of South Africa, and parts of southern Australia. According to Köppen, *Cs* is characteristic of only 1.7 per cent of the earth's land area; yet in spite of its limited extent it is one of the

most distinctive and best-known types. It is because *Cs* is so extensively developed within the Mediterranean Basin that the climatic type very commonly bears the name of that region.

359. Type Location. *Cs* climate characteristically is located on the tropical margins of the middle latitudes (30 to 40°), along the western sides of continents. Lying thus on the poleward slopes of the subtropical high-pressure cells it is intermediate in location between the dry subsiding air masses of the horse latitudes on the one hand and the rain-bringing fronts and cyclones of the westerlies on the other. Encroached upon by each of these systems during the course of a year as a result of the north-south shifting of wind belts, the Mediterranean latitudes are at one season joined climatically to the dry tropics and at the opposite season to the humid middle latitudes. Tropical constancy therefore characterizes them in summer, and middle-latitude changeability in winter. Emphatically, this is a transition type between the low-latitude steppes and deserts lying equatorward, and marine (*Cb*) and microthermal (*D*) climates farther poleward (Fig. 9.1).

As previously stated, *Cs* climate is usually confined to the western sides of continents, roughly between latitudes 30 and 40° (Fig. 6.4, Plate I). In both central Chile and California, mountains terminate the type abruptly on the land side, steppe and desert prevailing interior from the mountains. In South Africa and southwestern Australia, the farthest poleward extent of these continents carries them barely to Mediterranean latitudes, so that the dry-summer subtropical climates occupy southern and southwestern extremities rather than distinctly west-coast locations. Only in the region of the Mediterranean Basin, which is an important cool-season convergence zone and a route of winter cyclones, does this type of climate extend far inland, perhaps for 2,500 miles or more. It is the relative warmth of the Mediterranean Sea in winter, and the resulting low-pressure trough coincident with it, that makes the Mediterranean Basin a region of air-mass convergence with a resulting development of fronts and cyclones (Fig. 9.8). Interiors and eastern margins of continents, with their tendencies toward monsoon wind systems, and summer maxima of rainfall, are opposed to the development of *Cs* climates, more especially their characteristic rainfall regime. It will bear repeating, also, that the eastern sides of subtropical continents (30 to 40°), while like the western sides in being under the influence of a subtropical anticyclone in summer, are affected by the unstable air of the *western* parts of the cell, and hence summer rainfall is likely to be abundant.

TEMPERATURE

360. Subtropical in Character. Both because of its latitudinal location and because of its characteristic position on the continents, *Cs* climate is assured of a temperature regime in which cold weather is largely absent (Figs. 9.2, 9.3). Usually the winter months have average temperatures of between 40 and 50°, and the summer months between 70 and 80°, so that mean annual ranges of 20 to 30°+ are common. These are relatively small for the middle lati-

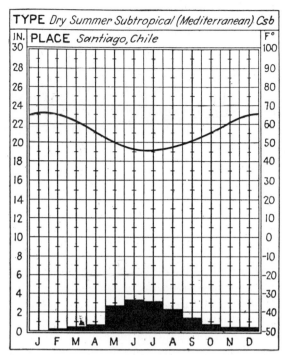

FIG. 9.3. A Southern Hemisphere dry subtropical station with cool summer (*Csb*).

tudes but are larger than those of most tropical climates, except possibly the low-latitude steppes and deserts.

361. Marine Locations (*Csb*).[1] Based upon the degree of summer heat, which in turn is a function of location, two subdivisions of Mediterranean climate are recognized, *Csa* and *Csb*. *Csa*, with warm or hot summers, is characteristically located back from the coast and farther inland than the cool-summer subtype, *Csb*, which fronts upon cool coastal waters. Coastal southern California, Mediterranean Chile and South Africa, the Atlantic Coast portions of the European–North African *Cs*, the more southerly and coastal parts of Mediterranean Australia, and certain subtropical highland areas in the Middle East are the most noteworthy examples of the regions with *Csb* climate. Littoral locations are likely to have somewhat modified

[1] In the Köppen symbols *Csb* and *Csa*, letter *b* indicates cool summers with the temperature of the warmest month under 22°C., or 71.6°F., but with at least 4 months over 10°C., or 50°F. The letter *a* indicates hot summers with the temperature of the warmest month over 22°C., or 71.6°F.

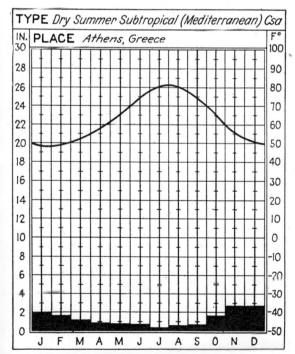

FIG. 9.2. A dry subtropical station with hot summer (*Csa*).

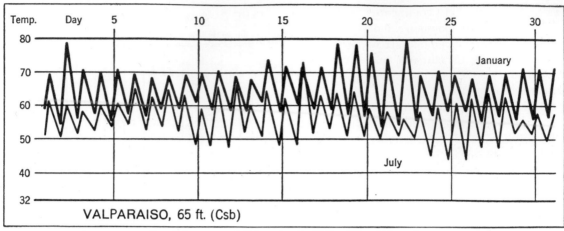

FIG. 9.4. A coastal *Csb* station in Chile. (*After Jefferson.*)

Mediterranean conditions. Summers are unusually cool, owing partly to the general marine location, but this condition in many instances is accentuated by the cool ocean currents offshore (Figs. 9.3, 9.4; see data for Santa Monica, p. 296). Thus Mogador, on the Atlantic Coast of Morocco, has a hot-month temperature of only 68.5°, while San Francisco records only 59°, and Valparaiso, Chile, 66°. Fogs of marine origin are frequent, as they are along the desert coasts somewhat farther equatorward. Retarded maxima are common, so that August is often warmer then July. Winters are unusually mild, frost being practically unknown. Thus the average cool-month temperature at Valparaiso, Chile, is 55°; Perth, Australia, 55°; and San Francisco, 50°. In such marine locations the annual temperature range is uncommonly small, approximately 9° at San Francisco and 11° at Valparaiso. Daily ranges are likewise small (Fig. 9.4).

362. Interior Locations (*Csa*).[1] Interior from the coast a short distance, however, *Cs* climate has a more continental temperature regime (see data for Red Bluff, Calif., p. 296). Winters, of course, are still mild, for the latitude is distinctly subtropical, and in most regions mountains or bodies of water protect against severe importations of low temperatures from higher latitudes. Redlands, an interior station in

California, has a January temperature of 51°, which is only slightly cooler than coastal stations in similar latitudes. Summers, however, are distinctly hotter than in marine locations (July at Redlands, 77°; Santa Monica, on the coast, 66°) so that annual ranges may be 15° greater (Fig. 9.2).

The most extensive area with *Csa* climate is the borderlands of the Mediterranean Sea in southern Europe, North Africa, and western Asia.[1] The warm waters of the Mediterranean Sea do not have a marked cooling effect upon its coastal areas so that *Csb* is lacking throughout. These same warm waters act to produce a trough or center of low pressure in winter which causes the Mediterranean to be a strong convergence and frontal zone in the cooler season and the route of many eastward-moving cyclones. It is these disturbances, following the Mediterranean trough of low pressure, which carry winter rainfall deep into the interior so that *Csa* climates are spread over an extensive area. Other *Csa* areas are interior southern California and the more interior sections of Mediterranean Australia.

363. Summer Temperatures. Except along cool-water coasts summer temperatures in *Cs*

[1] For an interpretation of the Köppen symbols, see preceding footnote and Appendix A.

[1] For a comprehensive treatment of this most extensive area of *Cs* climate, see Erwin R. Biel, Climatology of the Mediterranean Area, *Miscellaneous Report* 13, Institute of Meteorology, University of Chicago, 1944; V. Conrad, The Climate of the Mediterranean Region, *Bull. Am. Meteorological Soc.* Vol. 24, pp. 127–145, April, 1943.

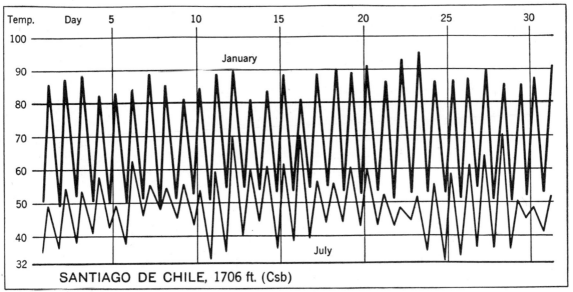

FIG. 9.5. An interior *Csb* station at an altitude of 1,700 ft. in Chile. Compare with Fig. 9.4. (*After Jefferson.*)

climates have many temperature resemblances to those of tropical steppes and deserts slightly farther equatorward. Thus, Red Bluff in the Sacramento Valley has a July temperature of 81.5°, which is distinctly tropical in nature and approximately 16° higher than the July average at Santa Monica, Calif., farther south but situated on a cool-water coast. Stations in Mediterranean Europe have average hot-month temperatures approximating 75°; those of North Africa are in the neighborhood of 80°. Summer days, quite obviously, are likely to be excessively warm (Figs. 9.5, 9.6). On the other hand, they are not sultry, for relative humidity is low. Dry

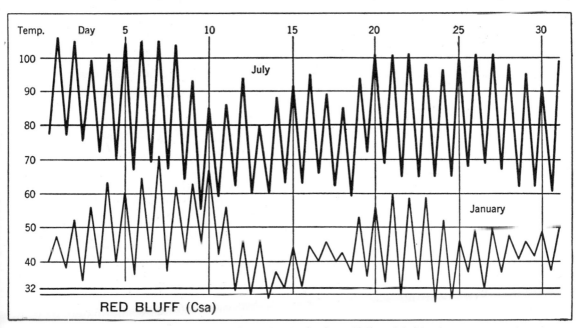

FIG. 9.6. An interior *Csa* station in the Great Valley of California.

heat like that of the steppes and deserts is the rule, and oppressive, muggy weather is almost unknown. The averages of the daily maxima of cities in the Great Valley of California are usually between 85 and 95+°. Sacramento in 1949 had 20 days in July and 13 days in August with maxima over 90°; while the respective figures for Red Bluff were 29 and 22 days. Sacramento has recorded a temperature as high as 114°, and Red Bluff 115°. The clear skies, dry atmosphere, and nearly vertical sun are ideal for rapid and strong diurnal heating in *Csa* locations.

However, these same conditions that give rise to high midday temperatures with a blazing sun are quite obviously conducive to rapid nocturnal cooling, so that there is marked contrast between day and night. This feature is typical of most dry climates. At Sacramento, in the Great Valley, hot, clear, summer days, with afternoon temperatures of 85 to 100°, are followed by nights when the thermometer sinks to between 55 and 60°. The daily range for this same city in July, 1949, was 36.6°, a figure thoroughly characteristic of deserts. The relatively cool nights, following hot, glaring days, are much appreciated by the inhabitants of Mediterranean climates (Figs. 9.5, 9.6). A light overcoat may feel distinctly comfortable when motoring on a summer night. One 24-hr. period is much like another in summer, for sun is in control.

364. Winter Temperatures. It is for the characteristically mild, bright winters, with delightful living temperatures, that Mediterranean climates are justly famed. Peoples of the higher latitudes seek them out as winter playgrounds and health resorts. Even interior locations have average cold-month temperatures 10 to 20° above freezing. Thus Sacramento has an average January temperature of 46°, Marseilles 43°, Perth, Australia, 55°, and Rome 44°. In southern California, in January, midday temperatures rise to between 55 and 65° and at night drop to 40±° (Sacramento 39° and Los Angeles 45.5°; Figs. 9.4, 9.5, 9.6).

The growing season is not quite the whole year, for frosts occasionally do occur during the three winter months. To say that the growing season is 9± months does not, however, adequately describe the situation, for while freezing temperatures are by no means unknown during midwinter months, they occur on only relatively few nights, and rarely are they severe. During a period of 41 years at Los Angeles, there were 28 in which no killing frost occurred, or, in other words, the growing season was 12 months in length. In 1947 at Red Bluff, Calif., there were 20 nights, and at Sacramento 12, when the temperature dropped below 32°. The lowest temperature ever recorded at Los Angeles is 28°, at Naples 30°, and at Sacramento 17°. Even on

Temperatures for Selected Mediterranean Cities

	Av. Annual Minimum	Absolute Minimum	Av. Annual Maximum	Absolute Maximum
Valencia	31	19	99	109
Naples	30	24	94	99
Athens	29	20	100	105

* W. J. Kendrew, "Climates of the Continents," p. 246, Oxford University Press, New York, 1927.

the very occasional nights when temperatures do slip a few degrees below freezing, the following day sees them well above 32° again. Never does the thermometer stay below the freezing point for the entire day. Such frosts as do occur are usually the result of local surface cooling, following an importation of cold polar air, the low temperatures being confined to a shallow layer of surface atmosphere and particularly to depressions in which the cool dense air has collected. For this reason such sensitive crops as citrus are characteristically planted on slopes. Occasionally fires must be lighted among the citrus trees in order to prevent serious damage from freezing. Upon first thought it may seem odd that in Mediterranean climates, where frosts are neither frequent nor severe, unusual losses should result from low temperatures. But it is this infrequency and the small degree of frost that make it so treacherous, since the mild winters tempt farmers to grow types of crops, such as out-of-season vegetables and citrus, that are particularly sensitive to cold.

365. *Weather Controls Associated with Frost.* Typical weather controls that produce occasional killing frosts in California are illustrated by Fig. 9.7, which portrays atmospheric condi-

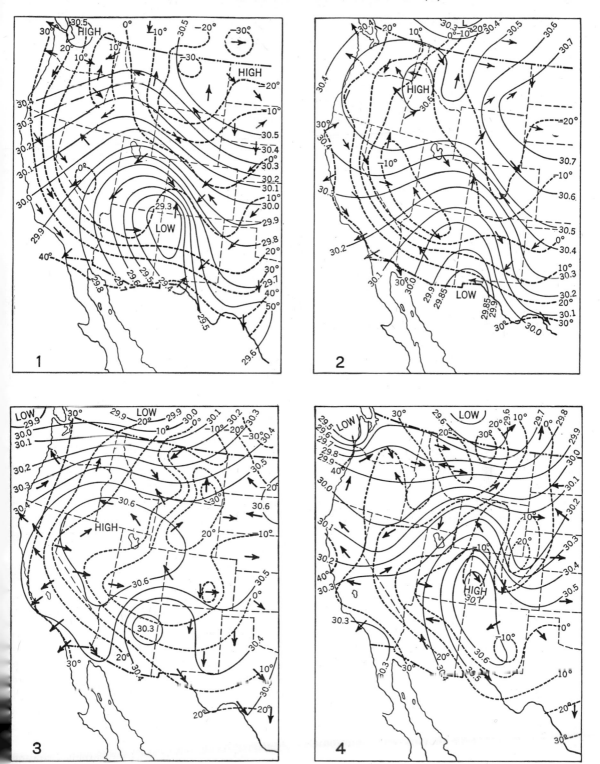

FIG. 9.7. Weather controls giving rise to killing frosts in California in January. Four successive days are shown.

tions in the American Southwest for Jan. 5 to 8 inclusive, 1913. A well-developed low traveling on a southerly track, with steep gradients on its poleward side, was followed by an inpouring of cold polar continental air associated with a large anticyclone which spread southward over the whole southwest. The clear skies and dry air of the anticyclone permitted strong nocturnal cooling in the already chilly air for several nights in succession. Citrus fruit was subjected to temperatures below freezing on four successive night periods: 4 hr. on the first night, 4 hr. on the second, 13 hr. on the third, and 9 hr. on the fourth. The temperature was generally below

fell during the hot summers when evaporation is high, semiarid conditions would be the result. But coming as it does in the cooler seasons, much less is evaporated, and more, therefore, is available for vegetation. As a result, Mediterranean climate is more correctly described as subhumid than as semiarid. The name *dry-summer subtropical* is useful, therefore, in distinguishing this climate from its wetter counterpart, the *humid subtropical* climate, located on the eastern sides of continents in similar latitudes.

Lying as they do between steppe and desert on their equatorward sides and the rainy marine climate *Cb* farther poleward, *Cs* climate shows a

Climatic Data for Representative Dry-summer Subtropical Stations (Cs)

Red Bluff, California (Csa)

	J	F	M	A	M	J	J	A	S	O	N	D	Yr.	Range
Temp.	45	50	54	59	67	75	82	80	73	64	54	46	62.3	36.3
Precip.	4.6	3.9	3.2	1.7	1.1	0.5	0.0	0.1	0.8	1.3	2.9	4.3	24.3	

Santa Monica, California (Csb)

	J	F	M	A	M	J	J	A	S	O	N	D	Yr.	Range
Temp.	53	53	55	58	60	63	66	66	65	62	58	55	59.5	13.6
Precip.	3.5	3.0	2.9	0.5	0.5	0.0	0.0	0.0	0.1	0.6	1.4	2.3	14.8	

Perth, Australia (Csa)

	J	F	M	A	M	J	J	A	S	O	N	D	Yr.	Range
Temp.	74	74	71	67	61	57	55	56	58	61	66	71	64	19
Precip.	0.3	0.5	0.7	1.6	4.9	6.9	6.5	5.7	3.3	2.1	0.8	0.6	33.9	

Mogador, French Morocco (Csb)

	J	F	M	A	M	J	J	A	S	O	N	D	Yr.	Range
Temp.	57	59	60	63	65	68	68	68	69	67	63	59	64	12
Precip.	2.2	1.5	2.2	0.7	0.6	0.1	0.0	0.0	0.2	1.3	2.4	2.0	13.2	

freezing on this occasion for a total of 30 hr.; below 25° for 12 hr., and below 20° for 2 hr. The prevalence of cyclones and anticyclones in winter causes that season's temperature regime to be somewhat less regular and periodic than that of summer when sun control is dominant (Figs. 9.5, 9.6).

PRECIPITATION

366. Amount. Rainfall is generally less than moderate, 15 to 25 in. being a fair average. More characteristic than the amount of rain, however, is its distribution over the year; for there is a pronounced maximum during the cooler months, summer being nearly, if not absolutely, dry (Fig. 9.2). This feature of dry summers and wet winters causes the climate in question to be unique among those of the world, no other *humid* type having such emphatic summer drought. If the relatively modest amount of rain typical of Mediterranean climate

gradual increase in rainfall from its equatorward to its poleward margins. This is well illustrated by three California cities, arranged in order from south to north. San Diego, farthest south, has only 9.6 in. of rain, Los Angeles 15.6 in., and San Francisco 23.3 in. Precipitation also tends to increase from the interiors toward the coasts, except where elevations may modify the rule.

367. Seasonal Distribution. Seventy-eight per cent of Los Angeles' precipitation falls during the period December to March inclusive, and less than 2 per cent during June to September inclusive. The rainfall regime, therefore, is alternately that of the deserts in summer and of the cyclonic westerlies in winter when rain is relatively abundant. This seasonal alternation of summer drought and winter rain results from a latitudinal shifting of wind and rain belts with the sun's rays, poleward in summer, bringing Mediterranean latitudes under the influence

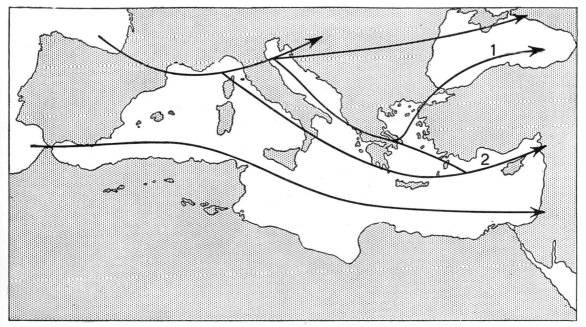

FIG. 9.8. Winter cyclone tracks in the Mediterranean Basin. (*After Kendrew.*)

of the subtropical anticyclone, and equator-ward in winter when they are brought within the zone of middle-latitude fronts and cyclones (Fig. 9.8, 9.9). Rainfall therefore is chiefly of frontal or cyclonic origin (Fig. 9.10). In Pacific North America in summer stable anticyclonic air prevails along the coast southward to beyond southernmost California (Fig. 9.11). Its basal layers having been chilled over the waters of the North Pacific and over the coastal cur-rents, this is relatively poor material out of which to obtain summer precipitation. In winter, Mediterranean California's rains are associated with an overrunning of colder air masses by mT air, or by mT or mP air being forced up over highland barriers.

368. Snowfall. A snow cover is absent at low elevations, and even snowfall is rare. Over Mediterranean central and southern California (excluding the mountains) annual snowfall averages less than 1 in., and there is none at all along the coast from San Luis Obispo southward. In all Mediterranean lowland regions snow is so rare that it is a matter for comment when it does fall. Where highlands are present in Mediter-ranean latitudes, as they commonly are, they

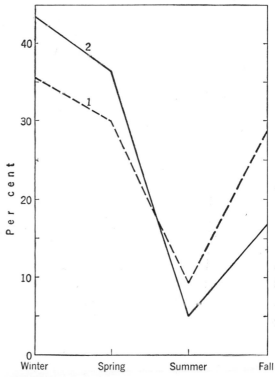

FIG. 9.9. Seasonal frequency (per cent) of cyclones on tracks 1 and 2 in the Mediterranean Basin as shown in Fig. 9.8. (*After Conrad.*)

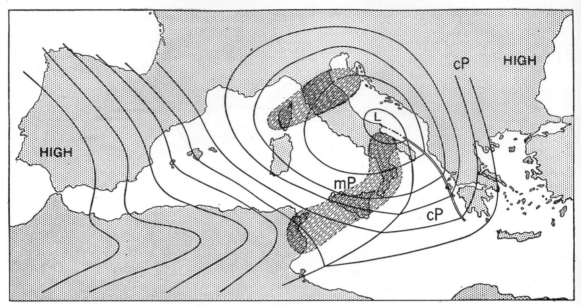

FIG. 9.10. A winter cyclone in the Mediterranean Basin producing widespread cloud and precipitation. Areas with precipitation are shaded. The precipitation of the *Cs* climates is predominantly from cyclonic storms.

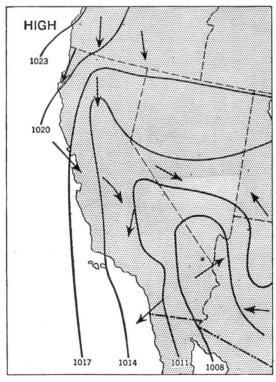

FIG. 9.11. The dry summer months of *Cs* climates are associated with strong subsidence in the stable eastern parts of the subtropical anticyclone.

usually have an abundance of snow. Not only is the total precipitation increased over that in the lowlands, but, because of the lower temperatures, much of it falls as snow. Because of the decreased temperatures these highlands are probably more commonly *Ds* than *Cs*. Some of the heaviest snowfall anywhere in the United States is on the windward western slopes of the Sierra Nevada mountains of California at elevations of 7,000 to 8,000 ft. At Summit, Calif. (7,017 ft.), the average annual snowfall is in excess of 400 in., while 697 in. or more than 60 ft. have been recorded in a single season. Tamarack, Calif. (about 8,000 ft.), has more than 500 in. of snowfall annually, and 884 in. have been recorded in a single year. Snow falls in the Atlas region of North Africa from November to April and in protected places lasts well into the summer. In south and middle Greece at elevations of 2,000 to 2,500 ft., there is relatively abundant snowfall that remains on the ground for several weeks. Heavy snowfall is also characteristic of the highlands of northern Iran and Afghanistan. This snowfall of Mediterranean highlands provides an invaluable source of water for irrigation in the adjacent lowlands.

369. Origin of the Precipitation. Precipitation over lowlands is largely of the frontal type associated with cyclonic storms. Since these climates, even in winter, lie along the equatorward margins of the westerlies and the principal cyclonic storm tracks, it is not to be expected that precipitation will be excessive. Most of the storms pass well to poleward, so that Mediterranean latitudes may be some distance from their centers, but even so, cloudy weather and showers may extend as far south as Los Angeles and beyond. These are the usual conditions. The greater the distance of a region from the storm center the less influence does the low have upon weather conditions. Perhaps less than one-tenth of the storms that cross the northern Pacific Coast region have any effect upon the weather of San Diego in extreme southern California. Occasionally a cyclone enters the country from the southwest, or one of the northern storms moves southward so that its center approaches close to Mediterranean latitudes, and under these conditions general rains may occur throughout the region.

370. Winter Rainfall and Cloudiness. But although winter is the rainy season, it is by no means dismal and gloomy as are the west-coast regions farther poleward at that season. Since Mediterranean latitudes usually are on the equatorward sides of the storm centers, and far removed from most of them, they experience a less persistent cloud cover, and sunshine is abundant even in winter. To be sure, winters are considerably cloudier than summers, but still they are bright and sunny. In interior Mediterranean California midsummer months have over 90 per cent of the possible sunshine, but in winter this is reduced to 50 per cent or less, although farther south in the vicinity of Los Angeles it reaches 60 to 70+ per cent. Dull, gray days with persistent, long-continued rain are by no means rare, but showery conditions with a broken sky are more common. After the rain the sun seems to shine more brilliantly than ever in the washed and dust-free atmosphere. These winter showers often are fairly heavy, more so than in regions farther poleward which lie nearer the storm centers. At Red Bluff there are 11 rainy days

in December, 12 in January, and 10 in both February and March. On the average, rain falls on only 7 days in the San Bernardino–Los Angeles region in January, the rainiest month. Bellingham, Wash., and Los Angeles, Calif., have almost identical amounts of January precipitation (3.4 and 3.3 in., respectively); yet it falls on 17 days at Bellingham and on only 7 at Los Angeles. In other words, precipitation falls harder but less frequently, and with a less persistent cloud cover, in the Mediterranean latitudes. Even the rainiest months have few days when one is kept indoors because of precipitation, while at the same time the relatively abundant sunshine, in conjunction with the mild temperatures, makes these regions ideal winter resorts and playgrounds.

371. Summer Drought and Sunshine. Summers in the dry-summer subtropics are periods of brilliant sunshine, extremely meager precipitation, nearly cloudless skies, and desert-like humidity except along the coast. Thus Sacramento has no rain at all in July and August, and in those months the percentage of the possible sunshine received is 95 and 96, respectively. Afternoon relative humidity is in the neighborhood of only 30 to 40 per cent. Los Angeles has, on the average, only one rainy day during the three summer months; San Bernardino has two; and Red Bluff three. The low rainfall, dry heat, abundant sunshine, and excessive evaporation, characteristic of interior Mediterranean summers, are ideal for out-of-doors drying of fruits on a large scale. In spite of the summer heat, thunderstorms are rare, except possibly in the mountains or hills, two to four a year being the usual number in southern California. The dry, settling air of these regions in summer is scarcely conducive to the formation of cumulus clouds.

Coastal regions, especially if paralleled by cool ocean currents that are kept exceptionally cool by upwelling, are characterized by high relative humidity and much fog. Rarely does it remain foggy over the coastlands for the entire day, the mists usually being burned off by the ascending sun after 9 or 10 A.M. Nights, however, may be damp and unpleasant. The coast of California is one of the foggiest areas in the United States, parts of the littoral having 40 days per year with dense fog. The coastal redwood forests of central and northern California derive a portion of their necessary summer moisture from the prevalent fogs, while summer crops of beans and certain other vegetables on the coastal terraces of southern California are also made possible by moisture from this same source. Summer fogs are frequent also along the Atlantic Coast of Morocco, Cape Spartel having on the average 28 days with fog in summer. These coastal sections with their cool, humid, and less sunny summers are really a subtype of general *Cs* climate.

372. Dependability of Precipitation. Like most subhumid climates, this one suffers from a rainfall that is none too reliable, although it fluctuates less than a summer-maximum regime having the same amount (Fig. 8.2). At San Bernardino, Calif., where the annual rainfall averages 16 in., during a 48-year period it has been as low as 5.5 and as high as 37. In 5 of the 48 years it has been below 10 in. At Santiago, Chile, rainfall is below normal in 7 out of 10 years, a few excessively wet years making up the deficiency. The somewhat precarious, as well as subhumid, character of the precipitation compels a relatively great dependence upon irrigation.

SEASONAL WEATHER

373. Summer. Daily weather is less fickle in the subtropical climates than it is farther poleward, where the conflict of air masses and the development of fronts and cyclones is more characteristic. Because the subtropical climates border the low latitudes, where sun control and diurnal regularity of weather prevail, they possess many of the tropic's weather characteristics. This is particularly true at the time of high sun, or summer, when they are essentially a part of the low latitudes. Thus a typical summer day in the *Cs* type is almost a replica of one in a low-latitude desert. Moreover, one day is much like another. Drought, brilliant sunshine, low relative humidity, high daytime temperatures, and marked nocturnal cooling are repeated day after day with only minor variations. Diurnal regularity is the keynote of weather at that season. Along seacoasts, and for a short distance inland,

the daily sea breeze is often a marked phenomenon, greatly meliorating the desert heat. Regions with *Cs* climates are famous for their well-developed sea breezes, the cool water offshore and the excessive heating of the dry land under intense insolation providing ideal conditions for strong daytime indrafts of air.

374. Autumn. In autumn, winds become less regular and uniform. As the cyclone belt creeps equatorward, following the sun's rays, an occasional low with its associated cloud cover and rain makes itself felt. The dry and dusty land begins to assume new life under the influence of increasing precipitation. Temperatures are still relatively high, and this, together with the increased humidity, gives rise to some oppressive and sultry days. As sun control loses something of its summer dominance, daily weather becomes more uncertain, and "spells of weather" become more frequent. On the front of an advancing cyclone, importations from the tropical desert may cause a temporary reestablishment of desiccating summer heat, to be followed by importations of cooler air from higher latitudes with the passing of the storm center.

375. Winter. Winter witnesses an increase in the frequency and strength of cyclones, and it is in that season that irregular, nonperiodic weather changes are most marked. Rainy days, brought by lows the centers of which are often well poleward from Mediterranean latitudes, are sandwiched between delightfully sunny ones, in which the days are comfortably mild, even though the nights may be chilly with occasional frosts. The relatively abundant rainfall of this period, together with the mild temperatures, leads to a greenness of winter landscape uncommon throughout most of the middle latitudes where winter is a dormant season.

376. Spring. Spring is a delightful season of the Mediterranean year: fresh and yet warm. On the whole it is cooler than autumn. This is the harvest period for many grains. Passing cyclones gradually become fewer as summer approaches, but nonperiodic weather changes are still significant. Importations of hot, parching air (in the Mediterranean Basin called *sirocco*, and in California *Santa Ana*), from the already superheated low-latitude deserts, precede the cyclonic centers. These sirocco winds, with temperatures of $100 \pm °$, relative humidities of 10 to 20 per cent, and blowing for a day or two without halting, may do serious damage to vegetation. Fine, choking dust, at times almost obscuring the sun, accompanies the temperature importation. Following the storm center, the hot sirocco winds are replaced by chilly importations from higher latitudes, these northerly winds going by the name of *mistral* in southern France and *bora* in the eastern Adriatic. Such cyclonic winds are particularly well marked in lands bordering the Mediterranean Sea, where traveling lows are relatively numerous, and where an extraordinarily large and hot desert lies to the south and cold lands behind the bordering highlands to the north. The cool-season temperature gradients along the northern margins of the Mediterranean Basin are extraordinarily steep.

ASSOCIATED FEATURES OF THE PHYSICAL EARTH IN *Cs*, DRY-SUMMER SUBTROPICAL CLIMATE

377. Native Vegetation. Mediterranean woodland is predominantly a mixed forest of low, or even stunted, trees and woody shrubs. Tall trees are rare. Where climatic and soil conditions are most favorable, the virgin forest is composed of low, widely spaced trees with massive trunks and gnarled branches. The appearance is not unlike that of a thinly stocked young orchard. Between the trees the ground is completely or partially covered by a pale, dusty, bush vegetation, which very much resembles the soil in color. From a distance, therefore, it may appear as though the ground were almost bare of small plants. In all of them woody parts are more prominent than foliage. As a protection against evaporation the tree trunks are encased in a thick, deeply fissured bark, this feature being perfectly exemplified by the cork oak. Leaves, too, which are small, stiff, thick, and leathery, with hard, shiny surfaces, are designed to prevent rapid losses of water.[1] The olive tree

[1] It is this leaf characteristic which has given the Mediterranean woodland the name *sclerophyll*.

with its massive trunk, gnarled branches, thick fissured bark, and small, stiff, leathery leaves is very representative of Mediterranean sclerophyll woodland in regions of hot (*Csa*) summers.

Even more common than the woodland composed of low trees and shrubs described above is a vegetation mantle consisting principally of shrubs and bushes in which there may be some stunted trees. This bush thicket is known as *chaparral* in California and *maqui* in lands bordering the Mediterranean Basin. In places the woody shrubs form a thick and relatively tall cover; in others it is short and sparse. The species that compose the chaparral are not identical in the several Mediterranean regions; yet the general appearance is much the same in all. In the California chaparral, highland live oak, scrub oak, sumac, and wild lilac are among the most common species. Chaparral in some regions may represent the original vegetation cover. In other sections it is the underwood remaining after the low trees of the original woodland have been destroyed. The chief economic importance of chaparral usually lies in its watershed protection.

Because in the *Cs* climates the period of maximum heat and maximum rainfall do not coincide, grass, which has only surficial roots, is not well suited to this climatic environment. It is not absent, however, but frequently exists in the form of scattered patches or outliers of the adjacent steppes. In parts sparse grasses may form the cover between the stunted trees and bushes. Among the large subcontinental regions with Mediterranean climate, grasses are most important in California and parts of southern Australia. In California much of the floor of the Great Central Valley was originally covered with a desert bunch grass of rather high grazing quality but of low carrying capacity.

378. Zonal Soils. There appears to be no single dominant mature soil type characteristic of the Mediterranean realm. This probably results from the unusual variety of surface configuration, geological formations, and vegetation conditions which prevail there. Structural or erosional plains are of rare occurrence, so that there are few flattish areas of hard rock where mature residual soils could develop.

Because of the widespread occurrence of hill land throughout the realm, immature residual soils cover extensive areas. Such soils are likely to be thin, coarse, and somewhat droughty in nature. In the widespread regions of hard limestones bordering the Mediterranean Sea, where rocky hills are conspicuous, there has developed a strikingly red soil known as *terra rossa*. Terra rossa soils, while friable and permeable to water, are of only modest fertility. Where slopes are sufficiently gentle so that mature soils can develop, they usually show resemblances to the gray-brown podzolic and to the subtropical red and yellow types. The percentage of mineral plant foods is low to moderate in amount, and the humus content likewise. Considerable parts of the residual-soil slope lands are uncultivated, being either wasteland or covered with a shrub vegetation providing poor forage for livestock.

Most emphatically the fresh, young, alluvial soils are the attractive sites for cultivation throughout the Mediterranean realm. Plains are largely aggradational in origin, being collections of alluvium in tectonic basins or eroded valleys in the midst of hill land, or delta fans between spurs of hills along the coast. Soils and surface configuration combine, therefore, to make floodplains, alluvial fans, and deltas the most attractive agricultural locations. Not only do such sites provide the most fertile soils and moderate slopes, but, since they owe their origin to running water, they also are the most likely locations for possible development of irrigation. Even where streams are not permanent, irrigation water often can be obtained from subterranean supplies contained in the unconsolidated and porous alluvial materials.

Ca (f and w), Humid Subtropical Climate

379. Three principal differences distinguish the humid subtropical (*Caf*) from the dry-summer subtropical climates (*Cs*): (*a*) The former is characteristically located on the eastern rather than on the western sides of continents; (*b*) on the average it has a more abundant precipitation; and (*c*) this precipitation is either well distributed throughout the year or else concentrated in the warm season. Even where the warm-season maximum is not emphatic, summer is still humid and usually has adequate rainfall for crops. Summer drought, which is so characteristic of *Cs* climate, is completely absent in *Ca*. It is differences *b* and *c*, listed above, having to do with amount and seasonal distribution of precipitation, that permit differentiation of the humid subtropical and the dry-summer subtropical climates. The *Ca* type as used in this classification includes Köppen's *Cfa* and his *Cwa* of middle latitudes.

380. Type Location. In latitudinal position the two subtropical climates are similar, both of them being on the equatorward margins of the intermediate zones but with the wet phase extending somewhat farther equatorward. Thus while Mediterranean climates lie roughly between latitudes 30 and 40°, perhaps it is more accurate to say that the humid subtropical climates usually lie between parallel 25 and 35 or 40°. However, the emphasis needs to be placed upon the similarity of the latitudinal positions, rather than upon their contrasts (Fig. 9.1).

But while the two subtropical types, *Cs* and *Ca*, have similar latitudinal locations, they are, on the other hand, relatively dissimilar in their positions on the continents, for *Ca* is typically situated on the *eastern* side of land masses and hence to the east of the dry interiors (Fig. 9.1). Only in Eurasia are small areas of *Ca* (the Po Valley and the lower Danube Basin) found to the west of the dry central part of the continent. Of chief significance in favoring this east-side location is the less stable nature of the mT air masses in the western portion of the subtropical anticyclones which affect the subtropical eastern parts of continents in summer. Consequently while it is the *eastern* limb of an anticyclone which produces the summer drought in California, it is the *western* limb of such a cell which permits of abundant summer rainfall in southeastern United States.

In some *Ca* regions also, particularly northern India and parts of China, there is a tendency toward a monsoon wind system which carries warm, moist, unstable mT air deep into the interior in summer. Such a monsoon tendency which causes a prevalence of cool, dry land air in winter, and of warm, moist mT air in summer, favors a seasonal rainfall regime which is the very antithesis of that which characterizes Cs climate. Thus eastern and southern Asia which experiences relatively well-developed monsoons has the only Ca regions where the third letter of the climatic symbol is w (winter dry) instead of f (no dry season). On Plate I it may be noted that northern India and parts of southern China have the symbol Caw, while all other humid subtropical areas are Caf.

Comparison of Rainfall Regimes at Subtropical Stations on the Eastern and Western Sides of Continents

Stations	Lat.	Rainfall (in inches)		
		Winter half year	Summer half year	Annual
San Luis Obispo (*Cs*)	35°N.	18.7	2.7	21.4
Hatteras (*Ca*)	35°N.	26.3	28.7	55.0
Mogador (*Cs*)	32°N.	10.6	2.6	13.2
Chungking (*Ca*)	30°N.	10.4	31.5	41.9
Perth (*Cs*)	32°S.	28.9	5.0	33.9
Sydney (*Ca*)	34°S.	26.2	21.7	47.9
Valparaiso (*Cs*)	33°S.	18.3	1.4	19.7
Rosario (*Ca*)	33°S.	10.5	24.4	34.9

Since warm ocean currents ordinarily parallel the subtropical *eastern* coasts, while cool waters are more common along *western* littorals in similar latitudes, this provides an additional reason why a warm-summer type such as Ca favors an east, rather than a west, coast location.

Lying as they do on the equatorward margins of the middle latitudes, and just beyond the poleward margins of the tropics, the humid subtropical, like the dry-summer subtropical, climate is a transitional type. But here the similarity in location ends; for while Cs (Mediterranean) climate is characteristically bordered by low-latitude steppe and desert on its equatorward side, humid subtropical climate is terminated on that frontier by humid tropical types, Aw and Af. This contrast has a marked effect upon the kinds of temperature importations from the low latitudes in the two types, parching dry heat accompanied by dust in the one case, and humid sultry heat in the other. On their poleward sides as well they make contact with contrasting types; for while Cs generally grades into the mild rainy marine climate (Cb), humid subtropical not infrequently makes contact with severe continental climate (Da). This is particularly true of North America and Asia where there are extensive land masses in the higher middle latitudes. On their landward, or western, margins humid subtropical climates gradually grade into dry types characteristic of the continental interiors (Figs. 6.4, 9.1).

TEMPERATURE

381. Temperatures Like Those of Csa. In temperature characteristics the humid subtropics are relatively similar to Csa climate (Figs. 9.12, 9.13). This similarity is not un-

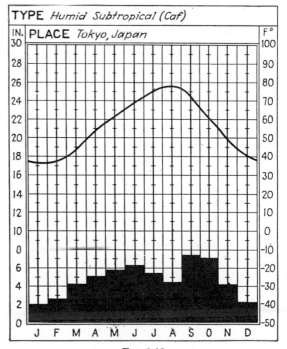

FIG. 9.12.

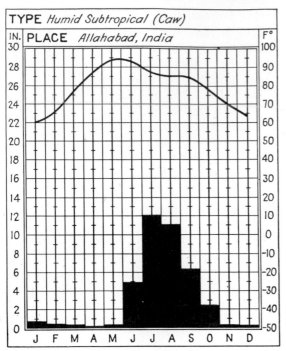

TYPE *Humid Subtropical (Caw)*

PLACE *Allahabad, India*

FIG. 9.13. Where rainfall is highly concentrated in mid-summer, as it is in much of the *Ca* region of northern India, it may have the effect of somewhat reducing the temperature in July and August. As a consequence the maximum temperature is experienced in late spring before the summer solstice.

expected, since the two types roughly correspond in their latitudinal locations. Because warm, instead of cool, ocean currents wash the subtropical eastern coasts of continents, there can be no distinctly cool littorals such as are characteristic of the *Csb* coasts. Cool, foggy stations, like San Francisco or Mogador, are absent.

382. Summer. Average hot-month temperatures of 75 to 80° are characteristic. According to the definition of *a*, the temperature for the warmest month must be above 71.6°. Along the immediate coasts, especially of the smaller Southern Hemisphere land masses, they are as often below as above 75°. But everywhere summers are distinctly warm to hot, and this is particularly true of North America and Asia. Thus July temperatures average 82° at Charleston, S.C.; 82° at Montgomery, Ala.; and 81° at Shanghai, China; while those of January, normally the warmest month in the Southern Hemisphere, average 77° at Brisbane, Australia;

77° at Durban, South Africa; and 74° at Buenos Aires, Argentina. Not only is the air temperature high, but absolute and relative humidity are likewise. In the American South Atlantic and Gulf States, where *mT* air almost completely dominates in summer, the average July relative humidity (8 P.M. reading) is 70 to 80 per cent. The high humidity in conjunction with the high temperatures produces a sultry, oppressive condition with low cooling power. This is in contrast to the dry summer heat of *Csa* climate. Sensible temperatures, therefore, are commonly higher in the humid- than in the dry-summer subtropics, even when the thermometer registers the same. Summer heat in the American Gulf States closely resembles that of the tropical *Af* and *Aw* climates. At New Orleans during June, July, and August the average temperatures are 2 to 3° higher than they are at Belém in the Amazon Valley, while the amount of rainfall is nearly the same. In the humid subtropics of Japan and China whites and wealthy natives often quit their usual places of residence during summer and go to high-altitude stations as they do in the genuine tropics. The average of the daily maxima in July throughout most of the American cotton belt is between 90 and 100°, while the highest temperatures ever observed are usually between 100 and 110° (Figs. 9.14, 19.15, 9.16). Thus Montgomery, Ala., has experienced a temperature of 106° in July and 107° in August; and Savannah, Ga., 105° in July.

383. Night Temperatures. Not only are the days hot and sultry, but the nights are oppressive as well, the humid atmosphere with more cloud preventing the same rapid loss of heat that takes place in the drier air and clearer skies of *Csa* climates. The sultry nights are an additional item of resemblance to the wet tropics. The slower night cooling results in relatively small diurnal ranges, usually only one-half to two-thirds as great as those in the dry-summer subtropics. As an illustration: The averages of the July maxima for Sacramento and Montgomery are 89 and 91°, respectively, their average July minima 58 and 72°, giving a diurnal range of 31° for Sacramento and 19° for Montgomery,

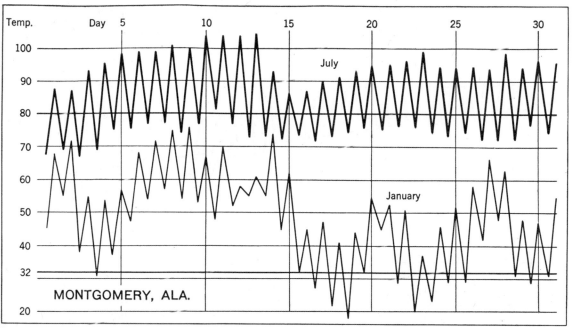

FIG. 9.14. A humid subtropical (*Ca*) station in the American cotton belt. Note the strong periodic, or solar, control in summer. In winter, on the other hand, air-mass or storm control is more conspicuous.

the difference being due chiefly to the cooler nights at the California city (Figs. 9.14, 9.15, 9.16, 9.6). Since the sun is very much in control of the daily weather, one day in summer is relatively like another in the humid subtropics, although there are to be sure some nonperiodic variations (Fig. 9.14).

384. Winter. Winters are, of course, rela-

tively mild in subtropical latitudes, cool-month temperatures usually averaging between 40 and 55°. Thus Montgomery, Ala., has an average cool-month temperature of 49°; Shanghai, China, 38°; Buenos Aires, Argentina, 50°; and Sydney, Australia, 52°. Southeastern United States receives warm, humid, tropical air from the Gulf of Mexico and the tropical Atlantic even

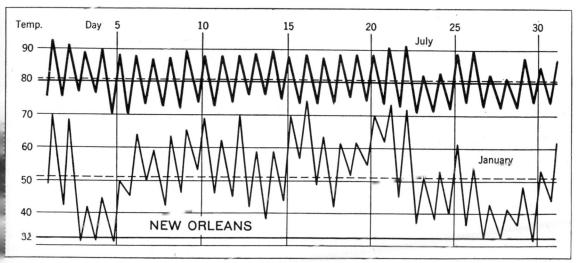

FIG. 9.15. Winter is characterized by more nonperiodic temperature variations than summer.

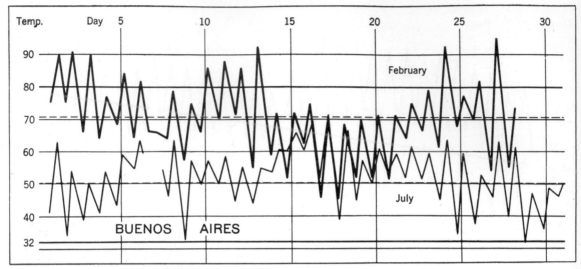

FIG. 9.16. A humid subtropical station in Argentina. (*After Jefferson.*)

in winter, but the normal seaward pressure gradient of that season makes progress inland of mT air a more sporadic thing than in summer. Usually the winter indrafts of tropical air are associated with passing cyclones.

Annual ranges of temperature in the Ca climates are usually small, although there is considerable variation, depending upon the size of the continent and the latitudinal location of the particular station. At Buenos Aires the annual range is only 23° and Sydney, 19°, but at Montgomery it is 33°, and it is 43° at Shanghai. Apparently the larger the land mass and the better the development of monsoon winds, the colder are the winters and the larger the annual ranges. In eastern Asia the strong monsoonal outpouring of cold cP air in winter from the large continent to the rear results in the lowest *average* winter temperatures in those latitudes for any part of the world. Thus Mobile, Ala., and Shanghai, approximately in the same latitude, have average January temperatures of 52 and 38°, respectively. After subtropical China, southeastern United States has the lowest average winter temperatures of any of the humid subtropical regions. Here, as in eastern Asia, there is a well-developed, although less strong, winter-monsoon tendency, the prevailing winter winds being north and northwest and consequently from the cold interior and higher latitudes. In eastern United States, the more numerous and better developed moving cyclones and anticyclones, as compared with eastern and southern Asia, tend to disrupt the monsoonal winds. The humid subtropical regions of the Southern Hemisphere, which because of the size or the latitudinal positions of their respective land masses have no severe continental climates on their poleward margins, receive no such invasions of severe cP air and are consequently milder.

The midday temperatures in winter are likely to be pleasantly warm, the thermometer usually rising to 55 or 60°. On winter nights temperatures of 35 to 45° are to be expected. These certainly are not low, but combined with a characteristically high humidity they are likely to produce a sensible temperature which is distinctly chilly and uncomfortable. Summer is so much the dominant season that little thought is given to the heating systems in homes, and as a result they are likely to be inefficient and ineffective. Consequently one is often more uncomfortable indoors than he is in colder regions farther poleward where adequate provision is made for winter heating.

385. *Minimum Temperatures and Frost.* It is to be expected that the growing season, or period between killing frosts, will be long. It is usually at least seven months and from that up to nearly, if not quite, the entire year. Even though freezing temperatures may be *expected* during a period of several months, they actually occur on only a relatively few nights of the winter season. As in the *Cs* climates, so too in *Cw*, the long growing season and infrequent severe frosts make them ideal regions for sensitive crops and for those requiring a long maturing period. There is scarcely any part of the humid subtropics which has not at some time or another experienced freezing temperatures, although along the tropical margins of some *Ca* regions frost is rare. In sections of the Southern Hemisphere humid subtropics, frost does not occur every winter and usually is light when it does come. Thus the average lowest winter temperature at Brisbane, Australia, is 37°, and at Sydney 39°. The lowest temperature ever recorded at Buenos Aires is 23°; at Montevideo, Uruguay, 20°; and at Brisbane, Australia, 32°.

In the humid subtropics of both the United States and China minima are considerably lower than those of the Southern Hemisphere continents, Shanghai having experienced a temperature as low as 10°, and Montgomery, Ala., −5°. New Orleans, with a normal January temperature of 55°, has the extremely low absolute minimum of 7°. One of the distinguishing features of the South Atlantic and Gulf States of the United States, a region where the *average winter temperatures* are relatively high, is the unusually *low winter minima*, even lower than those of China. Thus while southeastern China has lower *average* winter temperatures, the American humid subtropics have severer *cold spells* and consequently lower minima. Severe killing frosts are of annual occurrence, and temperatures as low as 10° have been recorded along the ocean margins of all of the Gulf States (Fig. 9.17). No other part of the world near sea level in these latitudes experiences such low winter minima. Serious damage to sensitive vegetation results from these cold spells. The occasional severe invasions of *cP* air which characterize the winter weather of the seaboard states of the American Gulf and South Atlantic can be attributed to the open nature of the North American Continent east of the Rocky Moun-

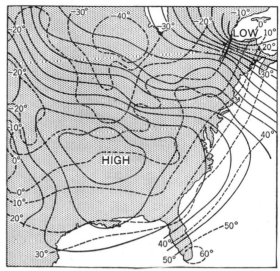

FIG. 9.17. Weather controls giving rise to killing frosts in the American humid subtropics. A well-developed anticyclone advancing from the northwest as a mass of polar continental air produced a minimum temperature of 20° at New Orleans and 8° at Memphis. The isotherm of 20° fairly well parallels the Gulf and South Atlantic Coasts. (*United States Daily Weather Map*, Feb. 9, 1933, 8 A.M., *E.S.T.*)

tains, which permits the surges of cold *cP* air to move rapidly southward into subtropical latitudes with only moderate modifications. In the Mediterranean region of California, mountain barriers tend to retard such severe invasions of cold air, so that there the absolute minima are much higher. Thus, while commercial citrus production extends north to about 38° in California, it is confined to regions south of latitude 30 or 31° in southeastern United States. In China the more hilly and mountainous surface configuration prevents such unrestricted latitudinal importations of cold *cP* air.

PRECIPITATION

386. Amount and Distribution. Rainfall is relatively abundant within the humid subtropics, but still there are considerable differences within the several regions. Probably the spread of 30 to 65 in. includes the various amounts characteristic of most of the humid subtropical regions. On the landward frontiers of this type, where it makes contact with steppe climates, rainfall reaches the lowest totals.

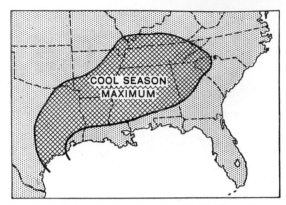

FIG. 9.18. Subtropical southeastern United States has an extensive area where there is more precipitation in the winter half year than in the summer half year.

Either precipitation is well distributed throughout the year (*Caf*), so that there is no dry season, or, in some parts, winters are distinctly dry (*Caw*) (Figs. 9.12, 9.13). Never is summer a drought season. Over the *Ca* areas as a whole summers are somewhat more rainy than winters, although usually winters are far from dry. It is particularly where monsoons are well developed, as in parts of southern China, northern India, and northeastern Australia, that winters are emphatically drier than summers. (See data for Benares, India, below.) On Plate I the symbols *Caw* are shown for these regions. In other parts *Caf* prevails. A considerable area within the *Ca* region of southeastern United States located inland from the Gulf Coast and east and west of the Mississippi has more rain-

fall in the cool season than in the warm, although this is exceptional (Fig. 9.18).

387. Warm-season Rainfall. A considerable part of the summer rainfall at low elevations originates in convectional storms, many of them accompanied by thunder and lightning. In fact, the American humid subtropics are the most thundery part of the United States, a large portion of that area having over 60 electrical storms a year, while a small part of Florida has over 90. These storms are mostly of local origin, resulting from strong surface heating of unstable *mT* air masses. The normal high temperatures and high humidity of the prevailing *mT* air in southeastern United States provide an ideal environment for vigorous development of local convection. In all the *Ca* regions warm, humid tropical air masses move in over the heated land surfaces in summer and are warmed at their bases, thereby increasing instability and promoting convectional overturning.

In addition to the convectional rain, falling from cumulus-type clouds, a considerable part is also obtained from weak cyclonic storms associated with frontal convergence zones and, in the late summer and early fall, from tropical hurricanes as well. In many respects the weak summer cyclones of the humid subtropics are like the weak tropical lows, having less definite tracks and more variable speeds than do the usual cool-season cyclones of middle latitudes. In the weak, shallow lows, rain often falls

Climatic Data for Representative Humid Subtropical Stations (Ca)

Charleston, South Carolina

	J	F	M	A	M	J	J	A	S	O	N	D	Yr.	Range
Temp.	50	52	58	65	73	79	82	81	77	68	58	51	66.1	31.4
Precip.	3.0	3.1	3.3	2.4	3.3	5.1	6.2	6.5	5.2	3.7	2.5	3.2	47.3	

Sydney, Australia

	J	F	M	A	M	J	J	A	S	O	N	D	Yr.	Range
Temp.	72	71	69	65	59	54	52	55	59	62	67	70	63	20
Precip.	3.6	4.4	4.9	5.4	5.1	4.8	5.0	3.0	2.9	2.9	2.8	2.8	27.7	

Benares, India (*Caw*)

	J	F	M	A	M	J	J	A	S	O	N	D	Yr.	Range
Temp.	60	65	77	8.7	91	89	84	83	83	78	68	60	77	31
Precip.	0.7	0.6	0.4	0.2	0.6	4.8	12.1	11.6	7.1	2.1	0.2	0.2	64.3	

Chungking, China

	J	F	M	A	M	J	J	A	S	O	N	D	Yr.	Range
Temp.	48	50	58	68	74	80	83	86	77	68	59	50	67	38
Precip.	0.7	0.9	1.3	4.0	5.3	6.7	5.3	4.4	5.8	4.6	2.0	0.9	41.9	

Memphis, Tennessee

	J	F	M	A	M	J	J	A	S	O	N	D	Yr.	Range
Temp.	41	44	53	62	70	78	81	80	74	63	52	43	62	30
Precip.	4.9	4.3	5.4	5.1	4.2	3.2	3.4	3.4	2.8	2.9	4.2	4.3	48.3	

steadily from gray, overcast skies and is general over larger areas than is true of thunderstorm precipitation.

Parts of the Asiatic *Ca* region in China and Japan are characterized by a rainfall regime which shows an early summer and a late summer maximum with a midsummer secondary minimum. The two summer maxima are probably attributable to cyclonic precipitation associated with northward advance and southward retreat of the polar front. (See rainfall data for Chungking, China, above.) The more persistent cloud cover and heavier precipitation associated with the early summer rainfall maximum tends to retard somewhat the normal advance of summer temperatures so that August with its clearer skies is the time of maximum heat.

Hurricane rainfall is largely confined to the American and Asiatic humid subtropics, contributing to the late summer and fall rainfall maximum characteristic of parts of these regions. Not only are the heavy late-summer and early-autumn hurricane rains occasionally disastrous to ripening crops and the cause of serious floods, but the accompanying violent winds may play havoc with coastwise shipping and port cities. In the Swatow typhoon of August, 1922, 40,000 Chinese are estimated to have perished, chiefly by drowning.

In spite of the plentiful summer rainfall characteristic of the humid subtropics, sunshine is relatively abundant, although much less so than is true of summer in *Csa* climates. Montgomery, Ala. receives 73 per cent of the possible sunshine in June and 62 per cent in July.

388. Cool-season Rainfall. In winter the land surface in the humid subtropics is likely to be colder than maritime air arriving from tropical source regions. As a result the poleward movement of such an air mass over the cooler land results in a chilling of the air at its base with a resulting increase in stability. As a consequence local convection resulting from surface heating, which is so prevalent in summer, is uncommon in winter. Only as the stabilized tropical maritime air masses are forced to rise over relief barriers or are involved in convergences along fronts and in cyclonic systems

does precipitation usually occur. Winter rainfall over lowlands, therefore, is chiefly frontal or cyclonic in origin. It is, as a consequence, usually accompanied by a general and persistent cloud cover extending over wide areas, from which precipitation may fall steadily during 12 to 36 hr. On the whole it is less intense, but of longer duration, than that in summer thunderstorms. Because of more numerous cyclones in winter that season is cloudier than summer. At Shanghai, China, in an average January, only 2 in. of rain falls, but there are 12 rainy days, while the 6 in. of August precipitation fall on only 11 days. Each rainy day in August, therefore, accounts for three times as much precipitation as a rainy day in January. Montgomery, Ala., which has 73 per cent of the possible sunshine in June, receives only 49 per cent in January and 44 per cent in December. Gray, overcast days with rain may be unpleasantly chilly.

Snow falls occasionally when a vigorous winter cyclone swings well equatorward, but it rarely stays on the ground for more than a few days. In the coastal parts of the American Gulf States snow does not fall so frequently as one day a year, and the snow cover is likewise of less than one day's duration. On the northern margins, however, 5 to 15 days are snowy, and the ground may be covered for an equally long period.

SEASONAL WEATHER

389. Irregular nonperiodic weather changes are usually less marked in the humid subtropics than they are farther poleward where the conflict between air masses is more marked and fronts more numerous. A majority of the storms in eastern United States, following a track that approximately coincides with the Great Lakes and the St. Lawrence Valley, do not greatly affect the Gulf States. It is more especially when the cyclones and anticyclones move on the southern circuit that the cotton belt feels their influence. In *summer*, when the frontal belt, or storm belt, is farthest poleward, and the sun is largely in control, irregular weather changes are at a minimum (Figs. 9.14, 9.15). Weak cyclones resembling those of the wet tropics may bring

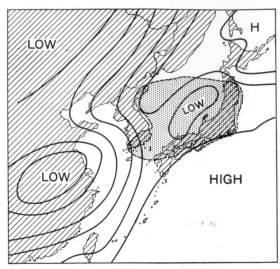

FIG. 9.19. A characteristic weather type of the summer-monsoon period in eastern Asia. Cyclonic storms are responsible for most of the summer precipitation in eastern Asia. Area of precipitation shaded. (*After Japanese weather map*.)

some gray days with general widespread rains, but these storms are not associated with marked temperature changes. Humid, sultry days with frequent thundershowers, each day much like the others, are the rule. The thermometer rises to

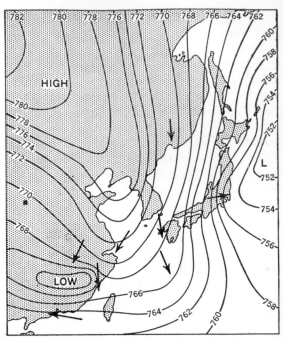

FIG. 9.21. A winter weather type in eastern Asia. Cold *cP* air of the winter monsoon prevails in the north but south of the Yangtze river in China a cyclonic storm causes cloud and precipitation. (*After Chu*.)

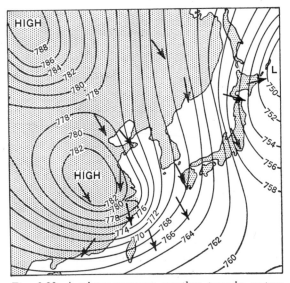

FIG. 9.20. A winter-monsoon weather type in eastern Asia. Here the outflowing winter monsoon has been intensified so that cold-wave conditions are produced in subtropical China and heavy snows result on the Japan Sea side of Japan. (*After Chu*.)

about the same height each day and sinks to similar minima each night. *Late summer and fall* are the dreaded hurricane season, and although these storms are not numerous, their severity more than makes up for their infrequency. Sunny, autumn days furnish delightful weather, although the equatorward-advancing cyclonic belt gradually produces more gray, cloudy days and unseasonable temperature importations as winter closes in. In *winter* the storm belt is farthest equatorward, so that irregular weather changes are most frequent and extreme at that time. Importations of tropical air on the front of an advancing cyclone may push the day temperatures to well above 60°, or even 70°, while the following *cP* air masses may reduce the temperature as much as 30° within 24 hr., resulting occasionally in severe freezes. Bright sunny winter days are distinctly pleasant and exhilarating outdoors. *Spring* again sees the retreat of the cyclonic belt and the gradual reestablishment of regular diurnal sun control (Figs. 9.19, 9.20, 9.21).

ASSOCIATED FEATURES OF THE PHYSICAL
EARTH IN *Ca*, HUMID SUBTROPICAL
CLIMATE

390. Native Vegetation. The abundant climatic energy, exhibited in both rainfall and temperature, characteristic of this climate, has induced a correspondingly abundant vegetation cover, usually of forests, although in sections of more moderate rainfall grasses may replace trees. The single large world region with *Ca* climate where grasslands predominate is in South America. Over much of the Argentine Pampa and Uruguay the original vegetation cover was tall grass.

No single type of forest predominates in the *Ca* climate, although one composed of mixed broadleaf and conifer trees is common. In some parts the broadleaf trees comprising the forest are deciduous and in others evergreen. Evergreen broadleaf appears most common in the Asiatic and Australian *Ca* regions. In the *Ca* region of the United States coniferous forests occupy the sandy, droughty upland portions of the Coastal Plain, while deciduous broadleaf forests are characteristic of its wetter bottom lands. The southern coniferous forest is composed chiefly of longleaf-loblolly slash pines. Most common trees comprising the bottomland broadleaf forest are cypress, tupelo, red gum, cottonwood, ash, and numerous other varieties which are suited to wet and periodically inundated sites. In the upland mixed forest to the north and west of the conifer belt, where the soils are less sandy, oak, chestnut, and pine are the most numerous trees.

391. Zonal Soils. High temperatures and relatively abundant year-round precipitation cause chemical weathering and leaching to be unusually rapid in the *Ca* regions. Since there is practically an absence of frozen ground, there is no interruption of chemical weathering even in winter, so that the processes are continuous throughout the year. It is to be expected, therefore, that the regolith cover will be deep. In some places as much as 50 ft. of regolith overlies the bedrock. Such depths are suggestive of conditions in the wet tropics.

392. *The mature red and yellow forest soils* of the humid subtropical realm are characteristically of low fertility. This tends partly to offset the effects of the realm's highly productive climate. The soil inferiority is not unexpected, however, considering the high leaching power of the climate and the low humus-producing character of the forest vegetation. In a general way, the red and yellow soils of the humid subtropics resemble those of the wet tropics, although the former are not so completely leached. The quantity of mineral plant foods is characteristically low, although there are significant amounts of lime, nitrates, potash, and phosphorus. While commonly overlain by a thin layer of leaf mold, or undecomposed leafy material, the amount of humus incorporated within the soil body is small. Among the heavier textured soils, such as those of the American Piedmont, structure is inclined toward being coarse and nutlike, but, under cultivation, structural deterioration is relatively rapid. Light sandy soils, such as those of the American Gulf and Atlantic Coastal Plain, are almost without structure but are nevertheless friable and easily worked. These sandy soils are likely to be even poorer than are the heavier textured ones, their large pore space speeding up the leaching processes.

393. *Grassland Soils.* Where grasslands, instead of forests, are the prevailing natural vegetation, the soils belong to a very different group and are potentially much more productive. In general, subtropical grasslands are located in regions with somewhat less than the normal amount of precipitation, so that leaching processes are less active. At the same time, the grass cover returns a much larger amount of organic matter to the soil than do trees. As a result, mineral plant foods are more abundant, humus content higher, structure better, colors darker, and chemical reaction less acid, in these grassland soils of the prairie and chernozem types, than is true of the more widespread and characteristic red and yellow soils developing under forest. They are capable, therefore, without expensive applications of fertilizer, of sustaining a much more continuous cropping than are the red and yellow soils. It is the South American humid subtropics, especially the

Argentine Pampa and Uruguay, which have the most extensive development of these fertile grassland soils within the realm. The productivity of the Pampa is almost proverbial. Within the humid subtropical region of the United States, particularly in Alabama, Mississippi, and Texas, are certain belts underlain by easily decomposed marls which, because of soil peculiarities, originally had a grass rather than a tree cover. These were not only "islands" of grass in the midst of forest, but likewise "islands" of highly productive prairie soil surrounded by the infertile subtropical red and yellow soils. The drier western margins of the American humid subtropics have other scattered areas of dark-colored grassland soils. They are likewise prominent on the high veld of southeastern Africa.

Cb, Cc, Marine Climate

394. Type Location. The name given to this climate suggests that it resembles that over the adjacent ocean. These mild, marine climates characteristically occupy positions on the western or windward sides of middle-latitude continents, poleward from about 40°, where the onshore westerly winds import to them conditions from the oceans (Figs. 6.4, 9.1, Plate I). In their general atmospheric characteristics, therefore, they are like the seas over which the prevailing air masses originate. Where land areas are relatively narrow, as, for instance, in the case of islands, such as Tasmania, New Zealand, and Great Britain, or where the continent extends for only a short distance into the belt of westerlies, as do Australia and Africa, marine climate may not be completely limited to the western littoral. Extensive development along east coasts of large middle-latitude continents is unlikely (in spite of the proximity of oceans), by reason of the severe temperatures resulting from leeward location and the monsoon wind systems. Only where land masses are very narrow, or where they extend barely into the middle latitudes, is east-coast location possible.

On its equatorward margins this *Cb* climate characteristically makes contact with the *Cs* type. Unlike the latter, and because of its higher

latitude, usually it is not strongly encroached upon by the subsiding air masses associated with the subtropical anticyclones, and thus does not experience a pronounced dry summer season. On its poleward side *Cb* climate extends far into the higher middle latitudes, where it is eventually terminated by either the subarctic or the tundra type. The far poleward extension of this mild climate is the result of oceanic control offsetting normal latitudinal control. Warm ocean currents, which parallel the west coasts of continents in middle latitudes, tend to accentuate the normal tempering effects of the ocean proper.

The depth to which *Cb* climate extends into the interiors of continents is determined largely by surface configuration. Where mountains closely parallel the west coasts, as in North and South America and Scandinavia, marine climate is restricted to relatively narrow strips of territory seaward from the highlands. But where extensive lowlands prevail, as in parts of western Europe, the effects of the sea are carried well inland and *Cb* climates have greater east-west extent. On their land sides marine climates are characteristically bordered by severe continental types, either dry or humid. In North America where highlands closely parallel the west coast, *Cb* climate west of the mountains is replaced by *B* climate to the east. In Europe on the other hand, where the westerlies from the ocean have freer entrance, *Cb* climate gradually passes over to humid *D* climates (Fig. 10.1).

TEMPERATURE

395. Summer. Although there are good and sufficient grounds for objecting to the use of the word "temperate" as applied to many middle-latitude climates, it is relatively suitable for the particular one under discussion (Figs. 9.22, 9.23). Summers are moderately cool and, while more or less ideal for human efficiency and comfort, are somewhat too low for the best growth of some cereal crops. The characteristically cool summer should be emphasized as one of the principal contrasts between this third of the triumvirate of mild mesothermal climates, on the one hand, and the two subtropical types, on

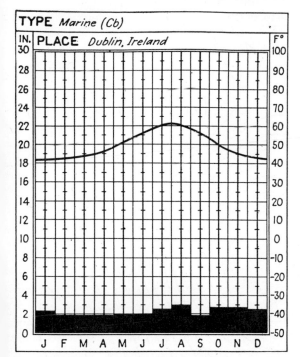

FIG. 9.22. A lowland *Cb* station in western Europe. Note the small range of temperature and the modest amount of precipitation well distributed throughout the year.

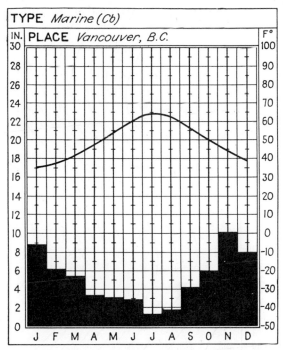

FIG. 9.23. A *Cb* station in western North America, backed by highlands. Here the precipitation (60 in.) is greater than for most lowland stations and there is a pronounced maximum in winter. The strong winter maximum is most characteristic of those parts of *Cb* which are closest to *Cs*.

the other (Figs. 9.24, 9.25). In the warm season these west coasts are several degrees below the average temperature for the latitude, although to be sure, the negative anomaly of summer is not nearly as striking as is the plus anomaly of winter. Seattle, Wash., has a mean July temperature of 63°; Dublin, Ireland, 60°; and Paris, France, 65.5°. Night cooling is not rapid in these humid, cloudy, marine climates, considerably less so than is characteristic of Mediterranean summers. The average of the daily minima in July is only 55° at Seattle and 51° at Bellingham, Wash., while the daily maxima are 73 and 72°, respectively, so that the normal diurnal range is in the neighborhood of only 20° (Figs. 9.26, 9.27, 9.28). Occasional hot days may occur when a passing disturbance temporarily halts the invasion of cool sea air and substitutes instead air of land or tropical origin. Under such conditions both Seattle and Bellingham have experienced a temperature as high as 96°, and Paris, 100°. Severe and prolonged hot waves, however, are few (see temperature data, p. 317).

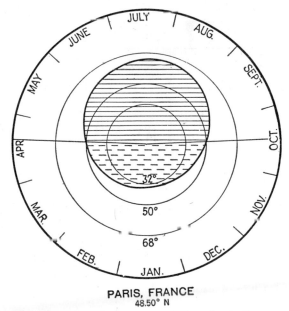

PARIS, FRANCE
48.50° N

9.24. Thermograph of a marine (*Cb*) station in Europe. (*After Hartshorne.*)

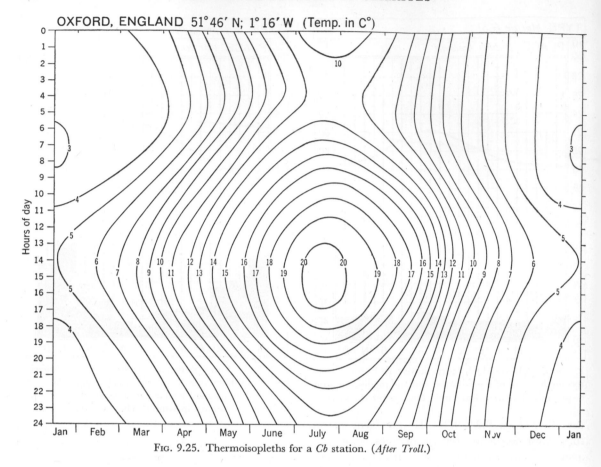

FIG. 9.25. Thermoisopleths for a *Cb* station. (*After Troll.*)

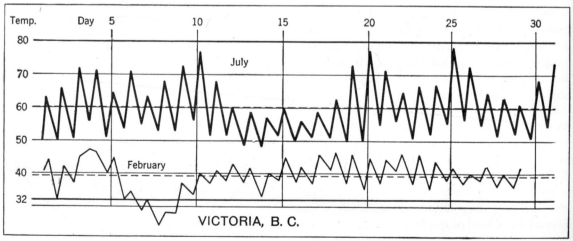

FIG. 9.26. A marine (*Cb*) station in western Canada. Note the small diurnal range, especially in winter. (*After Jefferson.*)

A great majority of the cyclonic disturbances which affect these west coasts are strongly occluded and therefore lacking in extensive warm sectors which would tend to produce frequent spells of warm weather and as a consequence higher average summer temperatures.

396. Winter. Winters, on the whole, are more abnormally mild for the latitude than the summers are cool. This is particularly the case with western Europe where a great mass of warm water, known as the North Atlantic drift, lies offshore. Thus the most marine parts of Western Europe are 20 to 30° too warm for their latitudes in January, while western North America, with its less conspicuous warm current, is 10+° too mild. In winter, isotherms tend to parallel these coasts rather than follow the lines of latitude, indicating the dominance of land-and-water control. The decrease in temperature is much more rapid from the coast toward the interior than it is going poleward. Thus Paris is 7° colder in January than Brest which is 310 miles nearer the ocean, while in Norway the heads of some of the longest fiords are 10° colder than the open coasts. Hammerfest on the coast of Norway at 71°N. is an ice-free port, while icebreakers are required to keep open the harbor of Hamburg (54°N.). January averages

of 35 to 50° in western Europe are matched by others of 0 to −40° in the continental climates of interior Asia in similar latitudes.

397. *Winter Minima and Frosts.* The average cold-month temperature at London is 39°; Seattle 40°; Valentia, Ireland, 45°; and Valdivia, Chile, 46°. Annual ranges are small: 15° at Valentia, 23° at London, 13.5° at Valdivia, and 24° at Seattle. For Seattle the average of the January daily minima is 35°, so that on a majority of nights frost is absent. At Paris frost occurs on about one-half of the nights in the three winter months, while in London the thermometer remains above the freezing point on more January nights than it goes below. It is rare for London to have a temperature below 15°, while 4° is the lowest minimum ever recorded. At Seattle the thermometer has fallen as low as 3°. The prevailingly cloudy skies and humid atmosphere in winter tend to decrease daytime heating and to retard nighttime cooling, so that a flat temperature curve with small diurnal temperature range is characteristic. Clear days show greater ranges (Figs. 9.26, 9.27, 9.28).

Frosts are more frequent, as well as more severe, and the frost-free season shorter, than in *Cs* climates. Nevertheless the growing season is unusually long for the latitude, 180 to 210 days

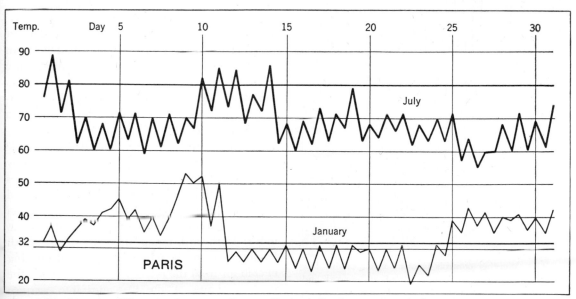

Fig. 9.27. A marine (*Cb*) station in western Europe. Nonperiodic air-mass control of temperature is conspicuous.

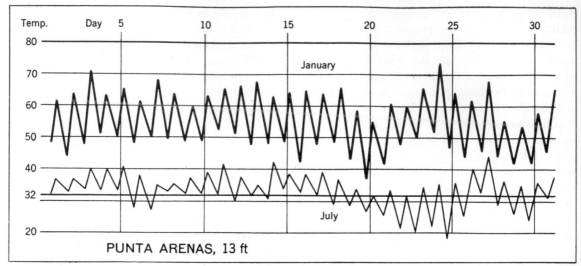

FIG. 9.28. Daily maximum and minimum temperatures for the extreme months at a cool marine station in extreme southern Chile (*Cc*). The average temperature of the warmest month at Punta Arenas is below 50°, but since its average annual temperature is above 32° it is scarcely genuine tundra. (*After Jefferson.*)

being characteristic of the American North Pacific Coast region. Seattle has only 4 months when temperatures below freezing are to be expected. However, winter is usually severe enough to produce a dormant season for plant

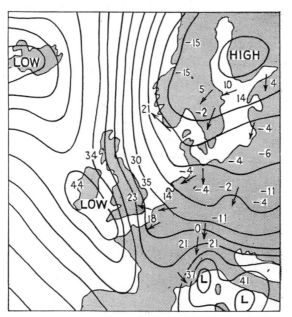

FIG. 9.29. Weather controls favoring unseasonably low temperatures in western Europe. A high to the north and east is delivering *cP* air to the regions west and south. (*After Kendrew.*)

life, which is not true for the *Cs* climates farther equatorward. In the latter regions, although killing frosts occasionally occur, temperatures never remain below freezing during the entire 24 hr. Frost is almost entirely confined to night hours. Such is not the case in marine *Cb* climates, for during unusually cold spells temperatures may remain constantly below freezing for a period of several days. Midday temperatures of normal winter days are relatively high, however, the average of the daily maxima for January at Seattle being 44.5°, and the daily range less than 10°. On the whole, the day-to-day temperature changes are much less regular in winter than in summer, the former season being more completely controlled by the succession of cyclones and anticyclones.

398. *Cold Spells.* Severe cold spells in these marine climates characteristically are caused by invasions of cold polar continental air masses from the anticyclonic interiors. A well-developed winter high stationary over the Columbia Plateau region may force an approaching low to move southward along the American North Pacific Coast, to be followed by an out-pouring of cold air from the interior, which descends the western slopes of the Cascades into western Washington and Oregon. Northeasterly, and not northwesterly, winds bring the coldest weather to the American North Pacific Coast. The same is true for western Europe, where both unusually cold spells and abnormally cold winters are caused by a substitution of cold, dry north-easterly air of polar continental origin for the normal southwesterly winds from the sea (Fig. 9.29). During the unusual cold spell in Europe in February, 1929, the influence of the continental anticyclone and its polar air masses persisted for several weeks. During that spell, temperatures in eastern Kent, England, remained continuously below freezing for 226 hr., the Thames was frozen over in many parts, and practically the whole of the British Isles was frost-bound for 5 weeks (Kendrew). On the continent at this same time German coastal cities recorded temperatures below zero, while the Rhine was frozen throughout almost its entire course. But such invasions of *cP* air are infrequent in *Cb* climates, for, coming as they do from the northeast, they are opposed to the general westerly air movement of the middle latitudes. The American North Pacific Coast is further protected against *cP* invasions by mountain barriers.

Bordeaux, France, the respective means for these same months are 53 and 55°. The seasons of maximum and minimum temperatures are also somewhat retarded so that at Valencia, February is a trifle colder than January, and August is warmer than July.

PRECIPITATION

400. Amount. These are humid climates with adequate rainfall at all seasons (Fig. 9.22). The total amount, however, varies greatly from region to region, depending in a large measure upon the character of the relief. Where lowlands predominate, as they do in parts of western Europe, rainfall is only moderate, usually 20 to 30 in. But, on the other hand, where west coasts are elevated and bordered by mountain ranges, as is the case in Norway, Chile, and western North America, precipitation may be excessive, even reaching such totals as 100 to 150 in. Compensating for this contrast in amount is a further contrast in regional distribution, for, where lowlands exist, moderate rainfall prevails well into the interior of the continent; but, where coastal mountains intercept the rain-bearing winds, precipitation is

Climatic Data for Representative Marine Cb Stations

Valentia, Ireland

	J	*F*	*M*	*A*	*M*	*J*	*J*	*A*	*S*	*O*	*N*	*D*	*Yr.*	*Range*
Temp.	44	44	45	48	52	57	59	59	57	52	48	45	50.8	15
Precip.	5.5	5.2	4.5	3.7	3.2	3.2	3.8	4.8	4.1	5.6	5.5	6.6	55.6	

Seattle, Washington

	J	*F*	*M*	*A*	*M*	*J*	*J*	*A*	*S*	*O*	*N*	*D*	*Yr.*	*Range*
Temp.	40	42	45	50	55	60	64	64	59	52	46	42	51.4	24
Precip.	4.9	3.8	3.1	2.4	1.8	1.3	0.6	0.7	1.7	2.8	4.8	5.5	33.4	

Paris, France

	J	*F*	*M*	*A*	*M*	*J*	*J*	*A*	*S*	*O*	*N*	*D*	*Yr.*	*Range*
Temp.	37	39	43	51	56	62	66	64	59	51	43	37	50.5	27
Precip.	1.5	1.2	1.6	1.7	2.1	2.3	2.2	2.2	2.0	2.3	1.8	1.7	22.6	

Hokitika, New Zealand

	J	*F*	*M*	*A*	*M*	*J*	*J*	*A*	*S*	*O*	*N*	*D*	*Yr.*	*Range*
Temp.	60	61	59	55	50	47	45	46	50	53	55	58	53	16
Precip.	9.8	7.3	9.7	9.2	9.8	9.7	9.0	9.4	9.2	11.8	10.6	10.6	116.1	

399. Annual March of Temperature. In the most marine portions of these west-coast climates the march of the seasons is commonly retarded so that autumn is relatively warmer than spring. This is particularly true in western Europe where spring is more subject than autumn to invasions of cold air from the continent. At Valentia, Ireland, April has a mean temperature of 48°, while October registers 51°; at

concentrated close to the littoral. East of the mountains drought conditions may prevail. There is no doubt than an *extensive* distribution of *moderate* rains is economically more desirable than the concentration of large and unusable quantities on a mountainous coast. Unfortunately, Europe is the only one of the three continents extending well into the westerlies where the windward side of the land mass is freely open to the entrance of the rain-bearing winds. The precipitation of these marine climates has a high degree of reliability, and droughts are of rare occurrence.

401. Annual Distribution. With respect to annual distribution of precipitation, the thing to be emphasized is *adequate rainfall at all seasons*, rather than a particular season of excess or deficiency (Fig. 9.22). This does not necessarily mean that all months have much the same amount, but only that there is no such marked seasonal emphasis as exists in Mediterranean and savanna climates or in regions with strong monsoons. In other words, there is no dormant period for vegetation because of lack of rain. In very marine and mountainous locations it is not uncommon to find the cooler months having more precipitation, with the summers somewhat drier. Thus at Brest, France, 59 per cent of the year's rain falls in the winter half year, and 41 per cent in the summer half. Approximately the same seasonal distribution is characteristic of Valentia, Ireland. But on the whole this condition of winter maximum prevails only on exposed seaboard locations and ceases to be character-

FIG. 9.30. In western Europe it is principally the more maritime areas which show a cool-season maximum of precipitation.

istic a short distance inland (Fig. 9.30). Thus, while Brest shows a slight cool-season maximum, Paris, 310 miles farther inland, but still within the marine climate, has 55 per cent of the year's total in the summer half year. It has been suggested that this coastal winter maximum may, in part, be the result of lifting resulting from the frictional effects of the coast upon onshore highly saturated maritime air currents.[1] Throughout much of Europe's *Cb* climate, fall is the wettest season and spring the driest.

As a general rule, also, those regions of *Cb* climate which lie nearest to *Cs*, which are usually the equatorward sections of *Cb*, show a stronger summer minimum, and hence an over-all greater accent on winter, than is true for the type as a whole. This is not unexpected, for the same control in the form of a strengthened and poleward displaced subtropical anticyclone which causes the summer drought in *Cs* is likely to cause reduced summer rainfall in adjacent parts of *Cb*. Thus the *Cb* climate of the North America Pacific Coast south of 50° has a striking summer minimum of precipitation (Fig. 9.23); Vancouver has only 1.2 in. of rain in July and 1.7 in August, but 8.2 in December and 8.4 in January. Because in this region the rainfall of the wettest winter month is more than three times as much as that of the driest summer month, Köppen has designated its climate as *Cs*. But the whole region has too much rainfall (Vancouver has nearly 59 in.) for a typical *Cs* climate, and, although the summers are much drier than the winters, still the warm season is not a period of genuine drought as in *Cs* climates. Here luxuriant forests are typical of lowlands as well as of the mountain slopes, another feature that is not typical of *Cs* climates. In the exposed coastal sections of Chile's *Cb* region in the vicinity of 40 to 45°S. the winter half year has nearly three times as much rainfall as the summer half year.

402. Snowfall. In spite of the fact that winter is characteristically a wet season, snowfall is not

[1] Tor Bergeron, The Problem of Artificial Control of Rainfall on the Globe, Part II, The Coastal Orographic Maximum of Precipitation in Autumn and Winter, *Tellus*, Vol. 1, No. 3, pp. 15–32, August, 1949.

abundant at low elevations, temperatures being too high on the lowlands for much snow. "Snow is sufficiently rare in most of northwest Europe to be a topic of conversation when it lies more than a few days. . . . " (Kendrew). Paris has, on the average, 14 snowy days during the year. In the Puget Sound Lowland there are some 10 to 15 such days, and the duration of snow cover is approximately the same length. In the north-eastern part of the British Isles the lowlands experience about 25 days with snow, but the southwest coast has only 4. The snow that falls is wet and heavy, reflecting the relatively high winter temperatures. Upon the ground, it quickly turns to slush, making for unpleasant conditions underfoot.

Where mountains border these west coasts, receiving abundant orographic and cyclonic winter precipitation, snowfall is extremely heavy. On the western slopes of the Cascade Range 300 to 400 in. of snow fall on the average each year. Snowfall is likewise heavy on the western slopes of the British Columbia Coast Ranges, the Scandinavian Highlands, the mountains of southern New Zealand, and the southern Andes. In each of these regions the mountain snowfields have in the past given rise to numerous valley glaciers, which in turn have been responsible for the characteristically ir-regular, fiorded coasts.

403. Origin of Precipitation. Over low-lands the characteristic precipitation is cyclonic (frontal) in origin, falling as steady, long-con-tinued rain, often only drizzle, from a gray, leaden sky. It is in winter that these storms reach their maximum development, and it is at that time of year that cloudy, rainy days are most numerous. In spite of the fact that cyclones are weaker and less numerous in the warm seasons, because the absolute humidity is higher, and the entrance of lows into the continents is facilitated by lower pressures, summer rain may be nearly, if not quite, as great, although it falls in sharper showers on fewer days. Thus at London, July has 13 rainy days with 2.4 in. of rain, while in January the respective figures are 15 and 1.9. Summers, therefore, are usually brighter and sunnier than winters.

The relatively cool summers and the prev-alence of stable maritime air masses at that season are not conducive to the development of convectional systems, and thunderstorms are few. Coastal stations of the American North Pacific states record two to four such storms a year, although they are more numerous at higher elevations and farther inland where turbulence and overturning are induced by the rugged land surface. At Oxford, England, only 28 per cent of the rain in June, and 32 per cent of that in July, falls on days in which thunder is heard.

A distinguishing feature of the precipitation of these marine climates is the relatively small amount of rain that falls, considering the large number of cloudy, rainy days. Thus, although Paris has only 22.6 in. of precipitation, this is spread over 188 rainy days (average 0.12 in. for each rainy day). Seattle, with 33.4 in. of precipi-tation, has 151 rainy days; London has 24.5 in. and 164 rainy days; while Sumburgh Head, on the Shetland Islands, has 36.7 in. spread out over 260 rainy days. London has had 72 rainy days in succession. Dull, lowering skies, with low-hang-ing clouds and drizzle, are characteristic. An important factor causing a large number of cloudy and rainy days with only a modest amount of precipitation on lowlands is the great prevalence of strongly occluded cyclones.

Where coasts are precipitous, abundant rains of orographic origin supplement those from cyclones and the few convectional storms. Not only is the total precipitation greater in such regions, but the rate of fall is greater as well. Connor[1] has pointed out that the winter precipi-tation of the North America Cb climate is probably more frontal than orographic. During winter, the winds in the interior valleys and even along the coast are prevailingly easterly, so that some sort of persistent discontinuity, or front, exists between the locally generated cool easterlies of the mainland and coast and the warmer Pacific air masses moving in from the west. No doubt a considerable part of the so-

[1] A. J. Connor, "The Climates of North America, Canada," in Köppen-Geiger, "Handbuch der Klimat-ologie," Vol. 2, Part J, p. 345, 1938.

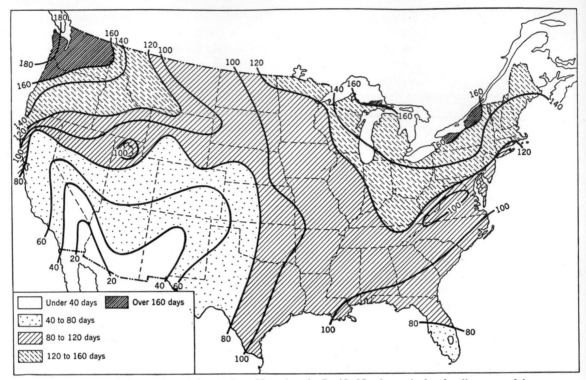

Fig. 9.31. Average annual number of cloudy days. Note that the Pacific Northwest is the cloudiest part of the country. Most of this cloudiness is in the cooler seasons.

called "orographic" rainfall is produced by the trigger effect of highlands upon conditionally or convectively unstable maritime air.

404. Cloudiness and Sunshine. Marine *Cb* climate is relatively unlike *Cs* in its features of humidity, cloudiness, and precipitation. Relative humidity is almost always high, and particularly so in winter. Much cloud is typical; indeed, these are some of the cloudiest climates of the earth. The American North Pacific Coast region has the highest cloudiness and least sunshine of any part of the United States, the mean annual cloudiness of that region being 60 to 70 per cent (Fig. 9.31). Over wide areas of western Europe cloudiness is greater than 70 per cent, the sun sometimes being hidden for several weeks in succession. Winter and fall, the seasons of maximum cyclones, are much darker and gloomier than spring and summer. Seattle, which has only 22 per cent of the possible sunshine in November and 21 per cent in December, has 65 per cent in July and 60 per cent in August, so that summers there are relatively

bright and pleasant. Valentia, Ireland, has only 17 per cent of the possible sunshine in December, but in May 43 per cent. But even though summers are sunnier than winters, they are still much cloudier than those of Mediterranean climates. Fog and mist are characteristic weather elements of the marine climate. The American North Pacific Coast has over 40 days with dense fog during the year; Bergen, Norway, has 37.7; and Fanö, Denmark, 53.6.

THE WEATHER ELEMENT AND SEASONAL WEATHER

405. The Nonperiodic or Cyclonic Element. Since cyclonic storms are numerous, it is to be expected that the weather will be dominated by these disturbances and their accompanying nonperiodic temperature and precipitation changes. The diurnal element, or sun control, is correspondingly weak. In spite of cyclonic control of weather, the associated temperature changes with the approach and passage of these disturbances are not nearly so striking as they are in the American Middle West, for example. The very moderate temperature changes stem from the fact that the air masses involved in the cyclonic circulations affecting *Cb* climates are characteristically of maritime origin so that temperature contrasts along fronts are not great. In addition, the strongly occluded nature of most cyclones precludes the existence of an extensive warm sector in a great majority of the disturbances, so that they are essentially converging systems of cool maritime air (Fig. 9.32). Nothing comparable to the contrasts between winter *cP* and *mT*-Gulf in interior North America is present. As previously noted, isotherms tend to parallel the coast, especially in the cooler seasons, so that imported temperatures from either north or south are not severe. To the west lies the ocean, so that it is only from the eastern interior that severe heat or cold can be derived and such air movement is opposed to the general west-to-east circulation of the middle latitudes.

There is greater nonperiodic variability in the precipitation element as controlled by these traveling disturbances. Sun-controlled convectional showers are only a feature of the warm season, and even then they are not dominant. Overcast days with light precipitation of frontal origin are numerous. When these cyclonic disturbances slow up in their movement or stagnate, as they commonly do, a succession of gray, dripping days is the result.

Winter, in spite of its mild temperatures, is a stormy period. The westerlies themselves are strongest at that season, and at frequent intervals the gradients are strengthened by passing cyclones. In coastal locations, gales are numerous as one storm follows another in rapid succession. The high seas generated by winter winds are strong enough to make navigation difficult, and unusually severe storms may do serious damage to shipping. The fog and mist make for poor visibility and add to the difficulties of navigation. Precipitation is relatively abundant and very frequent, most of it being in the form of rain rather than snow. Long periods of dark, gloomy, dripping weather are characteristic, so that winters are depressing and hard to endure. Between the frequent cyclones there are occa-

sional sunny days with crisper weather, but these are the exception rather than the rule. Night frosts are not unusual, especially when skies are clear, but ordinarily they are not severe. A pushing westward of *cP* air masses now and then leads to a succession of clear days in which temperatures may remain continuously below freezing.

As the days lengthen with the advance of *spring*, cyclones become fewer, and sunshine more abundant. The air is still cool, but the sun is warm, and in western Europe spring is acclaimed the most delightful season. *Summer* temperatures are pleasant for physical well-being, and, where sunny days are numerous, as they are in the American Pacific Northwest, a more charming summer climate would be hard to find (Fig. 9.33). More especially in the higher middle latitudes, or in very exposed marine locations, chilly, gray, overcast days are numerous even in summer. Rain is still relatively abundant, but it falls on fewer days than in

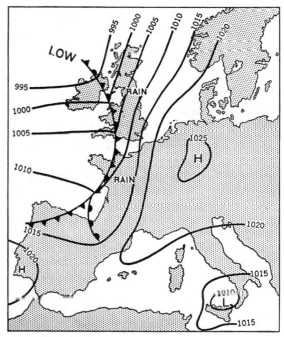

FIG. 9.32. A strongly occluded storm in western Europe, producing light but steady and widespread rainfall, a low ceiling, and low visibility. Most of the cyclones which affect western Europe are in an advanced stage of occlusion. Such storms are inclined to produce much cloud but only a modest amount of precipitation on lowlands.

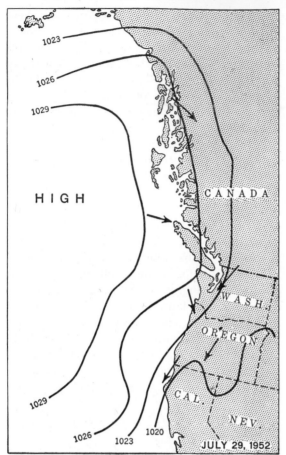

FIG. 9.33. The prevailingly fair weather and light rainfall characteristic of much of the *Cb* region of western North America in summer is attributable to the dominance of a warm-season anticyclone. Weather map of July 29, 1952.

winter. *Autumn* witnesses the equatorward swing of the storm belt again and, as a consequence, a rapid pickup in cloudiness and precipitation. On the whole, autumn is cloudier than spring. The season remains mild, however, so that September and October (Northern Hemisphere) are usually 2 or 3° warmer than their spring counterparts of May and April.

ASSOCIATED FEATURES OF THE PHYSICAL
EARTH IN *Cb*, MARINE CLIMATE

406. Native Vegetation. In these mild, humid, west-coast regions the original vegetation cover was principally forest, and because of the hilly and mountainous nature of large parts of the realm, trees still cover extensive areas. On the plains of western Europe the virgin forest was largely deciduous and mixed, with oaks

predominating, although linden, beech, and elm were also important. Conifers occupied chiefly the western margins of the Norwegian Highlands north of latitude 60°, certain sandy lands along the coasts, or highland areas. Centuries of occupancy by civilized peoples has greatly altered the original vegetation of western Europe (Fig. 7.12).

On the cool, raw, wind-swept Scottish Highlands in particular, where glacial scouring has removed most of the soil cover, and in other very exposed and windy locations, such as the rocky uplands of western Ireland and the higher elevations of Wales and England, forests are practically absent and heath and moor take their places. On both the drier heaths, and the wetter boglike moors, low evergreen shrubs, such as heather, gorse, brakes, and clumps of juniper, take the place of trees. Large parts of such areas are wasteland.

The North American segment of this realm is today the world's principal source of high-grade softwoods. Abundant rainfall, mild temperatures, and long growing season combine to produce a superior and luxuriant coniferous forest composed of large trees growing in relatively dense stands. Not only is the forest itself luxuriant, but the undergrowth as well is dense, so that in places it is almost impenetrable. Dominant timber trees vary with latitude and elevation. In northern California redwood forests, composed of enormous trees, many of them averaging 10 ft. in diameter, occupy the foggy western slopes of the Coast Ranges, while pines and cedars prevail farther inland. To the north, in Oregon, Washington, and southern British Columbia, Douglas fir is the outstanding tree, it being the most important timber tree of the Pacific Coast forests. Frequently it occurs in pure stands, but it is also mixed with hemlock and western red cedar. In size, Douglas fir ranks next to redwood, ordinarily attaining heights of 175 to 200 ft., and diameters of 3 to 6 ft. North of about latitude 50°, in British Columbia and Alaska, fir is less abundant, and spruce and western red cedar become the dominant timber trees.

Southern Hemisphere forests are dense and luxuriant in aspect, like those of Pacific North America, but are composed of very different species, most of which are greatly inferior in quality. At lower elevations the Chilean forest is hardwood in character, being composed chiefly of broadleaf evergreen trees, which become progressively more stunted toward the south. At higher elevations on the slopes of the Andes, conifers, some of them good timber trees, are more numerous. The New Zealand–Tasmanian–Australian segments of the realm have forests that resemble in many ways those of southern Chile.

407. Zonal Soils. As in the humid subtropics, so likewise in the marine climate, the weathering of rocks is relatively rapid, so that the regolith cover on flattish lands is commonly deep. Chemical decomposition and leaching are not quite so vigorous, owing to the lower temperatures, but, on the other hand, the wedge work of ice is more significant. The period of cold is usually very short, so that erosion and weathering are continuous over a large portion of the year.

Because of considerable variations in landforms, precipitation, earth materials, and vegetation within the realm, there is variety in the soils as well. Considerable areas of rough broken land exist in all four of the far-separated continental segments, and in such locations mature soils are of only minor extent. On the lowlands, however, allowing for a considerable number of exceptions and variations, mature forest soils are of the gray-brown podzolic variety. Podzolization is further advanced in the rainier, more marine sections, or where uplands prevail. Meadow and peat-bog soils are common. In the poleward portions of all four of the realm's principal segments, continental or mountain glaciers have altered the soil character through scouring and deposition, thereby hindering the development of mature profiles. Thin, stony soils, the result of ice scouring, are particularly characteristic of the Scottish and Scandinavian sections, while over the northern portions of the lowlands of maritime Europe (British Isles except southern England, Denmark, the North German Plain, and southern Scandinavia), till, outwash plain, and loess deposits are the parent material from which the soils have developed. Except in the regions of ice scouring, the general effect of glaciation has probably been to improve soils, although the deranged drainage has, no doubt, resulted in much wet soil of meadow and bog type. The sandy coastal-plain and outwash soils in northern Germany and Denmark are particularly infertile.

The gray-brown podzolic soils, to which type a majority of the mature soils in this realm belong, are the best of the world's forest soils. They are the least acid of that group, have a well-developed nutlike structure, and, although their content of organic matter and soluble mineral plant foods is not high, it is appreciably greater than in the other forest soils. One of the chief assets of the gray-brown podzolic soils is their well-developed structure, which makes them very amenable to improvement. Under constant cultivation they deteriorate, to be sure, but less rapidly than the other light-colored soils, and with less care and fertilizer they can be kept in good condition and fitted for a variety of crops. On the whole, then, they are potentially the most productive of their class, in both the natural and the improved states (Fig. 7.13).

408. Surface Configuration. More than in any other of the mesothermal realms, ice has been an agent in modeling the gradational landforms. In fact, it is the only one of the three C realms where glaciers have left appreciable imprint upon surface features. Except in Europe, the forms are almost exclusively those resulting from the work of mountain or valley glaciers. In the higher latitudes of Pacific North America, Norway, Scotland, southern Chile, and the southern part of New Zealand, highlands approach close to the seacoast. The heavy snowfall of these elevated windward coasts is conductive to permanent mountain snow fields and valley glaciers. Some exist even at the present time, but in past epochs valley glaciers apparently were much larger and consequently reached the sea, developing characteristic fiorded coast lines with numerous islands. Glacial troughs, hanging valleys, cirques, lakes, and the other normal features associated with erosion by valley glaciers characterize the adjacent highland slopes. Repetition of this pattern of rugged, island-studded, fiorded coasts and glaciated highlands within the four segments of the realm is extraordinarily striking.

CHAPTER 10: *The Humid Microthermal[1] Climates (D)*

409. Type Location. These are the climates where a genuine winter, emphasized by the usual snow mantle, is combined with a genuine, although many times short, summer to produce the characteristic annual climatic cycle. Fall and spring, the transition seasons, not only are brief, but are also chiefly composites of winter and summer weather elements. Colder and snowier winters, shorter frost-free seasons, and larger annual ranges of temperature distinguish the severe microthermal climates from the mesothermal types. This greater severity results primarily from locational differences, with respect both to (a) latitude and (b) positions on the continents, for microthermal climates lie poleward from the subtropical types (*Cs*, *Ca*) and occupy more interior and leeward locations on the great land masses than does the marine climate (*Cb*). Emphatically, microthermal climates are land-controlled and are, therefore, distinctly continental in their characteristics (Figs. 6.4, 10.1). It is because they are land-controlled, being associated with large continents in higher middle latitudes, that they are confined exclusively to the Northern Hemisphere. Only Eurasia and North America are able to produce them. Of the Southern Hemisphere continents, South America alone extends sufficiently far poleward to permit of severe climates, but the narrowness of that land mass south of latitude 35° prevents genuinely severe conditions in spite of the latitude. Microthermal climates are excluded from the western, or windward, coasts because of the dominance there of maritime air masses. They occupy, instead, the interiors of land masses and commonly extend

down to tidewater on their leeward, or eastern, sides, where, in spite of proximity to the sea, modified continental conditions likewise prevail.

The latitudinal spread of microthermal climate is from about 40° on the southern margins to 60° or 65° on the northern. On its northern frontier it is bounded by polar climate (*E*), the boundary between *D* and *E* being the isotherm of 10°C., or 50°F., for the warmest month. On its southern side *D* makes contact with the subtropical climates (*Cs* and *Ca*) of the mesothermal group.

Unlike the mesothermal climates, those of the microthermal group differ from one another substantially only in degree, and that chiefly in one element, temperature. For example, a *Ds* type of climate, comparable to the dry summer Mediterranean type (*Cs*) in the mesothermal group, is practically nonexistent in the microthermals. This considerable degree of similarity among the microthermal climates permits of a useful preliminary discussion of the group as a whole before the individual types are analyzed.

410. Temperature. Because of a wide latitudinal spread, there are marked temperature contrasts within those regions classed as microthermal. However, for any particular latitude, these climates are sure to have relatively severe seasons, so that annual ranges are large (Figs. 10.2, 10.3). Of the two extreme seasons, it is the winter cold, rather than the summer heat, which is most characteristic and distinctive. Nevertheless, summers are warm for the latitude. Not only are the seasons extreme, but they are likewise variable in temperature from one year to another. In marine climates, for instance, one winter is likely to be much like another, but

[1] Micro-, from the Greek word *mikros*, small. Microthermal, therefore, refers to "small," or low, temperatures.

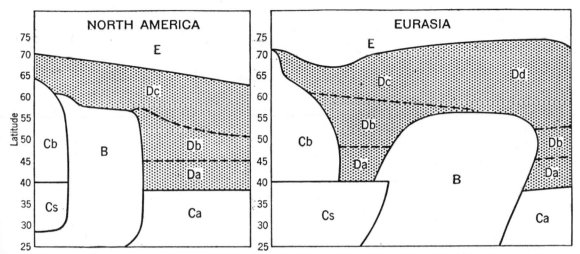

FIG. 10.1. Contrasting arrangement of the microthermal climates (*Da, Db, Dc-Dd*) in North America and Eurasia. Note that in Eurasia *D* climates are found both to the east and west of the dry interior, while in North America they are almost exclusively to the east of the *B* climates.

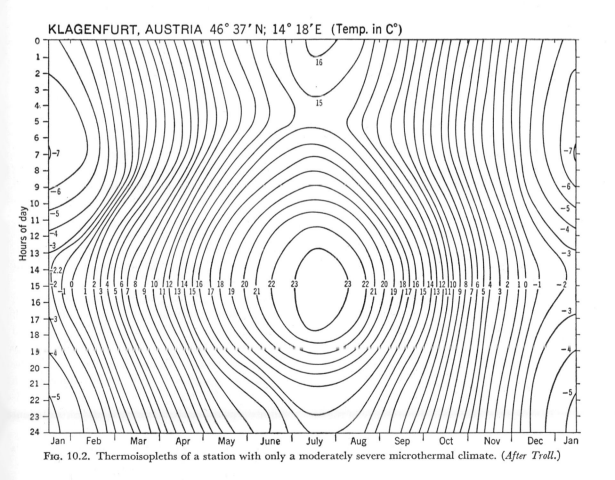

FIG. 10.2. Thermoisopleths of a station with only a moderately severe microthermal climate. (*After Troll.*)

wide departures from the normal seasonal temperature are characteristic of severe continental climates—in extreme instances as much as 30°.

411. *Effects of a Snow Cover upon Temperature.* Only in the microthermal, polar, and highland climates is the snow cover of sufficiently long duration to have a marked effect upon cool-season temperatures. Once a region is overlain by a snow mantle, the ground itself ceases to have much influence upon air temperature. Sunlight falling upon snow is largely reflected, so that little of the solar energy is effective in heating the ground or the atmosphere. Moreover, while loss of energy by earth radiation goes on very rapidly from a snow surface, the low conductivity of snow tends greatly to retard the upward flow of heat from the ground to replace that which is being lost. Observations made at Leningrad, after a fall of 20 in. of loose, dry snow, showed a temperature of $-39°$ at the surface, while the ground underneath recorded only 27°, a difference of 66°. *cP* air masses moving southward over this cold snow surface are modified only very slowly. Obviously, the effect of a snow cover is markedly to reduce winter temperatures. As spring advances, it acts to retard the warming of the air, for the reason that much of the solar energy is expended in melting the snow and ice. On the other hand, the snow cover tends to keep the ground warmer and prevents deep freezing.

412. Precipitation. Although winters are not without precipitation, summer is normally the season of its maximum. This seasonal distribution is related to the following conditions: (*a*) The specific humidity or reservoir of water vapor in the atmosphere is much less over the continents during the cold winter than it is in summer when temperatures are much higher. (*b*) During winter the subsiding air in the continental seasonal anticyclone is likewise conducive to low specific humidity. This same subsidence tends to develop a low-level inversion of temperature and thus increase the stability of the air mass, a condition which is opposed to precipitation. (*c*) The continental anticyclones, which develop over the colder parts of the land masses in winter, tend to repel or divert cyclonic storms. The diverging surface winds of these high-pressure cells are opposed to the origin of fronts. In summer, although cyclones may be fewer and weaker, they can nevertheless penetrate deeper into the continents. This applies particularly to the more severe microthermal climates, such as the subarctic, where the winter anticyclone is best developed. (*d*) Convection is at a maximum during the warm summer months, for at that season the warm land surface has a tendency to make unstable the air masses flowing over it. In winter, on the other hand, the cold snow surface has the effect of increasing air-mass stability. (*e*) Consequent upon the seasonal extremes of temperatures, and hence of pressure, a tendency toward a monsoon system of winds is developed, which leads to a strong inflow of warm humid tropical maritime air with high rainfall potentialities in summer, and to an outflow of dry cold polar continental air in winter.

It is almost impossible to overemphasize the significance in terms of climatic productivity of the fact that rainfall in microthermal climates characteristically reaches a maximum in summer. This is especially true where the total amount of precipitation is relatively modest as it is over extensive areas within this group. In tropical climates where the *temperature* growing season is 12 months in length, it matters not at all when the maximum precipitation comes. At any time of year there is ample heat to permit the rainfall to be effective for plant growth. Even in the subtropical parts of middle latitudes, California, for example, the winters, although not without frosts, still are so mild that a complete dormant season for plants is not imposed. In such regions, therefore, winter rainfall is of genuine direct value for crops. In microthermal climates, on the other hand, where relatively long and severe winters definitely limit the temperature season of plant growth and create a completely dormant season for vegetation, it is highly essential that the periods of sufficient warmth and sufficient rainfall coincide. Winter precipitation, much of it in the form of snow, is of no direct and immediate value to plants. The Mediterranean rainfall regime probably is the most efficient one for California, but for the Upper Mississippi Valley it would be disastrous. For the sake of emphasis, it bears repeating that coequal in importance with the *quantity* of rain that falls is the matter of its *distribution throughout the year*, or its *regime*.

Three principal types of climate are included within the microthermal group, viz., (a) *Da*, humid continental warm-summer climate; (b) *Db*, humid continental cool-summer climate; and (c) *Dc*, *Dd*, subarctic climate. The first two types, which are important agricultural climates, characteristically lie on the equatorward margins of the subarctic type, the latter occupying such high latitudes that agriculture ceases to be of great importance (Fig. 10.1).

Humid Continental Climates (*Da, Db*)

413. Location. Depending upon the presence or absence of mountain barriers, *Cb* climates of the west coasts change either abruptly or gradually into the more severe continental climates of the interiors (Plate I). In North America, where mountain chains parallel the west coasts, the change is sudden and abrupt; on the west European lowlands, on the other hand, it is very gradual. A further contrast distinguishes the two great Northern Hemisphere continents as regards arrangement of climates (Fig. 10.1). In North America, arid and semiarid conditions separate marine *Cb* climates from the continental climates farther east. This results from the abrupt halting of the moisture-bearing winds from the west by mountain barriers, so that to the leeward of the highlands it is dry. A humid marine climate (*C*), therefore, passes over directly into a dry continental one *BS(W)k*. In Eurasia, on the other hand, where, except in Scandinavia, the absence of high mountains permits the deep entrance of humid maritime air masses into the continent, humid continental climate lies both to the east and to the west of the dry interior. Consequently, this type is to be found in both central

and eastern Europe, as well as in eastern Asia (Plate I).

In North America the humid continental climates *Da* and *Db* lie poleward of latitude 35 or 40°. On their equatorward margins they pass over into the humid subtropical *Ca* type, and on their poleward sides they make contact with subarctic climate. This same arrangement is repeated in eastern Asia. In Europe, on the other hand, *Cs* replaces humid subtropical *Ca* climate on the southern frontier (Plate I).

On first thought it may seem odd that severe land-controlled climates should extend down to the sea margins on the eastern sides of continents. It is because these are leeward sides that the adjacent ocean is relatively ineffective in greatly modifying temperature conditions. The general atmospheric circulation in the middle latitudes is from west to east, so that polar maritime air masses from the ocean to the east find it difficult to move westward into the continent. The tendency toward monsoon wind systems along these eastern margins only accentuates the continentality, resulting in a prevalence of *cP* air in winter and some *mT* air in summer.

TEMPERATURE

414. Seasons Severe. Warm to hot summers and cold winters are characteristic of the humid continental climates, so that annual ranges are large. The monsoonal winds, bringing importations from lower latitudes in summer and from the higher latitudes in winter, tend only to emphasize further the normal seasonal severity. In general, the rigorousness of the climate increases from south to north and likewise from coasts toward the interior. Westerly winds and winter monsoons tend to carry continental air masses down to the eastern littorals, but there is some onshore wind of cyclonic and summer-monsoon origin which acts to meliorate conditions slightly, with the result that east coasts have *modified* continental climates. For example, at New York City and Omaha, Neb., in similar latitudes, but the former on the Atlantic Seaboard and the latter deep in the interior, the July temperatures are 73.9 and 76.8°, respectively, while their January temperatures are 30.9 and 21.8°. The

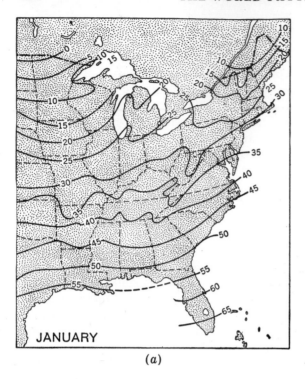

JANUARY

(*a*)

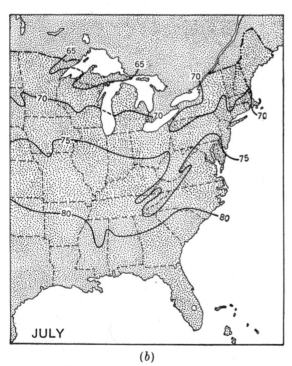

JULY

(*b*)

Fig. 10.3. Surface temperature gradients in the micro-thermal climates of central and eastern United States are much steeper in January (*A*) than in July (*B*).

annual range, consequently, is 43.0° at New York and 55.0° at Omaha. The higher atmospheric humidity of the air along the seaboard causes the summer heat to be more oppressive and sultry, and the winter cold more raw and penetrating, than are the drier extremes of the interior. The degree of marine modification is greatest where coasts are deeply indented, as, for example, in extreme eastern Canada.

415. Seasonal Gradients. Summer and winter in the continental climates present marked contrasts in latitudinal temperature gradient. (Compare with seasonal insolation gradients.) In the warm season the few isotherms that cross central and eastern United States are spaced far apart so that one does not experience marked temperature changes in going from north to south, the rate of change being in the neighborhood of 1° for every degree of latitude, or approximately 70 miles (Fig. 10.3). These same weak summer gradients are characteristic of eastern Asia. In winter, on the other hand, temperature changes very rapidly from north to south, in eastern United States the rate being 2.5° for each degree of latitude. Between Harbin, Manchuria, and Hankow, China, there is only 13° difference in July, but there is 42° in January. Between St. Louis and Winnipeg the January contrast amounts to 34.5°; the July contrast to only 13°. Obviously, there is much more reason for northerners to go south to escape winter cold than for southerners to go north to escape summer heat. The steeper temperature gradients of winter make possible much sharper temperature variations with changes in wind direction. The growing season varies greatly in length from north to south in the continental climates, approaching 200 days on the low-latitude margins and decreasing to 100± days on the subarctic side.

PRECIPITATION

416. Amount and Distribution. Rainfall decreases (*a*) from the seaward margins toward the interiors and (*b*) usually toward the higher latitudes as well. Thus along their interior margins the humid continental climates make contact with dry climates, and their interior sectors are definitely subhumid. The regions of the prairies, to be found in both interior Eurasia and North America, illustrate their drier subtype. For reasons previously stated, these land-controlled climates are likely to receive their abundant precipitation in the warm season, although winters are not necessarily dry. More especially it is (a) the deep continental interiors and (b) the regions of marked monsoonal tendencies in which summers are emphatically rainier than winters. At Peking in North China, a station typical of regions having well-developed monsoons, December and January have only 0.1 in. of precipitation, while July and August have 9 and 6 in., respectively. Omaha, Neb., typical of an interior regime in North America, has 0.7 in. in January and 4.7 in June. Over much of the United States *east* of the Mississippi, however, the discrepancy between winter and summer precipitation is not so marked. New York City, which receives 3.3 in. in each of the three winter months, has only slightly more, 4.1 and 4.3 in., in July and August, respectively. Its total for the year, however, is 42.5 in.

The western part of the *Da-Db* region in North America had an original vegetation cover of prairie grasses, and the prairie extended eastward in the form of a wedge across the state of Illinois (Fig. 10.4). This eastward projection of the grasslands into the forest has been interpreted as having a climatic origin.[1] The regional distinctiveness of the "prairie wedge" lies basically in its precipitation characteristics: (a) Low snowfall and low rainfall are typical of winter. (b) There is a greater risk of a large rainfall deficit in summer than is true of the forest regions to the north and south. (c) There are fewer days with precipitation, less cloud, and lower relative humidity in July and August than in the forested region to the north. (d) Dry summers in the prairie wedge are characterized by large positive departures from average temperatures and by frequent hot winds. The above climatic characteristics of the prairie wedge are related to the region's position in the

[1] John Borchert, The Climate of the Central North American Grassland, *Ann. Assoc. Am. Geographers*, Vol. 40, pp. 1–39, 1950.

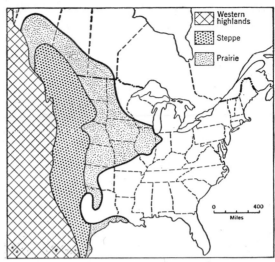

FIG. 10.4. Extensive areas in the western parts of the North American *Da-Db* are included within what is known as the "prairie wedge." Here the original vegetation was tall grass prairie, which was thrust eastward like a wedge into the humid forested areas of central United States. (*After Borchert.*)

general circulation pattern over North America, for it coincides approximately with the greatest mean transport of dry westerly continental air from the eastern base of the Rocky Mountains (Fig. 10.5).

417. *Early-summer Maximum.* In the more subhumid interior locations the period of maximum rainfall, more often than not, is in early summer and the late spring, rather than at the time of greatest heat (Fig. 10.6). This is the case in the Danube Basin and in the western part of the prairie region of the United States. At Belgrade, Yugoslavia, June is the wettest month, and May has more precipitation than July. At Omaha, June likewise receives the maximum amount. Lacking a forest mantle, the shallow snow cover of these subhumid lands melts rapidly with the advance of spring, and the dry earth warms quickly under the strong insolation. By May or June, therefore, the lower air has become relatively warm although the upper layers, in which there is a greater seasonal temperature lag, are still cool. Atmospheric instability, and consequently convectional overturning, is therefore greatest in early summer when there is a maximum temperature contrast between lower and

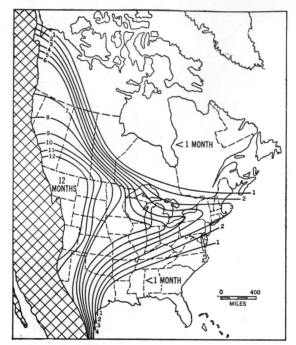

Fig. 10.5. Average number of months per year with a mean transport of dry continental air from the eastern base of the Rocky Mountains. It is this greater frequency of dry continental air, resulting in a unique combination of climatic characteristics, which produced the prairie wedge. (*After Borchert.*)

upper air. Later in the summer, even though surface temperatures are higher, there is less vertical contrast. The economic importance to agricultural production of having the year's rainfall relatively concentrated in the early part of the growing season cannot be overestimated. It is in their tillering period, which is spring and early summer, that cereals are developing stems and basal leaves and therefore require the greatest amounts of moisture. The maturing and

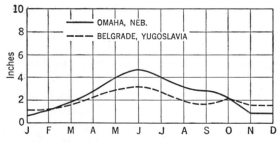

Fig. 10.6. Illustrating the early summer maximum of precipitation characteristic of extensive interior subhumid *Da-Db* regions.

harvesting season for grains preferably should be warm, bright, and dry.

418. Winter Precipitation. Winter precipitation is largely frontal in origin. In North America *mT* air masses moving poleward up the Mississippi Valley are continuously being chilled at their base, so that stability is increased and convectional overturning is unlikely. But usually the *mT* air masses do not advance very far northward before coming into conflict with denser polar air masses over which they are forced to ascend. Sometimes the front develops even before *mT* reaches the northern Gulf Coast and only occasionally does the tropical air advance at the surface farther north than the Great Lakes region. But even in winter *mT* air is sufficiently humid that when it is forced up over the colder air it yields moderate amounts of precipitation, which falls from a dull, gray, monotonous cloud cover that blankets the sky from horizon to horizon. The livelier skies of summer with their tumultuous cumulus clouds are largely lacking in winter. In northeastern Asia with its stronger winter monsoon the *cP* surges are so frequent that surface *mT* air is practically unknown in North China and Manchuria in the cool months. Winter precipitation in these regions is very meager.

Cool-season precipitation in *Da* and *Db* climates is partly in the form of snow, and a permanent snow cover, varying from a few weeks to several months in duration, is typical. Owing to the fact that (*a*) it takes 5 to 15 in. of snow to equal an inch of rain and (*b*) snow tends to remain on the ground while rain does not, the total less precipitation of winter may be more conspicuous and impressive than summer's greater amount. This contrast is further accentuated by the fact that the cyclonic winter precipitation is continuous over longer periods of time than are the sharper convectional showers of summer. In those parts of northeastern United States and Canada where winter cyclones are particularly numerous and well developed (Great Lakes region, St. Lawrence Valley, New England, and the Canadian Maritime Provinces) snow becomes excessively deep Thus northern New England and New York have more than 7 ft. of snowfall during an average winter, and the snow cover remains on the ground for more than 4 months. In parts of the Adirondack Mountains 150 in. or more of snow falls annually. Over the American Great Plains, on the other hand, it amounts to only 20 to 30 in.

419. Summer Precipitation. Summer rains in *Da-Db* climates have a larger proportion of their total in the form of convectional showers falling from cumulonimbus clouds. These summer showers are less extensive than the rains of winter, are of shorter duration, and are inclined to be more vigorous. In spite of the fact that the warm season has more total precipitation than winter, it has, at the same time, a smaller proportion of cloud. Thunder and lightning not infrequently accompany the summer showers. In Hungary, 61 per cent of the rain in June falls on days with thunderstorms (Kendrew). A fair percentage of the thunderstorms of continental climates are of the simple heat variety resulting from excessive surface heating. Some are associated with the fronts of cyclones. Steady cyclonic rains falling from gray, overcast skies are not absent, by any means, but this type of weather is less frequent in summer than in the cooler seasons when the polar front is farther equatorward. On the whole, cyclonic weather is most typical of the poleward margins of the continental climates.

SEASONAL WEATHER

420. Nonperiodic Weather Changes Characteristic. In no other types of climate are rapid and marked nonperiodic weather changes in winter so characteristic as in the humid continentals, for it is in these latitudes that the conflict between polar and tropical air masses reaches a maximum development. The spells of weather associated with the passage of cyclonic and anticyclonic storms are equally, if not more, numerous in the marine *Cb* climates, but in those locations the accompanying temperature changes are not nearly so severe. In central and eastern United States in particular, which is freely open to the movements of air masses from both north and south, storm control is especially strong. This North American *Da-Db* is the earth's most important *continental* region of cyclogenesis in middle latitudes. The weather element is less pronounced in eastern Asia, where unusually strong seasonal high- and low-pressure centers, with their monsoon wind systems, hinder cyclonic development, particularly in winter. Greater surface relief in eastern Asia likewise obstructs the free latitudinal movement of air masses. The net result is that the principal tracks of winter cyclones are located over the ocean to the east of Asia and there is much less storm actively over the continent itself than is true in North America.

It is in the cold season, when the sun has retreated farthest south, and with it the storm belt, that the continental climates experience the strongest nonperiodic control of weather. At that season the diurnal sun control is usually subordinate, and weather conditions are dominated by moving cyclones and anticyclones associated with rapidly shifting polar and tropical air masses and the fronts that develop along their boundaries. The daily rise and fall of temperatures with the sun many times are obscured by the larger nonperiodic oscillations caused by importations of temperature by air masses from polar and tropical latitudes (Figs. 10.18, 10.19). These sharp temperature changes are made possible by the steep thermal gradients of winter, which causes a north wind to be excessively cold, while a south wind, on the other hand, may import unseasonable warmth. Both cyclones and anticyclones tend to move faster, and to be larger, more frequent, and more severe in winter than at any other season. As a consequence, changes in temperature, wind, and weather in general are likewise more severe and more frequent in winter. In eastern United States there is a distinct concentration of winter storm tracks over the northeastern states; thus it is this region which experiences the most frequent weather changes. With increasing distance from the northeastern region of concentration, both to the south and to the west, storm control weakens, and less frequent weather changes occur.

In the deep interiors and higher middle latitudes of the continents the severe winter cold tends to develop what appears on the winter pressure chart to be a seasonal anticyclonic cell. In reality such cells are not static in character but rather are the monthly average of the numerous thrusts of polar air out of the subarctic source regions. These masses of dense cold air act to hold at bay the cyclonic storms, so that changeable cyclonic weather is somewhat less pronounced, and dry, cold, settled weather is more conspicuous. Although the number of clear days is relatively numerous, considering the small amounts of precipitation, cloudiness seems high. However, there are many gray days with stratus clouds on which no precipitation occurs.

421. Winter-weather Types. The usual cycle of weather changes with the passage of a winter cyclone, followed by an anticyclone, has been described in an earlier part of this book. But, on the other hand, there is an almost infinite variety of weather variations depending on the season, the differing intensity and extensiveness of the storms, the types and characteristics of the air masses and fronts involved, the

tracks taken by individual storms, and the contrasting patterns of high-level atmospheric circulation. As a consequence, it has thus far been impossible to work out a satisfactory classification of weather types. However, even the layman who is interested in weather is conscious of certain very general weather types, such as the cold wave, warm wave, mid-winter thaw, general snowstorm, gray overcast days with no precipitation, and numerous others. There are additional ones which are characteristic of seasons other than winter. A number of the more common weather types are illustrated by the sketches of synoptic conditions represented in Figs. 10.7 to 10.16. These are worthy of careful study, for microthermal climates are incapable of being understood apart from an understanding of the weather types which dominate their climates. Among the weather types of winter, which, because of their spectacular character, have gained a reputation out of proportion to their importance and frequency of occurrence, are the *blizzard* and the *cold wave*.

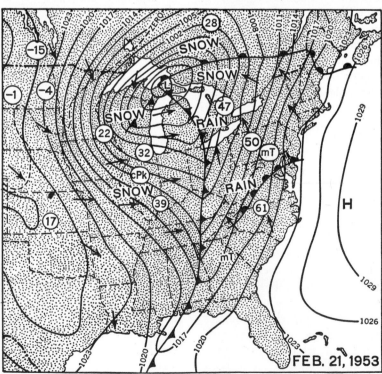

Fig. 10.7. An extensive winter storm over the general Great Lake's area which was accompanied by widespread precipitation, both snow and rain. Air temperature at 1:30 A.M. shown by figures within circles.

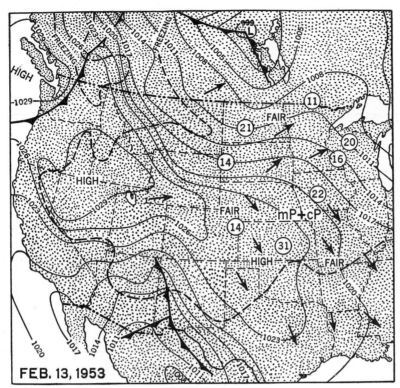

FIG. 10.8. Fine, clear winter weather over central United States associated with a high-pressure system composed principally of modified *mP* air from the Pacific. Temperatures at 1:30 A.M. shown by figures in circles.

422. *Blizzard.* This weather type is more than just a heavy snowstorm, for a genuine blizzard is "a gale of wind, zero cold, and drifting powdery snow." Actually, there may be no precipitation falling at the time; yet the air is filled to a height of several hundred feet by swirling masses of dry, finely pulverized snow, whipped up from the freshly fallen cover. Sometimes the sun can be perceived shining wanly through the shroud of flakes. It is the combination of wind, cold, and blinding snow that makes these storms dangerous to both man and beast who may be caught out in them. In the famous blizzard of Jan. 12, 1888, over the American Northern Plains states, winds of 50 miles an hour were recorded, accompanied by temperature of 20° below zero. In this storm between two and three hundred persons are reported to have lost their lives, and thousands of cattle perished. The genuine blizzard, although extremely rare in the eastern states, occurs occasionally in the Middle West but is most truly representative of the western Prairie and Plains states. Under the name of *buran*, the blizzard is also known to the prairie lands of Russia and Siberia.

On the synoptic chart this weather type is associated with unusually steep pressure gradients in fresh polar continental air on the rear of a well-developed cold front. The frontal precipitation in the cyclone lays down the necessary new cover of loose, soft snow. The violent northwest winds and rapidly falling temperatures on the rear of the cold front provide the remaining prerequisites.

423. *Cold Wave.* More frequent and less restricted in areal distribution than the genuine blizzard, the cold wave is also a typical phenomenon of humid continental winters and particularly of the American sector. Not every sharp drop in temperature is a cold wave, for to be an authentic one (*a*) the thermometer must fall a certain number of degrees within 24 hr., and (*b*) it must drop below a certain fixed minimum. In northern United States for a genuine winter

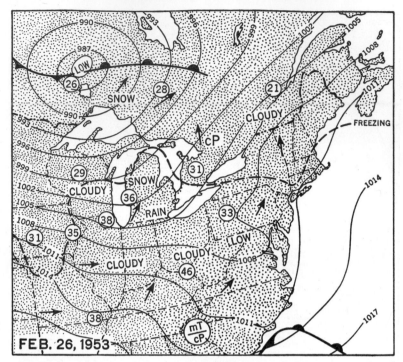

FIG. 10.9. A relatively extensive cyclone traveling on a northern track and giving rise to mild, cloudy weather with light precipitation over extensive areas of north central United States. Temperatures shown are for 1:30 A.M.

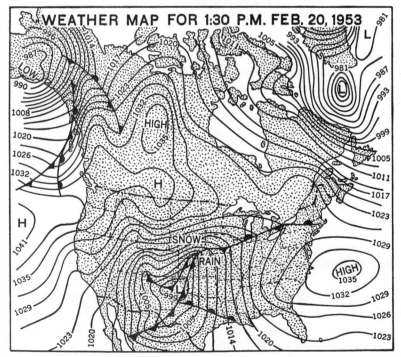

FIG. 10.10. A well-developed winter storm originating in the Texas area and following a track to the northeast. Such storms characteristically bring heavy precipitation, much of it in the form of snow.

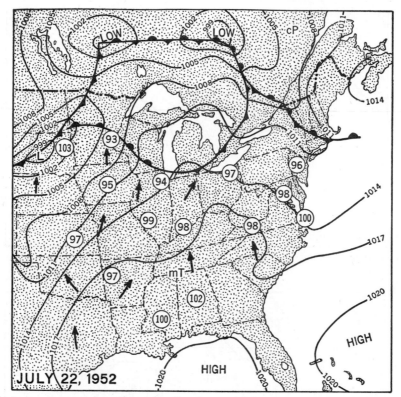

Fig. 10.11. A July heat wave over the whole central and eastern part of the country. Temperatures shown are the maxima for the 12 hr. preceding. *mT* air from the anticyclone over the Gulf is the dominant control.

cold wave the temperature must fall 20° within 24 hr. and must at least reach a minimum of zero. This weather type is associated with a rapid invasion of a *cP* air mass following a cold front (Fig. 5.16). It is usually preceded by mild weather with rain or snow on the front of a retreating cyclone. The sharp drop in temperature, which is the cold wave, occurs when the wind shifts from a southerly to a northerly direction, or in other words, when the cold front separating tropical and *cP* air is passed. The lowest temperatures, however, may not be reached during the blowing of the strong northwest wind but, rather, a day or two later in the calm air near the center of the anticyclone, when radiation and conduction produce the maximum surface cooling.

424. Summer Weather. Compared with winter, with its strong nonperiodic storm control, summer is more under the influence of the sun, with consequent diurnal regularity of weather. The polar-front storm belt swings northward with the sun, leaving the humid continental regions on its southern margins. As a result weather becomes more stable. Temperatures are much the same over wide areas. Not only are cyclones and anticyclones fewer and weaker, but the normal seasonal temperature gradients are also weak, so that importations from north or south cannot bring such violent changes. Several days in succession with south winds, however, may force the maximum temperatures to 90+° and occasionally even to 100° and over. *Diurnal* variations in wind velocity and temperature are characteristic. Cumulus clouds and afternoon thunderstorms tend partially to replace the sullen, gray skies and long-continued spells of precipitation characteristic of winter. Summer has some of the aspects of tropical weather.

Cyclones and anticyclones, while both less frequent and weaker in summer, nevertheless

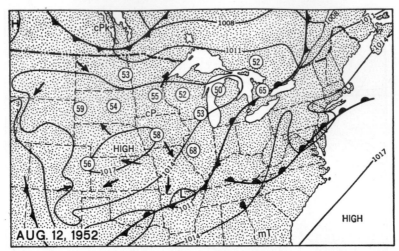

FIG. 10.12. A spell of fine, cool summer weather has been produced by a high-pressure system composed of fresh *cP* air. Temperatures are for 1:30 A.M.

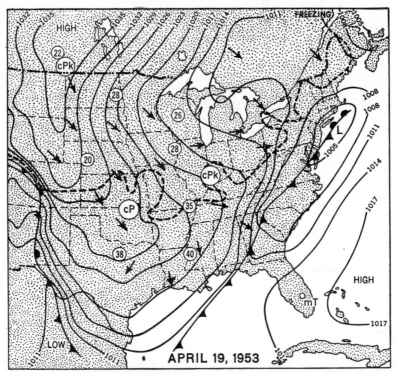

FIG. 10.13. A cold anticyclone in April with northwest winds carries low temperatures into subtropical United States and results in a severe freeze in the north central states.

serve to break the regularity of sun-controlled weather during that season. *Hot waves, convectional* and *frontal thunderstorms, summer cool waves,* and *drought spells* are a few of the more common weather types of the hot season. Spells of unusu-

ally hot weather, with maximum temperatures of over 90° on several successive days, are usually caused by long-continued importation by southerly winds of tropical air masses. The arrangement of storm areas on the weather map for such an invasion of tropical air is nearly opposite to that for cold waves. Hot waves occur with northward-sloping barometric gradients, when a relatively stagnant high centers over the south and southwest, and a weak, slowly moving low, with little cloud, lies to the north (Fig. 10.11). Cold-front thunderstorms are associated with elongated V-shaped lows in which there is a distinct wind-shift line (Fig. 5.32). Preceded by days with south winds and high temperatures, the heat wave is broken when the eastward-advancing cold front, with its general turbulence and thunderstorms, is reached, and the wind shifts to northwest. The delightfully cool polar air on the rear of such a storm brings the summer cool waves. Many of the summer drought spells in the humid continental regions of the United States appear to be associated with the development of an anticyclonic condition over the Gulf States, which blocks the normal northward

progress of mT air and substitutes for it the dry subsiding air of the anticyclone.

425. Spring and Fall Weather. Spring and fall, the transition seasons, witness a more even struggle between storm and sun control. At times the one and then the other is in the ascendancy, so that there is something of an oscillation between summer and winter conditions. Mild, warm days in April and early May, with regular diurnal rise and fall of the thermometer, resembling summer, may be followed by a reestablishment of winter conditions as a passing cyclone lays down a snow cover, and the following polar air mass drops the temperatures to an unseasonable frost. Continental climates are famous for their fickleness of spring weather (Figs. 10.13, 10.14, 10.15, 10.16).

Autumn brings some of the loveliest days of the entire year but likewise some of the rawest, gloomiest weather. Bright, clear weather with

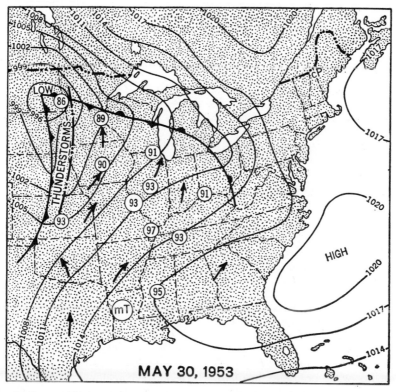

Fig. 10.14. A spring heat wave over central United States occasioned by a northward flow of mT air into a low centered over the Dakotas. Note the squall line, with thunderstorms, in advance of the cold front. Temperatures shown are the maxima for preceding 12 hr.

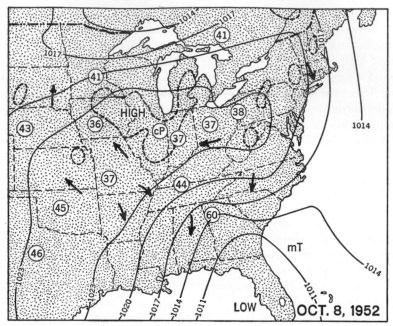

Fig. 10.15. Fine, clear weather in October produced by a mass of *cP* air associated with a large cold anticyclone. Temperatures shown are for 1:30 A.M. 32°-isotherm shown by dashed line.

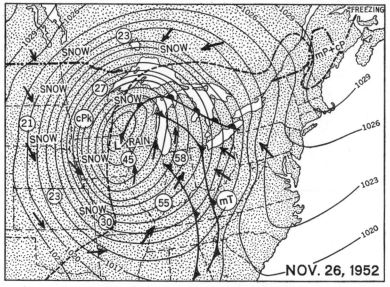

Fig. 10.16. A well-developed autumn storm accompanied by extensive precipitation in the form of snow and rain and by strong winds. Temperatures shown are for 1:30 A.M.

warm midday temperatures and crisp, frosty nights comes with polar-air-mass control. A reestablishment of hot-wave gradients in October and November after severe frost, and perhaps even snow, causes a temporary return of summer conditions. The result is those much-cherished spells of warm weather with hazy, smoky atmosphere, known as *Indian summer*. But well-developed cyclonic storms of this season may also bring those raw gray days with chilly rain, and occasionally a temporary snowy winter landscape may be produced as early as October.

Da, Humid Continental Climate, Warm Summer (Daf and Daw)

426. Type Location. This warm-summer phase of humid continental climates is sometimes designated as "corn-belt climate," because much of the world's commercial maize crop is grown in regions having its imprint. It is also occasionally called the "oak-maple-hickory climate" because of its reasonably strong regional coincidence with that hardwood-forest association.

Because this is the milder of the two humid continental climates, it is to be expected that, characteristically, it will be located on the southern margins of the general microthermal group. On its poleward side is the more severe cool-summer phase of continental climate (Db), while to the south is one or the other of the mesothermal subtropical types (Figs. 6.4, 10.1, Plate I). The boundary between Da and Db is the 22°C., or 71.6°F., isotherm for the warmest month. It is obvious, by reason of the latitudinal location, that warm-summer humid continental climate (Da) is the mildest and most equable of all those included within the microthermal group.

In the United States this subtype includes a tier of states, extending from cental Kansas and Nebraska on the west to the Atlantic Seaboard and including, besides those states mentioned, Iowa, northern and central Missouri, Illinois, Indiana, Ohio, and portions of Pennsylvania, Maryland, New Jersey, and Connecticut. The American corn belt lies within its borders. In Europe the Da type prevails chiefly in the south-central portions of that continent—the Danube and Balkan States and the upper Po Valley of Italy. It is on the plains of the Danube and in the Po Valley that much of Europe's maize crop is grown. The third principal region, in eastern Asia, includes much of North China and most of Korea. This Asiatic segment is where the monsoon regime of winds and rainfall is particularly well developed, so that Daw is more common than Daf.

TEMPERATURE

427. Summers are characteristically long, warm, and humid, this condition being asso-

ciated with the general prevalence of conditionally unstable mT air masses (Fig. 10.17). The American and the Asiatic Da regions have summer temperatures that are subtropical or even tropical in character (July at Des Moines 77°; St. Louis, 79°; Tientsin, 81°; Mukden, Manchuria, 77°). The European Da on the whole has less intense summer heat, July averages more often being under than above 75° (Bucharest, 73°; Milan, 75°). Typical American corn-belt cities have average July temperatures in the neighborhood of 75°. Summers are not only warm, but they are inclined to be relatively humid as well, so that a summer month contains a large number of sultry, oppressive days when the inhabitants experience great physical discomfort. At Urbana, Ill., in the heart of the corn belt, where the average July temperature is 75°, the mean of the daily maxima is 85.7°, while the highest temperature ever recorded is 105°. Not only are the days hot, but, because of the high absolute humidity, nocturnal cooling is not rapid, so that nights, too, are often uncom-

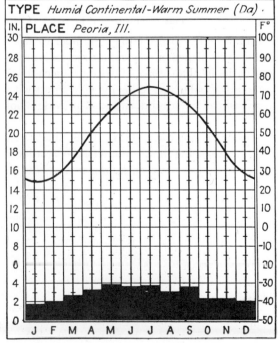

FIG. 10.17. A representative station with Da climate located in the corn belt of the United States. Note the summer maximum of precipitation.

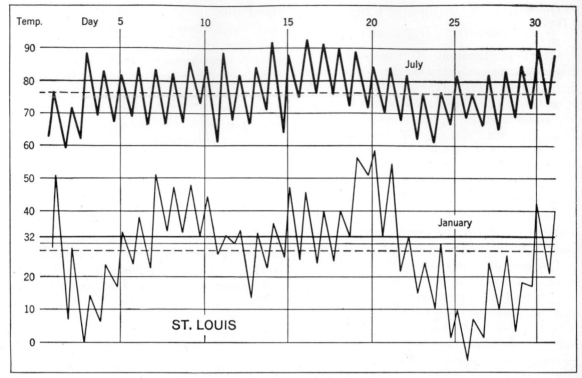

FIG. 10.18. A *Da* station. Note the stronger air-mass control of daily temperatures in winter as compared with summer.

fortably warm. Urbana has a July mean daily minimum temperature of 64°. Summer weather with its prevalence of tropical air masses is much less variable than that of winter. Occasional invasions of polar air, following cold fronts with their associated thunderstorms, provide cool spells that now and then interrupt the standard succession of hot days (Figs. 10.18, 10.19). In addition to being hot, summers are relatively long, the period between killing frosts being in the neighborhood of 150 to 200 days. As a result, these are productive climates agriculturally.

428. Winters are likely to be relatively cold but with spells of mild, disagreeable, and sometimes foggy weather, associated with tropical air masses, sandwiched in between the periods of cold. The average January temperature at Urbana is 25.6°, and the average of the daily minima is only 17.5°, although 25° below zero has been known to occur (Figs. 10.18, 10.19).

Climatic Data for Representative Da Stations

Peoria, Illinois

	J	F	M	A	M	J	J	A	S	O	N	D	Yr.	Range
Temp.	24	28	40	51	62	71	75	73	65	53	39	28	50.8	51.6
Precip.	1.8	2.0	2.7	3.3	3.9	3.8	3.8	3.2	3.8	2.4	2.4	2.0	34.9	

New York City

	J	F	M	A	M	J	J	A	S	O	N	D	Yr.	Range
Temp.	31	31	39	49	60	69	74	72	67	56	44	34	52.1	43.0
Precip.	3.3	3.3	3.4	3.3	3.4	3.4	4.1	4.3	3.4	3.4	3.4	3.3	42.0	

Bucharest, Rumania

	J	F	M	A	M	J	J	A	S	O	N	D	Yr.	Range
Temp.	26	29	40	52	61	68	73	71	64	54	41	30	50.7	47.5
Precip.	1.2	1.1	1.7	2.0	2.5	3.3	2.8	1.9	1.5	1.5	1.9	1.7	23.0	

Peking, China

	J	F	M	A	M	J	J	A	S	O	N	D	Yr.	Range
Temp.	24	29	41	57	68	76	79	77	68	55	39	27	53	55
Precip.	0.1	0.2	0.2	0.6	1.4	3.0	9.4	6.3	2.6	0.6	0.3	0.1	24.9	

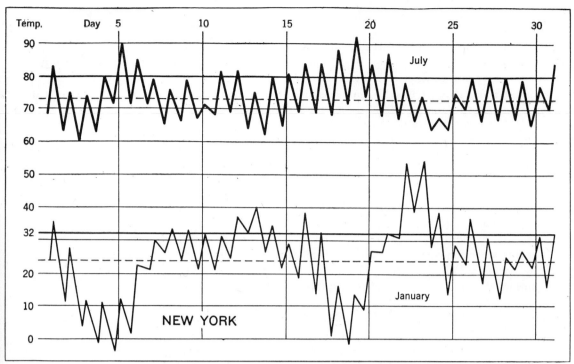

FIG. 10.19. A *Da* station along the Atlantic Seaboard of the United States. Air-mass control is most conspicuous in winter.

St. Louis has an average January temperature of 32°; Bucharest, Rumania, 25.5°; and Peking, China, 23.5°. Monthly averages, however, are not of great value for describing winter temperatures, since the latter are composed of such wide variants. Since the *Da* climate is bounded by such opposite temperature conditions on its northern and southern frontiers, it is to be expected that marked temperature contrasts can be produced through importations by north and south winds bringing polar and tropical air masses.

PRECIPITATION

429. Amount. In terms of the total amount of precipitation, most of the world regions possessing humid continental climate with warm summers suffer from too little, rather than too much rainfall. Thus much of the Asiatic and European *Da*, and the western portion of this climatic region in the United States, are all subhumid in character, with grass as the prevailing type of natural vegetation. It is chiefly Korea, Japan,

the eastern and central portions of the American *Da* region, and highlands elsewhere that are fortunate in having more than 30 in. of precipitation. Occasional crop failures as a result of drought are characteristic of the subhumid portions. This is especially true in North China where, because of the very dense population, drought years are likewise famine years.

430. Annual Distribution. Summer rains predominate, the warm-season maximum being particularly marked in (*a*) the more subhumid portions or (*b*) where monsoons prevail (Fig. 10.17). This is fortunate, for in regions with severe winters, and where precipitation is none too bountiful, it is especially necessary for rainfall to be concentrated in the growing season for crops. More of the warm-season rain is derived from convectional showers than is true for cooler climates farther poleward. With such local thundershowers the cloud cover is usually of short duration, so that relatively abundant sunshine and high temperatures are possible in spite of moderate summer rainfall. The warm summertime convectional rains have the advantage of permitting a maximum of sunshine and heat along with an abundance of rain. Such a condition is ideal for the corn crop. At Peoria, Ill., though there is a distinct concentration of rainfall in the warm months, it is this same season that has the largest amount of sunshine. For example, July has 3.77 in. of precipitation, falling on 10 rainy days, and 75 per cent of the possible sunshine. January, with only 1.8 in. of precipitation and 9 rainy days, has only 47 per cent of the possible sunshine. Emphatically, summers are more sunny than winters, even though the rainfall is heavier. Days with thunderstorms are numerous, averaging 40 to 60 a year in the American corn belt. Many of these are local storms associated with strong insolational surface heating in potentially unstable mT air.

Winter precipitation is usually less than that of summer. Only in Korea, Japan, parts of central Europe, and central and eastern United States can winters be classed as distinctly humid (Daf) (Fig. 10.20). North China represents the opposite extreme, for at Peking the combined precipitation of the three winter months is only 0.4 in., as compared with 18.7 in. for the three summer months (Daw). This reflects the well-developed system of monsoon winds which dominates eastern Asia. The dry winters and strong continental winds characteristic of North China cause it to be a dusty region with extensive loess deposits. The western margins of the American corn belt also have a relatively marked winter minimum in precipitation, with only 2 to 4 in. during December to February inclusive. Central Europe has somewhat more in winter but still only about one-half the normal amount that falls in summer. In these two latter regions, however, the winter minimum is not sufficiently marked to warrant the symbol Daw.

431. Snowfall. A portion of the winter precipitation falls as snow, although it is usually less than one-half the season's total. At Peoria, Ill., perhaps one-third or one-fourth of winter's precipitation is in the solid form. Over the American corn belt snow falls on 20 to 30 days of the year, the total amounting to 10 to 40 in.

The number of days with snow cover varies from 10± on the southern margin to 60+ on the poleward side. Heaviest snows result from those cyclonic storms that loop well to the south, so that the middle tier of states is covered by the northeastern and northwestern storm quadrants. Since, in general, more storms pass to the north than to the south of the American corn belt, southerly importations and rain are frequent, even in winter. In the Da region of central Europe snow falls on 20 to 30 days out of the year (Bucharest, 20.6; Belgrade, 26.1; Budapest, 30.7). Snowfall in the Daw region of Asia is extremely meager, and the ground is free from snow much of the time.

Db, Humid Continental Climate, Cool Summer (Dbf and Dbw)

432. Type Location. This more severe phase of humid continental climate lies on the poleward side of the warm summer type and between it and subarctic climate (Fig. 10.1). It is sometimes designated as the "spring-wheat" type, since that important commercial crop reaches its most specialized development in the subhumid parts of Db. This is scarcely the case in the more humid parts, however. In North America the type is found in general east of the 100th meridian and includes the northern tier of states in the United States and portions of southern Canada as well (Plate I). In Eurasia it includes most of Poland, eastern Germany, southern Sweden, and a large part of the central Russian plain between latitudes 50 and 60°+. Beyond the Urals it extends on into Siberia as a narrow strip in the vicinity of latitude 55°. In much of European Russia and Siberia it is terminated on the south by steppe climate. The third large representative area is in northeastern Asia, more especially central and northern Manchuria, southeastern Siberia, and northern Japan.

TEMPERATURE

433. Temperatures Relatively Extreme. Because of its characteristic location in higher latitudes, temperatures are somewhat lower than in the Da type farther south (Figs. 10.20, 10.21,

10.22). This is much more emphatically the case with winter than with summer, for while the hot months are only 5 to 10° cooler, average winter temperatures are 10 to 30° lower. It is the severer winters, then, that chiefly account for the larger annual ranges. Summers are usually moderately warm for a few months, the average July temperatures being about 65 to 70° (Grand Forks, N.D., 69°; Montreal 69°; Moscow 66°; Barnaul, Siberia, 67°; Sapporo, Japan, 69°). But the climate is handicapped by reason of the relatively short duration of summer. Thus, while Indianapolis (*Da*) has 7 months the average temperatures of which are over 50°, Fargo and Winnipeg have only 5. Frost comes early and remains late, so that the growing season is only 3+ to 5 months in length, which is insufficient for a number of crops. Offsetting somewhat the two handicaps of shorter and cooler summers is the advantage of the longer days that prevail in the higher latitudes. Thus, at the time of the Northern Hemisphere summer solstice, Winnipeg has a daily period of insolation which is more than 1 hr. longer than that of St. Louis.

434. Summer. Midday temperatures in July are likely to be warm to hot, especially when the sun is shining. Overcast days, on the other hand, are inclined to be chilly. It is not unusual to experience summer days with temperatures of 90 and above (Fig. 10.21). In a recent summer, Bismarck, N.D., had 20 days when the thermometer reached 90° or above and 4 when it touched or exceeded 100°. The next year there were 14 days with 90° or above, but none that reached 100°. Hot waves, similar in origin to those in the regions farther south, do occur, but they are

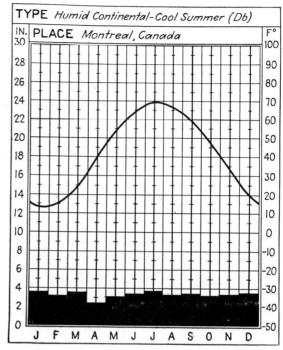

FIG. 10.20. Note the absence of any strong seasonal maximum of precipitation. Owing to the large number of winter cyclones, northeastern United States and adjacent parts of Canada have a large amount of snow.

usually not quite so severe or so long. There are, on the other hand, more spells of cool weather associated with polar air masses than in the *Da* type, for, in North America at least, *Db* is closer to the tracks of summer cyclones. It is the more frequent invasions of cool polar air that draw down the general summer average.

435. Winter is characteristically the dominant season. At Barnaul, Siberia, the January average is −2°; Bismarck, N.D., 8°, Sapporo,

Climatic Data for Representative Db Stations

Montreal, Canada

	J	F	M	A	M	J	J	A	S	O	N	D	Yr.	Range
Temp.	13	15	25	41	55	65	69	67	59	47	33	19	42	56
Precip.	3.7	3.2	3.7	2.4	3.1	3.5	3.8	3.4	3.5	3.3	3.4	3.7	40.7	

Moscow, U.S.S.R.

	J	F	M	A	M	J	J	A	S	O	N	D	Yr.	Range
Temp.	12	15	23	38	53	62	66	63	52	40	28	17	39	54
Precip.	1.1	1.0	1.2	1.5	1.9	2.0	2.8	2.9	2.2	1.4	1.6	1.5	21.1	

Winnipeg, Canada

	J	F	M	A	M	J	J	A	S	O	N	D	Yr.	Range
Temp.	−4	0	15	38	52	62	66	64	54	41	21	6	35	70
Precip.	0.9	0.7	1.2	1.4	2.0	3.1	3.1	2.2	2.2	1.4	1.1	0.9	20.2	

Vladivostok, U.S.S.R.

	J	F	M	A	M	J	J	A	S	O	N	D	Yr.	Range
Temp.	5	12	26	39	48	57	66	69	61	49	30	14	40	64
Precip.	0.1	0.2	0.3	1.2	1.3	1.5	2.2	3.5	2.4	1.6	0.5	0.2	14.7	

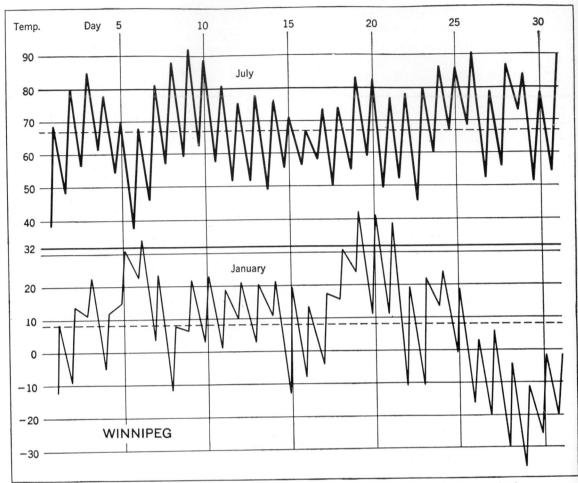

FIG. 10.21. A representative station with humid continental climate with cool summers (Db).

Japan, 21°; Uppsala, Sweden, 24°. But these averages are composed of very unlike temperature elements, since the succession of fronts and air masses brings much subzero weather as well as some that is distinctly above freezing (Fig. 10.21). At Bismarck, although the average January temperature is 8°, the average of the daily minima is −2.8°. Even the highest temperatures on most January days are well below freezing, for the mean of the daily maxima for that month is only 18.0. At Winnipeg the mean of the daily maxima for January is 6.2°, and of the daily minima −14.7°. The comparable figures for milder Quebec are 17.7° and 1.6°. In a recent January Bismarck had 5 days in which the temperature did not rise to zero and

13 in which it was constantly above zero. There were 14 days in which the minimum temperatures went below −10°. The lowest temperature for that particular year was about −37° although −45° has been recorded. But winter differ greatly from year to year in the continenta climates, for the following January Bismarck had only 1 day with temperature below −10° as compared with 14 the previous year. Large nonperiodic air-mass-controlled temperature fluctuations within a short period of time ar likewise characteristic, changes of 40° within 2 hr. being relatively common at Bismarck. O Mar. 3, 1913, a rise from −15 to nearly 50° wa recorded.

In the western portions of Europe's D

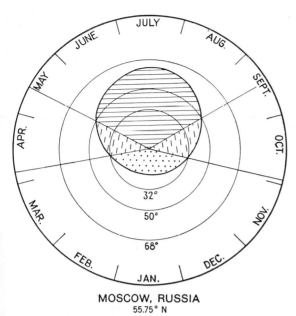

MOSCOW, RUSSIA
55.75° N

FIG. 10.22. Thermograph of a representative *Db* station in Europe. (*After Hartshorne.*)

(Germany, Poland, southern Sweden), although summers are cool so that the region must be classified as *b*, the winters are not correspondingly severe (Fig. 10.22). The mean January temperature of Berlin (31°) and Posen (29°), for example, are higher than for many *Da* regions in eastern Asia and eastern United States. This European section of *Db* is exceptional in that it is influenced to a considerable degree by maritime air masses that make its summers cool and at the same time keep its winters moderate. It is almost impossible to find stations in the European *Db* whose annual temperature curves closely match those of the North American *Db*. If they correspond in July, then the American stations are colder in January, and if the winter temperatures correspond, the American *Db* stations will have warmer summers. In general, the *Db* of Asia is the most severe, and that of Europe the least.

PRECIPITATION

436. Amount and Seasonal Distribution. Generalization is difficult concerning any total amount of precipitation characteristic of this climate. Interior North America, Siberia,

and Manchuria are representative of subhumid sections where rainfall is commonly less than 25 or 30 in. and in parts even less than 20 in. Eastern United States and Canada, northern Japan, and the western portions of Europe's *Db* region are representative of the more humid sections. It is in the former, or subhumid, group, that precipitation is more strikingly concentrated in the short period of warmth, winters being relatively dry. Thus Bismarck with only 17.4 in. of precipitation has 3.4 in. in June, the rainiest month, and only 0.5 in. in each of the two driest months, January and February. At Winnipeg, with an annual rainfall of 20.2 in., four to five times as much falls in July as in February, and at Vladivostok the comparable figures are 14.7 with 3.5 in. in July and 0.1 in. in January. In those regions with more abundant annual precipitation previously noted, especially eastern North America, winters are much less dry. In New England and the Maritime Provinces of Canada, where tracks of cyclones converge, winters have nearly, if not quite, as much precipitation as summers. For example, at Quebec, which has a total of 40.7 in., July has 4.3 and January 3.4 in., while Portland, Me., has slightly more precipitation in January (3.9 in.) than in July (3.4 in.). See Fig. 10.20.

As compared with *Da*, a much smaller proportion of the summer precipitation in *Db* climates originates as a result of surface heating of conditionally unstable air. Local heat thunderstorms, therefore, are not so numerous. More common is frontal summer rainfall, although, since the obliquely ascending warm air along the discontinuity surface is often conditionally unstable, the resulting precipitation may be showery in nature and associated with frontal thunderstorms. Drizzly cyclonic days are more frequent than in the types farther south, which are farther removed from the principal summer storm tracks. The prevalence of polar air masses in winter tends to reduce the amount of precipitation in that season. The winter precipitation is predominantly frontal in origin, falling chiefly as snow from gray, leaden skies.

437. Snowfall. Because of the lower winter temperatures, much more of the cool-season

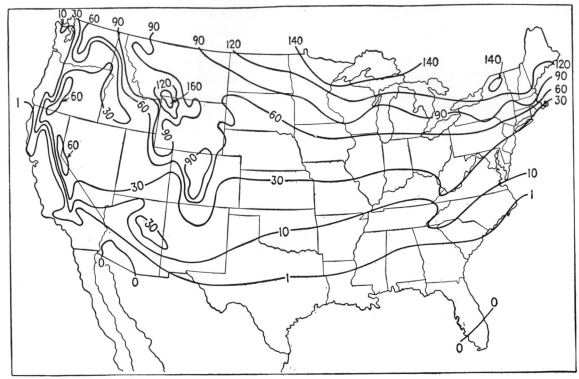

Fig. 10.23. Number of days with snow cover.

precipitation is in the form of snow than is true of the *Da* type to the south. In northern Minnesota there are 60 to 80 days with snowfall, the total amount being 40 to 60 in., while there is a durable snow cover for 120 days (Fig. 10.23). A similar situation with respect to duration of snow cover holds for northern New England, while the total snowfall there amounts to more than 80 in. The actual amount of snow is much less along the drier interior margins of this type, but, owing to the low temperatures, the number of days with snow cover may be quite as long. Ríga in Latvia has 72 days with snowfall and Warsaw in Poland 59 days. At Sapporo in western Hokkaido snow mantles the ground from November to April, and from January through March the snow cover averages about 40 in. in depth. Because of the long and continuous snow cover in *Db* climates, polar air masses advancing southward are not rapidly modified and made milder by these cold surfaces. The result is an increased severity of winter temperatures.

ASSOCIATED FEATURES OF THE PHYSICAL EARTH IN *Da*, *Db*, HUMID CONTINENTAL CLIMATES

438. Native Vegetation. *Grasslands.* Forests in the more humid portions and tall-grass prairie in the subhumid interiors are the characteristic arrangement of natural vegetation within the *Da*, *Db* regions (Fig. 7.12). In the United States and Canada, tall-grass prairies with deciduous woodlands along the streams originally prevailed throughout the eastern portions of the plains states and extended eastward as a >-shaped entrant into the forest belt as far as western Indiana, covering southern Minnesota, Iowa, northern Missouri, and central Illinois. The reason for this eastward extension of prairie into the forest appears to be of climatic origin. Extensive grasslands likewise exist on the Danube plains, in southeastern Russia, southwestern Siberia, and in northern China and Manchuria.

In the virgin state, these prairies provided

some of the finest natural grazing land on the earth. On the whole, however, they represent a natural environment in which it is possible to produce high-grade field crops, and prairie lands are, therefore, too valuable to be left permanently in grass and used for grazing. In the United States, most of the tall-grass prairie has been replaced by cultivated crops and is now the finest part of agricultural North America. In most of the other prairie segments of the realm mentioned above, crops have likewise replaced grass. Only in a few places is the grazing of animals on natural prairie grasses an important part of the regional economy.

439. *Forests.* Throughout the more humid portions of the realm, forests of a variety of types are characteristic. A representative north-south cross section of the humid continental forests would show conifers predominating toward the northern margins of the realm, with mixed forests and purer stands of deciduous hardwoods prevailing in the milder latitudes with warm summers. This rough latitudinal zonation is conspicuous in both eastern North America and in Europe, and in less perfect form is repeated in eastern Asia as well. Without doubt, forests of the humid continental realm were originally among the finest and most extensive of the earth. For decades they were the world's principal sources of lumber, and they still are important producers. However, because they were composed of such superior trees, and because of ready accessibility, they have suffered rapid cutting, so that over much the larger part of the original forested area in eastern United States only remnants of the superior virgin forest remain.

440. Zonal Soils. *Forest Soils.* Throughout the humid forested portions of the humid continental climates, soils with gray-brown coloration predominate (Fig. 7.13). These soils, which are characteristic of the *Cb* climates as well, have already been described for that subdivision, so that it is unnecessary to repeat much of what has been said. Gray-brown podzolic soils are particularly characteristic of the deciduous and mixed forests, which occupy all but the poleward margins, or the elevated and sandy portions, of the humid *Da, Db* regions. Here annual leaf fall from the deciduous trees and heavy underwood is a powerful factor in providing humus and maintaining a base status in the soil. Moreover, for a considerable part of the year, when the deciduous vegetation is bare of leaves, much sunshine reaches the earth, activating an important soil fauna. Earthworms, which are numerous, are effective in causing a rather even distribution of humus throughout the upper foot or so of soil. In fertility, structure, and adaptability, these are the best of the earth's forest soils.

On the cooler poleward margins, at higher altitudes, or where soils are sandy, podzolization processes are more active, with the result that soils are inferior. In the locations described above, needle trees are likely to replace hardwoods. Where the parent material is sandy, and poor in basic elements, podzol profiles develop most rapidly. In such soils heath plants and conifers, which require a minimum amount of mineral plant food, are particularly at home. The inferior structure, low humus content, and thoroughly leached nature of *podzols*, which ordinarily are overlain by a layer of raw acid humus, brands them as one of the world's poorest soils.

441. *Grassland Soils.* Where rainfall is somewhat less and tall prairie grasses instead of forests predominate, there have developed fertile, dark-colored, *prairie* and *chernozem* soils, types that are the antithesis of podzols. Such excellent soils in a measure help to compensate for the less abundant, and likewise somewhat less reliable, character of the rainfall.

Prairie soils represent a transition type between the humid gray-brown podzolic soils on the one hand, and the subhumid and semiarid chernozems on the other. In humid continental United States, which is the only *Da, Db* region (except possibly Manchuria) containing a large area of prairie soils, they extend as a north-south belt from western Minnesota through eastern Nebraska, Kansas, and Oklahoma into central Texas and then eastward as a >-shaped projection which includes Iowa, southern Minnesota, northern Missouri, and central Illinois. Rainfall is sufficient to cause considerable leaching of the soil, so that there is no zone of lime accumulation, and the soil is neutral in reaction. Nevertheless, the amount of humus, potash, and phosphates is high, and dark colorations predominate. Loessial materials are usually abundant. Although soil structure, which tends to be finely granular, is not so perfect as that of the chernozems, it is nevertheless good, so that tillage is easy. Unfortunately, the prairie soils, which among mature soils rank next to chernozems in quality, do not prevail over very extensive portions of the earth's surface. While not quite the aristocrat among soils that chernozem is, prairie soils, on the other hand, characteristically occupy regions of somewhat greater rainfall, so that their *total* agricultural environment is superior.

Along the subhumid margins of the humid continental realm, and in places extending slightly beyond into the semiarid steppe, chernozem, the real king among mature soils, is characteristic. Chernozem soils too, develop under tall prairie grasses, but in the distinctly subhumid sections where leaching is less pronounced. High in organic material and therefore dark in color, strong in quantity of basic minerals, and of excellent crumbly, granular structure, only immature fresh alluvial materials can equal the chernozems in quality. Like the prairie soils, they characteristically occupy flattish plains areas. Proximity to dry climates makes likely a strong element of loess in the regolith. Within the humid continental realm are two extensive chernozem regions: (*a*) in central North America from Saskatchewan and Alberta in Canada southward to central Texas, and (*b*) in southeastern Russia and extending into southwestern Siberia. Smaller fragments are found in northern Manchuria and in southern Siberia. Unfortunately, these most excellent of mature soils develop under rainfall conditions which handicap their most complete utilization.

442. Landforms. Particularly within the *Db* portions of the humid continental climates in Europe and North America recent continental glaciation has significantly modified the surface features and drainage. Where relief was rela-

tively great, or the bedrock resistant, as, for instance, in New England, northern New York, and southeastern Canada, erosion was dominant, so that not only was much of the original regolith mantle removed, but the summits of hills were planed down and valleys gouged out. In such regions knobby hills with rounded, bare-rock summits, many of them polished and striated, together with numerous ice-eroded basins filled with lakes, are characteristic.

In general, throughout the glaciated parts of *Db* regions, however, features resulting from glacial deposition are much more widespread than are those caused by erosion. The deposited till sheet is thin in some places and thick in others. On the hilltops it is often only a veneer, while adjacent valleys may be deeply buried. Where retreat of the ice was relatively continuous and without significant haltings, the till surface exhibits typical swell-and-swale configuration, the arrangement of features being largely without a readily observable pattern. Morainic belts of irregular rounded hills and kettle depressions, sometimes arranged in concentric pattern, mark the haltings of the ice front.

Throughout the recently glaciated areas of Europe and North America, drainage is strikingly immature. Rivers occupy newly adopted valleys and often appear to wander aimlessly through a maze of unsystematically arranged depressions in the till surface. As a consequence, lakes and swamps are numerous and the rivers contain falls and rapids.

Dc, Dd,[1] Subarctic Climates (*Dcf, Dcw, Ddw*)

443. Location. This is the extreme in continental climates, subarctic having the largest annual ranges of any type. It is found only in the higher middle latitudes (50 or 55 to 65°) of the great Northern Hemisphere continents (Figs.

[1] In the Köppen symbols, c = cool summers with only 1 to 3 months above 10°C., or 50°F.; d = cold winters with the temperature of the coldest month below -38°C., or -36.4°F. Predominantly this type is *Dc*, for only in extreme northeastern Siberia is there an area of *Dd*.

6.4, 10.1, Plate I). On its poleward side it makes contact with tundra, one of the polar climates. This northern boundary is approximately the isotherm of 50° for the warmest month (usually July), which is critical because it closely coincides with the poleward limit of tree growth. Beyond the July isotherm for 50°, in the tundra, lowly vegetation forms, such as mosses, lichens, and bushes, predominate. Subarctic climate, on its southern margin, usually makes contact with the cool-summer phase of humid continental climate (Db) or, in places, with middle-latitude steppes and deserts. To the subarctic lands of Eurasia, with their extensive coniferous forests, the Russians have given the name *taiga*, and this term has come to be applied not only to the comparable region in North America but likewise to the type of climate that characterizes both of them. Thus subarctic and taiga are, to a large degree, regionally synonymous. The Eurasian subarctic area extends from Sweden and Finland in Europe, across the whole of the continent to the coast of Siberia. It widens toward the Pacific, or leeward, side as continentality increases. In North America the Dc belt stretches from Alaska on the Pacific, across Canada to Labrador and Newfoundland on the Atlantic.

TEMPERATURE

444. Summer. Long, bitterly cold winters, very short summers, and brief springs and autumns are characteristic (Figs. 10.24, 10.25, 10.26). Since the isotherm of 50° for the warmest month has been accepted as the poleward boundary of this type of climate, at least one month must have an average temperature of 50° or above. At Yakutsk, Siberia, nearly 62°N., representing the extreme in subarctic climates (Ddw), July, the warmest month, has an average temperature of 66°, which is higher than the same month at London or Berlin and 9° higher than July at San Francisco. Midsummer daily maxima of 80° are common at Yakutsk, and the thermometer occasionally reaches 90°. The absolute maximum is 102°. At this same station, however, June and August have mean temperatures of only 59 and 59.5°, respectively. It

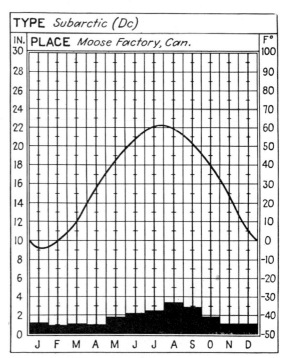

TYPE *Subarctic (Dc)*

PLACE *Moose Factory, Can.*

FIG. 10.24. Cool summers, severe winters, and modest precipitation are characteristic of subarctic climate. Note the summer maximum of precipitation.

needs to be emphasized that, at Yakutsk, there are only three months in which the mean temperatures exceed 50°, for both May and September have averages in the low forties. At Fort Vermilion, at 58°27'N. in Canada, another representative subarctic station, July is cooler than it is at Yakutsk, having an average temperature of only 60°, while June and August are 55° and 59°, respectively. The mean of the daily maxima in July is 74°; and of the minima, 46°. Temperatures over 90° have been recorded at Fort Vermilion in both June and July. Subarctic summer days, then, are pleasantly warm and occasionally even hot (Figs. 10.27, 10.28).

445. *Long Summer Days.* Somewhat compensating for the short and none too warm summers are the unusually long days in these higher latitudes. Thus, while the intensity of sunlight is not so great, the large number of hours during which the sun shines is an offsetting factor. Moreover, the short nights do not permit a long period of cooling. For example, at latitude 55°N., June days average 17.3 hr. of possible

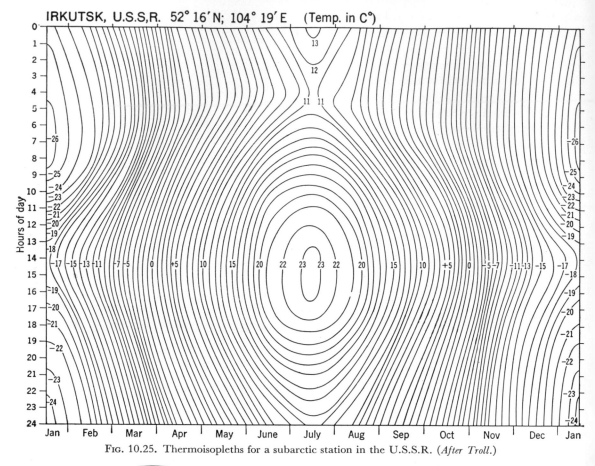

FIG. 10.25. Thermoisopleths for a subarctic station in the U.S.S.R. (*After Troll.*)

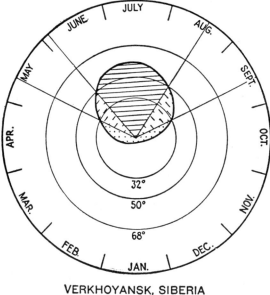

VERKHOYANSK, SIBERIA
67.5° N

FIG. 10.26. Thermograph of a station with a severe subarctic climate (*Dd*). (*After Hartshorne.*)

sunshine; latitude 60°N., 18.8 hr.; and latitude 65°N., 22.1 hr. Moreover, since twilight continues when the sun is as much as 18° below the horizon, it is evident that in summer the hours of darkness are very much limited. In the more northerly portions of the subarctic lands, at the time of the summer solstice, one can read a paper outdoors even at midnight.

446. *Growing Season.* Unfortunately, the subarctic lands have very short periods that are entirely without frost. The growing season in the Mackenzie Valley of Canada varies from about 50 to 75 days, and many stations must expect freezing temperatures in July and August in at least half of the years. A shift of wind to the north at any time brings with it the chill of the ice-laden Arctic. Thus, while it is the occasional *midwinter* frosts which are dangerous in the subtropical climates, it is, on the other hand, the *midsummer* frosts which are of special significance in this subarctic type. The characteristic

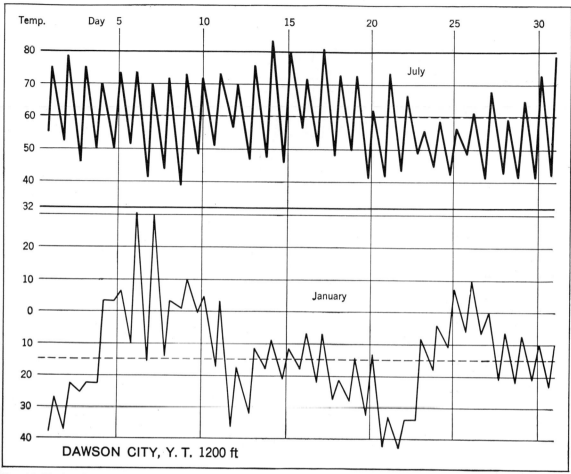

Fig. 10.27. A subarctic station in Canada. Note the stronger nonperiodic air-mass control in winter. Summer shows greater diurnal regularity.

coolness, shortness, and precariousness of the growing season are the most serious handicaps of the subarctic climates for agricultural development. In fact, these are the principal conditions that have retarded permanent settlement, so that at the present time much of the subarctic land is either totally unoccupied or at best has a meager sprinkling of frontier farmers or of people engaged in exploiting the mineral, forest, and wild-animal resources.

447. Winter follows on the heels of summer with only a very brief intervening autumn season. Frosts may arrive in late August, and ice begins to form on pools in September. By the middle of October navigation for small craft is made difficult on the subarctic lakes of Canada. At Verkhoyansk, Siberia, the mean temperature drops 40° from October to November. Subarctic Siberia holds the records for minimum temperatures at low elevations, perhaps even lower than those of polar climates. Verkhoyansk (*Ddw*), in the northeastern part, boasts an average January temperature of 59° below zero, while an absolute minimum of −90° was recorded in February, 1892.[1] This, of course is an

[1] Based upon a 4-year record, 1931 to 1933 inclusive, it would appear as though Oimekon, located about 400 miles southeast of Verkhoyansk, might displace the latter station as the cold pole of the earth in winter. During the summer months temperatures at Oimekon and Verkhoyansk were about the same, but for the rest of the year Oimekon was colder. The average January temperature in 1931 at Oimekon was −68.3°F. and a minimum temperature of −89.9° was observed on Feb. 6, 1933. See *Geog. Rev.*, Vol. 25, pp. 684–685, 1935.

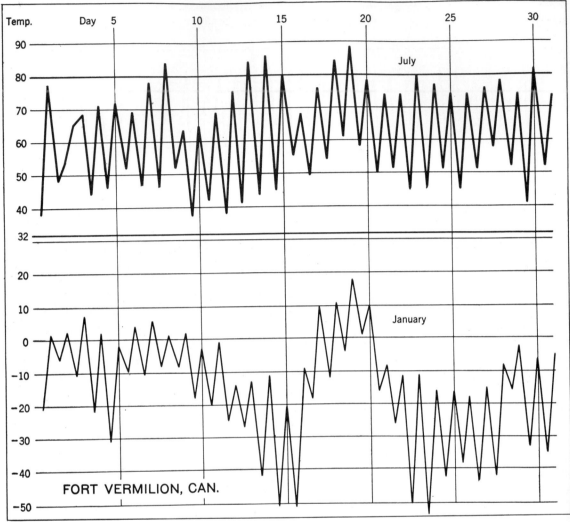

Fig. 10.28. A subarctic station in Canada.

extreme case. At Yakutsk, however, where July has an average temperature of 66°, the January mean drops to approximately −46°, producing an annual range of 112°. For 7 months at Yakutsk the average temperatures are below freezing, and during 5 months they are below zero. No other type of climate can show such contrasts between summer and winter temperatures. Again, it needs to be emphasized that it is the excessively cold winters, rather than any unusual temperature peculiarity of the summers, which cause these much greater mean annual ranges of temperature in the taiga, as compared, for instance, with those of the *Da* and *Db*

climates. If temperature curves for the several *D* types are superimposed, the summer portions do not offset greatly, while the bottoms, or winter parts, of the curves are likely to be much farther apart, the latter condition being due to the colder subarctic winters. The smaller differences in summer temperatures between the humid continental and the subarctic climates are, nevertheless, much more significant as far as agricultural land use is concerned than are the much greater winter contrasts. A July average of 60° as compared with 75° has far greater consequences than January contrasts of 40°, provided the averages are well below freezing anyway. It needs to be kept in mind that the subarctic regions of North America and Eurasia are portions of the general source regions for polar air masses which so much influence weather conditions farther south.

Concerning the subarctic Siberian winter, Hann writes:

"It is not possible to describe the terrible cold one has to endure; one has to experience it to appreciate it. The quicksilver freezes solid and can be cut and hammered like lead; iron becomes brittle, and the hatchet breaks like glass; wood, depending upon the degree of moisture in it, becomes harder than iron and withstands the ax so that only completely dry wood can be split. Every step in the dry snow can be heard for long distances; the bursting of the ice cover and the frozen ground sound like the cannonading of distant batteries."

The low winter temperatures of the northeastern Siberia are not so hard to bear as one might imagine, for air movement is usually slight, skies are clear, and, since absolute humidity is very low, the air is physiologically dry. For example, when air at $-20°$ and relative humidity of 80 per cent comes in contact with the human body and is heated to $60°$, the relative humidity falls to nearly 2 per cent.

Subarctic winters in North America are not quite so severe as are those of Siberia. This comes about in part as a result of Asia's being a broader land mass. In addition, however, the mountains of eastern Siberia tend effectively to dam up the outflow of cold winter air, thereby aiding in an excessive accumulation of it over Asia, resulting in the great continental anticyclone. No such blocking effect is possible in less mountainous eastern Canada, with the result that such representative stations as Moose Factory, Dawson, and Fort Good Hope show average January temperatures of -4, -22, and $-32°$, respectively. Annual ranges at these stations are 66, 82, and 93, respectively. At Dawson, in the Yukon, at $64°3'N$. the thermometer, on an average January night, falls to approximately $-29°$ and rises to nearly $-16°$ during the warmest hours of the day (Figs. 10.27, 10.28). During the three winter months at this station the average of the daily maxima does not reach zero. The lowest temperature ever recorded is $-64°$.

The excessive and long-continued cold of the subarctic winters causes large parts of these regions to be permanently frozen down to great depths. Over extensive areas of the subarctic lands only the upper few feet thaw out during the short summers. The depth to which frost penetrates and the depth of the summer thaw vary greatly from one part of the subarctic lands to another. Cleveland Abbe notes the case of a mine in the Klondike (Yukon) which passed out of the permanently frozen zone at a depth of 220 ft.

Just as long days are characteristic of subarctic summers, so long nights are characteristic of the winters. For example, on Dec. 21 all places on the $60°N$. parallel can receive a maximum of only 5.7 hr. of sunshine, while on latitude $65°N$. the maximum is only 3.3 hr. These long daily periods of darkness are not only depressing and hard to bear, but they are, in a considerable measure, responsible for the low winter temperatures.

Spring, like autumn, is a short and inconspicuous season. At Yakutsk there is a difference of $25°$ between the mean temperatures of April and May, and $18°$ between May and June. The

Climatic Data for Representative Subarctic Stations (Dc, Dd)

Fort Vermilion, Alberta, Canada (58°27'N.)

	J	F	M	A	M	J	J	A	S	O	N	D	Yr.	Range
Temp.	−14	−6	8	30	47	55	60	57	46	32	10	−4	26.7	74.3
Precip.	0.6	0.3	0.5	0.7	1.0	1.9	2.1	2.1	1.4	0.7	0.5	0.4	12.3	

Moose Factory, Ontario, Canada (51°16'N.)

	J	F	M	A	M	J	J	A	S	O	N	D	Yr.	Range
Temp.	−4	−2	10	28	42	54	61	59	51	39	22	5	30.4	65.6
Precip.	1.3	0.9	1.1	1.0	1.8	2.2	2.4	3.3	2.9	1.8	1.1	1.2	21.0	

Yakutsk, Siberia, U.S.S.R.

	J	F	M	A	M	J	J	A	S	O	N	D	Yr.	Range
Temp.	−46	−35	−10	16	41	59	66	60	42	16	−21	−41	12	112
Precip.	0.9	0.2	0.4	0.6	1.1	2.1	1.7	2.6	1.2	1.4	0.6	0.9	13.7	

average April temperature at Yakutsk is like that of Madison, Wis., in January, while May is only 4 to 5° lower than April at Madison.

PRECIPITATION AND HUMIDITY

448. Amount. Precipitation in subarctic climates is usually meager (Fig. 10.24). Over much of the Siberian taiga it is no more than 15 in., while most of Subarctic Canada receives less than 20, and parts receive less than 15, in. It is principally along the oceanic margins in both Eurasia and North America that rainfall exceeds 20 in. In most middle-latitude climates these small amounts, characteristic of the taiga, would be classed as semiarid, but where such low temperatures and, therefore, low evaporation rates prevail, and where the ground is frozen so much of the year, the precipitation is sufficient for forest growth. The relatively low precipitation is associated with (a) the prevailing low temperatures and correspondingly low specific humidity, (b) a strong continental winter anticyclone, with settling air and diverging winds, and (c) the large size of the land masses in these subarctic latitudes.

449. Annual Distribution. Precipitation is concentrated in the warmer months. Though the total amounts are small, they are adequate in most years for whatever meager cropping takes place, since precipitation is concentrated in the short growing season. At Yakutsk, where the total annual rainfall is 13.7 in., August is the wettest month with 2.6 in., and February the driest with 0.2 in. At Dawson in the Yukon the total is 12.5 in., with 1.5 in July and 0.8 in January (0.7 in. in February and 0.5 in March). Winter, with its low temperatures, meager specific humidity, strong anticyclone with settling air, and seaward-moving winds, presents a total setup that is antagonistic to precipitation. It is over east central Siberia, in particular, that winters are especially dry, the three winter months there having only 10 per cent of the annual precipitation, while the three summer months have 58 per cent. This is the region of most intense cold and strongest anticyclone.

Over the more interior and continental portions of the subarctic lands, because of the prevalence of the stationary cold-season anticyclone, winters are likely to have much bright, clear weather, but east central Siberia, in the neighborhood of Verkhoyansk, the "cold pole" of the earth, is especially cloudless. There summers are more cloudy than winters, the average being less than $\frac{3}{10}$ in winter, but almost $\frac{7}{10}$ in August. In its prevailingly clear skies, northeastern Siberia is like southern Italy, while in winter the amount of cloud is nearly as low as that of the desert. One traveler writes, "The air in these high latitudes is remarkably clear, the color of the sky is a blue-violet, like the dress of the Sistine Madonna; sounds can be heard for long distances, so that one can hear the bark of a dog 20 km. away" (Hann). The meager cloud cover during long winter nights is an additional factor favoring low temperatures. Over interior subarctic Canada, cloudiness is not far from $\frac{5}{10}$ in both winter and summer. Winter days often are cloudy even when there is no precipitation, considerable low status cloud and ground fog occurring during that season.

450. Winter Precipitation. Over lowlands the winter precipitation, practically all of it in the form of snow, is frontal in origin. The prevalence of the continental anticyclone tends to repel or hold at bay moving cyclones, so that these snow-bearing storms are most frequently forced to follow the southern margins of subarctic regions, rather than being permitted to move directly across their centers. In North America, over the center of the continent, the principal winter storm tracks loop well southward. This fact that principal winter cyclonic tracks tend to avoid the centers of subarctic regions helps to explain the meager winter precipitation. But the few fronts that do cross these areas yield sufficient precipitation, in the form of relatively dry, hard snow, so that a permanent snow cover, lasting 5 to 7 months, is common. Because of the shelter provided by the forest, little melting or evaporation occurs, so that the winter snows accumulate to a depth of 2 to 3 ft. in the taiga. This same protection of the forest leads to slow melting of the snow cover in spring. In parts of Siberia, winter precipitation is so meager that sleighing is sometimes diffi-

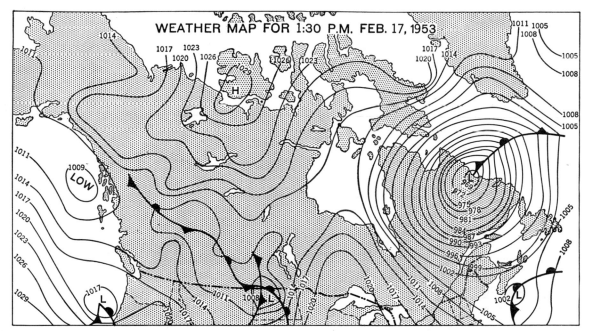

FIG. 10.29. A well-developed storm, accompanied by strong winds and extensive precipitation over the subarctic and tundra region of northeastern Canada.

cult. Strong winter winds with snow, giving blizzard-like weather, are not nearly so characteristic of the taiga as they are of the prairies to the south and the treeless tundra to the north. This is largely due to the fact that the forest cover acts to break the force of the winds and to prevent the surface snow from being swept back into the air.

451. Summer Precipitation. Summer, the season of maximum temperatures, highest specific humidity, and deepest penetration of maritime air masses under the influence of the summer monsoon, provides conditions that are relatively most favorable for rainfall. Warm-season precipitation is largely frontal in origin, even that associated with thunderstorms. Thunderstorms are not numerous, the total number in the Mackenzie Valley of Canada being in the neighbourhood of 5 to 10 a year. Fort Vermilion, in the Mackenzie Valley, has on the average 5.3 rainy days in June, 9.1 in July, and 7.5 in August. Comparable data for Dawson, in the Yukon, are 11.7, 10.3, and 10.9.

452. Seasonal Weather. The nonperiodic weather element is generally less marked in the subarctic lands than it is in the continental climates farther south. Winter in the taiga has much anticyclonic weather with settling air and light to moderate winds. The greater the continentality and the stronger the winter anticyclone, the clearer, drier, and colder the weather. Occasional cyclones bring gray skies with hard, dry snow (Fig. 10.29). Cyclones are often more numerous in the short transition seasons than in the dead of winter, for in the latter season the subarctic lands are included within the source regions of those great masses of cold anticyclonic air which periodically surge equatorward affecting even the lower middle latitudes. Summer weather is likewise rather settled, although cyclones make themselves felt in occasional rains and in importations of warm and cold air. A strong invasion of cP air from higher latitudes can cause freezing temperatures even in midsummer. Hot waves are rare but by no means unknown

ASSOCIATED FEATURES OF THE PHYSICAL EARTH IN Dc, Dd, SUBARCTIC CLIMATES

453. Native Vegetation. Subarctic Eurasia and North America are covered by softwood forests, designated as taiga (Fig. 7.12). In their immensity and monotony these forested subarctic lands are like the sea, and travelers are impressed with their emptiness and silence. Even animal life is not abundant. They are among the largest and least-known wildernesses of the earth. Unlike tropical forests, these of the subarctic are composed of a relatively few species, most of which are xerophilous in character. This is predominantly a forest of needle trees, although mixed growth is common. Conifers usually occupy in the neighborhood of 75 per cent of the area, with such deciduous trees as birch, poplar, willow, and alder comprising much of the remainder. In both North America and Eurasia spruce and fir are usually the dominant coniferous trees, although larch and pine are plentiful. Dense deciduous thickets characteristically spring up in areas where conifers have been destroyed. Although a forested realm, the subarctic climate is not genuinely favorable to forests. Trees are not closely spaced, nor are they impressive in size, their diameters rarely exceeding $1\frac{1}{4}$ ft. even on the southern margins of the taiga. Because of the evergreen character of the forest, and its high-latitude location, little sunlight reaches the earth. Where it does penetrate, the ground is clothed with bush vegetation. In darker places mosses and lichens tend to replace bushes, while in the deepest shade even these lowly forms disappear and the ground is smothered in a muffling blanket of needles. As a potential supply of lumber and other forest products the subarctic taiga is not nearly so valuable as its extensiveness might seem to indicate. Neither the size of the trees nor their density of stand is impressive.

454. Zonal Soils. The creation of a regolith mantle in the subarctic climates is accomplished by both mechanical and chemical means. To a greater extent than in realms farther south, frost action is probably responsible for regolith in the taiga. Exposed rock surfaces are broken up by frost action into coarse fragments, and sharp angular promontories are characteristic. Nevertheless, although chemical weathering is halted during a long period when the ground is frozen, it becomes active during the short summer. The abundance of surface moisture at this time. in association with the very acid humus cover, produces intensive leaching. On the whole, however, rock weathering is probably much slower in the subarctic than in humid regions farther equatorward. Over much of the North American taiga, and in western North Europe as well, soils are developed from glacial till.

455. *Podzols.* An impoverished soil environment is characteristic of the subarctic realm. Probably in no other, except the polar realm, is this handicap so striking. With an infertile soil, combined with a climate of low potentialities, the subarctic lands offer what appear to be almost insurmountable difficulties to large-scale agricultural settlement.

Over the realm as a whole, gray, ash-colored podzols prevail (Fig. 7.13). In fact the subarctic realm is the earth's type region of podzol development. Lacking in an important soil fauna, excessively leached, low in humus, and of miserable structure, these are among the most infertile of the earth's mature soils. The dominant feature in the development of podzols is the intense leaching resulting from the excess of precipitation over evaporation in the presence of a raw, acid humus cover composed of semidecomposed conifer needles. The underlying B horizon, enriched by materials removed from above, is often compact and impervious, retarding drainage, and making root penetration difficult. Except where the parent material contained a high percentage of sand, mature soils in the subarctic realm are likely to be structureless and powdery when dry, and dense and difficult to work when damp. They have a tendency to bake, forming extremely hard clods if plowed when too wet. Heavy applications of lime, and large quantities of fertilizer are required in order to make podzols even moderately productive.

As a result of deficient drainage, which is so widespread throughout the subarctic realm, bog soils, high in peat material, are very common. Over large areas, too, particularly in Finland, Scandinavia, and the region of ancient crystalline rocks surrounding Hudson Bay, glacial scouring has removed much of the regolith cover so that soils are thin, and bedrock exposures and scattered boulders are abundant. In a few restricted "warm oases" along some of the river valleys, vegetation has a semisteppe aspect, and, in these, darker-colored and relatively more fertile soils prevail. Such spots today are frontier settlement "islands" in the midst of taiga and podzols.

456. Drainage and Landforms. After climate and soils, probably the third ranking handicap to settlement within the subarctic realm is the widespread deficient drainage. This prevalence of poorly drained land is partly the result of a permanently frozen subsoil, a condition which prevails throughout the higher latitudes of the realm. As a consequence, proper underdrainage is impossible. Over all of subarctic North America, with the exception of the Yukon Basin of Alaska, and in Scandinavia, Finland, and western Russia, the abundance of lakes and swamps is a consequence of deranged drainage resulting from recent glaciation. Many of the lakes occupy ice-scoured basins; others lie behind morainic dams in stream courses. The name Finland, derived from "fen land," suggests the prevalence of lakes and marshes in that country where they occupy in the neighborhood of one-third of the entire area.

Still another cause of the realm's deficient drainage is associated with the fact that many of its principal streams flow poleward. Such northward-flowing rivers thaw out in their upper and middle courses while the lower portions are still frozen and are therefore unable to carry drainage waters. As a result, where lowlands prevail, widespread spring inundations are the result. Because of the frozen subsoil and relatively low temperatures these flood waters disappear very slowly. The most extensive area of swamp forest resulting from spring inundation is in the drainage basins of the Ob and Enisei (Yenisei) rivers in flattish western Siberia.

457. *Landforms.* The Siberian taiga and interior Alaska are the two large regions within the subarctic climate in which indigenous surface features, resulting largely from normal river erosion, prevail. All other parts of this climatic realm have suffered glaciation and consequently exhibit numerous landforms associated with that gradational agent. Within no other climatic type have continental ice sheets covered such extensive areas as in the subarctic. In fact, all the principal centers of Northern Hemisphere ice sheets, in both Europe and North America, lie within this realm. Although entirely a coincidence, the principal centers also are in regions of resistant, ancient, crystalline rock. These regions of ice origin, Fenno-Scandia in Europe, and Laurentia in Canada, are the two most extensive ice-scoured regions of the earth. Not everywhere is soil absent, to be sure, for between the outcrops of bare rocks, and interspersed between lakes, are other areas of glacial deposit. In some of the depressions old lake sediments exist, while others are swamps filled with decaying vegetation. Lakes in rock-eroded basins are among the most conspicuous features.

Farther away from the centers of ice origin in both subarctic Europe and North America, where the ice was more heavily loaded with materials, and where less resistant sedimentary rocks prevailed, aggradational, rather than degradational, features are more common. Erosion was not absent by any means, but it was less effective than deposition. Where moraines are composed chiefly of small materials and weak sedimentary boulders, they do not retain a rugged appearance for a long period of time. On the other hand, in closer proximity to the regions of resistant crystalline rock, where large crystalline boulders are numerous in the till, moraines are likely to be more rugged and conspicuous.

CHAPTER 11: *Polar Climates and Highland Climates*

E, Polar Climates

458. As the tropics are characterized by lack of a cool season, so the polar regions are wanting in a period of warmth. It is the prevalence of monotonous heat that typifies the low latitudes. In the high latitudes monotonous and long-continued cold is the greatest handicap. Certain explorers to the contrary, the polar areas cannot be made to appear warm by noting that occasional days with temperatures over 80° have been experienced beyond the Arctic Circle. "One swallow does not make a summer," nor do a few warm days determine the general climatic character of a region.

459. Phenomena of Light and Darkness. A distinctive feature of the polar climates is their peculiarity with respect to periods of light and darkness. At the poles the sun is out of sight entirely for approximately 6 months, while for an equal period it is constantly above the horizon, although never very high in the heavens, so that insolation is weak. At the Arctic and Antarctic Circles, which lie near the equatorward margins of polar climates, the daily period of sunlight varies from 24 hr. at the time of the summer solstice to a complete lack of sunlight at the winter solstice. At points between the poles and the $66\frac{1}{2}°$ parallels the lengths of the periods of sunlight, and absence of sunlight, are intermediate in character between the two extremes noted.

These peculiarities of daylight duration introduce new conceptions of certain climatic phenomena. Thus diurnal range has less significance in a region that may have continuous day or continuous night. The annual march of temperature has an altered appearance, since, for instance, at the North Pole, there is no incoming direct solar radiation for a period of 6 months. Loss of heat by terrestrial radiation goes on continuously, however, so that a minimum temperature should be reached somewhat before the spring equinox.

460. Locations and Boundaries. Polar climates are largely confined to the high latitudes of the earth. Somewhat similar conditions can be found at high altitudes in a great variety of latitudes. But these latter regions of continuous cold usually are very isolated and fragmentary and in this book are included within the group designated as highland climates (Fig. 6.4).

The poleward limit of forest is usually accepted as marking the boundary separating the cold climates from those of the intermediate latitudes. In continental locations this vegetation boundary approximately coincides with the isotherm of 50° for the *warmest month*, so that this seasonal isotherm is commonly employed in defining the outer margins of the polar climates.[1] It is significant that, while for the boundary of the humid tropics a *cool-month* isotherm is employed, a *warm-month* isotherm serves in the same way for polar climates. It suggests that while a period of coolness is of critical importance for plants and animals in the low latitudes, a period of warmth is much more significant in high latitudes. In the Northern Hemisphere the July isotherm of 50° swings well poleward of the Arctic Circle over most of Asia and Alaska, reasonably well coincides with it over lowland Europe, but is to the

[1] In order to exclude certain cool marine climates which are not distinctly polar in nature, the definition might further stipulate a mean annual temperature of 32° or below. If this were done, such marine tundra areas as the southern tip of South America would be excluded.

south of the 66½° parallel over much of eastern North America and Greenland. There, because of large inland bodies of water, the cool Labrador Current, and the Greenland ice cap, summers are distinctly cooler than in Asia. In the Southern Hemisphere the only conspicuous land area possessed of polar climates is the ice-covered Antarctic continent. North of the equator it is the Arctic Sea borderlands of Eurasia and North America, together with extensive island groups north of both continents, and ice-covered Greenland, which are included. In both hemispheres the lands with polar climates are important source regions for those polar air masses which so markedly affect the weather of middle latitudes.

Since the *Arctic* is almost a landlocked sea, while the *Antarctic* is a seagirt land, certain important climatic differences are to be expected between the two regions. As a consequence of its single land mass being centered at the pole and surrounded on all sides by extensive oceans of uniform temperature, the Antarctic shows much greater uniformity and simplicity in its climate than does the Arctic. Wind and pressure systems are symmetrically developed about the South Pole, and there is little change in these elements throughout the year, while lack of symmetry and seasonal variations in these controls are characteristic of the north polar regions.

461. Temperature and Precipitation. Polar climates claim the distinction of having the lowest *mean annual*, as well as the lowest *summer*, temperatures for any part of the earth. In spite of the long duration of sunshine in summer, temperatures remain low, the rays being too oblique to be genuinely effective. Moreover, much of the solar energy is reflected by the snow and ice or is consumed in melting the snow cover and evaporating the water, so that neither the land surface nor the air adjacent to it becomes warm. Winters are bitterly cold, but there is some doubt as to whether the thermometer ever sinks as low in the polar regions as it does in the subarctic climate of northeastern Siberia. In spite of the cool summers, winter cold is sufficiently severe to develop large annual ranges.

Precipitation is meager throughout the high latitudes. Over large parts of the land areas it is less than 10 in. But in spite of its meagerness, the low evaporation permits of some runoff, part of it in the form of glaciers. It is because of the low evaporation and the small amount of melting that great permanent snow and ice fields several thousand feet thick have been able to accumulate on Greenland and the Antarctic continent, and this in spite of the low precipitation. A dearth of polar precipitation does not seem unusual when one considers the prevailingly low specific humidity which must accompany the low temperatures. The reservoir of water vapor is small at all times. Moreover, in these latitudes there is a general settling of the cold upper air masses which creates a condition unfavorable to condensation. Precipitation is usually heavier in the warmer months when the moisture supply is most abundant.

462. Tundra and Ice Caps. Polar climates are here subdivided into two types, with the *warmest-month* isotherm of 0°C., or 32°F., serving as the boundary between them. Where the average temperatures of all months are below freezing, the growth of vegetation is impossible, and a permanent snow-and-ice cover prevails. These are the *ice-cap climates*. Where one or more of the warm-season months has an average temperature above 32° (but not over 50°) so that the ground is free from snow for a short period, and a meager and lowly vegetation cover is possible, the climate is designated as *tundra*.

ET,[1] Tundra Climate

463. Location. Tundra climate is transitional in character between the ice cap, or region of perpetual snow and ice, on the one hand, and middle-latitude climates, usually subarctic, on the other (Fig. 6.4, Plate I). Its accepted equatorward and poleward boundaries are the warmest month isotherms of 50 and 32, respectively. These temperatures are significant because of their reasonable coincidence with vegetational boundaries: the poleward limit of forest in one case and of practically all forms of plant life in the other.

[1] *ET* warmest month below 50°F. (10°C.) but above 32°F. (0°C.).

Tundra climate over land areas is almost exclusively confined to the Northern Hemisphere. In the Antarctic, ocean prevails in those latitudes where the tundra would normally develop. Only the most northerly fringes of the Antarctic continent, and certain small Antarctic islands have sufficiently warm summers for them to be included. The most extensive tundra areas are the Arctic Sea margins of both North America and Eurasia. Most of the Arctic archipelago of the former continent, as well as the coastal fringe of Greenland, is likewise included.

TEMPERATURE

464. Summer. It becomes obvious that much of the larger part of the earth's tundra climate over the lands is continental rather than marine in character. As a result continentality in temperature characteristics is a distinguishing feature of most tundra areas. Long, bitterly cold winters and very short, cool summers are the rule (Figs. 11.1, 11.3). By the definition of boundaries for tundra climate, previously stated, the average temperature of the warmest

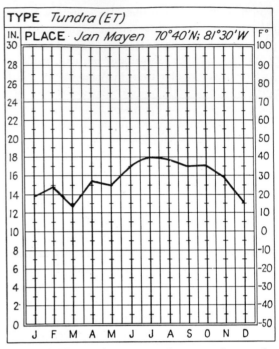

Fig. 11.2. Temperature curve for a marine tundra station. Due to the relatively mild winters for this latitude the annual range of temperature is comparatively small.

month can be no lower than 32° and no higher than 50°. The cool character of the summer is therefore relatively fixed. Raw and chilly, the warmest months of the tundra resemble March and April in southern Wisconsin and are like January in the American cotton belt (Fig. 11.2). Usually only 2 to 4 months have average temperatures above freezing, and killing frost is likely to occur at any time. Summer cool waves in middle latitudes are associated with air masses moving southward from the tundra and subarctic areas. Along coasts, where water, ice, and land are in close proximity, fog is very prevalent. These fogs may last for days at a time and are extraordinarily depressing. Under the influence of unusually long summer days, the snow cover begins to disappear in May, and the lakes are usually rid of their ice cover in June. Because of the permanently frozen subsoil, subsurface drainage is deficient, and bog and swamp prevalent. Myriads of mosquitoes and black flies make life almost unbearable for man and beast alike during the summer period of wet earth.

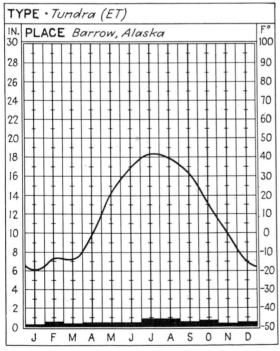

Fig. 11.1. A continental tundra station. Note the very meager precipitation and the large range of temperature.

At Ponds Inlet, Canada, a tundra station at 72°43′N., where the average July temperature is 42°, the thermometer in that month rises to about 49° during the warmest hours of the day and, on the average, sinks to 35 or 36° at "night." Daily ranges in summer are relatively small, for the sun is above the horizon for all or a greater part of the 24-hr. period. On most July "nights" no frost occurs, but on the other hand it is not unusual for the thermometer to slip a few degrees below freezing (Fig. 11.4). Warm days occur now and then, Ponds Inlet having recorded, on at least one occasion, a temperature of 77°. Chesterfield Inlet, another tundra station in Canada, has experienced 84°, but of course these high temperatures are a rare exception and not the rule.

465. Winter. While summer temperatures are not greatly different from one tundra region to another, there are greater variations in the winters. Thus along the Arctic coasts of Siberia,

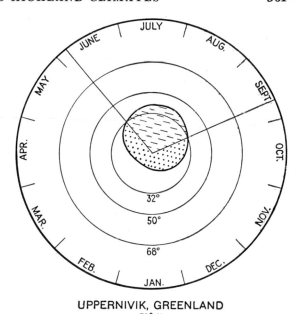

UPPERNIVIK, GREENLAND
73° N

Fig. 11.3. Thermograph for a representative *ET* station. (*After Hartshorne.*)

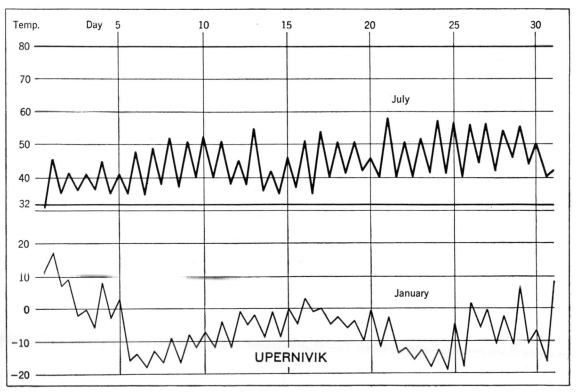

Fig. 11.4. A tundra station in Greenland.

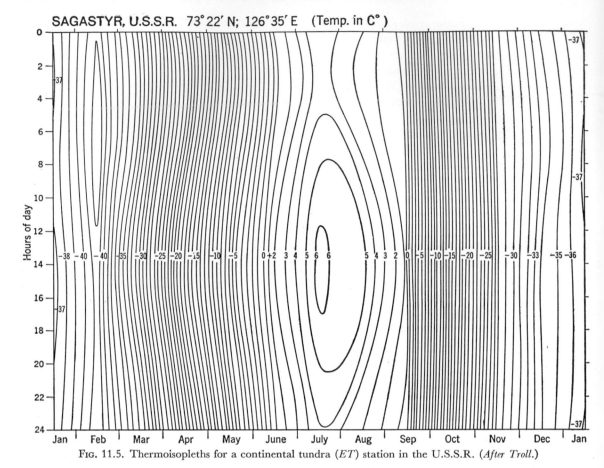

SAGASTYR, U.S.S.R. 73°22′ N; 126°35′ E (Temp. in C°)

FIG. 11.5. Thermoisopleths for a continental tundra (*ET*) station in the U.S.S.R. (*After Troll.*)

average January and February temperatures are in the neighborhood of −35 or −40°, and it is appreciably colder farther inland. At this season winds in general are from the bitterly cold sub-arctic region to the south, and these importations serve only further to intensify the severity of temperatures in the tundra. Without doubt, the tundra of northeastern Siberia, the winter-month averages of which are below −40°, represents the extreme condition. Along the Arctic borderlands of North America winters are not quite so severe. A coastal station in Labrador

shows a January mean of −8°; Ponds Inlet in Canada records an average of −28° for January, −30° for February, and even −24° for March (Fig. 11.1). At the latter station, 5 months, November to March inclusive, have average temperatures below zero, while 9 are below freezing.

PRECIPITATION

466. Amount and Distribution. Over most of the tundra lands precipitation is not over 10 or 12 in. (Fig. 11.1). In portions of eastern Arctic

Climatic Data for Representative Tundra Stations (ET)
Sagastyr, Siberia, U.S.S.R. (73°N., 124°E.)

	J	F	M	A	M	J	J	A	S	O	N	D	Yr.	Range
Temp.	−34	−36	−30	−7	15	32	41	38	33	6	−16	−28	1	77
Precip.	0.1	0.1	0.0	0.0	0.2	0.4	0.3	1.4	0.4	0.1	0.1	0.2	3.3	

Upernivik, Western Greenland (73°N., 56°W.)

	J	F	M	A	M	J	J	A	S	O	N	D	Yr.	Range
Temp.	−7	−10	−6	6	25	35	41	41	33	25	14	1	16.5	50.6
Precip.	0.4	0.4	0.6	0.6	0.6	0.6	0.1	1.1	1.0	1.1	1.1	0.5	9.2	

Canada, particularly Labrador peninsula, it is somewhat greater. Low summer temperatures and winter anticyclonic conditions are, in general, not conducive to abundant precipitation, while convectional effects are largely absent. Summer and autumn, the warmest seasons, are likewise the periods of maximum precipitation throughout the tundra as a whole. In the more marine locations, where cyclones are greater in number, fall and winter may show larger totals than summer. Precipitation is principally cyclonic, or frontal, in origin. Much of that which falls in the warm season is in the form of rain, with occasional wet snows. The meager winter snowfall is usually dry and powdery in character so that it forms a very compact cover. It is only this very compact snow, 2 in. of which may equal an inch of rain, that the Eskimos use in constructing their igloos. The actual amount of dry, sandlike snow that falls is not easy to measure, since it is often accompanied by strong blizzard winds which heap it up in depressions and on the lee sides of hills, while at the same time sweeping bare the exposed surfaces. There are no forests, as in the taiga, to break the force of the wind and hold the snow cover. Stefansson estimates that 75 to 90 per cent of the surface of Arctic lands is nearly free of snow at all seasons. Both as a result of the small amount of snow and as a result of its strong tendency to drift, sledging commonly is difficult.

SEASONAL WEATHER

467. There appears to be conflicting testimony concerning the character of winter weather in the tundra. Undoubtedly this results from the fact that conditions vary from one part of the Arctic to another and also that successive winters are unlike. Certainly the variability of winters is much greater than that of summers. In some years clear, cold, anticyclonic conditions appear to prevail, while in others, at least in some parts, cyclones with accompanying blizzards follow each other in rapid succession. In general, however, the principal belts of cyclones lie south of the tundra, so that winters in both the Eurasian and North American sectors probably have much anticyclonic weather

(Fig. 11.4). The dryness of the air leads to rapid evaporation from the human body, and explorers report the prevalence of torturing thirst. Blizzards on the treeless tundra are fearful weather phenomena, their low temperatures, gale winds, and driving snow combining to force all living creatures to seek shelter.

The transition seasons of spring and fall are somewhat unlike; "autumn is a quiet dying away of nature, spring a sudden awakening." Both seasons are likely to be more stormy than winter. Autumn, without doubt, is one of the worst seasons for severe storms, since at that time bodies of water are still unfrozen, and their surface temperatures are markedly in contrast with those of the rapidly cooling lands. Spring likewise is stormy, for by March and April the belt of maximum cyclones is again retreating poleward.

Summer is a relatively quiet and uniformly cool season (Fig. 11.4). The wet, swampy ground makes the air damp and raw. Fogs are common and the sky is often gray and cheerless. Snow is not unusual even in summer.

ASSOCIATED FEATURES OF THE PHYSICAL EARTH IN *ET*, TUNDRA CLIMATES

468. Native Vegetation. Two vegetation rings are recognized in the tundra, these closely corresponding to the character of summer temperature. The outermost belt is included between the warm-month isotherms of about 50 and 40°. It therefore represents the section with warmest summers. Within this belt, or ring, which includes much of the tundra of Eurasia and North America (except the extreme coastal margins), together with the coasts of southern Greenland, a close meadow or heath type of cover prevails. The vegetation consists chiefly of mosses, lichens, sedges, flowering and bushy plants, together with stunted birches, willows, and aspen. The dominant character over large areas is determined by the carpet of moss and lichens. On the equatorward margins, where it goes over into taiga, bushes become taller and more numerous, so that the tundra here is too luxuriant to be typical.

Where the mean temperature for the warmest

month sinks below 40°, as it does along the extreme poleward margins of Eurasia and North America, as well as in northern Greenland, and the North American Arctic archipelago, more of a desert tundra prevails. In this belt the higher plants are much rarer, and the areas of bare earth, or those covered by a scanty mantle of mosses and lichens, are more extensive.

469. Zonal Soils. Throughout the tundra, mechanical weathering associated with frost action is dominant. Chemical weathering and microbiological activity are not entirely suppressed, but certainly, as a result of the long period of frozen earth and of the low temperatures even in summer, they are much less pronounced than in warmer climates. As a consequence of the emphasis upon frost weathering, uplands are likely to have angular forms, and a mantle of loose, angular, rock fragments commonly covers elevated hard rock areas of moderate slopes.

As a potential resource, tundra soil, no matter what its quality, is of little consequence, since it is associated with a climate that makes impossible the growing of domesticated plants of economic importance. Mature soils are completely leached and are excessively poor in plant foods. Below the thin horizon of raw humus or peat, and 2 to 3 in. of gray topsoil, is a grayish-blue, sticky loam of semifluid consistency, this latter layer being the characteristic mark of the tundra. When the surface of the tundra becomes frozen, the semifluid, grayish-blue horizon is held under pressure owing to the expansion of water at temperatures below 39.5°. This leads either to an eruption through the thin, frozen layer, or in other cases to the formation of hummocks.

Within the tundra soil water melts in the summer, producing a layer of thick mud which tends to creep downslope producing bulges and terraces. This process is known as *solifluction*. The rate of mud flowage reaches a maximum during the warmer hours of the day when it may attain a rate of several feet an hour. On flat ground the diurnal freeze and thaw in the tundra soil layer results in a system of polygonal ground. On highlands these cracks may be filled with stones

as a result of the alternating freeze and thaw of the soil water, developing stone polygons. On slopes the stone polygons may gravitate downslope to produce very conspicuous stone stripes.

In tundra regions of recent continental glaciation, as for instance in North America and Europe, and especially where resistant crystalline rocks prevail, the soil cover may have been largely removed. In such regions, the principal soil accumulations are in the depressions, although thin, stony glacial till may mantle the scraped and polished bedrock as well.

EF, Ice-cap Climate [1]

This least well-known among the world's climatic types is characteristically developed over the great permanent continental ice sheets of Antarctica and Greenland and over the perpetually frozen ocean in the vicinity of the North Pole. Only fragmentary data from occasional exploring expeditions have been obtained from these deserts of snow and ice where the average temperature of no month rises above freezing.

470. Pressure and wind systems in the polar areas are still a highly controversial topic. The former widely held concept of the existence of a permanent surface anticyclone over the ice caps of Antarctica and Greenland, with a diverging system of easterly winds, has required modification in the light of later observations. On the other hand, there is no prevailingly accepted substitute concept. No attempt will be made here to review the numerous ideas concerning the circulation systems of the polar areas.[2] In general, explorers have reported a prevalence of downslope winds on the ice caps but, on the other hand, upslope winds are experienced (Fig. 11.6). This prevalence of downslope winds suggests the existence of prevailing radial wind systems over Greenland and Antarctica which are of the gravity type.

---

[1] *EF* warmest month below 0°C., or 32°F.
[2] On this topic, see Yale Mintz and Gordon Dean, The Observed Mean Field of Motion of the Atmosphere, *Geophysical Research Papers*, No. 17, pp. 23–41, 1952, Air Force Cambridge Research Center; "Compendium of Meteorology," pp. 917–964.

They originate as a result of subsidence and surface cooling over the ice and flow down the slopes of the ice caps toward the surrounding seas. Along the steep margins of ice plateaus these gravity winds may reach gale force in local areas. At Eismitte in central Greenland near the crest of the ice cap the wind velocity averaged only 10 miles an hour. In Greenland at least, there is frequent penetration of the ice cap by moving cyclones bringing cloud and snow and causing variable winds. Less is known about the interior of Antarctica.

471. Temperature. The mean annual temperature of interior Greenland has been calculated to be −26°; that of the South Pole −22 to −31°; that of the North Pole −9°. These, without doubt, are the lowest annual temperatures for any portion of the earth. Observed temperatures for the *warmest* months in the

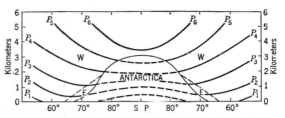

Fig. 11.6. Hypothetical distribution of zonal pressure and wind in the south polar area. (*After Meinardus, Mintz and Dean.*)

neighborhood of the South Pole, at the time of continuous insolation, were −9° (December) and −19° (January). A temperature of −58° has been recorded in the Antarctic continent in this season. Unquestionably, therefore, Antarctica has the distinction of being the earth's coldest spot in summer. While the North Pole and interior Greenland are certainly below freezing in July and August, they are far from

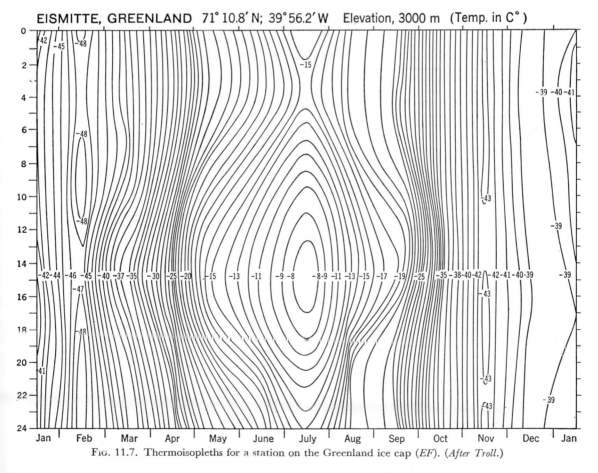

Fig. 11.7. Thermoisopleths for a station on the Greenland ice cap (*EF*). (*After Troll.*)

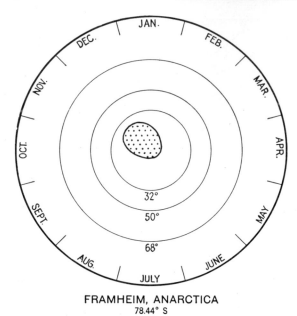

FRAMHEIM, ANARCTICA
78.44° S

FIG. 11.8. Thermograph for an *EF* station. (*After Hartshorne.*)

zero. It is not impossible that in some of the wind-protected depressions of that region, cold-month and minimum temperatures are as low as those of northeastern Siberia. At Eismitte in interior Greenland the unreduced averages of January and February are −42° and −53°, while the minimum temperatures fell to −84° or −85°. These appear to be somewhat lower than the mean minimum temperatures at Verkhoyansk, Siberia.

Conditions on the ice caps all favor low temperatures. During a considerable part of the year the sun is completely below the horizon, and even during the period of continuous sunlight the solar rays are very oblique and without much energy. Because of the excellent reflecting properties of the snow and ice surface, probably 80 per cent or more of the solar radiation reaching the ice-cap surface is reflected back into the atmosphere. A part of the remaining 20 per cent is consumed in evaporating the ice and snow. On the other hand, the relatively dry air permits of excessive earth radiation whenever the sky is clear, and there is little warming of the snow surface by conduction from below. The result is a practically permanent surface temperature inversion reaching up to considerable heights.

Climatic Data for an Ice-cap Station (EF)
Eismitte (Wegener), Interior Greenland (70°54′N., 40°42′W., 9,941 ft.)

	J	F	M	A	M	J	J	A	S	O	N	D	Yr.	Range
Temp.	−42	−53	−40	−24	−4	+4	+12	+1	−8	−32	−46	−37	−22	65
Precip.	No data													

being as cold as the south polar plateau at the time of continuous day. To be sure, the figures given above are for interior portions of Antarctica and hence represent extreme conditions. Along the margins of that continent warm-month temperatures are considerably milder

(McMurdo Sound 25°, Little America 21°). At Eismitte on the ice plateau of Greenland the average temperatures of the three midsummer months are above zero but well below freezing (see data above). At these temperatures a good deal of midday melting goes on so that the surface of the ice cap is cut by the channels of innumerable swift-flowing rivulets (Figs. 11.7, 11.8).

During the period when the sun is constantly below the horizon, excessively cold weather prevails, although exact and reliable data are not available. On the Antarctic plateau the average winter-month temperatures are probably in the neighborhood of 30 to 40° below

472. Precipitation. If little is known about the temperatures of the ice-cap climates, still less is known concerning their precipitation. There is no doubt that it is meager, and nearly all of it falls as snow, most of it in the form of dry, hard, sandlike particles which are readily driven before the wind. The origin of the precipitation over the ice caps is not well understood. In such regions, although rivers are practically absent, there is some loss by evaporation as well as through glaciers moving out to the sea in the form of icebergs. Enough precipitation must be accounted for to offset these losses. The precipitation at the South Pole has been estimated to be around 1 to 2 in. (water equivalent) and that

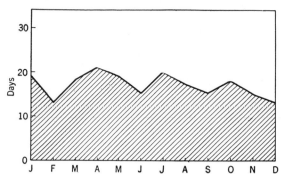

Fig. 11.9. Days with precipitation at Eismitte on the Greenland ice cap. (*After Loewe.*)

for the whole of Antarctica as about $3\frac{1}{2}$ in. (Fig. 11.9).

No doubt a portion of the inland snow has its origin in the cyclonic storms that pass along the margins of the ice plateaus. Still more originates in the moving cyclones that pass in over the ice cap. Precipitation may, in part, result from condensation in the form of fine ice particles, or as hoarfrost, within the descending air as it reaches the intensely cold ice surface. The rate of deposit is exceedingly slow, no doubt, but since it is fairly continuous, the total amount may be considerable. At Eismitte in interior Greenland (9,941 ft.) the recorded average cloudiness was between $\frac{5}{10}$ and $\frac{6}{10}$ with a maximum in the season of least cold. The cloud forms were predominantly stratus, cirrus, and cirrostratus. There were 204 days on which precipitation fell, the larger part of it cyclonic in origin. Considering the prevailing atmospheric conditions over the ice caps, this figure of days with precipitation seems unusually high. From a study of the snow layers marking the yearly accumulations of snow at Eismitte, it was established that the average annual snowfall at that station over a period of 21 years was 12 in., or 3 to 4 in. of water. Seasonal concentration was not conspicuous.[1] It appears then that cyclones do cross the Greenland ice cap and they probably account for a large part of the snowfall. Certainly the weather element is a prominent feature of the climate so that the concept of a permanent anticyclone is scarcely tenable.

H, Highland Climates[1]

473. Altitude and Exposure as Climatic Controls. Next to the distribution of land and water, elevation above sea level probably is the most important control causing differences in climate in similar latitudes. The climatic effects of such elevated land masses as mountains and plateaus are expressed through the two factors (a) *altitude* and (b) *exposure*.

It needs to be emphasized, however, that there is no such thing as a *highland type of climate* in the same sense that there is an *Af* or a *Cs* type. Almost endless varieties of local climates exist within a mountain mass, the atmospheric conditions varying markedly with altitude and exposure and of course with latitude as well. The enclosed valley or plateau is very different climatically from the exposed peak; windward slopes contrast markedly with those having leeward positions, while flanks inclined toward the sun are dissimilar to those oppositely inclined. And each of these in turn is different at various *altitudes* and *latitudes*. Above an elevation of 5,000 or 6,000 ft. marked differences in temperature are conspicuous between sunshine and shade, wind and calm. Representative temperature and rainfall curves for highland climates scarcely can be said to exist, and only the most flexible generalizations are broadly applicable.

474. Methods of Classification of Highland Climates. It is essentially impossible to represent on a small-scale map the almost limitless variety of climates which prevail within the world's highlands. Not only are weather stations few in such regions, but in addition the profusion of local climates makes it impossible for the weather data of most stations to be representative of anything but a very restricted area.

[1] Fritz Loewe, "Klima des Grönländische. Inlandeises," Vol. II, Part K of "Handbuch der Klimatologie" by Köppen and Geiger, Berlin, 1935. See also by the same author, The Greenland Ice Cap as Seen by a Meteorologist, *Quart. Jour. Roy. Meteorological Soc.,* Vol. 62, pp. 359–377, July, 1936.

[1] Hann, "Handbook of Climatology." See also Roderick Peattie, "Mountain Geography," Harvard University Press, Cambridge, Mass., 1936, expecially Chaps. I, II, and III.

The far greater variety and localism of climates in highlands as compared with lowlands is associated with the fact that, to those controls making for climatic variations over the earth in a horizon direction, are added others related to altitude and exposure changes. Moreover, the latter change very abruptly so that different climates can be found in close vertical juxtaposition. In highland climates a third dimension has been added which greatly increases the complications.

Köppen attempts to classify highland climates by employing the same system of climatic types and their limiting boundaries as are described for a hypothetical continent of low and uniform elevation. In other words, the system applied to a horizontal arrangement is assumed to fit a vertical zonation as well. This assumption appears to be based upon the fact that temperature decreases poleward along a horizontal plane and likewise vertically, and as a consequence the temperature of a particular latitude should be duplicated at some given altitude. In other words, the average annual temperature of a lowland station at latitude 40° might be duplicated at several thousand feet elevation in the tropics. Thus Quito, Ecuador, almost on the equator at 9,300 ft. elevation, has a mean annual temperature very similar to that of St. Louis, Mo., in the middle latitudes. Actually the two stations have totally different climates, however, for St. Louis has a difference of 47° between its warmest and coldest months, while Quito has only 0.7 of one degree difference. Yet Köppen classifies Quito's climate as mesothermal (*C*) since all months have an average temperature under 18°C., or 64.4°F., while its coolest month is over 0.°C., or 32°F. Actually, it is far from being mesothermal in the same sense that a lowland middle-latitude station warrants that same classification.

The unique and distinctive feature of highland climates is their large difference in temperature between day and night. The intense insolation by day and the equally rapid loss of heat by radiation at night results in large ranges of temperature within each 24-hr. period. Throughout much of the tropics the cool climates of the high altitudes show far greater temperature changes between day and night than they do between the seasons. One is forced to conclude that a system of climatic classification designed for lowland climates is not applicable to those in highlands.

There appears to be no simple, and at the same time satisfactory, way of representing the variety of highland climates on a small-scale map. In this book a compromise has been employed. Where there are extensive highlands of only moderate elevation above the surrounding lowlands, these often have been included within the general climatic type characteristic of the surrounding lowlands, even though they represent a modified form of the lowland climate. Highlands of greater elevation have been included within one general group designated as highland climates, and the distinctive characteristics of the group are set forth in the textual materials.

475. Atmospheric Pressure in Mountains. At low elevations the minor changes in air pressure from day to day, or from season to season, are directly imperceptible to the human body. As a consequence, it is as a climatic control, and rarely as a climatic element, that pressure has been included in the discussions of types of climate. However, the very rapid decrease in the atmosphere's weight with increasing elevation and the very low pressures that prevail in high mountains and plateaus cause this element to be a somewhat more important one in highland climates. At an elevation above sea level of about 17,500 ft., pressure is reduced to approximately one-half of its sea-level value. The highest human habitations are found below this level, although there are said to be settlements in Tibet and the Bolivian Andes the elevations of which approach it. Physiological effects (faintness, headache, nosebleed, nausea, weakness) of decreased pressure aloft are experienced by most people at altitudes above 12,000 to 15,000 ft. Sleeplessness is common, and exertion is difficult. Usually mountain sickness is a temporary inconvenience which passes away after a week or so of residence at high altitudes. Some persons, however, never become acclimated to the reduced pressure.

TEMPERATURE AND INSOLATION

476. Insolation. Intensity of sunlight increases aloft in the cleaner, drier, thinner air of mountains. This is to be expected, since dust, water vapor, cloud particles, and other principal reflecting, scattering, and absorbing elements of solar radiation in the atmosphere are much more abundant at lower elevations. On a clear day probably three-fourths of the insolation penetrates to 6,000 ft., but only one-half to sea level. The great relative intensity of the sun's rays attracts the attention of nearly all persons going to high elevations. On Mont Blanc (15,781 ft.) the intensity of solar radiation is approximately 26 per cent greater than at Paris (200 ft.). At the time of the summer solstice the amount of sunlight received by Tibet is nearly one and a half times as great as that falling upon the neighboring lowlands in India (Hann).

Insolation not only is more intense in the higher altitudes, but it also is proportionally

changes resulting from increased elevation is the decrease in air temperature (about 3.3° per 1,000 ft.), and this in spite of the increased intensity of insolation. Quito, Ecuador, on the equator, at an elevation of 9,350 ft., has an average annual temperature of 54.7°, which is 25° lower than that of the adjacent Amazon Lowlands. But although the clear, rare air at that elevation, which is incapable of absorbing and retaining much energy, remains chilly, the sun is intensely strong. It is a climate of *cool shade and hot sun*. Viscount Bryce has the following to say concerning his experience on the Bolivian plateau: "The keen air which this elevation gives has a fine bracing quality, yet there are disadvantages. One is never warm except when actually in the sunlight. . . . The inhabitants get accustomed to these conditions and shiver in their ponchos, but the traveler is rather wretched after sunset and feels how natural was Sun worship in such a country."

Climatic Data for a Highland Station in the Tropics

Quito, Ecuador (9,350 Ft.)

	J	F	M	A	M	J	J	A	S	O	N	D	Yr.	Range
Temp.	54.5	55.0	54.5	54.5	54.7	55.0	54.9	54.9	55.0	54.7	54.3	54.7	54.7	0.7
Precip.	3.2	3.9	4.8	7.0	4.6	1.5	1.1	2.2	2.6	3.9	4.0	3.6	42.3	

richer in the shorter wavelengths of energy, or the violet and ultraviolet rays. One therefore burns and tans quickly in mountain sunlight. The greater therapeutic quality of this short-wave radiation is one reason for establishing many sanatoriums in the higher altitudes.

477. Soil Temperature. Associated with the greater intensity of insolation at higher elevations is the excess of surface or soil temperatures over air temperatures. Thus, although the thin, dry mountain air is incapable of readily absorbing and retaining either the solar or the terrestrial energy, the land surface, on the other hand, is highly absorptive of the intense insolation and as a consequence attains a relatively high daytime temperature. Compared with the prevailingly cool air, therefore, soil temperatures of mountains are relatively high. The effect upon plant growth is marked.

478. Air Temperature. Probably of most fundamental importance among the climatic

Vertical temperature gradients along mountain slopes are many times steeper than the most severe winter horizontal gradients on lowlands. In the low latitudes, by a railroad trip of only a few hours, one can be transported from tropical to polar climates. This fact of steep vertical temperature gradients in mountains is particularly significant in the low latitudes, where, as a result of the prevailing high temperatures of the lowlands, people look with favor upon elevated regions where they are able to escape the oppressive heat. Largely because of their lower temperatures, elevations in the tropics commonly become the centers of concentration for native population. In tropical Latin America, for instance, the capital cities of Venezuela, Colombia, Bolivia, and five of the Central American republics are on highlands. In India, the so-called "hill stations" of the sub-Himalayas, such as Darjeeling, Simla, Murree, and Naini Tal, at elevations of 6,500 to 7,500 ft.,

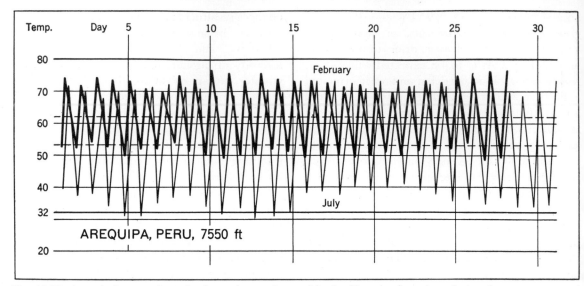

FIG. 11.10. A tropical mountain station located at moderate altitudes. Note the diurnal regularity of temperatures and the greater diurnal range in winter (July), which is the period of least cloud and precipitation.

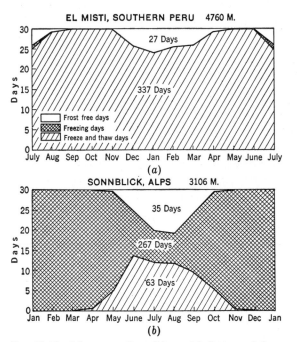

FIG. 11.11. A large number of days with freeze and thaw are characteristic of high elevations in the tropics. This feature expresses itself strongly in the vegetation, weathering, and soil characteristics. Freeze-and-thaw days are much fewer in middle latitude highlands and freezing days more numerous. (*After Troll.*)

become havens for residents from the lowlands during the long hot season.

479. Diurnal Temperature Changes. Mountains and high plateaus have been called the radiation windows of the earth, since the thin dry air at higher altitudes facilitates the entry of strong solar radiation by day and the rapid loss of heat by terrestrial radiation at night. Rapid daytime heating and nighttime cooling is the result, so that large diurnal ranges of temperature are characteristics of highland climates (Fig. 11.10). In tropical highlands this marked temperature change between day and night stands in great contrast to the very slight temperature changes between the averages for the months and the seasons. At high altitudes in tropical highlands, especially in the *tierra helada*, the large diurnal range of temperature results in a very large number of days with night freezing and daytime thawing (Fig. 11.11). Such a frequent oscillation between freeze and thaw has striking effects upon weathering processes, soil formation, and vegetation characteristics. A distinctive feature of the climate of high tropical mountains is the combination of large *diurnal* temperature variations and small *seasonal* ranges.

480. Seasonal Temperatures and Annual Ranges. The lower temperatures at elevated sites have led to the statement that mountains in the tropics enjoy perpetual spring. Quito's annual temperature of 54.7°, for instance, is not greatly unlike the May average at Madison, Wis. However, the great variety of elevations within a tropical mountain mass obviously results in all gradations of temperature.

But although the thermometer stands lower on a tropical mountain than it does on an adjacent lowland, both locations have a similar uniformity in average monthly and daily means. Small seasonal ranges, and the same monotonous repetition of daily weather, belong alike to tropical highlands and tropical lowlands (Fig. 11.12). At Quito, for instance, the temperature difference between the warmest and coolest months is only 0.7°, which is even smaller than that of the Amazon Lowlands in the same latitude. Mexico City at 7,474 ft. and farther poleward has an *average annual temperature* 17° below that for Veracruz on the coast; yet their

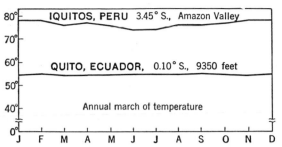

FIG. 11.12. A comparison of the annual march of temperature at Iquitos, a tropical lowland station, and at Quito, a tropical highland station. Note the generally lower temperature at Quito. On the other hand, a small annual range of temperature is characteristic of both stations.

annual ranges are almost identical—11.5 and 11°, respectively. One climatologist has aptly described both the difference and the similarity in the annual march of temperature between

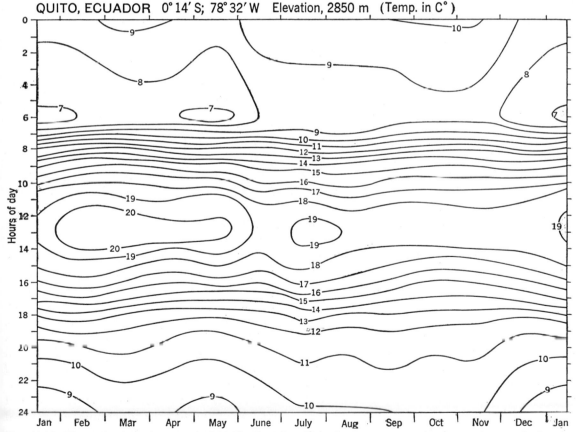

FIG. 11.13. Thermoisopleths for a tropical highland station. Note that temperature changes much more during the 24-hr. period than it does from month to month. (*After Troll.*)

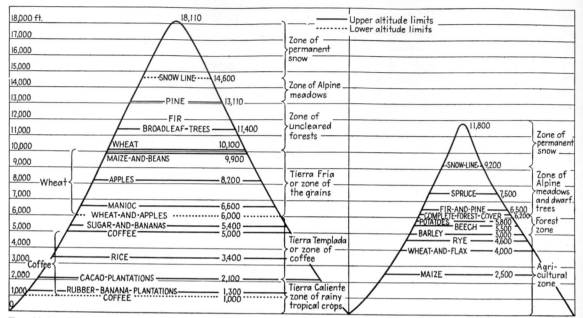

FIG. 11.14. Vertical temperature zones and altitude limits on a tropical mountain (left) and a middle latitude mountain (right). (*After Sapper.*)

lowlands and highlands in the same latitude in the following manner: "The pitch changes; the tune remains the same." As a general rule it may be stated that seasonal temperature contrasts, or mean annual range, increase with latitude in both highland and lowland stations and that the annual ranges for highland and lowland stations in similar latitudes are of the same general magnitude. Highland climates in the tropics present the unique feature of a cold climate having a small mean annual range of temperature. This is quite in contrast to cold climates in middle latitudes where annual ranges are characteristically large. The small annual ranges in tropical highlands have some resemblance to those of marine locations farther poleward (Fig. 11.13).

481. Temperature Zones on Tropical Highlands. As a consequence of the steep temperature gradients that characterize mountains, several zones of climate, with characteristic vegetation covers and crops, may be recognized (Fig. 11.14). In mountainous parts of tropical Latin America, four such zones commonly are delimited, *viz.*, the *tierra caliente* (hot lands), *tierre templada* (temperate lands), *tierra fria* (cool

lands), and the *tierra helada* (land of frost). Quite naturally these altitudinal belts are not defined by identical elevations throughout the entire tropics. In general, the bounding elevations become lower with increasing distance from the equator. The lowest zone, or *caliente*, normally extends from sea level to 2,000 to 3,000 ft. (annual temperature roughly 83 to 75°). Where precipitation is abundant, it is characterized by a luxuriant vegetation cover of trees or of trees and tall grass and by such crops as rubber, bananas, and cacao. The *tierra templada* lies above the *caliente* and extends up to 6,000 to 6,500 ft. (temperature roughly 75 to 65°). Within this climatic belt is produced a great variety of crops, among them coffee, maize, tea, cotton, and rice. *Tierra fria*, lying above the *templada*, prevails up to 10,000 to 11,500 ft. (temperature 65 to 54°). There middle-latitude crops such as wheat, barley, apples, and potatoes are at home, and the pastoral industries frequently are well developed. At still higher elevations is the *tierra helada* which is above the tree line and beyond the agricultural zone. Here are the alpine pastures which are terminated along their upper margins by the permanent snow fields. Close to the equator where there is no dry season the grass formation of the *tierra helada* is relatively thick and it remains green throughout the year. This is known as the *paramo*. With increasing distance from the equator, a dry season becomes characteristic so that the alpine grasses are dry for a part of the year and are subjected to burning. This is the *wet puna*. As the dry season becomes longer with increase in latitude, the grass cover becomes less dense and the

482. Middle-latitude Highlands. While within the tropics mountains and plateaus may be climatically desirable because of their lower temperatures, this same characteristic causes highlands in the middle latitudes to be climatically inferior to lowlands. The difference lies in the fact that tropical lowlands have an *excess* of heat, so that any reduction of temperature with altitude usually is counted as an advantage, both for human comfort as well as for

Horizontal and Vertical Arrangement of the Climatic Vegetation Belts in the Tropical Andes
(After Troll)

Number of humid months	Tierra caliente	Tierra templada	Tierra fria	Tierra helada
12 11 10	Tropical evergreen and semideciduous transition forest	Tropical mountain forest	Tropical altitude-and-fog forest	Paramo
9 8	Tropical moist savanna (forest and grassland)	Tropical moist valley vegetation (forest and grassland)	Tropical moist sierra vegetation (moist sierra brush)	Moist *puna*
—7— 6 5	Tropical dry savanna (forest and grassland)	Tropical dry valley vegetation (forest and grassland)	Tropical dry sierra vegetation (dry sierra brush)	Dry *puna*
4 3	Tropical thorn savanna (forest and grassland)	Tropical thorn valley vegetation (forest and grassland)	Tropical thorn sierra vegetation (thorn sierra brush)	Thorn *puna*
—2—	Tropical semidesert	Tropical valley semidesert	Desert sierra	Desert *puna*
—1— 0	Tropical desert	Tropical valley desert		

wet puna changes gradually to *dry puna* and then into *thorn puna* and finally *desert puna*. Thorn and desert puna are characterized by thorny shrubs and cactus. Grazing is the principal form of land use in the *paramo* and *puna*. Above heights of 14,000 to 15,000 ft. is usually encountered the zone of perpetual snow. Local trade of considerable importance, fostered by this temperature zonation of products, is carried on among the inhabitants at various altitudes.

the greater variety of products that can be grown. In the middle latitudes, on the other hand, even the lowlands usually are none too warm, so that reduction of temperature with altitude, causing a cooler summer and shorter growing season, materially decreases the opportunities for agricultural production. In other words, there are fewer *utilizable* temperature zones in middle-latitude highlands (Fig. 11.14).

Climatic Data for a Representative Altitude Station in Middle Latitudes

Longs Peak, Colorado (8,956 Ft.)

	J	F	M	A	M	J	J	A	S	O	N	D	Yr.	Range
Temp.	23	22	26	33	41	51	55	55	48	39	31	24	37	33
Precip.	0.7	1.2	2.0	2.7	2.4	1.6	3.6	2.2	1.7	1.7	0.9	0.9	21.6	

483. Temperature Inversions Characteristic of Highland Climates. One of the characteristic phenomena of mountain regions, especially those of middle latitudes, is the larger diurnal and seasonal ranges of temperature in the valleys as compared with the slopes. On summer days the protected valley, receiving much radiant energy from the surrounding slopes, may become warmer than the flanks above, where winds provide better ventilation. At night, and especially in winter, on the other hand, the basins become reservoirs of cold air draining from surrounding slopes. In a region of such uneven surface and varied exposures as mountains provide, air drainage is accentuated, and temperature inversions are therefore unusually well developed. This is further aided by the briefer daily period of sunshine, as well as the calmer, more stagnant air in the protected valley. Not only are the basins colder, but they likewise are foggier. A pall of gray fog may enshroud the Swiss Foreland for a week at a time. In going down into a mountain valley on a warm summer evening one does not need an instrument to note the increasing dampness and coolness of the air. From the valleys of Carinthia, in the Austrian Alps, where temperature inversions are well developed and vertical increase in temperature in winter is well known, comes the following proverb: "If you climb in winter up a stair, one less coat you will need to wear" (Hann). It often happens that on a winter day one can ascend from damp, cold, dark, sunless weather in the valley and come out suddenly on the slopes above, into a "wonderland of sunshine and beauty" where the air is clear, mild, and dry.

484. Highlands as Temperature Divides. Highlands commonly function as barriers to the free movement of air masses, and by so doing act as a shelter to areas on the leeward sides. Steep horizontal temperature gradients may be the result. Thus the great highland mass of the Himalayas and Tibet north of India and Pakistan act to prevent the invasion of Hindustan in winter by the cold continental air masses from central and northern Asia which so greatly affect the winter temperatures of eastern Asia.

The protective effect of the mountains is made clear by a comparison of the January temperatures of stations in India-Pakistan and in China in similar latitudes. The northern high-

| Lahore | 53° | Calcutta | 65° |
| Shanghai | 38° | Canton | 50° |

land rim of the Mediterranean Basin likewise acts to block the free movement of cold winter air into southern Europe. Thus while Bucharest and Uskub in the Balkans show January temperatures of 26° and 29°, Salonika south of the highlands records 41°, Athens, 46°, and Trieste, 39°.

PRECIPITATION

485. Increased Precipitation in Mountains. The amount of precipitation increases with altitude. In the tropics, at least, this increase appears to continue only up to a certain altitude, called the *zone of maximum precipitation*, above which there is a decline. The evidence is not conclusive relative to the existence of such a zone in middle-latitude highlands. The heaviest rains normally fall at those altitudes where air ascends most rapidly after the temperature has reached the dew point. So much condensation occurs in this zone that at higher elevations the drier air masses yield less rain. The fact that highlands tend to induce increased precipitation is verified by observation of the mean annual precipitation chart, on which mountain areas are conspicuous as "islands" of heavier rainfall compared with the surrounding lowlands. Note, for example, the case of the Pacific Coast mountains of North America, the Himalayas in southern Asia, and the Alps in Europe. The increase of precipitation as caused by highlands is of multiple origin. This topic has been discussed in an earlier section of the book.

Of great consequence in terms of power resources is the heavy precipitation associated with most highlands. This accumulation of water (including snow) at high elevations represents a reservoir of potential energy, for as it flows to lower levels its energy may be harnessed to produce hydroelectric power. The potential water power of an area obviously depends upon two factors: (*a*) the amount of precipitation and (*b*) the extent of its fall, which in turn is directly related to the height at which the precipitation reaches the earth's surface.

It is especially in dry climates, no matter in what latitude, that the heavier rainfall of highlands is of such critical importance. In regions of drought, mountains, besides being "islands" of heavier precipitation, are islands of heavier vegetation cover and more abundant agricultural production as well. In both arid and semi-arid lands, highlands not infrequently bear a cover of forest in contrast to the meager grass and shrub vegetation of the surrounding drier lowlands. The Black Hills of western South Dakota are "black" because their dark-green forests present such a color contrast with the tawny-hued steppes surrounding them. Not only are settlements attracted to the humid slopes and to the well-watered mountain valleys, but streams, descending from the rainier highlands, carry the influence of highland climate far out on the dry lowlands. Thus the Yemen Highlands in southern Arabia, and the adjacent lowlands watered by its rivers, are a garden spot and the principal center of settlement in that otherwise largely desert country. In eastern North Africa the Ethiopian (Abyssinian) Highlands are a similar "culture island," while the Nile floods have their origin in this same mountain knot. The waters of the Colorado River, with its principal sources in the Rocky Mountains, make possible the agricultural utilization of the dry Imperial Valley of southern California, over 700 miles distant. From the Andes come the 50 or more small streams that, crossing the Peruvian Desert, nourish the parallel irrigated strips of that otherwise waste land.

486. Windward and Leeward Slopes. As indicated previously, highlands usually have wetter windward slopes and a drier leeward side, the latter being described as the *rain shadow*. It may be pointed out, however, that on the leeward side, also, there is likely to be an increase in precipitation with elevation just as is the case on the windward, or weather, side. This results from the fact that the ascending current on the windward side does not begin to descend immediately upon reaching the crest of a mountain range, but continues to ascend for some distance even beyond the crest. As a consequence there is a spillover of the heavy windward precipitation on to the higher leeward slopes.

It is likewise noteworthy that the lifting effect of a highland barrier upon approaching air masses begins at some distance out in front of the marked change in slope, so that rainfall may be increased perceptibly over the lowlands on the windward side of mountains. Lowlands on the leeward side are likely to be much drier. Thus there has been observed a strong increase in rainfall within the flat lowlands of northern Java 25 miles or more away from the mountains.

In summary, it may be said that the windward sides of mountains are more cloudy and rainy and have smaller temperature ranges, while leeward of highlands the climate is drier, sunnier, more variable in temperature, and with a tendency toward increased continentality.

487. Snowfall and the Snow Line. Because of the lower temperatures in highlands, snow falls more frequently and abundantly, and remains on the ground for a longer period, in mountains than on the surrounding lowlands. It is the slow melting of deep accumulations of snow in highlands that supplies many lowlands with an abundant and continuous supply of water throughout the warmer seasons. Considerable interest attaches to the permanent, or year-round, snow fields in highlands and to the changing elevation of the snow line which marks the lower boundary of permanent snow. As a general rule, the elevation of the snow line becomes increasingly higher with decreasing latitude, which suggests the higher temperatures toward the equator. From the table on p. 376 it is seen that the highest snow line is not found at the equator but instead in two zones to the north and south of it where precipitation is lower in amount. Thus while latitude, or zonal temperatures, largely accounts for the general latitudinal variations in the altitude of the snow line, there are bound to be large departures from the zonal average caused by differences in amounts of precipitation, seasonal distribution of precipitation throughout the year, and exposure to the

Mean Altitude of the Snow Line in Various Latitudes
(After Landsberg)

Latitude	0–10	10–20	20–30	30–40	40–50	50–60	60–70	70–80
			Northern Hemisphere					
Elevation, ft.	15,500	15,500	17,400	14,100	9,900	6,600	3,300	1,650
			Southern Hemisphere					
Elevation, ft.	17,400	18,400	16,800	9,900	4,900	2,600	0	0

sun. As a rule the snow line is lower on windward slopes where precipitation is heavier than on drier leeward slopes, and is also lower on those shadier slopes inclined away from the sun. A winter maximum of precipitation also tends to lower the snow line. In some places these controls are cumulative in their effects, and in others they counteract and oppose. The fact that the snow line on the warmer southern slopes of the Himalayas is 2,500 ft. lower in elevation than on the cooler northern slopes reflects the much heavier precipitation on the former.

WINDS

488. On exposed mountain slopes and summits, where ground friction is small, winds are usually strong. Mountain valleys, on the other hand, are particularly well protected against violent winds. Owing to the great variety of relief and exposure in highlands, there are also a number of local winds characteristic of such areas. The diurnal reversal of wind direction,

upslope by day and downslope by night, has been discussed previously under the heading of *mountain and valley winds.*

489. Foehn, or Chinook. Still another local vertical wind, characteristic of mountains, is the cyclonic-induced *foehn,* which in the United States and Canada is known as the *chinook.* It is a relatively warm, dry wind which descends a mountain front when a cyclonic storm causes air to cross the range from the opposite side of the divide (Fig. 11.15). For example, as a well-developed low travels southeastward down the Great Plains, paralleling the Rocky Mountain front, air is induced to ascend over the Rockies from the western side and descend their eastern slopes. The relatively high temperature and aridity of the chinook originate as follows: As the air ascends on the western side of the Rockies, condensation occurs, so that the rising air reaches the top of the divide with much of its moisture gone *but still retaining a relatively high temperature* as a result of liberation of heat of condensation during ascent. As this air descends

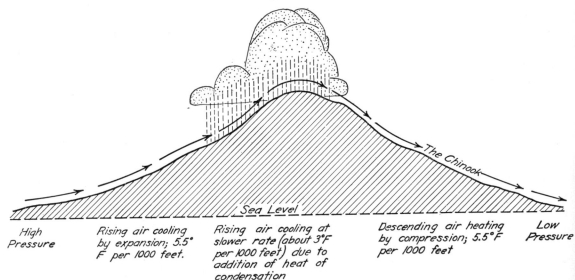

| High Pressure | Rising air cooling by expansion; 5.5° F per 1000 feet. | Rising air cooling at slower rate (about 3°F per 1000 feet) due to addition of heat of condensation | Descending air heating by compression; 5.5°F per 1000 feet | Low Pressure |

FIG. 11.15. Diagrammatic representation of foehn, or chinook, winds.

on the side of the mountain toward the cyclone, it is further heated by compression and made relatively drier, so that it arrives at the eastern base of the Rockies as a mild, arid wind (Fig. 11.16). The warmth of the chinook, therefore, is of dual origin: (a) heat of condensation and (b) heat resulting from compression. Usually its temperature is not over 40° in winter, but this appears very warm, by contrast at least, after a period of anticyclonic weather with intense cold. If snow lies on the ground, it vanishes as if by magic before the warm blast of the chinook. A rise in temperature of 40° within 24 hr. is not unusual. At Kipp, Mont., there is the extraordinary record of a 34° rise within an interval of 7 min. The genuine chinook country is the High Plains at the eastern foot of the Rockies from southern Colorado northward to the limits of settlement in Canada. The milder winters of this western portion of the plains, as compared with regions farther east, are associated with the prevalence of these local mountain winds. Here the snow cover is less persistent, so that grazing can go on throughout the winter.

Foehn winds are by no means confined to the eastern Rocky Mountain foothill country but, on the contrary, are found in almost all mountain areas where cyclonic storms are prevalent. No doubt the region where they are best known is the Swiss valleys on the northern side of the Alps. As a cyclone moves across Europe north of the Alps, southerly winds at first descend the northern slopes, warming and drying as they progress. But if this southerly current is to be maintained, it eventually must be fed from the south side of the mountains, where, during ascent, heat of condensation is probably added. Owing to the frequency of foehns, certain of the northern Swiss valleys may well be called climatic oases in winter. On the average there are about 48 foehn days during the year, the minimum being in summer. In spring they greatly aid in freeing the valleys of their winter snow cover and so accelerate the time of beginning

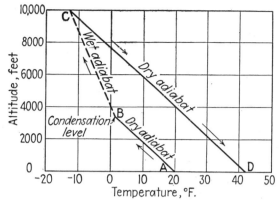

Fig. 11.16. Illustrating the cause of the relatively high temperatures associated with a foehn, or chinook, wind.

farming operations. Autumn foehns are appreciated because they hasten the ripening of grapes, thereby lessening the danger from frost.

DAILY WEATHER

490. In highlands the weather changes within the 24-hr. period are likely to be greater than they are on adjacent lowlands. Violent changes from hot sun to cool shade, from chill wind to calm; at one period gusts of rain or possibly snow, and then again intense sunlight—such is the erratic nature of the daily weather. Even within the tropics, the complex sequence of daily weather stands out in marked contrast to the uniformity of temperature conditions between the months.

"The night and early mornings are cold and raw, but the powerful sunshine raises the temperature rapidly, and by noon it feels hot in the sun, though in the shade it is still cool. About midday clouds gather and there is often a violent thunderstorm in the afternoon with heavy rain, hail, and frequently snow. These clouds and storms are essentially convectional, and they die away after the heat of the day which caused them. . . . The early mornings are fine, and the air at these great altitudes (Quito, Ecuador) is remarkably clear; but in the afternoons the clouds hang low over the gloomy landscape, and hail, snow, and rain chill the air, so that the mountains are almost invariably hidden."[1]

[1] Kendrew, "Climates of the Continents," p. 320.

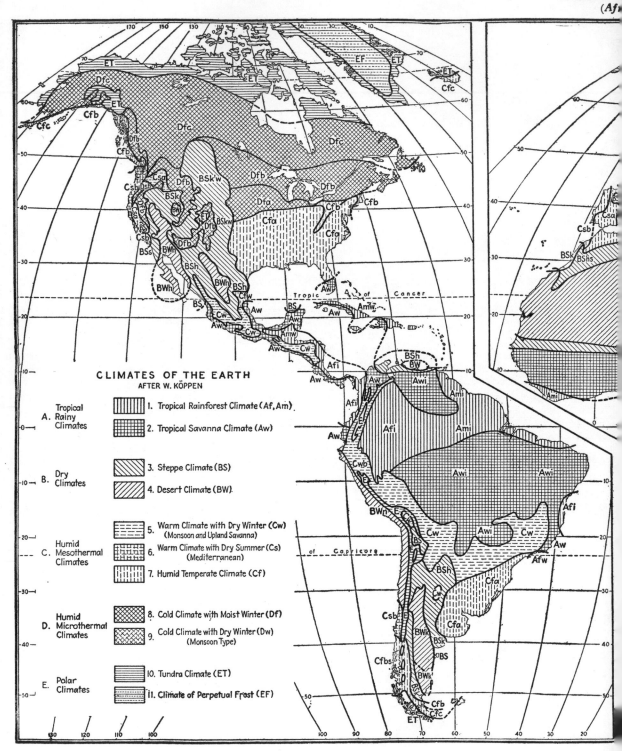

CLIMATES OF THE EARTH
AFTER W. KÖPPEN

A. Tropical Rainy Climates
   1. Tropical Rainforest Climate (Af, Am)
   2. Tropical Savanna Climate (Aw)

B. Dry Climates
   3. Steppe Climate (BS)
   4. Desert Climate (BW)

C. Humid Mesothermal Climates
   5. Warm Climate with Dry Winter (Cw) (Monsoon and Upland Savanna)
   6. Warm Climate with Dry Summer (Cs) (Mediterranean)
   7. Humid Temperate Climate (Cf)

D. Humid Microthermal Climates
   8. Cold Climate with Moist Winter (Df)
   9. Cold Climate with Dry Winter (Dw) (Monsoon Type)

E. Polar Climates
   10. Tundra Climate (ET)
   11. Climate of Perpetual Frost (EF)

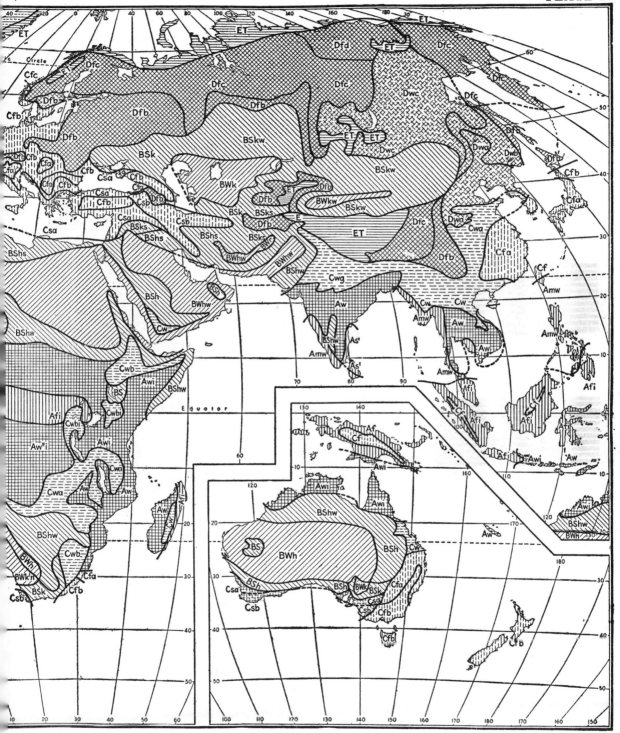

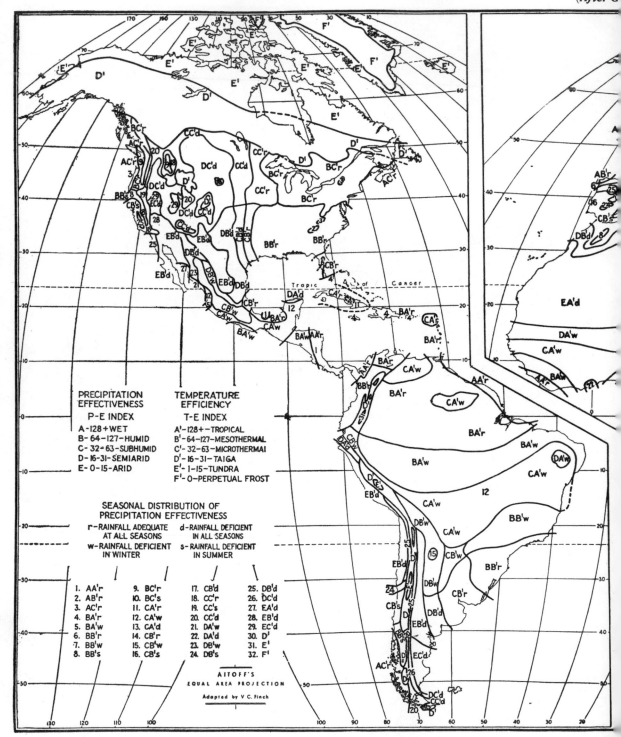

PRECIPITATION
EFFECTIVENESS
P-E INDEX

A-128+WET
B-64-127-HUMID
C-32-63-SUBHUMID
D-16-31-SEMIARID
E-0-15-ARID

TEMPERATURE
EFFICIENCY
T-E INDEX

A'-128+-TROPICAL
B'-64-127-MESOTHERMAL
C'-32-63-MICROTHERMAL
D'-16-31-TAIGA
E'-1-15-TUNDRA
F'-0-PERPETUAL FROST

SEASONAL DISTRIBUTION OF
PRECIPITATION EFFECTIVENESS

r-RAINFALL ADEQUATE   d-RAINFALL DEFICIENT
   AT ALL SEASONS   IN ALL SEASONS

w-RAINFALL DEFICIENT   s-RAINFALL DEFICIENT
   IN WINTER   IN SUMMER

1. AA'r	9. BC'r	17. CB'd	25. DB'd
2. AB'r	10. BC's	18. CC'r	26. DC'd
3. AC'r	11. CA'r	19. CC's	27. EA'd
4. BA'r	12. CA'w	20. CC'd	28. EB'd
5. BA'w	13. CA'd	21. DA'w	29. EC'd
6. BB'r	14. CB'r	22. DA'd	30. D'
7. BB'w	15. CB'w	23. DB'w	31. E'
8. BB's	16. CB's	24. DB's	32. F'

AITOFF'S
EQUAL AREA PROJECTION

Adapted by V C. Finch

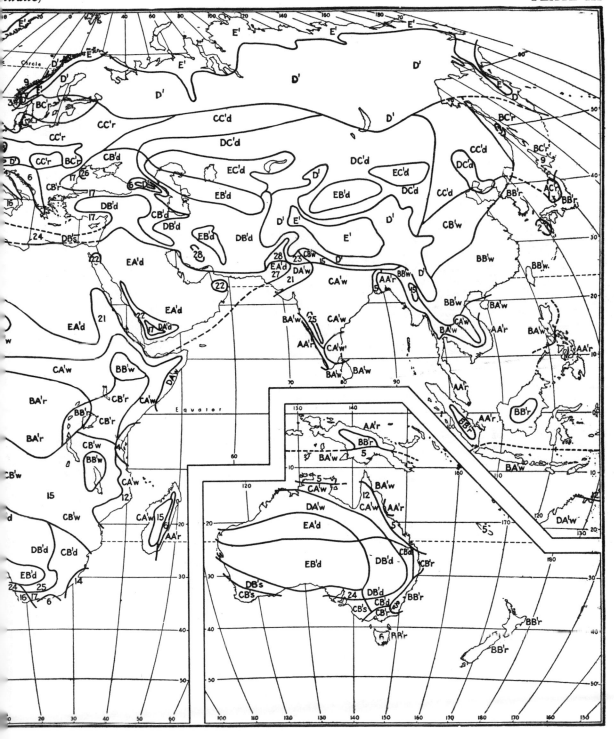

PLATE III

Appendixes

APPENDIX A: *Köppen's Classification of Climates*

Köppen recognizes five principal groups of world climate which are intended to correspond with five principal vegetation groups. The *five* climatic groups, each designated by a capital letter, are as follows: *A*, tropical rainy climates with no cool season; *B*, dry climates; *C*, middle-latitude rainy climates with mild winters; *D*, middle-latitude rainy climates with severe winters; and *E*, polar climates with no warm season. Each of these in turn is subdivided into climatic types based upon the seasonal distribution of rainfall or the degree of dryness or cold. The small letters *f*, *s*, and *w* indicate the seasonableness of precipitation; no dry season (*f*); dry season in summer (*s*); dry season in winter (*w*). The capital letters *S* and *W* are employed to designate the two subdivisions of dry climate; semi-arid, or steppe (*S*), and arid, or desert (*W*). Capital letters *T* and *F* are similarly employed to designate the two subdivisions of polar climate; tundra (*T*), and ice cap (*F*). The table below shows the Köppen scheme of five main climatic groups and eleven climatic types. The parentheses indicate that the combinations *As* and *Ds* rarely occur, and for this reason they are not recognized as among the principal climatic types.

Köppen's Climatic Groups and Types

Climatic group	Symbol	Dry period	Degrees of dryness of cold	
Tropical rainy climates	A	f (s) w		
Dry climates	B	. . . . .	S	W
Warm temperate rainy climates	C	f s w		
Cold snowy forest climates	D	f (s) w		
Polar climates	E	. . . . .	T	F

A CLIMATES

A: Tropical rainy climates; temperature of the coolest month above 64.4° (18°C.). With monthly temperatures lower than 64.4° certain sensitive tropical plants do not thrive. This is the realm of plants known as megatherms which need continuously high temperatures and relatively abundant precipitation. Within the *A* group of climates two main types are recognized, one in which there is adequate precipitation throughout the year, while the other contains a distinctly dry season which affects vegetation adversely.

Af: tropical wet climate; *f*: rainfall of the driest month is at least 2.4 in. (6 cm.). Within this climate there is a minimum of seasonal variation in temperature and precipitation, both remaining high throughout the year.

Aw: tropical wet and dry climate; *w*: distinct dry season in low-sun period or winter. A marked seasonal rhythm of rainfall characterizes *Aw* climates; at least one month must have less than 2.4 in. (6 cm.). Temperature is similar to that in *Af*.

Other small letters used with *A* climates are as follows:

m (monsoon): short dry season, but with total rainfall so great that ground remains sufficiently wet throughout the year to support rainforest. *Am* is intermediate between *Af* and *Aw*, resembling *Af* in amount of precipitation and *Aw* in seasonal distribution. In both *Aw* and *Am* the rainfall of the driest month is below 2.4 in. (6 cm.). Whether it is *Aw* or *Am* depends upon the total amount of rainfall and the amount occurring in the driest month. For example, when the total annual rainfall is 50 in. the boundary between *Aw* and *Am* is 1.94 in. for the driest month; less than this is *Aw*; more than this, but less than 2.4 in., is *Am*. At 60 in. annual total the *Am/Aw* boundary is 1.55: at 70 in., 1.15; at 90 in., 0.34. The boundary between *Am* and *Aw* is expressed by the formula $a = 3.94 - r/25$, where *r* is the annual rainfall in inches and *a* the rainfall during the driest month. If with a given annual rainfall the rainfall of the driest month is greater than the value of *a* as obtained by the preceding formula, the climate is *Am*; if smaller than *a*, it is *Aw*.

w':   rainfall maximum in autumn.

w'': two distinct rainfall maxima separated by two dry seasons.

s: dry season during high-sun period (rare).

i: range of temperature between warmest and coldest months less than 9° (5°C.).

g: Ganges types of annual march of temperature; hottest month comes before the solstice and the summer rainy season.

B CLIMATES

B: Dry climates, in which there is an excess of evaporation over precipitation. No surplus of water remains, therefore, to maintain a constant groundwater level so that permanent streams cannot *originate* within *B* climates. The amount of precipitation that falls is not sufficient data with which to determine the *B*-climate boundaries, since the effectiveness of precipitation in providing moisture in the ground for plants is dependent upon the rate of evaporation, which in turn varies directly with temperature. Rain that falls during a hot summer obviously is less effective than the same amount falling in a cool winter. Köppen's formulas for identifying arid and semiarid climates, therefore, are obliged to involve not only the annual temperature and the total annual rainfall, but likewise the season of maximum precipitation. There are two main subdivisions of *B* climates, the arid, or desert, type, *BW* (*W* from the German word, *Wüste*, meaning "desert"), and the semiarid or steppe type *BS* (*S* from the word *steppe*, meaning dry grassland).

BW: arid climate or desert.

BS: semiarid climate or steppe; for precise definitions of steppe and desert boundaries see formulas at end of this section on *B* climates.

Other small letters used with *B* climates are as follows:

h (*heiss*): average annual temperature over 64.4° (18°C.). *BWh* and *BSh* therefore are low-latitude, or tropical, deserts and steppes.

k (*kalt*): average annual temperature under 64.4° (18°C.). *BWk* and *BSk* therefore are middle-latitude, or cold, deserts and steppes.

k':   temperature of the warmest month under 64.4° (18°C.).

s: summer drought; at least three times as much rain in the wettest winter month as in the driest summer month.

w: winter drought; at least ten times as much rain in the wettest summer month as in the driest winter month.

n (*Nebel*): frequent fog. *BWn* and *BSn* climates are usually found along littorals paralleled by cool ocean currents.

Formulas for Identifying Steppe (BS) and Desert (BW) Margins, in Which r Is the Annual Rainfall in Inches and t the Average Annual Temperature in Degrees Fahrenheit

	Boundary between BS and Humid Climates	Boundary between BW and BS
Rainfall evenly distributed	$r = 0.44t - 8.5$	$r = \dfrac{0.44t - 8.5}{2}$
Rainfall max. in summer; at least ten times as much rain in the wettest summer month as in driest winter month	$r = 0.44t - 3$	$r = \dfrac{0.44t - 3}{2}$
Rainfall max. in winter; at least three times as much rain in the wettest winter month as in driest summer month	$r = 0.44t - 14$	$r = \dfrac{0.44t - 14}{2}$

C CLIMATES (MESOTHERMAL)

C: Warm temperate rainy climates; average temperature of coldest month below 64.4° (18°C.) but above 26.6° (−3°C); average temperature of warmest month over 50° (10°C.). The average temperature of 26.6° (−3°C.) for the coldest month supposedly roughly coincides with the equatorward limit of frozen ground and a snow cover lasting for a month or more. Within the *C* group of climates three contrasting rainfall regimes are the basis for recognition of three principal climatic types, *viz.*, the *f* type with no dry season; the *w* type with a dry winter; and the *s* type with a dry summer.

Cf: no distinct dry season; difference between the rainiest and driest months less than for *w* and *s*, and the driest month of summer receives more than 1.2 in. (3 cm.).

Cw: winter dry; at least ten times as much rain in the wettest month of summer as in the driest month of winter. This type of climate has two characteristic locations: (1) elevated sites in the low latitudes where altitude reduces the temperature of the *Aw* climates which prevail in the adjacent lowlands, and

(2) mild middle-latitude monsoon lands of southeastern Asia, particularly northern India and southern China.

Cs: summer dry; at least three times as much rain in the wettest month of winter as in the driest month of summer, and the driest month of summer receives less than 1.2 in. (3 cm.).

Other small letters used with *C* climates are as follows:

a: hot summer; average temperature of the warmest month over 71.6° (22°C.).

b: cool summer; average temperature of warmest month under 71.6° (22°C.).

c: cool short summer; less than 4 months over 50° (10°C.).

i: same as in *A* climates.

g: same as in *A* climates.

x: rainfall maximum in late spring or early summer; drier in late summer.

n: same as in *B* climates

D CLIMATES (MICROTHERMAL)

D: Cold-snowy forest climates; average temperature of coldest month below 26.6° (−3°C.), average temperature of warmest month above 50° (10°C.). The average temperature of 50° (10°C.) for the warmest month approximately coincides with the poleward limits of forest. *D* climates are characterized by frozen ground and a snow cover of several months' duration. Two principal subdivisions of the *D* group are recognized: the one, *Df*, with no dry season, and the other, *Dw*, with dry season in winter.

Df: cold climate with humid winters.

Dw: cold climate with dry winters; characteristic of northeastern Asia where the winter anticyclone is well developed.

Other small letters used with *D* climates are as follows:

d: average temperature of coldest month below −36.4° (−38°C.). Letters *f*, *s*, *w*, *a*, *b*, and *c* are the same as in *C* climates.

E CLIMATES

E: Polar climates; average temperature of the warmest month below 50° (10°C.). In the higher latitudes once the temperatures are well below freezing and the ground frozen it makes little difference to plant life how cold it gets. Rather it is the intensity and duration of a season of warmth which is critical. For this reason a warm-month isotherm is employed as the poleward boundary of *E* climates. Two climatic subdivisions are recognized: one, *ET*, in which there is a brief growing season and a meager vegetation cover, and the other, *EF*, in which there is perpetual frost and no vegetation.

ET: tundra climate; average temperature of the warmest month below 50° (10°C.) but above 32° (0°C.).

EF: perpetual frost; average temperature of all months below 32° (0°C.). Such climates persist only over the permanent ice caps.

APPENDIX B: *Supplementary Climatic Data for Selected Stations*

(T., temperature in degrees Fahrenheit; Rf., rainfall in inches)

Af, Am, Tropical Wet and Monsoon (Rainforest)

Af

	Jan.	Feb.	Mar.	Apr.	May	June	July	Aug.	Sept.	Oct.	Nov.	Dec.	Year
1. T.	81	81	81	79	79	78	77	78	78	79	80	81	79.3
Rf.	5.6	4.5	5.4	10.9	20.5	23.9	23.2	16.0	9.1	6.9	4.1	5.7	135.8
2. T.	82	81	80	77	74	71	70	70	73	76	79	81	76
Rf.	30.9	22.2	32.2	22.2	13.2	8.0	4.2	5.4	3.7	3.8	8.1	11.7	165.6
3. T.	79	80	79	80	80	79	79	79	79	79	79	79	79
Rf.	13.5	9.9	11.9	14.0	12.6	13.0	11.8	13.7	16.1	20.0	20.7	19.4	177.6
4. T.	78	79	79	79	80	80	80	79	79	79	78	78	79
Rf.	10.8	7.9	9.8	10.8	10.7	8.7	6.3	8.9	8.4	14.8	15.7	13.2	125.9
5. T.	77	77	78	78	79	79	79	80	80	79	79	78	79
Rf.	18.6	14.4	10.3	8.0	6.6	6.5	4.9	3.8	3.4	4.8	8.6	14.7	104.6
6. T.	81	81	81	81	81	81	81	81	81	81	81	81	81
Rf.	11.5	8.9	8.6	8.1	5.6	5.1	6.8	3.9	5.2	5.6	5.7	8.9	83.9
7. T.	81	81	81	80	80	80	80	80	80	81	81	81	81
Rf.	11.5	11.9	17.9	14.0	19.8	15.8	15.5	13.8	13.6	11.4	14.0	17.3	176.5
8. T.	78	79	80	80	79	77	76	76	76	77	78	79	78
Rf.	2.6	6.5	10.0	8.6	17.0	18.6	10.1	9.3	19.3	24.7	10.6	6.5	143.8
9. T.	78	78	76	77	76	74	74	76	76	77	78	78	77
Rf.	10.2	9.8	12.2	6.5	10.0	7.4	6.6	4.6	8.7	7.2	8.4	11.5	103.1
10. T.	79	79	80	81	81	80	81	82	83	83	82	81	81
Rf.	7.9	4.6	7.2	6.0	11.1	11.7	9.9	6.5	3.1	2.9	6.7	11.1	88.7
11. T.	80	80	81	82	83	82	82	82	82	82	81	80	81.3
Rf.	18.4	9.6	8.0	4.1	5.9	7.3	6.5	8.1	9.4	10.0	14.7	17.7	119.7

Am

	Jan.	Feb.	Mar.	Apr.	May	June	July	Aug.	Sept.	Oct.	Nov.	Dec.	Year
12. T.	74	74	74	72	72	71	70	71	71	71	72	73	72.0
Rf.	1.6	2.7	5.9	9.1	8.1	4.5	2.6	3.3	7.6	8.9	5.9	2.0	62.2

(T., temperature in degrees Fahrenheit; Rf., rainfall in inches)

	Jan.	Feb.	Mar.	Apr.	May	June	July	Aug.	Sept.	Oct.	Nov.	Dec.	Year
13. T.	75	75	76	78	79	78	78	78	78	78	78	76	77.3
Rf.	2.7	1.5	1.8	1.8	3.6	7.9	8.8	9.6	7.4	6.6	7.0	4.7	63.4
14. T.	80	80	80	79	79	77	75	75	76	76	78	79	78
Rf.	1.9	3.7	8.0	8.9	12.0	21.5	29.3	27.2	20.7	16.9	6.3	2.6	159.0
15. T.	80	80	81	82	81	80	78	78	79	79	80	80	80
Rf.	16.9	12.5	9.1	7.0	6.0	4.5	2.6	2.3	5.7	5.0	9.4	13.5	94.5
16. T.	81	82	84	85	84	80	79	79	80	80	81	81	81.3
Rf.	0.8	0.8	1.7	3.7	11.4	27.8	25.3	12.5	9.2	12.9	6.7	1.9	114.7
17. T.	80	80	82	83	83	82	81	81	81	81	80	80	81.0
Rf.	3.2	1.9	4.3	9.7	10.9	7.3	4.4	3.2	4.8	13.4	11.8	5.1	80.0
18. T.	80	80	80	81	81	80	80	80	80	80	80	79	80
Rf.	3.7	1.6	1.6	4.3	12.4	13.3	16.0	14.8	12.5	15.1	20.7	11.4	127.4
19. T.	80	80	80	80	80	80	81	82	83	83	82	81	81
Rf.	8.3	8.0	8.1	8.4	6.6	3.9	1.8	1.3	1.4	4.6	4.5	8.2	65.1
20. T.	70	73	79	83	84	82	81	81	82	82	78	72	79
Rf.	0.1	0.2	0.5	2.0	13.7	49.4	53.7	42.5	24.6	11.6	5.0	0.6	203.8
21. T.	77	79	84	87	84	81	80	80	81	82	80	77	81
Rf.	0.2	0.2	0.3	1.4	12.1	18.4	21.5	19.7	15.4	7.3	2.8	0.3	99.6
22. T.	78	78	79	80	80	79	79	79	80	80	79	79	79
Rf.	13.0	12.8	7.8	5.1	4.0	3.7	2.6	1.7	2.9	4.5	5.5	8.5	72.1
23. T.	81	82	82	82	82	80	79	78	79	80	81	81	80.7
Rf.	0.4	0.3	1.2	4.1	11.5	20.0	35.6	36.6	28.5	12.6	5.1	1.4	157.3

Aw, Tropical Wet and Dry (Savanna)

	Jan.	Feb.	Mar.	Apr.	May	June	July	Aug.	Sept.	Oct.	Nov.	Dec.	Year
24. T.	79	81	84	86	84	82	82	82	82	81	80	79	81.7
Rf.	0.9	0.1	0.3	1.7	8.3	12.6	11.1	11.0	13.3	11.1	3.7	3.1	77.2
25. T.	76	78	81	85	90	90	88	86	85	82	79	77	83.1
Rf.	1.1	0.3	0.3	0.6	1.8	2.0	3.8	4.5	4.8	11.1	13.6	5.3	49.2
26. T.	71	71	71	73	75	77	78	78	78	77	75	72	75
Rf.	3.7	4.3	3.8	2.3	1.9	1.1	1.3	1.5	1.5	1.9	4.2	4.1	31.6
27. T.	76	77	78	79	80	81	82	81	81	80	78	77	79
Rf.	1.2	2.5	3.7	6.5	9.4	4.1	2.7	5.4	7.3	6.6	3.4	1.3	54.1
28. T.	77	77	77	78	80	81	82	82	82	81	79	78	79
Rf.	1.0	0.6	1.0	1.2	4.3	4.1	1.7	3.7	4.1	7.5	3.1	1.0	33.9
29. T.	69	71	73	76	79	82	84	84	82	79	74	70	77
Rf.	1.9	1.5	1.3	1.3	3.5	4.3	3.4	4.5	6.8	5.6	2.3	1.7	38.1

(T., temperature in degrees Fahrenheit; Rf., rainfall in inches)

	Jan.	Feb.	Mar.	Apr.	May	June	July	Aug.	Sept.	Oct.	Nov.	Dec.	Year
30. T.	74	75	76	76	77	80	80	79	80	81	79	75	78
Rf.	. . . . . .	. . . . . .	. . . . . .	. . . . . .	0.2	2.9	10.9	19.6	10.0	3.7	0.2	0.1	47.6
31. T.	80	82	83	81	79	77	76	76	77	78	79	79	79
Rf.	0.1	0.8	1.5	4.2	5.4	4.6	5.2	5.8	4.9	4.3	1.8	0.3	38.9
32. T.	70	75	83	90	89	87	87	86	85	83	76	71	82
Rf.	0.1	0.1	0.2	1.1	5.8	5.5	3.3	4.6	5.7	4.7	1.6	0.4	35.1
33. T.	75	77	79	82	83	84	84	84	82	80	78	76	80
Rf.	2.4	1.1	0.9	0.9	2.4	2.2	2.0	1.5	6.9	10.6	13.9	9.6	54.4
34. T.	76	76	80	83	86	84	81	81	81	82	81	77	81
Rf.	0.1	0.1	. . . . . .	. . . . . .	0.7	19.9	24.0	14.5	10.6	1.9	0.4	. . . . . .	72.4
35. T.	78	79	79	78	78	78	77	78	78	77	77	77	77.9
Rf.	5.0	7.0	4.6	7.2	5.6	0.4	0.0	2.7	3.8	6.5	7.6	10.2	62.6
36. T.	79	79	79	79	79	78	77	78	79	80	81	81	79
Rf.	15.7	14.8	8.7	2.5	1.2	0.4	0.2	0.1	. . . . . .	0.8	3.4	10.0	57.8
37. T.	84	83	84	84	82	79	77	79	83	85	86	85	83
Rf.	15.9	12.9	10.1	4.1	0.7	0.1	0.1	0.1	0.5	2.2	4.8	10.3	61.8

BS, BW, Dry Climates
BS, Steppe

	Jan.	Feb.	Mar.	Apr.	May	June	July	Aug.	Sept.	Oct.	Nov.	Dec.	Year
38. T.	54	55	57	58	61	64	67	68	67	63	59	56	61
Rf.	1.8	1.9	1.5	0.6	0.3	0.1	0.1	0.1	0.1	0.4	0.9	1.8	9.6
39. T.	53	57	69	81	89	93	89	87	85	76	63	55	75
Rf.	0.9	1.0	0.8	0.5	0.7	1.4	5.1	4.7	2.3	0.3	0.1	0.4	18.1
40. T.	61	65	75	85	92	93	86	84	84	80	70	63	78
Rf.	0.4	0.3	0.4	0.2	0.6	2.6	8.3	7.3	3.2	0.3	0.1	0.3	24.0
41. T.	88	88	88	87	82	77	76	79	85	89	90	90	85
Rf.	9.7	5.9	4.3	1.0	0.4	0.1	. . . . . .	. . . . . .	0.1	0.5	2.2	4.2	28.4
42. T.	86	85	85	83	76	71	70	73	77	81	85	86	80
Rf.	6.2	6.1	3.8	1.4	0.6	1.0	0.2	0.2	0.1	. . . . . .	0.9	3.7	24.2
43. T.	34	42	48	61	71	80	85	83	77	66	51	42	62
Rf.	1.6	1.0	1.9	1.4	0.5	0.1	0.2	. . . . . .	0.1	0.3	1.0	1.3	9.3
44. T.	57.9	59.0	65.5	74.1	82.4	86.1	89.6	90.2	86.5	79.5	70.1	61.5	75.2
Rf.	2.7	1.9	0.9	0.5	0	0	0	0	0	0.1	1.4	2.9	10.4
45. T.	57	60	65	71	74	72	70	70	68	65	61	57	65.7
Rf.	0.4	0.3	0.7	0.2	1.2	4.5	6.1	5.2	4.5	1.4	0.5	0.4	25.4

(T., temperature in degrees Fahrenheit; Rf., rainfall in inches)

	Jan.	Feb.	Mar.	Apr.	May	June	July	Aug.	Sept.	Oct.	Nov.	Dec.	Year
46. T.	58	62	68	73	79	82	82	83	78	71	64	57	71.4
Rf.	0.5	0.5	0.7	1.1	1.2	2.3	2.1	2.0	4.4	2.4	1.3	1.0	19.5
47. T.	16	19	32	47	58	69	75	73	64	50	34	22	46.4
Rf.	0.5	0.5	0.9	1.8	2.5	3.0	2.7	2.1	1.1	0.8	0.5	0.5	16.9
48. T.	23	26	38	50	58	64	70	68	58	48	35	28	47
Rf.	1.0	0.8	0.3	0.4	0.9	1.2	1.1	1.1	0.8	0.6	1.0	0.9	10.1
49. T.	20	23	32	44	52	60	68	57	56	45	33	25	44
Rf.	0.9	0.6	0.8	1.1	2.1	2.3	1.1	0.7	1.2	0.9	0.7	0.8	13.6
50. T.	30	32	39	47	57	67	72	71	62	51	39	32	50
Rf.	0.4	0.5	1.0	2.1	2.4	1.4	1.8	1.4	1.0	1.0	0.6	0.7	14.3
51. T.	81	83	87	88	85	81	80	80	81	82	82	79	82
Rf.	0.0	0.2	0.2	1.1	3.1	5.4	5.9	7.1	4.3	2.8	0.6	0.0	30.6
52. T.	76	74	70	63	55	49	49	54	61	67	71	75	63.6 *Bsk*
Rf.	2.8	3.1	3.0	1.3	0.9	0.3	0.4	0.4	0.7	1.0	1.7	2.4	18

BW, Desert

	Jan.	Feb.	Mar.	Apr.	May	June	July	Aug.	Sept.	Oct.	Nov.	Dec.	Year
53. T.	83	82	77	68	60	54	53	58	66	73	79	82	68.6
Rf.	1.8	1.7	1.2	0.7	0.7	0.6	0.4	0.4	0.4	0.7	1.0	1.6	11.2
54. T.	55	59	65	70	77	85	91	90	84	72	61	56	72 *Bwh*
Rf.	0.4	0.5	0.4	0.1	......	......	0.1	0.5	0.2	0.2	0.3	0.4	3.1
55. T.	61	61	63	64	65	67	68	68	69	68	65	62	65
Rf.	0.5	0.5	0.5	......	......	......	......	0.5	0.5	0.5	0.5	1.0	4.5
56. T.	55	59	68	76	86	94	99	97	92	80	68	58	78
Rf.	Practically nil												
57. T.	59	63	70	78	85	90	91	90	88	82	72	62	77
Rf.	Practically nil												
58. T.	55	57	63	70	76	80	82	82	78	74	65	58	70
Rf.	0.4	0.2	0.2	0.2	......	......	......	......	......	......	0.1	0.2	1.3
59. T.	49	54	61	71	81	90	95	94	88	80	63	53	73
Rf.	1.2	1.3	1.3	0.9	0.2	......	......	......	......	0.1	0.8	1.2	7.0
60. T.	65	68	75	81	85	87	84	82	82	80	74	67	78
Rf.	0.5	0.5	0.4	0.2	0.1	0.9	2.9	1.5	0.5	......	0.1	0.1	7.6
61. T.	71	71	69	65	63	62	60	61	63	64	67	69	66
Rf.	Practically nil												
62. T.	60	60	59	58	57	55	55	54	55	58	59	60	58 *Bwk*
Rf.	......	0.1	0.2	0.2	0.4	0.3	0.2	0.4	0.3	......	0.2	0.1	2.3

(T., temperature in degrees Fahrenheit; Rf., rainfall in inches)

	Jan.	Feb.	Mar.	Apr.	May	June	July	Aug.	Sept.	Oct.	Nov.	Dec.	Year
63. T.	84	82	77	68	60	54	52	58	66	74	80	82	70
Rf.	1.8	1.7	1.3	0.9	0.6	0.6	0.4	0.4	0.4	0.7	0.9	1.3	11.1
64. T.	73	75	81	81	93	93	90	88	89	89	82	75	84.0
Rf.	0	0	0	0	0.1	0.3	1.8	2.6	0.7	0.2	0	0	5.7
65. T.	19	21	32	48	64	73	77	74	63	50	37	26	49
Rf.	0.5	0.3	0.4	0.5	0.7	0.7	0.5	0.5	0.5	0.4	0.4	0.5	5.9
66. T.	22	34	47	61	70	77	80	76	59	56	40	26	55
Rf.	0.3	......	0.2	0.2	0.8	0.4	0.3	0.7	0.3	......	......	0.2	3.5

Cs, Dry Summer Subtropical (Mediterranean)

	Jan.	Feb.	Mar.	Apr.	May	June	July	Aug.	Sept.	Oct.	Nov.	Dec.	Year
67. T.	55	56	57	61	65	70	73	75	72	67	60	56	64
Rf.	5.1	4.2	4.8	2.7	1.7	0.5	......	0.1	1.4	3.3	6.4	5.5	35.7
68. T.	52	55	59	67	69	77	82	85	76	70	62	54	67
Rf.	1.3	1.2	1.4	1.1	0.7	0.3	0.2	......	0.3	0.5	1.5	0.9	9.4
69. T.	46	50	54	58	63	69	73	72	69	62	53	46	57
Rf.	3.8	2.9	3.0	1.6	0.8	0.1	......	......	0.2	0.9	2.1	4.0	19.4
70. T.	44	46	50	55	61	68	72	71	66	59	51	46	57
Rf.	1.7	1.4	1.9	2.2	1.7	1.1	0.7	0.8	2.4	3.8	2.8	2.1	22.6
71. T.	45	47	51	57	64	71	76	76	70	62	53	46	60
Rf.	3.2	2.7	2.9	2.6	2.2	1.6	0.7	1.0	2.5	5.0	4.4	3.9	32.7
72. T.	51	52	55	58	64	71	76	77	73	67	59	53	63
Rf.	3.2	2.7	2.8	1.9	1.1	0.7	0.2	0.4	1.8	3.2	3.3	3.6	25.0
73. T.	48	49	52	59	66	74	80	80	73	66	57	52	63
Rf.	2.0	1.7	1.2	0.9	0.8	0.7	0.3	0.5	0.6	1.6	2.6	2.6	15.5
74. T.	46	48	53	39	68	75	80	79	72	66	56	49	63
Rf.	4.3	3.3	3.2	1.7	1.3	0.6	0.1	......	0.7	1.7	3.6	5.2	25.7
75. T.	44	48	51	59	66	70	73	73	71	67	56	49	61
Rf.	6.2	4.6	3.5	1.5	0.3	......	......	......	......	0.4	2.5	5.7	24.7
76. T.	74	74	70	64	58	54	52	54	57	62	67	71	63
Rf.	0.7	0.7	1.0	1.8	2.8	3.1	2.7	2.5	2.0	1.7	1.2	1.0	21.2
77. T.	52	53	54	55	57	61	63	64	64	61	56	53	58
Rf.	5.0	3.9	3.5	1.4	0.6	0.1	......	0.3	0.3	0.9	1.6	3.8	21.4
78. T.	49	51	53	54	56	57	57	58	60	59	56	51	55
Rf.	4.8	3.6	3.1	1.0	0.7	0.1	......	......	0.3	1.0	2.4	4.6	22.2
79. T.	51	52	54	58	60	67	70	71	68	62	57	52	60
Rf.	3.6	3.5	3.4	2.6	2.0	0.8	0.2	0.2	1.4	3.3	4.3	4.1	29.4

(T., temperature in degrees Fahrenheit; Rf., rainfall in inches)

	Jan.	Feb.	Mar.	Apr.	May	June	July	Aug.	Sept.	Oct.	Nov.	Dec.	Year
80. T.	67	66	62	56	51	46	46	48	52	56	61	66	56
Rf.	......	0.1	0.2	0.6	2.6	3.2	3.2	2.1	1.2	0.5	0.3	0.2	14.2
81. T.	67	66	65	61	59	56	55	56	58	59	62	64	61
Rf.	......	......	0.6	0.2	3.5	5.8	4.8	3.2	0.8	0.4	0.1	0.3	19.7
82. T.	70	70	68	63	59	56	55	56	58	61	64	68	62
Rf.	0.7	0.6	0.9	1.9	3.8	4.5	3.7	3.4	2.3	1.6	1.1	0.8	25.3

Ca, Humid Subtropical

	Jan.	Feb.	Mar.	Apr.	May	June	July	Aug.	Sept.	Oct.	Nov.	Dec.	Year
83. T.	35	34	40	51	59	67	74	78	70	59	49	39	55
Rf.	7.7	4.9	4.1	4.2	3.7	5.2	6.2	5.2	7.4	5.7	7.2	9.1	70.6
84. T.	42	43	48	58	64	71	78	80	74	64	55	46	60
Rf.	3.1	3.5	5.2	8.1	7.4	13.2	9.3	7.3	8.6	4.6	3.3	3.3	76.9
85. T.	81	80	78	72	67	63	64	66	70	73	76	80	72
Rf.	5.5	5.1	4.3	5.2	4.6	2.7	2.2	1.6	3.1	5.5	5.9	6.2	50.9
86. T.	40	43	51	62	70	78	83	83	75	65	54	44	62
Rf.	0.8	1.1	2.0	4.2	5.0	6.2	7.8	6.8	4.0	3.6	1.5	0.6	43.6
87. T.	39	41	50	59	68	76	79	78	72	69	49	41	59
Rf.	4.8	4.2	5.1	4.4	3.8	4.2	4.1	3.5	3.5	2.4	3.5	3.9	47.4
88. T.	33	34	44	54	65	74	78	76	69	58	45	36	56
Rf.	3.5	2.9	4.0	3.1	3.6	3.7	3.4	3.3	2.6	2.5	2.9	3.1	38.6
89. T.	34	35	43	54	64	72	77	74	68	57	46	36	55
Rf.	3.2	3.0	3.5	3.3	3.6	3.9	4.4	4.0	3.1	3.1	2.5	3.1	40.7
90. T.	79	77	71	64	55	49	47	51	56	63	71	76	63
Rf.	2.1	1.9	1.8	1.9	1.9	1.9	2.0	1.8	1.9	1.6	1.8	2.0	22.6
91. T.	73	73	71	66	61	56	55	57	60	64	68	71	64
Rf.	5.9	7.5	6.5	5.9	5.6	4.6	4.5	3.8	3.9	3.2	4.1	5.9	61.4
92. T.	48	50	58	68	74	80	83	86	77	68	59	50	67
Rf.	0.7	0.9	1.3	4.0	5.3	6.7	5.3	4.4	5.8	4.6	2.0	0.9	41.9
93. T.	45	45	51	60	65	71	78	80	75	66	57	48	62
Rf.	3.5	3.3	6.1	9.1	9.6	13.9	11.2	7.4	8.7	5.1	3.7	3.5	85.1
94. T.	72	72	69	63	57	51	51	51	55	58	65	69	61
Rf.	2.7	2.8	3.2	4.5	3.5	3.2	2.5	3.6	3.4	2.6	3.2	3.6	38.8
95. T.	77	77	73	66	59	54	54	57	61	66	72	76	66
Rf.	4.4	3.8	3.7	3.8	1.8	0.9	1.0	1.3	1.9	4.4	3.6	4.8	35.4
96. T.	77	76	70	62	56	49	51	52	57	62	69	75	63
Rf.	3.7	3.2	5.3	3.1	1.8	1.5	1.0	1.5	1.6	3.5	3.4	5.3	34.9

(T., temperature in degrees Fahrenheit; Rf., rainfall in inches)

	Jan.	Feb.	Mar.	Apr.	May	June	July	Aug.	Sept.	Oct.	Nov.	Dec.	Year
97. T.	74	73	69	61	55	50	49	51	55	60	66	71	61
Rf.	3.1	2.7	4.4	3.5	2.9	2.5	2.2	2.5	3.0	3.5	3.1	3.9	37.3
98. T.	74	72	67	60	53	47	47	49	54	59	66	71	60
Rf.	2.0	2.2	2.6	2.2	1.1	0.9	1.0	1.0	1.6	2.3	2.0	2.1	21.0
99. T.	54	57	63	70	76	82	84	83	80	73	63	57	70
Rf.	4.5	4.3	4.6	4.5	4.1	5.4	6.5	5.7	4.5	3.2	3.8	4.5	55.6
100. T.	54	56	63	70	76	82	84	83	80	73	63	57	70
Rf.	3.4	3.0	2.9	3.1	3.4	4.2	4.0	4.7	5.7	4.3	3.9	3.7	46.3
101. T.	51	54	60	66	73	79	80	80	77	68	58	52	67
Rf.	4.7	5.2	6.4	4.9	4.4	5.4	7.0	7.1	5.3	3.5	3.7	4.9	62.5
102. T.	47	51	58	65	73	79	80	80	75	65	56	49	65
Rf.	5.2	4.8	5.5	5.0	4.3	4.0	4.6	3.4	3.3	2.6	4.3	5.0	52.0
103. T.	60	59	63	70	77	81	82	82	81	76	69	63	72
Rf.	1.3	1.8	2.7	5.3	12.0	15.8	14.0	14.6	9.7	5.1	1.7	1.1	85.1
104. T.	37	39	44	55	62	69	76	78	71	60	51	41	56.9
Rf.	2.2	2.8	4.4	4.9	5.7	6.5	5.3	5.7	8.7	7.4	4.2	2.1	59.9
105. T.	61	66	77	87	93	93	86	84	84	79	69	62	78.5
Rf.	0.7	0.5	0.4	0.1	0.3	4.7	12.0	11.0	6.3	2.3	0.3	0.2	38.8

Cb, Cc, Marine

	Jan.	Feb.	Mar.	Apr.	May	June	July	Aug.	Sept.	Oct.	Nov.	Dec.	Year
106. T.	34	34	36	42	49	55	58	57	52	45	39	36	45 *Cfc*
Rf.	9.0	6.6	6.2	4.3	4.7	4.1	5.7	7.8	9.2	9.3	8.5	8.9	84.3
107. T.	38	38	40	44	48	54	57	56	53	47	42	39	46 *Cf*
Rf.	2.2	2.1	2.4	1.9	2.3	1.7	2.8	2.7	2.2	3.0	3.0	3.2	29.5
108. T.	45	45	47	50	55	60	65	64	61	56	50	46	54
Rf.	2.6	2.4	2.2	2.1	2.4	1.5	1.3	1.9	2.5	3.4	3.1	3.7	29.1
109. T.	58	58	55	52	47	44	42	44	48	51	53	56	51
Rf.	3.4	2.7	3.0	2.7	3.2	3.2	3.0	3.1	2.8	3.0	3.3	3.5	36.9
110. T.	62	62	59	55	51	47	46	48	51	54	57	60	54
Rf.	1.8	1.5	1.7	1.9	1.8	2.2	2.1	1.9	2.1	2.2	2.5	2.0	23.7
111. T.	60	59	57	54	51	49	46	46	49	51	53	57	53
Rf.	2.9	3.2	6.4	9.3	15.3	17.5	15.4	13.5	7.3	5.0	4.4	4.8	105
112. T.	67	67	66	61	57	54	52	52	55	57	60	64	59
Rf.	2.6	3.0	3.1	3.3	4.4	4.8	5.0	4.2	3.6	3.6	3.3	2.9	43.8
113. T.	69	70	68	65	62	59	58	58	60	62	65	68	64
Rf.	1.2	1.3	1.8	2.0	2.4	1.7	1.9	2.1	2.2	2.1	2.1	1.7	22.5

(T., temperature in degrees Fahrenheit; Rf., rainfall in inches)

		Jan.	Feb.	Mar.	Apr.	May	June	July	Aug.	Sept.	Oct.	Nov.	Dec.	Year
114.	T.	68	68	65	60	54	51	49	51	54	58	61	65	59
	Rf.	1.9	1.7	2.2	2.3	2.2	2.1	1.8	1.8	2.4	2.6	2.2	2.3	25.5
115.	T.	36	38	42	47	54	59	63	62	56	49	43	38	48
	Rf.	8.6	6.1	5.3	3.3	3.0	2.7	1.3	1.7	4.1	5.9	10.0	7.8	59.8
116.	T.	39	42	46	51	57	61	67	66	61	54	46	41	53
	Rf.	6.7	5.5	4.8	3.1	2.3	1.6	0.6	0.6	1.9	3.3	6.5	6.9	43.8
117.	T.	38	38	37	41	44	49	51	51	48	44	41	38	43
	Rf.	6.7	5.3	4.9	3.7	3.3	2.6	3.2	3.6	4.7	6.1	6.5	6.6	57.2
118.	T.	52	51	48	44	39	36	35	37	40	44	47	50	44
	Rf.	1.4	1.2	1.7	1.6	1.6	1.2	1.2	1.2	1.1	0.8	1.1	1.4	15.5
119.	T.	32	32	33	35	41	46	51	51	47	42	35	32	40
	Rf.	5.4	7.1	5.6	3.4	5.0	2.7	2.3	3.1	5.8	8.4	6.8	7.2	62.8

Da, Humid Continental, Warm Summer

		Jan.	Feb.	Mar.	Apr.	May	June	July	Aug.	Sept.	Oct.	Nov.	Dec.	Year
120.	T.	28	28	36	47	58	67	72	70	64	53	42	32	50
	Rf.	3.8	4.0	4.0	3.5	3.9	3.2	4.3	4.5	3.7	3.7	3.6	3.7	45.9
121.	T.	25	28	35	48	59	68	73	71	62	52	41	31	49
	Rf.	0.9	0.7	1.1	1.1	1.3	2.3	2.1	1.2	1.4	1.1	1.6	1.3	16
122.	T.	32	38	46	55	63	70	75	73	66	56	44	36	55
	Rf.	2.4	2.3	2.7	3.4	4.1	3.3	2.8	3.2	3.5	4.7	4.3	3.0	39.8
123.	T.	29	34	43	52	62	67	72	71	63	55	43	34	52
	Rf.	1.2	1.3	1.6	2.3	2.8	3.2	2.7	1.9	1.7	2.2	1.7	1.7	24.4
124.	T.	22	25	37	51	63	72	77	75	66	55	39	27	51
	Rf.	0.7	0.9	1.3	2.8	4.1	4.7	4.0	3.2	3.0	2.3	1.1	0.9	29.0
125.	T.	26	27	37	47	58	68	74	73	66	55	42	30	50
	Rf.	2.1	2.1	2.6	2.9	3.6	3.3	3.4	3.0	3.1	2.6	2.4	2.1	33.2
126.	T.	−2	5	24	42	56	66	72	69	58	40	21	3	38
	Rf.	0.1	0.2	0.4	0.9	1.7	3.8	4.5	4.1	1.8	1.3	0.3	0.2	19.3
127.	T.	8	14	30	47	60	71	77	75	61	48	29	14	44
	Rf.	0.2	0.3	0.8	1.1	2.2	3.4	6.3	6.1	3.3	1.6	1.0	0.2	26.5
128.	T.	27	28	35	45	57	68	72	69	63	52	41	32	49
	Rf.	3.7	3.5	4.1	3.8	3.7	3.1	3.5	4.2	3.4	3.7	4.1	3.8	44.6
129.	T.	32	34	44	56	66	75	79	77	70	58	45	36	56.0
	Rf.	2.3	2.6	3.5	3.8	4.5	4.6	3.6	3.5	3.2	2.8	2.9	2.5	39.8

(T., temperature in degrees Fahrenheit; Rf., rainfall in inches)

Db, Humid Continental, Cool Summer

		Jan.	Feb.	Mar.	Apr.	May	June	July	Aug.	Sept.	Oct.	Nov.	Dec.	Year
130.	T.	12	15	25	40	49	56	61	59	51	42	28	19	38
	Rf.	0.5	0.6	0.7	0.8	2.3	2.9	2.6	2.5	1.3	0.7	0.7	0.5	16.1
131.	T.	5	11	24	41	51	57	61	59	50	41	25	14	37
	Rf.	0.9	0.6	0.7	0.8	0.8	3.2	3.5	2.4	1.4	0.7	0.7	0.8	16.5
132.	T.	−4	0	15	38	52	62	66	64	54	41	21	6	35
	Rf.	0.9	0.7	1.2	1.4	2.0	3.1	3.1	2.2	2.2	2.2	1.1	0.9	20.2
133.	T.	16	16	25	38	49	59	65	63	57	46	33	23	41
	Rf.	2.2	1.8	2.1	2.3	3.1	3.5	3.1	2.8	3.2	3.0	3.0	2.5	32.6
134.	T.	22	21	30	42	54	64	69	67	60	49	37	27	45
	Rf.	2.8	2.4	2.4	2.3	2.8	2.7	2.8	2.8	2.7	2.6	2.6	2.5	31.4
135.	T.	24	23	28	35	43	51	59	60	54	45	37	29	41
	Rf.	5.4	5.0	4.6	4.3	3.6	3.6	3.8	3.7	3.8	5.4	6.0	5.4	54.6
136.	T.	7	10	20	38	54	63	68	63	51	39	25	11	37
	Rf.	0.5	0.4	0.6	0.9	1.6	2.2	2.4	2.4	1.6	1.1	1.0	0.7	15.4
137.	T.	3	6	17	38	58	66	71	67	55	39	24	11	38
	Rf.	1.1	0.8	1.0	0.9	1.4	2.0	1.7	1.3	1.3	1.2	1.2	1.2	15.2
138.	T.	0	3	14	34	52	63	68	62	51	35	17	6	33
	Rf.	0.8	0.6	0.6	0.6	1.3	1.7	2.2	1.8	1.1	1.3	1.1	1.1	14.2
139.	T.	23	22	32	37	44	50	58	63	59	50	39	29	42
	Rf.	1.3	1.0	2.2	2.9	3.7	3.7	3.8	4.3	5.6	3.8	3.3	2.3	37.9
140.	T.	24	23	27	38	49	57	62	59	50	41	32	25	41
	Rf.	1.3	1.1	1.2	1.2	1.7	2.0	2.7	2.8	2.0	2.1	1.7	1.6	21.4
141.	T.	21	20	25	34	46	57	62	60	52	42	32	25	40
	Rf.	1.8	1.4	1.4	1.4	1.8	1.8	2.2	2.9	2.5	2.6	2.5	2.4	24.7
142.	T.	18	18	24	36	48	59	63	60	51	41	30	22	39
	Rf.	1.0	0.9	0.9	1.0	1.6	2.0	2.5	2.8	2.1	1.8	1.4	1.2	19.3
143.	T.	30	33	38	48	57	63	66	65	58	49	39	33	48
	Rf.	1.7	1.4	1.6	1.5	1.9	2.3	3.0	2.3	1.7	1.7	1.7	1.9	22.7
144.	T.	30	32	37	46	56	63	66	64	58	48	38	32	47
	Rf.	1.3	1.0	1.6	1.5	2.4	2.4	3.4	2.8	2.0	1.5	1.5	1.5	22.9
145.	T.	29	33	40	50	59	65	68	67	60	50	39	32	49
	Rf.	1.5	1.3	1.8	2.0	2.8	2.7	3.1	2.7	2.0	1.9	1.8	1.8	25.4
146.	T.	26	29	35	46	57	63	66	64	56	46	36	30	46
	Rf.	1.2	1.1	1.3	1.5	1.9	2.6	3.0	2.9	1.9	1.6	1.5	1.5	22.1
147.	T.	21	23	31	45	57	64	67	65	57	46	34	24	44
	Rf.	1.1	0.8	1.5	1.7	1.7	2.4	3.0	2.4	1.7	1.7	1.5	1.5	21

(T., temperature in degrees Fahrenheit; Rf., rainfall in inches)

Dc, Dd, Subarctic

	Jan.	Feb.	Mar.	Apr.	May	June	July	Aug.	Sept.	Oct.	Nov.	Dec.	Year
148. T.	−58	−48	−24	9	36	56	60	52	36	6	−34	−51	3
Rf.	0.2	0.1	0.1	0.2	0.3	0.9	1.0	1.0	0.5	0.4	0.3	0.1	5.0
149. T.	26	26	31	39	46	54	57	56	49	41	34	28	41
Rf.	4.3	3.0	3.4	2.5	2.2	1.9	2.8	3.4	4.4	5.0	3.9	3.4	40.2
150. T.	−11	−7	7	21	35	45	55	55	46	27	6	−8	22
Rf.	0.1	0.1	0.1	0.2	0.5	1.1	0.5	1.8	2.1	0.7	0.2	0.2	7.5
151. T.	8	9	18	30	41	53	60	56	46	34	22	12	33
Rf.	0.9	0.7	0.8	0.7	1.2	1.8	2.4	2.4	2.2	1.6	1.2	0.9	16.8
152. T.	−23	−11	4	29	46	57	59	54	42	25	1	−13	23
Rf.	0.8	0.8	0.5	0.7	0.9	1.3	1.6	1.6	1.7	1.3	1.3	1.1	13.6

Dfd (handwritten beside row 148)

DWb (handwritten beside row 150)

ET, Tundra Climate

	Jan.	Feb.	Mar.	Apr.	May	June	July	Aug.	Sept.	Oct.	Nov.	Dec.	Year
153. T.	−19	−13	−14	−2	21	35	40	39	31	16	0	−15	10
Rf.	0.3	0.2	0.2	0.3	0.3	0.3	1.1	0.8	0.5	0.8	0.4	0.4	5.6
154. T.	4	−2	−2	8	23	35	42	40	32	22	11	6	18
Rf.	1.4	1.3	1.1	0.9	0.5	0.4	0.6	0.9	1.0	1.2	1.0	1.5	11.8
155. T.	22	21	24	30	35	42	48	48	43	35	28	24	33
Rf.	2.7	2.6	2.1	1.6	1.4	1.5	1.8	2.0	2.4	2.5	2.5	2.6	25.7
156. T.	32	33	31	27	19	15	13	15	20	25	28	31	24
Rf.	1.5	1.5	1.8	1.7	1.3	1.2	1.2	1.4	1.0	1.0	1.4	0.9	15.9
157. T.	19	19	24	31	40	47	50	47	41	34	26	21	33.1
Rf.	3.3	2.7	3.4	2.4	3.6	3.0	3.3	3.8	6.0	5.9	4.4	3.1	44.9

ET (handwritten beside row 153)

EF, Ice Cap Climate

	Jan.	Feb.	Mar.	Apr.	May	June	July	Aug.	Sept.	Oct.	Nov.	Dec.	Year
158. T.	24	16	4	−9	−11	−12	−15	−15	−12	−2	14	25	1
Rf.	No data												
159. T.	22	(9)	(−7)	−24	−27	−29	−34	−34	−29	−14	8.6	24	−13.3
Rf.	No data												

EF (handwritten beside row 158)

H, Highland Climates

	Jan.	Feb.	Mar.	Apr.	May	June	July	Aug.	Sept.	Oct.	Nov.	Dec.	Year
160. T.	58	58	59	59	59	58	57	57	57	58	58	58	58
Rf.	3.7	3.5	4.5	9.6	6.5	3.2	2.6	3.3	2.9	8.4	9.6	5.6	63.4
161. T.	40	42	50	56	58	60	62	61	59	55	48	42	53
Rf.	0.6	1.1	1.8	3.8	8.7	24.9	32.3	26.1	18.4	4.5	0.8	0.2	122.7
162. T.	55	56	59	61	62	59	58	58	58	57	55	55	58
Rf.	2.9	1.4	2.0	4.3	6.0	4.1	5.0	7.0	7.3	9.7	8.2	4.4	62.3

(T., temperature in degrees Fahrenheit; Rf., rainfall in inches)

		Jan.	Feb.	Mar.	Apr.	May.	June	July	Aug.	Sept.	Oct.	Nov.	Dec.	Year
163.	T.	60	62	65	64	66	64	62	61	61	62	59	59	62
	Rf.	0.6	1.9	2.8	3.4	3.0	5.7	11.0	12.1	7.6	0.8	0.5	0.2	49.6
164.	T.	54	57	61	64	65	64	62	62	61	59	56	54	60
	Rf.	0.2	0.2	0.5	0.8	1.9	3.9	4.5	4.6	3.9	1.6	0.5	0.2	22.8
165.	T.	54	57	61	64	65	64	63	63	62	61	58	54	61
	Rf.	0.4	0.3	0.4	1.1	3.5	6.8	5.8	6.0	5.5	2.5	0.9	0.4	33.6
166.	T.	16	16	17	24	31	37	41	41	37	30	23	17	27
	Rf.	5.7	6.7	6.7	8.1	7.8	11.2	12.3	10.8	8.3	7.2	4.8	6.1	95.7
167.	T.	17	19	31	43	50	58	63	61	54	43	32	22	41
	Rf.	0.4	0.3	0.3	0.2	0.2	0.2	0.5	0.5	0.3	0.2	. . . . . .	0.2	3.2

STATIONS FOR WHICH DATA ARE GIVEN ABOVE

Af, Am

1. Amboina, Moluccas
2. Cairns, Australia (17°S., 146°E.)
3. Padang, Sumatra
4. Pontianak, Borneo
5. Menado, Celebes
6. Ocean Island (1°S., 170°E.)
7. Jaluit, Marshall Islands (6°N., 170°E.)
8. Akassa, Nigeria
9. Iquitos, Peru
10. Georgetown, British Guiana
11. Sandakan, British North Borneo
12. Yaunde, Cameroons
13. Port-of-Spain, Trinidad
14. Duala, Cameroons
15. Seychelles (5°S., 55°E.)
16. Cochin, India
17. Colombo, Ceylon
18. Colón, Panama
19. Manáos, Brazil
20. Akyab, Burma
21. Rangoon, Burma
22. Jakarta, Java
23. Freetown, Sierra Leone

Aw

24. Saïgon, Indo-China
25. Madras, India
26. Honolulu, Hawaii
27. Port-au-Prince, Haiti
28. Kingston, Jamaica
29. Key West, Florida
30. Bathurst, Gambia (Africa)
31. Mongalla, Anglo-Egyptian Sudan
32. Mandalay, Burma
33. Nhatrang, Indo-China

34. Bombay, India
35. Bolobo, Belgian Congo
36. Kupang, Timor (10°S., 124°E.)
37. Darwin, Australia

BS

38. San Diego, California
39. Lahore, Pakistan
40. Jaipur, India
41. Wyndham, Australia
42. Broome, Australia
43. Tehran (Teheran), Iran
44. Bushire, Iran
45. León, Mexico
46. Monterrey, Mexico
47. Pierre, South Dakota
48. Kamloops, British Columbia
49. Helena, Montana
50. Denver, Colorado
51. Hillet Doleib, Anglo-Egyptian Sudan
52. Kimberley, South Africa

BW

53. Stuart, Australia
54. Yuma, Arizona
55. Cape Juby, Africa (28°N., 13°W.)
56. Insalah, Algeria
57. Aswan, Egypt
58. Cairo, Egypt
59. Baghdad, Iraq
60. Karachi, Pakistan
61. Iquique, Chile
62. Port Nolloth, Cape Province
63. Alice Springs, Australia
64. Khartoum, Anglo-Egyptian Sudan
65. Astrakhan, U.S.S.R. (46°N., 48°E.)
66. Kashgar, China (39°N., 76°E.)

Cs

67. Gibraltar
68. Marrakech, Morocco
69. Sacramento, California
70. Marseilles, France
71. Rome, Italy
72. Palermo, Sicily
73. Athens, Greece
74. Izmir, Turkey
75. Jerusalem, Israel-Jordan
76. Adelaide, Australia
77. San Luis Obispo, California
78. San Francisco, California
79. Lisbon, Portugal
80. Santiago, Chile
81. Valparaiso, Chile
82. Capetown, Cape Province

Ca

83. Niigata, Japan
84. Nagasaki, Japan
85. Asunción, Paraguay
86. Ichang, China
87. Nashville, Tennessee
88. Cincinnati, Ohio
89. Washington, D.C.
90. Dubbo, Australia
91. Port Macquarie, Australia (31°S., 153°E.)
92. Foochow, China
93. Kagoshima, Japan
94. Montevideo, Uruguay
95. Paraná, Argentina
96. Rosario, Argentina
97. Buenos Aires, Argentina
98. Bahía Blanca, Argentina
99. New Orleans, Louisiana
100. Galveston, Texas
101. Mobile, Alabama
102. Vicksburg, Mississippi
103. Hongkong
104. Tokyo, Japan
105. Allahabad, India

Cb, Cc

106. Bergen, Norway
107. Aberdeen, Scotland
108. Brest, France
109. Dunedin, New Zealand
110. Hobart, Tasmania
111. Valdivia, Chile
112. Auckland, New Zealand
113. Port Elizabeth, Cape Province
114. Melbourne, Australia
115. Vancouver, British Columbia
116. Portland, Oregon
117. Thorshavn, Faeroe Islands
118. Punta Arenas, Chile
119. Dutch Harbor, Aleutian Islands (54°N., 167°W.)

Da

120. New Haven, Connecticut
121. Odessa, U.S.S.R.
122. Milan, Italy
123. Belgrade, Yugoslavia
124. Omaha, Nebraska
125. Chicago, Illinois
126. Harbin, Manchuria
127. Mukden, Manchuria
128. Boston, Massachusetts
129. St. Louis, Missouri

Db

130. Calgary, Alberta
131. Edmonton, Alberta
132. Winnipeg, Manitoba
133. Marquette, Michigan
134. Toronto, Ontario
135. St. John's, Newfoundland
136. Kazan, U.S.S.R. (56°N., 49°E.)
137. Orenburg, U.S.S.R. (52°N., 55°E.)
138. Barnaul, U.S.S.R. (53°N., 84°E.)
139. Nemuro, Japan (43°N., 146°E.)
140. Uppsala, Sweden
141. Helsingfors, Finland
142. Leningrad, U.S.S.R.
143. Berlin, Germany
144. Breslau, Poland
145. Vienna, Austria
146. Warsaw, Poland
147. Kiev, U.S.S.R.

Dc, Dd

148. Verkhoyansk, U.S.S.R. (68°N., 133°E.)
149. Trondheim, Norway
150. Okhotsk, U.S.S.R. (59°N., 143°E.)
151. Archangel, U.S.S.R. (65°N., 41°E.)
152. Dawson, Yukon (64°N., 139°W.)

ET

153. Barrow Point, Alaska (71°N., 150°W.)
154. Spitsbergen (78°N., 14°E.)
155. Vardö, Norway (70°N., 31°E.)
156. South Orkneys (61°S., 45°W.)
157. Ivigtut, Greenland

EF

158. McMurdo Sound, Antarctica (78°S., 167°E.)
159. Little America, Antarctica

Highland Climates

160. Bogotá, Colombia (8,730 ft.)
161. Darjeeling, India (7,376 ft.)
162. Kodaicanal, India (7,688 ft.)
163. Addis Ababa, Abyssinia (8,000 ft.)
164. Mexico City, Mexico (7,411 ft.)
165. Puebla, Mexico (6,987 ft.)
166. Säntis, Switzerland (8,202 ft.)
167. Leh, Kashmir (11,503 ft.)

Index